Fundamentals of

ELECTRONICS *second edition*

PRENTICE-HALL INTERNATIONAL, INC., *London*
PRENTICE-HALL OF AUSTRALIA, PTY., LTD., *Sydney*
PRENTICE-HALL OF CANADA, LTD., *Toronto*
PRENTICE-HALL OF INDIA (PRIVATE) LTD., *New Delhi*
PRENTICE-HALL OF JAPAN, INC., *Tokyo*

Fundamentals of

ELECTRONICS *second edition*

MATTHEW MANDL

*Technical Institute and
Community College,
Temple University*

PRENTICE-HALL, INC.

Englewood Cliffs, N.J.

DEDICATED TO MY SISTER, FAY

© 1965 by
Prentice-Hall Inc.
Englewood Cliffs, N.J.

Current printing (last digit):

11   10   9   8   7   6

Library of Congress Catalog Card Number: 65-17802
Printed in the United States of America
33813C

PREFACE

Fundamentals of Electronics is a single-volume text covering not only the basic theory of electronics, but also the practical aspects. It has been specifically written for those planning a career in any of the various branches of electronics, including industrial control, automation, radar, microwave electronics, computer systems, communications, or allied fields. In this revised edition the topics have been divided into three primary sections:

1. Review of Electric Fundamentals
2. Principles of Electronics
3. Applications and Components

The first section reviews electron theory; it includes a study of subshells and atomic bond factors that provide a firm foundation toward an understanding of solid-state devices and transistors covered later. Included in the first section are the basic topics of current flow, fundamental circuit analysis, magnetism, and other material needed for acquiring the necessary groundwork for advanced studies. The topic features of the original chapters have been retained from the first edition, though the material has been reorganized and rearranged to improve topic sequence and upgrade the text structure.

The second section, which starts with vacuum-tube principles, also contains discussions of solid-state fundamentals, transistors, power supplies, amplification systems, oscillators, pulse factors, and miscellaneous electronic circuitry. Portions of the original material have been revised and brought up to date. Many chapters have been expanded since the first edition to cover new topics. The transistor section, for instance, has been enlarged, and a new chapter on solid-state fundamentals has been added. Additional solid-state components are discussed in the power supply section and other subsequent chapters. Similarly, the amplifier and oscillator chapters now contain greater emphasis on pulse-signal and circuit characteristics.

Topics in the third section include receiver circuitry, transducers, test instruments, switching and gating systems, magnetic amplifiers, and signal frequency multiplication and division. Receiver and transmitting principles are covered since their basic circuitry is also encountered in other branches of electronics, and because this information is essential for those who will ultimately be engaged in some aspects of research and design in the communications field. In addition, these principles round out the foundation acquired earlier and unify some of the application factors.

As with the first two sections of this text, the third section also contains several new chapters. These cover transducers, switching and gating, logic circuits, and control amplification. In *all* sections the emphasis has been on circuit and component analysis, and the aim has been to present explanations as clearly and thoroughly as possible.

The review questions given to the student at the end of each chapter for home and classroom usage have been expanded to meet the increased text coverage. The questions are so worded that a rereading of the chapters involved will funish the necessary answers. In most chapters, the number of practical problems have been increased to better illustrate practical applications and provide for added experience in solving typical circuit analysis and design equations. Most of the practical problems require numerical answers as opposed to the essay answers required for the review questions. Hence, self-checking facilities are provided by the answers to practical problems in the Appendix.

The Appendix lists the various reference data so essential to both the study of electronics and electricity. Included are a summary of the principles of logarithms along with appropriate tables, right-angle factors, and a table of trigonometric ratios, color coding, and other necessary information.

The author wishes to thank the practicing engineers, technicians, and electronic field men who have outlined the general scope of electronic knowledge which industry usually desires new employees to have. Grateful acknowledgment is also expressed herewith to the instructors in many technical schools and institutes who have contributed many valuable suggestions regarding the scope and topic sequence for this revised edition.

MATTHEW MANDL

Yardley, Pennsylvania

CONTENTS

Part **1**

Review of

Electric

Fundamentals

1

ELECTRONS, CHARGES, AND FIELDS

INTRODUCTION

The word *electronics* stems from the word *electron*. All phases of electricity and electronics are related to the movement of electrons through some conducting medium to constitute what is known as *current flow*. Electron movement also creates lines of force known as *fields* which are important because they permit the construction of such items as generators, transformers, capacitors, antennas, and numerous other electronic devices. Also, by altering the chemical composition of basic crystal elements to modify electron movement characteristics, it is possible to design the various solid-state units such as transistors, photo-diodes, and other units that are widely used at present.

The essential factors relating to the electron theory are reviewed in this chapter to serve as a foundation for the subsequent studies involving current flow, circuit behaviour, and component applications.

ATOMIC CHARGES

The atom is a closely-knit structure which consists of a central core, called a *nucleus,* and one or more electrons revolving around the core. The electrons are referred to as *planetary* electrons because the atomic struc-

3

ture resembles the solar planetary system. In the solar system each planet orbits at a different distance from the sun; likewise an atom with a number of electrons will have them revolving around the nucleus in orbits which are spaced at different distances from the nucleus.

In a fashion similar to the gravitational pull between the sun and its planets, there is also an attraction between the nucleus of an atom and its planetary electrons. The potential energy represented by the attraction between the nucleus and any particular electron of the atom is known as a *charge*. To distinguish between the charge of an electron and that of the nucleus, the charge of the electron is designated as *negative* (sometimes referred to as *minus*). The nucleus, on the other hand, is said to have a *positive* charge (also referred to on occasion as a *plus* charge). The positive charge of the nucleus, however, simply indicates the predominant or primary charge of the nucleus. It may be composed of a number of positively-charged particles (known as protons) as well as some particles with no charge which are known as *neutrons*. Other particles also exist, but for purposes of simplification, only the positively charged particles of the nucleus, the protons, will be considered here.

In a normal atom, the total value of the positive charge of the nucleus is equal to the total negative charge established by the planetary electrons surrounding the nucleus. Since the nucleus has a positive value, and the electrons have a negative value, they are equal though opposite in their charge relationship, and the atomic structure as a *whole* may be considered as having a *neutral* charge.

Because the nucleus has a positive charge and the electrons a negative charge, an attraction is created between the nucleus and the planetary electrons. This attraction is in conformity with one of the most basic laws of electricity, that is, *unlike charges attract, and like charges repel.* Hence, the individual electrons, having like charges (negative) repel each other, yet all are attracted to the positive nucleus.

ELEMENTS AND COMPOUNDS

There are many types of atoms, some having electrons in a single orbit, and others having electrons in several orbits. The number of electrons in an atom (as well as the composition of the nucleus) determines its type. The various types of atoms form the fundamental structure of *all* substances or matter which exists on earth and in the universe. When identical atoms are grouped together, they combine to form an *element,* and all matter is made up of either a single element or a combination of various elements.

The proton has considerably greater mass and weight than an electron. If the proton mass is taken to represent one, the mass of the electron is virtually negligible (actually less than $\frac{1}{1,800}$ of the proton weight).

Thus, even though the electrons revolve around the nucleus at high speeds, they constitute only a fractional portion of the total mass of an atom.

The simplest atom is that of the gas *hydrogen.* An atom of this gas consists of one proton and one electron, as shown in Fig. 1-1. This is a simplified illustration, since the electron can rotate at any angle, and its orbit may not be perfectly circular, as shown here. Because there is only one electron and one proton in the hydrogen atom, there is very little mass, and hence the element formed by combining such atoms has very little weight. For this reason, the lightweight gas elements are composed of atoms with few protons and electrons.

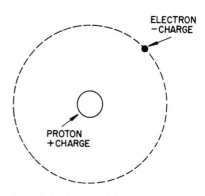

Fig. 1-1. Atom of hydrogen.

The next most simple atom is that of the gas *helium,* shown in Fig. 1-2. Here, there are two electrons in the single orbit around the nucleus. Also, there are two protons present, as well as two neutrons. When protons and neutrons coexist in the nucleus, they are tightly bound together, and the neutrons contribute to the total mass and weight of the nucleus. With the helium atom, as with the hydrogen atom, if each proton and neutron is considered to have a mass of one, the two neutrons with a mass of two and the two protons with a mass of two would represent a total weight of four.

Atoms with a larger number of electrons revolving around the central nucleus form other elements. The first orbit beyond the nucleus can accommodate only two electrons, so that additional orbits are present in most elements. The element *lithium,* for instance, has two electrons in the first orbit and another electron in the second orbit, as illustrated in Fig. 1-3. In many cases, more than

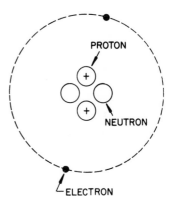

Fig. 1-2. Atom of helium.

two orbits are present, as shown later. The orbits are sometimes referred to as planetary *rings* or *shells.* An increase in the number of electrons around the nucleus forms other element atoms, such as *beryllium* with four electrons, *boron* with five electrons, *carbon* with six electrons, etc. A greater number of electrons forms such elements as gold, silver, copper, lead, oxygen, among many others. There are over one hundred known elements to date. The number of protons in a normal atom determines the atom's position in the so-called atomic series or list of standard atomic numbers. (See Appendix.)

Because there are over a hundred basic elements, they can be com-

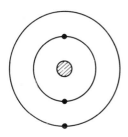

Fig. 1-3. Atom of Lithium.

bined in virtually an infinite number of ways to form what are known as *compounds*. Examples of compounds are such items as water (two parts hydrogen and one part oxygen) and table salt (sodium and chlorine). Mixtures of compounds form glass, stone, cloth, wood, and countless other substances. Since there are millions of the various atoms in even a small segment of a compound, one can recognize a compound even when the particles may be so small that a microscope is required to observe them. If a compound is divided into smaller and smaller sections, however, a point is finally reached where any additional division results in the dividing up of the fundamental elements themselves. Since these make up the element structure, their division results in the loss of the identifiable compound. Thus, the smallest particle of a substance which is still identifiable as such is known as a molecule, and it contains the minimum number of the various atoms forming the identifiable compound.

An element, even though made up of similar atoms, can also be considered as having a molecular structure. The molecule of an element such as atmospheric oxygen or hydrogen gas consists of two atoms only. (As shown later in this chapter, certain characteristics are established when atoms are brought close to each other to form elements. As also discussed, the atom itself may undergo some change with respect to its electrons when it is combined with other atoms to form an element such as iron.) In comparison to the element, the compound is made up of one or more similar atoms plus one or more dissimilar atoms, and the smallest combination of such various atoms is known as the molecule. Combinations of such molecules in large numbers form materials such as paper, plastic, bronze, etc.

SHELLS AND SUBSHELLS

As a foundation for the study of current flow, magnetics, solid-state devices, and other electronic factors, we must next consider the aspects of electron orbit characteristics. As mentioned earlier, the various orbital paths of the electrons around the nucleus are sometimes referred to as *shells* or *rings*. Each primary shell or ring can accommodate only a certain amount of electrons. All shells, except the first shell near the nucleus, are composed of two or more *subshells*.

As shown in Fig. 1-4, the first shell is a solitary one and can accommodate only two electrons. The second primary shell is composed of two

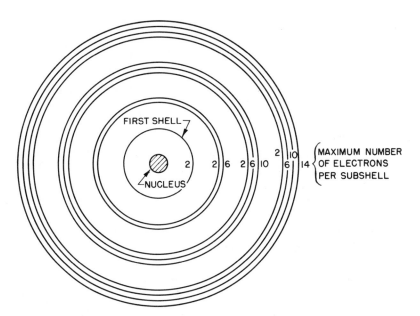

Fig. 1-4. Sequential arrangement of primary shells and subshells of an atom.

subshells, the one nearest the nucleus being capable of accommodating two electrons, the other subshell being able to contain up to six electrons. The third primary shell can consist of three subshells, the first of these being able to hold a maximum of two electrons, the second six electrons, and the third 10 electrons. The fourth primary shell may have no more than four subshells. As with the others mentioned, the first subshell can hold two electrons, the second six, and the third 10. The fourth subshell of the fourth primary ring can hold up to 14 electrons. Note that, in any primary shell group, the second subshell can contain *four more* electrons than the first subshell. Each succeeding subshell can contain four more electrons than the preceding subshell. In the next primary shell group, however, the first subshell again starts with two as the maximum number of electrons which it can contain.

All the outer shells need not, of course, be completely filled. With the lithium atom, for example, the first primary shell contains two electrons and the second primary shell contains only one electron. This single electron revolves in an orbit representative of the first subshell of the second primary shell group (see Fig. 1-3). *In a solitary atom* each shell and subshell, because of the strong nuclear attraction from the core, must be filled successively before subsequent shells can hold electrons. The electrons nearest the nucleus are those representative of the lowest *energy levels,* since they are firmly bound to the nucleus, particularly if the shells are filled. Electrons in the outer rings represent the highest energy levels and these electrons are most readily influnced and capable of being removed from the atom.

From the foregoing, it is evident that the first *primary* ring can contain two electrons, the second primary ring a total of eight electrons, the third primary ring a total of 18 electrons, and the fourth primary ring 32 electrons. Beyond the fourth primary ring are two additional rings, but these are never entirely filled, and it is not known how many they could hold, since there are only about one hundred known basic elements.

The number of electrons in the outer shell of an atom determines the stability of the atom. If the quota of electrons in an outer shell is filled, the atom is stable, and exhibits virtually no chemical reactions. Such a stable element is known as an *inert* element. Helium is inert since it has only two electrons and these completely fill the first primary shell. Neon is another inert element since it has two electrons in the first primary shell and eight electrons in the second primary shell, as shown in Fig. 1-5 (A). Argon, shown in Fig. 1-5 (B), is still another inert gas. Note, however, that while in the argon atom the first two primary shells are filled completely, the third primary shell is filled only with respect to its first two *subshells.* The third subshell is empty. Here, however, we still have an inert element, because the first two subshells are completely filled. The inert elements just mentioned will not combine with any other elements.

When the outer shell of an atom has less than its full quota of electrons, it can readily gain or lose electrons. In particular, atoms lacking only one or two electrons in their *outer* shell can easily acquire the additional elec-

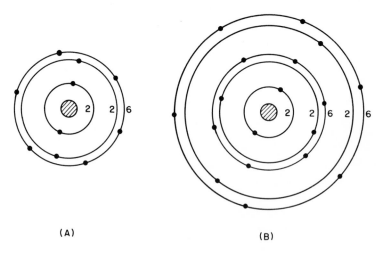

(A)   (B)

Fig. 1-5. Atoms of neon and argon.

trons to fill the quota of the outer ring. Atoms having only one or two electrons in the outer shell can readily lose such electrons.

ELECTRON MOVEMENT

Elements which have the ability to lose electrons are usually metals, while elements with a capacity for acquiring electrons are nonmetallic. Calcium, barium, and strontium each have two electrons in the outer shell, and hence these elements all have the ability to lose such electrons. These elements are often used as the sources of electrons in vacuum tubes, because they will emit electrons freely when heated. Metals such as aluminum, copper, silver, etc. have incomplete outer shells with only a few electrons of the full quota present. Hence, such electrons can be removed easily from the outer orbit. Copper, for instance, has a total of 29 electrons in each atom of the element. As shown in Fig. 1-6, the first three primary shells of the copper atom are completely filled; that is, the first three shells contain two, eight, and 18 electrons respectively, for a total of 28 electrons. The fourth shell has only one electron (actually in the first subshell of the fourth orbital ring). This solitary electron of the copper atom is a *free* electron, and hence can be removed rather easily. For this reason, copper is often utilized in electricity and electronics because its electrons can be subject to influence. If copper is formed into a

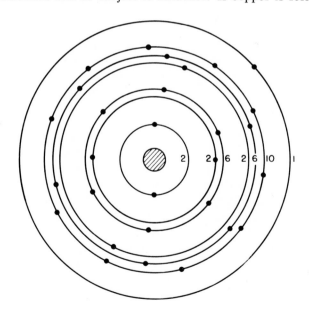

Fig. 1-6. Atom of copper.

length of wire, electron flow can be produced from one end of the wire to the other, by applying pressure to the electrons through use of a battery or other source of electric force. In copper, as in other elements, millions of atoms make up the structure. The single electron in the outer shell, as it travels in its orbit, may become equidistant between its own atom and an adjacent one. When this happens, it is not under the exclusive attraction of either nucleus, and can leave its own orbit to travel and enter another orbit of an adjacent atom. Hence, the electric pressure which is applied to such a free electron causes it to leave one atom and move on to the next. The second atom thus has a force applied to it, in the form of an arriving electron, and in turn transfers a free electron to the next atom. This progression of electrons through the copper wire is known as *current flow.*

When the outer shell of an atom is completely filled (or almost completely filled), electron movement *through* the element is difficult to produce, and consequently the substance becomes an *insulator,* which means that it is a nonconductor of electric current. When only a few electrons are part of the outer shell, that is, when the outer shell lacks a number of electrons to reach its full *quota,* the substance has the ability to permit current to flow through it, on application of electric pressure, and thus is known as a *conductor.*

IONS AND PLASMA

As mentioned earlier, because of the equality existing between the positive charge of the nucleus and the negative charge of the electrons of an atom, the net charge is neutral. In various branches of electronics, however, there are occasions where conditions are created which either remove or add electrons to the normal quota surrounding the nucleus of an atom. To define this altered atomic characteristic, the word *ion* is applied to an atom which is no longer neutral, but has either gained or lost one or more electrons from its original state. When an atom has more than the normal amount of electrons, an unbalanced condition is created between the planetary electrons and the nucleus, because the excessive electrons now cause the atom to be predominantly negative. Originally, the total negative electron charge was equal, though opposite, to the total positive nucleus charge. The added electrons, however, increased the negative charge above that of the positive charge of the nucleus. Hence, an atom having one or more electrons above its normal quota is known as a *negative ion.* Thus, when a number of atoms of this type are utilized, they are referred to as ions and serve many useful purposes in electronic devices.

Ions can also be formed by removing one or more electrons from an atom, creating an electron deficiency. Hence, if an atom has less than the normal amount of electrons in its planetary system, the positive charge of the nucleus will predominate. Such an atom is known as a *positive ion,* to distinguish it from the negative ion atom which has an excessive amount of electrons. Ions of both types are of particular importance in electronic applications using gas-filled vacuum tubes, cathode-ray tubes, as well as transistors, as shown later.

The term *plasma* is also applied to ionization, particularly to ionized gases forming a cloud of ions in a highly agitated state. As such, the plasma can be considered the equivalent to an electrical conducting fluid which can be acted on by magnetic fields. Because it is actually neither a true solid or liquid, it has been referred to as the fourth state of matter. The word plasma stems from the Greek word *plassein,* meaning "to form" or "to mold." While plasma is usually formed by gas ionization, it also applies to ionization in solid-state devices. Practical applications apply to all gas-filled electron tubes, thermonuclear fussion, missile re-entry problems, industrial processes for application of refractory coatings to base metals, as well as some aspects of metal shaping and welding processes.

Plasma temperatures start at approximately 10,000°F, and gas ionization causes molecular structures to break up into individual atoms with a loss of normal charge neutrality. In industrial utilization and research, magnetic fields are utilized as containers of the plasma, since solid materials disintegrate because of the extremely high temperatures. Plasma engineering and research are continuing to explore the potentials of this ionization cloud formed by basic atomic elements.

TYPES OF FIELDS

There are two types of fields: the electrostatic and the electromagnetic. Electrostatic fields are created when a condition of either insufficient or excessive electrons exists. Magnetic fields are created by the alignment of the orbital spins of electrons. Electrostatic fields can be produced by applying friction to objects, which also produces electron movement. If, for instance, a silk cloth is rubbed against a glass rod, it will tear electrons away from the rod and absorb them into its own atomic structure. As a result, the affected atoms of the glass rod will have an electron deficiency, and hence the rod is said to be *positively charged.* As mentioned earlier, an atom with one or more of its normal quota of electrons removed becomes a positive ion, and the net charge of the atom is positive. A group of such atoms, constituting a particular element, will cause that element to have a positive charge. Thus, rubbing the glass rod with silk caused an electron movement from the glass to the silk, and created a positive charge in the rod, and a negative charge in the silk.

A charged particle will produce *fields* which represent *lines of force* emanating from the particle. This is shown in Fig. 1-7 (A), where a charged particle has been suspended in air, and the dotted lines indicate the fields which exist around such a particle. These fields can be likened to tentacles of electricity which, though invisible, extend out from the charged particle in all directions. Such fields are known as *electrostatic lines of force,* and are capable of influencing other charged materials. Thus, if two charged glass rods are suspended as shown in Fig. 1-7 (B), the two rods will repel each other.

If a piece of flannel is used to rub a hard rubber rod, electrons are torn away from the flannel, by virtue of the friction produced. The electrons leave the flannel and are transferred to the rubber, setting up a negative charge in the latter. Thus, if two rubber rods are charged in this manner and suspended near each other, they will repel each other just as the glass rods did, because in either case the rule mentioned earlier, regarding the repulsion between like poles, applies here.

If the charged glass rod (positive) is suspended near the charged rubber rod (negative), the unlike poles will create an attraction, as shown in Fig. 1-7 (C), causing the rods to swing together. (Note that the lines of force of a positively-charged particle are shown with arrows pointing away from the particle, while the lines of force of a negatively-charged particle are shown with arrows pointing toward the particle.) If the particles are permitted to touch each other, the excessive amount of electrons in the negatively-charged particle will be transferred to the particle having an electron deficiency, thus cancelling the respective charges and making each item neutral again. A charged particle will hold its charge in a dormant or static state until it is discharged. The terms *electrostatic charge* and *electrostatic lines of force* are based on the word *static.*

Charles Coulomb (1736-1806) was the first to state the law of charged bodies:

> "The force between two electrically-charged bodies is inversely proportional to the square of the distance between the two, and directly proportional to the product of the two charges."

The electrostatic charge unit is called the *coulomb* in honor of this French scientist, and the unit is the quantity of charge carried by electrons

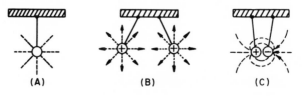

Fig. 1-7. Electrostatic lines of force in charged particles.

in the amount of 6.28 times the product of 10 multiplied by itself 18 times. Thus, to represent such a large number of electrons, a long string of zeros would be necessary, and hence an abbreviated method of writing such large numbers is used, as more fully detailed later.

While friction is not used for the generation of electric current in practical electronics, charged bodies and electrostatic lines of force are encountered frequently, and hence are an important phase of electronics.

Magnetic fields can also be demonstrated easily. If, for instance, a thin cardboard is placed over a bar magnet, and iron filings are sprinkled over the cardboard, the magnetizing force of the magnet will, in turn, magnetize the particles of iron. If the cardboard is now tapped gently, the iron filings will arrange themselves in a pattern representative of the magnetic field. The magnetic field is shown in Fig. 1-8, with the lines indicating a direction from the north pole of the magnet to the south pole. The lines form loops around the magnet (the open lines indicate that insufficient magnetism is present to influence the iron filings).

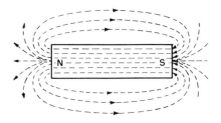

Fig. 1-8. Fields of bar magnet.

If two bar magnets are brought near each other, as shown in Fig. 1-9 (A), the fields of one interacts that of the other and, thus, the two influence each other. If the north and south poles of the two magnets are brought into close proximity, the unlike poles will *attract* each other, and *lines of force* are set up between them. If both north poles are brought close to each other, as in Fig. 1-9 (B), the lines of force are such that a *repelling* action occurs. Lines of force are not closed loops, like the fields around a single magnet, but instead extend from one pole to the other, as shown between the two magnets in Fig. 1-9 (A). Thus, the law previously stated, regarding the attraction between unlike charges (and the repulsion between like charges), also holds for the poles of magnets.

The force of either attraction or repulsion between two magnetic poles follows Coulomb's law with respect to the force between two charged bodies, and hence is inversely proportional to the square of the distance

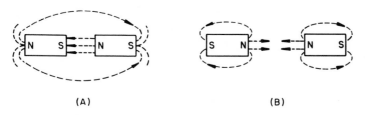

(A)   (B)

Fig. 1-9. Aiding and opposing fields of bar magnets.

between the two, and directly proportional to the product of the strength of the two charges. This law, expressed mathematically, then becomes:

$$\text{Force} = \frac{M_1 \times M_2}{D^2} \qquad (1\text{-}1)$$

where M_1 and M_2 represent the strength of each pole, and D represents the distance in centimeters between the poles.

The strength of M_1 or M_2 is expressed in terms of the *unit pole*. A unit pole has a strength such that it will exert a force of one dyne upon an equal pole in air (or vacuum) when the distance between the poles is one centimeter. The *dyne* is the unit of force in the centimeter-grams-second (cgs) system and is equal to the force required to produce, in a 1-gram weight mass, an acceleration of 1 centimeter per second for every second that the force is present. The dyne is an extremely small unit, 980 dynes equaling only 1 gram of force.

As an example of the use of this formula assume the north pole of a magnet with a unit pole strength of 100 is brought within 5 centimeters of the south pole of another magnet having a unit pole strength of 50. The calculation would then be:

$$\frac{100 \times 50}{5 \times 5} = \frac{5{,}000}{25} = \text{a force of 200 dynes}$$

THEORY OF MAGNETISM

Before undertaking an explanation of the electron-spin principle which produces magnetic lines of force, some factors relating to magnets in general should be discussed.

When a magnet is dipped into a pile of iron filings, a considerable quantity of the filings will cling to the ends of the magnet, but only a few iron particles will be attracted and held by the center portion of the magnet, as shown in Fig. 1-10 (B). This simple experiment proves that the magnetism is concentrated in the two ends of the magnet. These two areas or regions of concentrated magnetism are known as the *poles* of the magnet, with each pole possessing the same magnetic strength as the other.

If a bar magnet is suspended from the center by a string, it will turn until it is aligned with the natural magnetism of the earth, that is, in a general north-south direction. The pole of the magnet which points north is known as the *north-seeking pole* or simply *north pole* (N), while the other pole of the magnet is known as the *south-seeking pole,* or the *south pole* (S). This is the principle used in the compass, which consists of a magnetized needle-type indicator pivoted so as to rotate freely, and with the pointed end polarized to form the north-seeking pole. Actually, the magnetized needle of the compass points to the magnetic poles of the

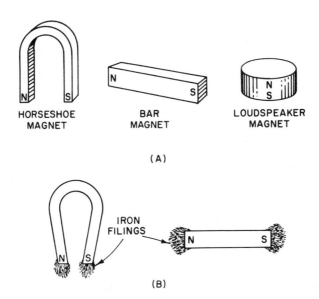

Fig. 1-10. (A) Magnet shapes (B) Filings show poles.

earth, and not to the geographic north and south poles. The north *magnetic* pole at 71°N. latitude, 96°W. longitude, is approximately 1,300 miles distant from the geographic north pole. The south *magnetic* pole, on the other hand, is 72-73°S. latitude, 156°E. longitude. Because of its magnetic poles, the earth can be considered a huge natural magnet.

As with other basic principles of electronics and electricity, early scientists focused their attention on magnetism and attempted to evaluate and explain it, as well as set up fundamental laws governing its behavior. One of these earlier scientists was the German physicist Wilhelm Weber (1804-1891), who made the proposition that each molecule of a magnetic substance was a permanent magnet in itself. Later, Sir James Ewing (1855-1935), the Scottish engineer and physicist, offered an explanation of magnetism based on Weber's earlier theory. In consequence, the Weber-Ewing concepts are known as the *molecular theory of magnetism.* According to this theory, the magnet molecules of magnetic material such as iron, steel, etc., are normally in a random arrangement, as shown in Fig. 1-11 (A), and their effect on each other is a neutralizing one; that is,

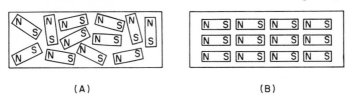

Fig. 1-11. Molecular theory of magnet formation.

the magnetic material has no over-all polarity and no attraction for other magnetic materials. When the material is magnetized, the molecules are in orderly arrangement, as shown in Fig. 1-11 (B), and one magnetic particle aids another to form a north polarity at one end and a south polarity at the other.

If the magnetic material shown in Fig. 1-11 (A) is iron, the magnet molecules can be aligned as shown in 1-1 (B), by bringing a permanent magnet close to the iron bar. The symmetrical arrangement of the molecules will then cause the iron bar to become a magnet. Upon removal of the permanent magnet, however, the molecules in the iron bar shift, and again become disorganized. In consequence, the iron bar loses its magnetic properties. If a steel bar is used, however, the molecules will remain positioned in their orderly and organized manner, and a permanent magnet results.

The modern concept of magnetism goes deeper than the older Weber-Ewing theory, and is based not on molecular structures, but on the *electron-spin* principle. This relates to the thteory that the individual electrons of an atom not only revolve around the nucleus in orbital paths, but also spin around their own axes just as the earth, in revolving around the sun, also turns on its own axis. Some of the atom's electrons spin in one direction, and others in the opposite direction. If as many electrons are spinning in one direction as the other, they tend to neutralize each other insofar as magnetic properties are concerned. Thus, iron, with 26 electrons to the atom, will be nonmagnetized if 13 electrons spin in one direction and 13 in the other.

As discussed earlier, the electrons around the nucleus of an atom have primary rings for their orbital travel as well as subshells. Thus, iron, with 26 electrons, would have an atom wherein the first ring contains two electrons, the second ring consists of two subshells of two and six electrons, and the third ring consists of three subshells of two, six, and eight electrons, for a total of 26 electrons. According to the modern concept, when the atoms are brought close together to form a solid metal, the outer subshell is disturbed, and free electrons are liberated (which are the ones that constitute current). Hence, an atom which is part of an element, is somewhat different from an atom isolated from the element, just as in the case of the oxygen atom when combined with others to form atmospheric oxygen, as discussed later.

An iron atom (as part of the element iron) is shown in Fig. 1-12, wherein a fourth ring is indicated containing two free electrons. The number of electrons in each ring and subshell is shown with the positive sign indicating electron spin in one direction and the negative sign indicating electron spin in the other. Here it is the third subshell of the third primary ring which is responsible for creating magnetic property. As shown, the

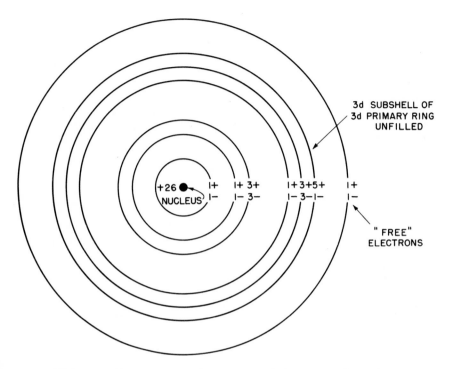

Fig. 1-12. Electron spins in iron atom. Polarity signs indicate direction of spin; electrons are still negative with respect to nucleus.

iron atom is in a magnetized state because there are 15 electrons spinning in one direction (+), and only 11 spinning in the other direction (−). If the iron atom were nonmagnetized, there would be three electrons spinning in one direction (+) in the third subshell of the third ring, and also three electrons spinning in the other direction (−), forming, as already mentioned, 13 in one direction and 13 in the other.

The iron element atom shown in Fig. 1-12 (in its magnetized state) acts as an individual (though infinitely small) permanent magnet. When a number of such atoms are grouped together to form the element iron, there is an interaction between the magnetic forces of the various atoms. Such interaction only occurs when atoms are in close proximity to each other. The interaction among the atoms making up the element permits the electron spins of one atom to influence the electron spins of adjacent atoms and thus to produce alignment. The alignment of the electron spins is confined to a small area or section of the material known as a *domain*. The atoms making up one domain all have parallel electron spins and hence the domain is magnetized in a particular direction. The fields of an external magnetizing force will tend to align all the domains in an element in a direction to produce a uniform magnetic field.

ATOM BONDS

The electrons in the *outer* orbit of the atom's planetary system are capable of binding the atom to that of an adjacent atom. This bonding property of atoms is responsible for the cohesive characteristics of matter which permit the formation of the materials and substances found in nature. The outer ring electrons which have such bonding properties with respect to the outer electron shell of adjacent atoms are known as *valence electrons*.

The number of electrons in the outer ring or subshells has an important bearing on the ability of the individual atoms of an element or compound to cling together and form solid substances such as copper, silver, gold, etc. Knowledge of how the number of electrons influences the binding characteristics of substances is of material aid in understanding current flow, transistor behavior, and other important electronic phenomena.

The binding characteristics of the atom fall into three general classes, the *ionic,* the *metallic,* and the *covalent.* The ionic bonds are those present in compounds. The metallic bonds are those established in metals, while the covalent bonds are the type encountered in the formation of transistors and other crystal structures.

Ionic bonds are created when metallic atoms (with only a few electrons in the outer shell) combine with atoms which have almost a full quota of electrons in their outer shells. With atoms having almost a full quota of outer ring electrons, there is a tendency to absorb electrons from metallic atoms, because a few electrons in the outer shell are easily lost. A typical example of this is the formation of ordinary table salt (sodium chloride) by combining the element *sodium* with the element *chlorine* to form a compound, as shown in Fig. 1-13. Note that the sodium atom has only one electron in its third ring (which could normally accommodate 18 electrons). The chlorine atom, on the other hand, has seven electrons in its third ring. Thus, the first two subshells of the third ring have almost their full quota of eight. Hence, when the sodium atom and the chlorine atom are brought closely together, an ionic bond is formed, because the chlorine atom captures a sodium valence electron. This results in the compound sodium chloride, wherein the sodium atom is now a positive ion, and the chlorine atom is a negative ion. The two ions are firmly bound together because of the attraction set up between the opposite charges of the two ions. This conforms to one of the laws of electricity, mentioned earlier, that like charges repel each other and unlike charges attract each other.

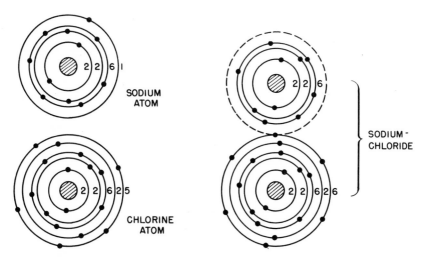

Fig. 1-13. Ionic bond formed by chlorine atom capturing a sodium valence electron.

In the case of the metallic sodium atom and the chlorine atom, the bond formed when sodium chloride is produced results in the outer shells of each atom having a full electron quota. The consequence is that this compound (if it is absolutely pure) is an insulator (a nonconductor of electricity). Each chlorine ion is attracted to a neighboring sodium ion and the various bonds which are formed create a cubic arrangement of atoms as shown in Fig. 1-14. Such a symmetrical arrangement forms a crystal, and the structure shown in the illustration is known as a *crystal-lattice*

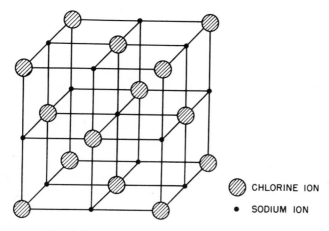

Fig. 1-14. Ion atoms in sodium chloride crystals.

network. Crystals formed by other elements have atoms arranged in other geometrical patterns depending on the molecular structure formed.

As already mentioned, atoms having only a few electrons present in their outer rings tend to give up such electrons readily, and such atoms usually form metals. When atoms having only a few electrons in the outer ring are combined, *metallic* bonds are formed to create solid materials. Since the outer rings or subshells are not completely filled, free electrons are present which can move from one atom to another. An outer ring electron spinning in its orbit may easily move into an orbit of an adjacent atom. This is particularly true at the instant when the free electron is at a point between the two atoms, and hence virtually equidistant from each nucleus. Therefore, if a free electron leaves one atom and enters an orbit of the next, it will leave behind a positive ion. This condition is only temporary, because the positive ion will capture an electron from another adjacent atom, and hence the free electrons can move about within the element at random. Upon application of electric power, however, all the free electrons can be made to move in orderly fashion from one atom to another, in a direction established by the manner in which the electric pressure is applied.

Covalent bonds are those in which outer ring electrons of similar atoms combine. A typical example of this is the hydrogen atom. Normally, the single atom does not have its outer ring completely filled (the ring can accommodate two electrons and only one is present). When such atoms are brought closely together, however, a bond is formed because each nucleus not only has its own electron revolving around it but also shares the electron of its neighbor, as shown in Fig. 1-15 (A). Neither nucleus can attract the adjacent electron more than the other nucleus; in this way the inert gas hydrogen is formed.

Another example of the covalent bond is that of normal atmospheric oxygen. The oxygen atom, by itself, has two electrons in the first ring and six in the second ring, as shown in Fig. 1-15 (B). When the two atoms are brought together, there is a sharing of two of the electrons by each

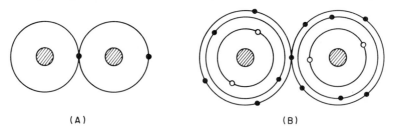

(A)   (B)

Fig. 1-15. Bonding of hydrogen atoms and of oxygen atoms.

atom nucleus. The first two subshells of the outer ring are, for all practical purposes, filled to their quota of eight, and a bond is formed.

Another example of covalent bonding of electrons occurs in either carbon, germanium, or silicon. Since covalent bonding is of prime concern in solid-state diodes, transistors, and other such items, it is discussed more fully in Chapter 12 on Solid-state Fundamentals.

REVIEW QUESTIONS

1. Briefly define the terms *electron, neutron, proton* and *atom.*

2. What are *planetary* electrons?

3. Explain the relationships of positive and negative charges with respect to the nucleus of an atom and its planetary electrons.

4. List the number of protons in each of the following atoms: Atomic No. 3; No. 6; No. 8; No. 30.

5. What are the essential differences between elements, compounds, and molecules?

6. List five elements and five compounds.

7. If an atom has an atomic No. 28, how many electrons does it contain? How many electrons are in each subshell of the second and third primary shells?

8. If an atom has 33 electrons, how many electrons are there in the outer ring subshells?

9. Explain what is meant by a free electron, and in what substances free electrons are usually found.

10. Explain what constitutes a positive ion and what constitutes a negative ion.

11. Briefly explain what is meant by *plasma* in electronics.

12. What are the basic characteristics of electrostatic and electromagnetic fields?

13. By simple drawings of two bar magnets, show which magnetic fields repel each other and which attract each other, and indicate which are the North and which are the South poles.

14. Briefly explain the older molecular theory of magnetism, and compare it with the newer theory of electron . . . spins.

15. Briefly define the term *unit pole,* and show its formula for finding the magnetic force in dynes.

16. What are valence electrons and what are their characteristics?

17. Explain why some substances are conductors of electricity and others are not.

18. Explain the essential differences between ionic and covalent bonds.

PRACTICAL PROBLEMS

1. The north pole of a magnet with a unit pole strength of 300 is brought within 2.5 centimeters of the north pole of another magnet with a unit pole strength of 150. What is the force of repulsion in dynes between the two?

2. If the same magnets in Problem 1 were separated by 5 centimeters, what would be the force of repulsion in dynes between the two?

2

ELECTRICAL

SOURCES AND

UNITS

INTRODUCTION

When free electrons move progressively from atom to atom in some conducting medium such as copper or silver they constitute what is known as current flow. In electric and electronic practices, a continuous path for current flow is created by interconnecting vacuum tubes, transistors, and other components to form what are known as *circuits*. These are employed to serve a number of purposes, among them the generation of necessary types of signals, the amplification of existing signals, and the modification of certain signals. The pressure applied to cause electron movement is called *voltage*.

The voltage necessary to force current through an electric circuit may be obtained from a number of sources. One source is the power supply (discussed in Chapter 14) which converts the a-c line potential of the power mains to direct current for application to the vacuum tubes or transistors of receivers, transmitters, or other electronic devices. Other sources of electric power include various batteries which are used in portable electronic work. A battery consists of a number of cells so wired to provide the voltage value desired. The cells create electron movement by a chemical reaction which occurs when the cell is wired into a circuit which provides a closed-loop path for the current flow.

PRIMARY CELLS

In each cell of a battery, two dissimilar conducting elements are brought into contact with a chemical composition known as an *electrolyte,* and the chemical reaction is such that electrons are forced out of one battery terminal and into the other, if an external path is provided for them. Without an interconnection between the battery terminals, no current flows, and there is little chemical action. As shown in Fig. 2-1, a flashlight bulb, or other device which completes the circuit, allows the electrons to flow from the negative terminal of the battery, through the bulb, and back into the battery via the positive terminal. The chemical reaction within the battery which causes electron movement can be likened to pressure forcing water through a pipe. Hence, the term *electromotive force* (emf) is applied to indicate the force which could cause electron movement (current flow) if the circuit were completed. The electromotive force is also known as *voltage*.

There are a number of battery types, many of which are chemically formed, and others which generate power by atomic means, as well as some which use sunlight for the generation of electric power. The atomic types utilize isotopes which are radioactive and can generate voltages. The sunshine battery, on the other hand, employs strips of silicon in a crystalline form. These silicon strips function on the same principle as the solid-state devices which are described in Chapter 12. Each strip is approximately two inches long and a half inch wide. When sunlight strikes these strips, electric energy is generated. The battery generates electricity from the wavelengths of visible light. The basic types of the most commonly used batteries are discussed in this chapter.

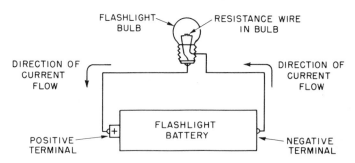

Fig. 2-1. Current flows from negative to positive terminal.

A battery, in its strictest sense, is a combination of basic energy-producing units known as cells. Each cell has available at its terminals a certain voltage, and when two or more such cells are placed in series, they form a battery of increased voltage. A primary cell is the type commonly used in flashlights and for some portable transistor radios. The cell principle in the chemical types is based on the fact that when two dissimilar metals (such as zinc and copper, or zinc and carbon) are placed in a solution of an acid, they act as a base. Electrons are then torn away from one metal element (the positive terminal), and flow internally and accumulate on the zinc element, making the latter negative. If zinc and carbon elements are employed, the zinc element is called the *negative electrode,* and the carbon section is called the *positive electrode.*

The primary cell utilized in flashlight batteries employs a chemical paste made up of sal ammoniac and zinc chloride, as the principal active ingredients. The chemical paste (or the solution in a wet battery) is called the *electrolyte.*

The chemical action of tearing electrons from the carbon plate and depositing them on the zinc electrode creates a potential difference between the two terminals of the cell. If a circuit is formed by connecting a resistor to the negative and positive terminals, the closed circuit will permit electrons to flow. The electrons flow out of the negative terminal of the cell, through the resistor, and into the positive electrode. Thus, the cell converts chemical energy into electric energy.

The *size* of the electrodes in such a cell has little influence in determining the potential developed. The emf of a single primary cell is 1.5 volts when new, and this will gradually decrease as the cell is utilized, or as it ages.

Figure 2-2 shows a cross section of the basic construction of a flashlight-type cell. The outside shell consists of a zinc can which, as previously mentioned, serves as the negative electrode. When the cell circuit is completed by adding a resistor across the terminals, the current flow through the cell consumes some of this zinc, because of the action of the electrolyte chemicals.

The separator consists of a pulpboard paper lining, coated with a layer of electrolyte paste made up of sal ammoniac, zinc chloride, and other material to form a thick consistency. This layer of electrolyte also separates the zinc from the depolarizing mixture, but permits the electrochemical action to continue between them. The depolarizing mixture contains manganese dioxide to combine with hydrogen as it accumulates, and carbon to provide conductivity. Other chemicals such as graphite are added, and the mixture also contains some of the sal ammoniac and zinc chloride previously mentioned.

The depolarized mixture aids in giving the cell much longer life than

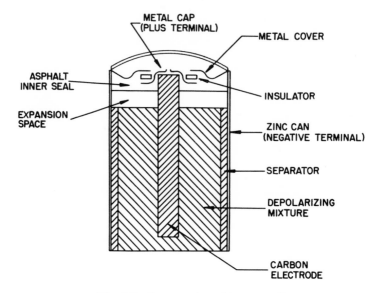

Fig. 2-2. Cross section of battery cell.

would normally be the case. Depolarization is a chemical reaction which the cell undergoes; this reaction occurs while the cell is not in use, and thus tends to "rejuvenate" the cell to some extent. For this reason, it is advantageous to use the cell intermittently.

The carbon elecrtode rod through the center is the *positive* terminal of the cell, and provides a conducting path for the current flow. This carbon electrode is composed of powdered carbon particles bonded together and made rigid by baking at a very high temperature.

An inner expansion space is provided to permit the cell contents to expand without causing the cell to bulge during use. The cell top is closed at the center by an asphalt inner seal. A metal cover is usually employed, which also closes the cell at the top and sides, minimizing breakage and bulging. This metal cover section is insulated from the metal cap that makes contact with the carbon positive terminal at the center top of the cell.

These primary cells can be combined in parallel to make a large A battery which furnishes more power than a single cell, or they can be used in series to provide higher voltage batteries, such as B and C batteries. Cell combinations are described more fully in Chapter 3.

Battery cells have an internal resistance determined by the type of chemicals used. The internal resistance of a primary cell is very low when the cell is new, but increases as the cell ages, and also as it is used. As the internal resistance increases (because of chemical changes), there is also a decrease of voltage across the terminals, and a decline in the power available from the cell. Internal cell or battery resistance is not easily measured with accuracy and, in practical applications, internal resistance values need not be known. Compensation for internal resistance is made by *bypassing,* a process described more fully in Chapter 13.

THE MERCURY CELL

Another type of cell which has been popular, for portable electronic equipment requiring low voltages, is the mercury cell. This cell uses a chemical compound of mercury for the electrolyte which provides for a fairly constant voltage over the life of the cell. For hearing aid usage, such cells have been made with a diameter of less than ½ inch and thickness near that of a 25-cent piece. Where extreme miniaturization is not a factor, the life of the mercury cell has been extended by increasing thickness to approximately ½ inch.

The mercury cell has a starting voltage of approximately 1.25, as compared to approximately 1.5 for the flashlight-type cell. For the mercury cell, however, the voltage decline during use is quite gradual, while with the flashlight-type cell there is an abrupt voltage decline during initial use. The small size of the mercury cell and its fairly constant voltage lend themselves advantageously to transistor circuit applications.

THE SECONDARY CELL

The secondary cell is a so-called *storage* cell to which electric energy is applied and converted into chemical energy. This chemical electric power is stored in the cell and reconverted into electric energy when the cell circuit is completed by placing a resistance material across it to permit current flow.

The storage battery used in automobiles is made up of a lead-acid type of secondary cells. In such batteries, the negative electrode of each cell is usually composed of a spongy lead, while the positive electrode is composed of lead peroxide. The two elements are immersed in an electrolyte of sulfuric acid. When current flows through the cell due to a closed circuit, some of the diluted sulfuric acid is transferred from the electrolyte chemical to the lead plates. Since sulfuric acid is heavier than water, there is a change in weight when the battery is fully charged, in relation to its discharged condition. A device known as a *hydrometer* is utilized to determine the condition of the cell by measuring the density of the electrolyte.

Actually, the storage battery does not "store" electric energy, but stores *chemical* energy. The latter is converted to electric energy when the circuit is completed by applying a resistor or resistive load to the battery. The

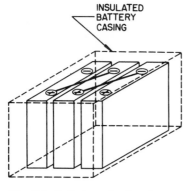

INSULATED
BATTERY
CASING

Fig. 2-3. Cells in series for storage battery.

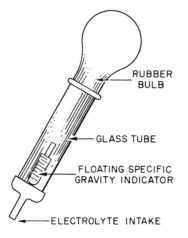

RUBBER
BULB

GLASS TUBE

FLOATING SPECIFIC
GRAVITY INDICATOR

ELECTROLYTE INTAKE

Fig. 2-4. Typical hydrometer.

amount of chemical energy which the battery is capable of storing depends on the area of the plates. Three secondary cell types are commonly employed to obtain a 6-volt battery, such as shown in Fig. 2-3. Six secondary cells are necessary for the 12-volt car battery. The entire battery is encased in a hard rubber or plastic case, with provision available, in the form of removable caps, for checking the water density versus electrolyte density in each cell.

The hydrometer has a small float, which is marked with a scale usually starting at 1,000 and ending at 1,300. Some scales also have color sections which are labeled *fully charged, half-charged,* and *discharged.* At full charge, the electrolyte is heavier, since it contains a greater amount of acid, and the specific gravity of the electrolyte is approximately 1,280, which corresponds to the markings on the hydrometer. Thus, when the battery is fully charged, the hydrometer will read near the 1,300 mark, while a completely discharged battery will be indicated by a hydrometer reading of approximately 1,100. A typical hydrometer is shown in Fig. 2-4.

BATTERY CHARGING

The lead storage cell, such as is used in automobiles, can be recharged after use. The charging device consists of a unit which furnishes at its terminals a voltage somewhat greater than the battery voltage. This higher voltage then forces current to flow through the battery in opposite direction to the current flow which occurs during the time the battery is normally discharging through a load.

The storage battery, as previously mentioned, has a chemical storage capacity proportionate to the activity and size of the plates utilized. This is generally expressed in *ampere hours,* which indicate how many hours the battery can deliver a given amount of current measured in amperes (the ampere is discussed in greater detail later in this chapter). Most batteries are rated at eight hours for a 100-ampere-hour battery. This would indicate that such a battery can supply 12.5 amperes of current continuously for eight hours (12.5 × 8 = 100 ampere hours).

The charging rate depends on the amount of current forced through the battery in opposite direction to what would flow during normal operation of the battery. The higher the charging potential, the greater the charging current which will flow.

Too high a charging rate will not only increase battery temperature, but will also generate an excessive amount of gas. Some gas in generated even at lower charging rates and, for this reason, no lighted matches or other open flames should be brought near a battery which is being charged. The 100-ampere-hour battery can be charged at a rate ranging between about 10 amperes to a fraction of an ampere. Some battery chargers start at a higher rate, then gradually reduce the charging rate in amperes as the battery nears full charge. A lower charging rate is recommended wherever possible. Higher rates should be used only when it is urgent to put the battery into service again as soon as possible.

The average life of the lead-type storage battery can be extended for several years by keeping the electrolyte at a good level above the plates. This means the periodic addition of pure water (or distilled water), as well as occasional checking to see that the charge level has not decreased to too low a value. The top of the battery should be kept clean, and the terminals may be coated with petroleum jelly to minimize the corrosion which is set up because of acid leakage.

When the battery is fully charged, there is a minimum danger of its freezing when exposed to extremely cold weather. When the battery is near the discharge level and the electrolyte reads about 1,100 on the hydrometer, the freezing point is approximately 20 degrees above zero. When the hydrometer reads 1,250 to indicate a fully charged battery, the freezing point is approximately 60 degrees below zero.

OTHER ELECTRIC SOURCES

Magnetism is also used for producing current flow through conductors and circuits. Both the permanent magnets and the so-called electromagnets (formed by passing current through a coil) produce the magnetic lines of force discussed in the preceding chapter. When a conductor, such as a wire (or a coil composed of wire) is moved through magnetic lines of force, a current flow is produced. This process is more fully described in Chapter 7. The principles of producing current flow by utilizing magnetic lines of force are employed in transformers, generators, and a variety of other electronic devices as subsequently detailed in Chapters 7 and 8.

Thermal (heat) processes are also used for creating electron movement. One thermal method consists in joining the ends of two dissimilar metals and heating the joined ends, as shown in Fig. 2-5 (A). A voltage appears at the open ends, and, if these open ends are connected to a suitable current path (a conductor), electric current will flow. This device, known as a *thermocouple,* finds applications in industry through its use for reading high temperatures (in commercial ovens or kilns), and as a temperature-sensitive device for high-frequency radio signal measurements, and also for use as a protective safety device.

Another use of the thermal process for production of electron movement is in an evacuated tube, as shown in Fig. 2-5 (B). By bringing a filament within the tube to a high temperature, a cloud of free electrons is produced, as more fully explained in Chapter 11.

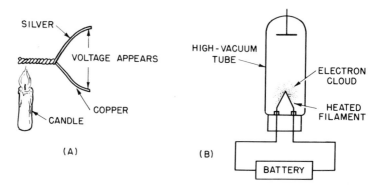

Fig. 2-5. Thermal process for electron movement.

Photoelectric emission is a term applied to still another process for creating electron movement, and hence current flow. This method consists in permitting light to strike certain sensitive materials such as selenium or cesium, which, in turn, will then emit electrons (see Fig. 2-6). Again, if a current path is provided, the amount of current which flows can be used as an indication of the amount of light striking the photosensitive surface. The uses of photoelectric emission are numerous and find application in burglar alarms, devices for turning lights on at night, television cameras, motion picture "sound on film" techniques, and

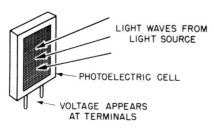

Fig. 2-6. Photoelectric emission.

other devices. Heinrich Hertz (1857-1894), the noted German scientist, is credited with the discovery of photoelectric emission.

UNITS OF CURRENT

From the foregoing discussion, it is evident that numerous methods exist for producing electron movement, or *current flow,* as it is more commonly known. All processes generate current quantities decidedly useful in practical electricity and electronics. Provisions must be made, however, to transfer electrons in the form of current flow through appropriate devices and circuits, and for such purposes a current flow path is provided by wires or other metals known as *conductors,* as mentioned in Chapter 1. The ability of a substance to conduct electric current is known as *conductivity.* Current can also be made to flow in substances other than metal, such as liquids, gases, or materials whose composition offers opposition to the flow and limits the amount of current to definite quantities. The unit of electric current is known as the *ampere,* named after André Ampère (1775-1836), the famous French experimenter and scientist. One ampere of current represents the exact quantity of electrons which flows past a given point in one second, and is equal to one coulomb. (See the earlier discussion on charges in Chapter 1.) The symbol for current is the capital letter *I.*

While many circuits have a current flow of one or more amperes, there are also numerous electronic devices wherein only a fractional portion of an ampere of current flows. The amount of current which flows in any electronic unit or device can be measured by means of a current-reading meter, as more fully detailed in Chapter 5.

UNITS OF RESISTANCE

All substances do not provide the same degree of conductivity, as mentioned in the foregoing discussion. Hence, some metals offer little opposition to current flow, while others will oppose current flow to a considerable degree. The opposition to current flow is known as *resistance,* and the unit of measurement for resistance is an *ohm,* named after George Ohm (1787-1854), the German professor who formulated the basic law relating to current flow, resistance, etc., described later, and known as *Ohm's law.* The symbol for resistance is the capital letter *R.* The Greek letter Ω (omega) is used to indicate ohm or ohms.

The standard which has been established for one ohm is the resistance provided at zero degrees centigrade, by a column of mercury having a cross-sectional area of one square millimeter and a length of 106.3 centimeters. When a substance is specially prepared to offer a given amount of resistance, it is known as a *resistor*. Resistors of all types are widely used in virtually all electric and electronic devices. Examples of types, plus practical factors, are discussed in Chapter 3.

UNITS OF CONDUCTANCE

The measure of how well a substance will permit current flow is known as *conductance*. Because conductance is functionally opposite to resistance, it is the reciprocal of resistance, and is therefore equal to the numeral *one* divided by the value of resistance, as expressed by the formula $1/R$. Thus, if a particular resistance is 1,000 ohms, the conductance is $\frac{1}{1,000} = 0.001$. Because conductance is the opposite of resistance, the unit for conductance is expressed as the word *ohm* spelled backwards, which becomes *mho*. Hence, the conductance for the last example is 0.001 mho. Generally, a fractional measurement of mho is used, known as the *micromho*. This is one-millionth of a mho. The symbol for conductance is the capital letter *G*.

UNITS OF ELECTRIC FORCE

As a brief review, electric pressure is required to move electrons, and thus establish current flow. Such electric pressure is known as *electromotive force,* and this is abbreviated as EMF or emf. The unit of emf is the *volt,* named after Alessandro Volta (1745-1827), the Italian researcher who first built a cell which provided emf, and which was the forerunner of our modern battery. Because the unit is known as the volt, emf is also referred to as *voltage,* with the symbol *E*. Hence, either *E* or emf designates voltage (electric pressure), and sometimes the word *potential* is also used. All these terms have the same meaning. *A volt is the quantity of electromotive force that will cause one ampere of current to flow through one ohm of resistance.*

The source of electrons, from a battery or other electric generating device, is referred to as the negative terminal or negative section of the unit. The terminal toward which electrons flow is designated as the positive terminal. Instead of referring to the two different types of potentials as charges, the term *polarity* is more often used. Thus, a flashlight cell may have a potential (emf) of 1.5 volts, with one terminal having a negative polarity and the other terminal a positive polarity.

Years ago, when electric phenomena were first observed, the battery polarities were thought to indicate that current flowed from the positive terminal to the negative terminal. This is still known as the *conventional current flow theory,* and is still referred to in some of the literature. For the study of electronics, however, the direction of electron flow is recognized as constituting also the direction of the current flow (from negative to positive). This concept is used throughout this text.

In practical electric or electronic applications, voltages of a fractional value will frequently be encountered, as well as voltages having values up in the thousands, depending on the amount of electric pressure necessary to force current flow through the resistances encountered in the various circuits and devices. Hence, fractional unit values of voltage are often in terms of a *millivolt* (one-thousandth of a volt) or *microvolt* (one-millionth of a volt). Thus, 0.001 volt can be expressed as 1 millivolt (1 mv), while 0.00003 volt can be expressed as 30 microvolts (30 μv). High voltages are often designated as *kilovolts* (kv), to indicate thousands of volts. Thus, 10 kilovolts represents 10,000 volts. Such terms simplify the designation of fractional voltages or high-value voltages, by substituting a prefix for the number of zeros which would have to be employed.

OHM'S LAW

The values of current, voltage, and resistance are all related, because the amount of current which flows is dependent on the amount of electric pressure (emf) applied and the opposition (resistance) encountered by the electron movement. These relationships were established by George Ohm, and were set down as specific formulas whereby an unknown quantity of either *R, I,* or *E* can be found when the values of any two of these are known. One of these formulas shows how the value of current (*I*) can be ascertained when voltage (*E*) and resistance (*R*) are known.

$$I = \frac{E}{R} \qquad (2\text{-}1)$$

This formula indicates that the amount of current flowing in a circuit is equal to the quotient obtained when the voltage value is divided by the resistance value. Thus, if there are 10 volts impressed across a 5-ohm resistor, the current flow through the resistor is 2 amperes.

An unknown value of either voltage or resistance can also be found by rearrangement of the formula. Voltage, for example, can be obtained if the values of current and resistance are known.

$$E = IR \qquad (2\text{-}2)$$

As this formula shows, an unknown voltage can be found by multiplying the current value by the resistance value. Thus, if the current flow through a 3-ohm resistance is 20 amperes, the voltage across the resistance is 60.

If the value of the resistance is desired, the known values of current and voltage are used for solving the problem by use of the formula:

$$R = \frac{E}{I} \qquad (2\text{-}3)$$

As an example, assume that the voltage across a resistance is 50, and the value of the current flow is 10 amperes. Dividing the E value by the I value indicates a resistance of 5 ohms.

UNITS OF ELECTRIC POWER

When voltage is applied to a conductor, current will flow, and the amounts of current flow and voltage represent a quantity of power. Such electric power can be used for heating purposes, operating a motor, or in other applications of electric energy. Since we cannot get power for nothing, a battery or other power source must be used to generate the energy needed. The electric power is measured by the amount of voltage multiplied by the quantity of current flow.

$$P = EI \qquad (2\text{-}4)$$

The unit of power is the *watt,* named after the Scottish inventor James Watt (1736-1819). One watt of power is equal to one ampere of current flow produced by one volt of electric pressure. Because the unit is the watt, the capital letter W is sometimes used to represent power, instead of the symbol P given in the previous formula.

When power is calculated in terms of time, the unit of energy is the *joule.* This is also known as the *watt-second,* and represents one watt of power for one second. In the measurement of ordinary electric power consumed in homes, the *kilowatt-hour* (kw-hr) is utilized, and this refers to 1,000 watts for one hour. In many electronic applications, however, only fractional power units are used, and the term *milliwatt* (mw) is then utilized for convenience, to express one-thousandth of a watt. Thus, 0.0005 watt $=0.5$ milliwatt.

Formula (2-4) solves for the amount of energy consumed in terms of unit watts. Hence, if 20 volts are present across a resistance, and 2 amperes of current flow, the amount of energy consumed equals 40 watts. If E is unknown, but I and R are known, the following formula can be used.

$$P = I^2R \qquad (2\text{-}5)$$

Thus, if 2 amperes of current are flowing and the *R* value is 10 ohms, the amount of power is:

$$P = 2 \times 2 \times 10 = 40$$

Power can also be found by

$$P = \frac{E^2}{R} \qquad (2\text{-}6)$$

Example: A voltage of 20 is measured across a resistance of 4 ohms. What is the power in watts?

Solution: Twenty squared equals $20 \times 20 = 400$. When this product is divided by the value of *R* (4 ohms), the answer is 100 watts.

Because power is also related to Ohm's law, the amount of power used can be employed in formulas for finding unknown values of current or voltage, as shown by Formulas (2-7).

$$I = \frac{P}{E}, \qquad R = \frac{P}{I^2}, \qquad E = \sqrt{PR}, \qquad I = \sqrt{\frac{P}{R}} \qquad (2\text{-}7)$$

Example: If the power consumed in a circuit is 50 watts and the circuit resistance is 800 ohms, what is the applied voltage?

Solution: Using the third equation of Formula (2-7)

$$E = \sqrt{50 \times 800} = \sqrt{40,000} = 200 \text{ volts}$$

UNITS OF MAGNETISM

In electricity and electronics, certain terms and unit values are employed to define the characteristics of magnetic materials. The types of magnetic materials also have names applied to them for easy recognition and reference. The following list, with definitions, covers the most commonly encountered.

Magnetic flux. The number of lines of force in a given area of magnetism. Magnetic flux is symbolized by the Greek letter phi (ϕ). The unit of magnetic flux is the *maxwell,* and represents one line of the magnetic flux. The maxwell is named after James Maxwell (1831-1879), the famous Scotch theoretical physicist.

Flux density. This is a term applied to the number of lines of force which pass perpendicularly through a square centimeter, and is symbolized by the capital letter *B*. The unit of flux density is the *gauss,* named after the German mathematician Karl Gauss (1777-1855).

Magnetic field intensity. This relates to the force (magnetic field strength) exerted by the field, and the unit is the *oersted,* named after Hans Oersted (1777-1851), the Danish physicist. An oersted represents the intensity of the magnetic field at a 1-centimeter distance from the unit magnetic pole (in air or vacuum). The symbol for the oersted is the capital letter *H.*

Magnetic Induction. The term applies to the magnetizing of a magnetic material by inducing into it the lines of force from a magnet. Thus, a bar of iron when rubbed with a permanent magnet can become magnetized through magnetic induction.

Permeability. This is a measure of the conductivity of magnetic flux through a material. Permeability is symbolized by the Greek letter μ (mu). It is the ratio of the flux which exists when using a certain material to the flux which would be present if air were used instead. The permeability of air is thus considered as unity (one), and all other materials have varying degrees of permeability above one. Soft iron, for instance, has better conductivity for lines of force than steel, because it has greater permeability. Other materials with high permeability include cobalt, ferrite, and certain alloys. High permeability materials find extensive use as cores of transformers.

Reluctance. The opposition offered by material to the magnetic flux is referred to as its *reluctivity* or *reluctance,* and it corresponds to the resistance to current flow in electric circuits. The symbol is the script letter $\mathcal{R}$.

Permeance. This term, seldom used, refers to the property which determines the magnitude of the flux in a material and is equal to the reciprocal of reluctance; the symbol is the script letter $\mathcal{P}$.

Retentivity. The ability of a material to retain magnetism after withdrawal of the magnetizing force is known as its retentivity. Steel, for example, having a higher retentivity, will retain more magnetism than iron.

Instead of classifying materials simply as magnetic and nonmagnetic, modern practices group materials into three primary classifications, as follows:

Diamagnetic Materials. This is the term used for materials which become only slightly magnetized, even though under the influence of a strong magnetic field. When a diamagnetic material is magnetized, it is in a direction opposite to that of the external magnetizing force, as shown in Fig. 2-7(A). Diamagnetic materials have a permeability of less than unity, and include such metals as copper, silver, gold, and mercury.

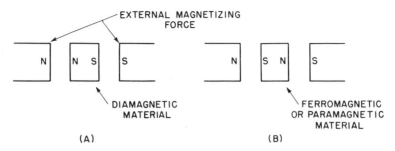

Fig. 2-7. Direction of magnetism for various materials.

Paramagnetic Materials. These materials become only slightly magnetized, even though under the influence of a strong magnetic field, as with the diamagnetic materials. The difference between the two, however, is that the paramagnetic materials become magnetized in the same direction as the external magnetizing field, as shown in Fig. 2-7(B). Permeability of the materials is greater than unity, though low compared to the ferromagnetic materials. Paramagnetic materials include aluminum, chromium, manganese, platinum, and also air.

Ferromagnetic Materials. The most important materials used in magnetic applications in electricity and electronics are the ferromagnetic materials. These are characterized by a very high permeability, and will become very strongly magnetized by a field relatively much weaker than that required for the other two types discussed. The direction of the induced magnetism is identical with that of the magnetizing field, as shown in Fig. 2-7(B), as with the paramagnetic materials. The permeability of ferromagnetic materials is not constant, but varies with the strength of the magnetizing field. Among the ferromagnetic materials, are iron, steel, cobalt, magnetite (lodestone), and alloys such as Alnico and Permalloy. Alnico derives its name from the metals used in the alloy: *al*uminum, *ni*ckel, and *co*balt (with some iron added). Permalloy (*perm*anent-*alloy*) contains iron and about four times as much nickel. Such newer alloys produce powerful magnets, and find extensive application in industry. Compared to soft iron, with a permeability of about 2,000, these alloys have permeability ratings ranging, under certain conditions, as high as 50,000 or more.

ABBREVIATED FORMS

To simplify explanations hereafter, it is expedient at this time to discuss the mathematical abbreviations utilized by engineers and technicians as a means for eliminating the necessity of writing long strings of zeros in very small fractional unit values or extremely large unit values. An understanding of these abbreviations will overcome the need for employing cumbersome numbers in referring to specific measured values.

As an illustration, the unit of electric current, the ampere, was previously indicated to consist of 6.28 electrons times the product of the figure 10 multiplied by itself 18 times. This enormous figure can be represented in much more simple form by setting it down as:

$$6.28 \times 10^{18}$$

This method of expression is known as the *Standard System of Scientific Notation* and is also called *engineers' shorthand,* because it is a method for writing large numbers in simple (abbreviated) form. Thus, if 10 is to be multiplied by itself, it is represented by 10^2 (*10 to the second power*). This expression, because it indicates that the 10 is to be multiplied by itself, represents 100. The expression 10^3 indicates the following multiplication process:

$$10 \times 10 \times 10 = 1{,}000$$

The basic number, here the "10" in 10^{18}, is called the *base,* and the raised (or superior) number is called the *exponent.*

Example: $6.28 \times 10^3 = 6{,}280.$

Note that the decimal point in 6.28 has been moved three places to the right in the answer. In using engineers' shorthand in the foregoing example, the initial figures were not changed, but only the decimal point. Similarly, 4.8×10^4 equals 48,000. Here the decimal has been moved four places to the right. The "shorthand" feature is more apparent when the exponent is a larger number: 6×10^8 equals 600,000,000. Thus, the engineers' shorthand expression is much simpler than writing the higher number out.

Scientific notation of *power of 10,* as it is also known, is also used with a minus sign. A minus power such as 10^{-2} moves the decimal two places to the left, because the exponent is -2.

Example: $8 \times 10^{-2} = 0.08.$

Again, the advantages of this kind of abbreviated notation are more apparent when the exponent is a larger number, such as 6.3×10^{-6} which, when written out, equals:

$$0.0000063$$

The expression 5×10^{-10} becomes:

$$0.0000000005$$

Since both fractional values in millionths and whole numbers in millions are encountered frequently in electronics, engineers' shorthand is quite useful in eliminating a long string of zeros:

$$10 = 10^1$$
$$100 = 10^2$$
$$1,000 = 10^3$$
$$10,000 = 10^4$$
$$100,000 = 10^5$$
$$1,000,000 = 10^6$$

$$0.1 = 10^{-1}$$
$$0.01 = 10^{-2}$$
$$0.001 = 10^{-3}$$
$$\text{one-millionth} = 10^{-6}$$
$$\text{one-millionth of a millionth} = 10^{-12}$$

$$100^0 = \text{one } (1)$$
$$100^1 = \text{one hundred } (100)$$
$$100^2 = \text{ten thousand } (10,000)$$
$$100^3 = \text{one million } (1,000,000)$$

In electronic work, it is not always convenient to use the unit expression of ampere, because only fractions of such current may be present. In such cases, the term milliampere and microampere are employed. *Milliampere* means one-thousandth of an ampere, and *microampere* means one-millionth of an ampere. The following list gives additional terms. These apply not only to current, but also to other units, as detailed in later chapters.

pico (micro-micro)	one-millionth of a millionth	(1×10^{-12})
nano (milli-micro)	one-thousandth of a millionth	(1×10^{-9})
micro	one-millionth	(1×10^{-6})
milli	one-thousandth	(1×10^{-3})
centi	one-hundredth	(1×10^{-2})
deci	one-tenth	(1×10^{-1})
deca	ten	(1×10^{1})
hecto	one hundred	(1×10^{2})
kilo	one thousand	(1×10^{3})
mega	one million	(1×10^{6})
giga	one thousand million	(1×10^{9})
tera	one million million	(1×10^{12})

REVIEW QUESTIONS

1. Define in your own words a primary cell.

2. Explain briefly what is meant by a secondary cell?

3. Briefly explain what materials can be used as a negative and a positive electrode in a cell.

4. What chemical composition may be used as a battery electrolyte?

5. When a storage battery is fully charged, is the chemical electrolyte heavier than when the battery has a low charge?

6. When is the lead-type storage battery more subect to freezing than otherwise?

7. Briefly explain two other processes besides battery usage for creating electron movements.

8. Define the word *resistance* with respect to current flow.

9. Give the unit terms for current, resistance, and conductance.

10. Briefly explain what is meant by electromotive force.

11. Explain what is meant by polarity and in which direction current flows with respect to polarity indications.

12. What determines the amount of electric power consumed by a resistor?

13. Define Ohm's law and give two equation examples of its application.

14. Briefly describe what is meant by field intensity and magnetic flux.

15. Briefly describe what is meant by permeability, and name three materials having high permeability.

16. Briefly explain what is meant by ferromagnetic materials, and compare them with the characteristics of diamagnetic materials.

17. (a) What whole number does 3.14×10^3 equal?
    (b) What whole number does 0.870×10^4 represent?

18. (a) What whole number does 15×10^6 equal?
    (b) What fractional number does 24×10^{-3} equal?
    (c) What fractional number does 340×10^{-4} equal?
    (d) What fractional number does $20,000 \times 10^{-6}$ represent?

PRACTICAL PROBLEMS

1. In an electronic fabrication control circuit, 845 volts appeared across a 1,300-ohm resistor. What amount of current flows through this resistor?

2. In an industrial electronic circuit a 9-ohm resistor was used to decrease the voltage applied to the filament of a tube. If the current through the resistor is 0.5 ampere, what voltage drop appears across the resistor?

3. In a test instrument for automation processes 2,000 volts dropped across a resistor which had 2.5 amperes of current flow through it. What is the value of the resistance?

4. In a plastic fabrication plant a heating element resistance of 500 ohms had 0.5 ampere of current flow through it. What is the power in watts dissipated by the resistor? What is the voltage drop across the resistor?

5. In a receiver a 400-ohm resistor had a 20-volt drop across it. What wattage is dissipated by the resistor? What amount of current flows through the resistor?

6. If a resistor dissipated 1,000 watts of power and the current through the resistor is 5 amperes, what is the value of the resistor? What voltage appears across the unit?

7. In a particular electronic device the voltage measured across a resistor was 0.02. What would this value be when expressed in millivolts?

8. A test instrument utilized for obtaining visual characteristics of electronic equipment uses 5,000 volts. How would this voltage be expressed in kilovolts?

9. A test instrument indicates that 0.03 amperes of current is flowing in an electronic circuit. In recording this information, how would the fractional current be expressed in milliamperes?

10. A delicate instrument is applied to a low-power device and reads 0.0004 ampere. Express this in milliamperes.

11. A broadcast station is rated as having a power of 50 kilowatts. How many watts of power does this represent?

12. A certain transistor radio has an audio output rating of 200 milliwatts. What is this in fractional wattage?

13. In measuring an antenna system, it is indicated that 250 microvolts is delivered to a receiver. Which of the following values also correctly expresses this voltage?

$$0.250 \quad \text{volt}$$
$$0.0025 \quad \text{volt}$$
$$0.00025 \text{ volt}$$

14. A certain frequency-modulation station transmits on 90 megacycles. How many cycles does this represent?

3

BASIC

RESISTOR

CIRCUITS

INTRODUCTION

The word *circuit* has already been introduced in Chapter 2, with a basic type illustrated in Fig. 2-1. A circuit is a combination of two or more electric or electronic components which are wired together in some specific manner to perform a required task. Circuits may be *closed* or *open* types, depending on their usage as needed at a given time. A flashlight with a switch, for instance, represents an open circuit when the switch has not been thrown to light the bulb. When the switch is closed, the circuit becomes a closed (or completed) circuit, and the amount of current flow is determined by the battery voltage and the resistance rating of the bulb.

An undesired characteristic is the *short circuit*. This comes about when the circuit resistance is abnormally low in comparison to the power source used. If, for instance, a copper wire were placed directly across a battery, the virtually zero resistance of the wire would permit such high current conductivity that all the current which the battery can furnish would flow. The copper wire, in such an instance, "shorts out" the battery and hence we get the term *short circuit*. Short circuits blow fuses, open circuit breakers, and impose a severe and possibly damaging load on the power source.

In this chapter the basic aspects of series and parallel resistor circuits are reviewed. Before analyzing these circuit characteristics, however, the practical factors regarding resistors should be understood, and hence are covered initially.

R-E-I RELATIONSHIPS

The voltage (electric pressure) required to cause a given amount of current to flow through a conductor or resistance, is dependent on the ohmic value of the resistance. This is exemplified by the application of Ohm's law, in a circuit where a resistance value of 10,000 ohms permits only 0.005 amperes (5 milliamperes) of current to flow at a potential of 50 volts. Raising the voltage to 100 doubles the amount of current flow to 0.01 ampere (10 milliamperes). At 50 volts, however, the amount of current flow can also be increased by reducing the resistance. Hence, in practical electric and electronic circuits, the amount of current is not only established or adjusted by voltage values, but also by using appropriate resistance in the form of physical resistors.

The amount of resistance within a conductor or a resistor depends on the composition of the unit, its cross section, length, and temperature. Wire usually has a high resistance at higher temperatures, while many nonmetallic substances offer lower resistance as the temperature rises. Pure soft-metal elements, such as silver and copper, have a very low resistance —so low in fact that when silver or copper wire of any sizable diameter is used, it can be considered as a conductor whose resistance to current flow is practically negligible, and usually not worth considering. (The current-carrying capacity of wire is covered more fully later in this chapter.) Harder elements or compounds, such as iron, metal alloys of iron (steel, for instance), or nichrome wire, have a measurable resistance, which can be made quite high if the wire diameter is made small.

Plastics, ceramic tile products, wood, glass, and many other materials offer such a high opposition to current flow that their resistance can be considered to be virtually infinite. Such materials can be used for supports or separators of current-carrying conductors and, because of their very high resistivity, will prevent the currents from straying from their assigned paths. Hence, such items act as an electric *insulation* between two sections which have current flow, and hence are known as *insulators*. (See Fig. 3-1.)

Commercial resistors differ widely in size and composition, in order to match the various requirements of their countless applications. Resistors

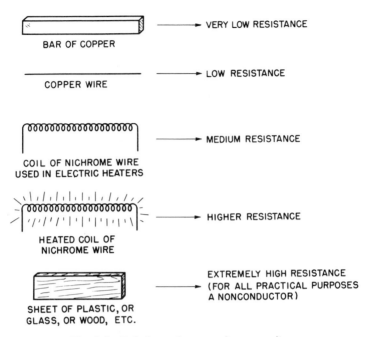

Fig. 3-1. Relative resistances of common items.

are rated both according to their ohmic value and their wattage. The ohmic value is, of course, an indication of the actual resistance expressed in ohms, such as 20 ohms, 1,000 ohms, or several megohms. (A *megohm* represents one million ohms; in some applications, values as high as 5 or 10 megohms are used.) The wattage rating of a resistor is directly related to the amount of heat generated and indicates how much heat is permitted in the resistor before the point is reached where there is danger of resistor damage. The amount of heat which a particular resistor will tolerate depends on the composition of the resistor, its heat dissipating factors, and the general cross-sectional area. Thus, if a resistor is designated as a 50-watt resistor, this resistor can withstand that wattage (when suspended in free air) without overheating excessively and burning out. In actual usage, however, a larger wattage-rating resistor than the one calculated is usually employed, even though this is somewhat more costly. The larger-rating resistor will operate at lower temperatures, and will thus have a longer life.

Various combinations of voltage and current values can provide a given wattage rating. For instance, a resistor consumes 50 watts when the applied voltage is 2, and 25 amperes of current is flowing. On the other hand, if 10 amperes of current is flowing and 5 volts are applied, the amount of energy consumed will again be 50 watts. Fifty watts will also be consumed if 50 volts are applied and 1 ampere of current flows.

Resistors are not only obtainable in a variety of shapes and sizes, but can also be formed from special wire, carbon alloys, or other materials. Wire-wound resistors use a special wire such as *nichrome,* which has valuable resistive characteristics, as mentioned earlier. Wire of this kind is capable of handling a considerable amount of current, and for this reason resistors fashioned from nichrome wire are employed where considerable wattage is encountered. Nichrome, or other special wire, is also used for the resistive elements of electric heaters and electric irons. In these devices, sufficient current is made to flow through the resistive element to generate the required heat. Such heating devices consume much more electric power than do ordinary light bulbs and consequently have a much higher wattage rating.

In electronic devices, the most popular type of resistor is the carbon-composition resistor. Such resistors use a mixture of carbon and other substances to establish a fixed value of resistance. Carbon resistors are small units, and are available in wattage ratings starting at ¼ watt and continuing through intermediate wattage sizes up to 2 watts. The carbon resistors are less expensive than the nichrome-wire types and therefore are extensively employed in receivers, high-fidelity systems, and low-power industrial devices.

Two basic types of fixed resistors are illustrated in Fig. 3-2. The one shown at the top is a wire-wound resistor, available in various wattage ratings from a few watts to well over 50 watts. In radio and television receivers, high-fidelity systems, and other comparable electronic devices, only a few wire-wound high wattage resistors are employed, and rarely are such resistors used with wattage ratings as high as 50 watts. Generally, when it is necessary to use wire-wound resistors, ratings ranging from 5 to 20 watts are utilized.

Fig. 3-2. Fixed resistors. (Courtesy International Resistance Co.)

The wire-wound resistor shown at the top of Fig. 3-2 has an adjustable center terminal, which connects to the internal resistance wire. This center terminal can be adjusted to procure an intermediate value of resistance below the value established between the two outer terminals.

It must be emphasized that the ohmic value of the resistor is independent of its wattage rating. A 20-ohm resistor can be purchased with a 1-watt rating, a 10-watt rating, or a 50-watt rating, as desired. Conversely, a 30-watt resistor could be purchased with an ohmic value of 10 ohms, 100 ohms, or 1,000 ohms.

The lower resistor of Fig. 3-2 is the standard carbon unit previously mentioned, and is used extensively in electronic devices. In order to facilitate identifying the resistance value in ohms, bands of color are painted on the body of the resistor. By *coding* a resistor in this manner, the necessity for measuring its value with a meter is eliminated. The fixed resistance value is indicated by several bands of color shown on the left of the resistor. Such identification is in accordance with the standard Color Code given in the Appendix. The carbon resistors are generally available in resistance value tolerances of 5% and 10%, as shown by the chart in the Appendix. The wattage ratings of such resistors are between ¼ watt and 2 watts, as required by the circuits in the resistors are used.

Frequently, the necessity arises for using a resistor which has provision for varying the resistance manually. Such variable resistors are required for volume controls in audio amplifiers and receivers, for level controls in test equipment, and for other applications described later. Variable resistors of this type are usually manufactured by depositing the carbon composition on a circular strip of paper, though there are occasions where resistance wire is wrapped around a circular form, when higher-wattage variable resistors are needed. In both the carbon and wire types, a sliding contact permits a change of the resistance value. Several variable resistor types are illustrated in Fig. 3-3. The one shown at the upper left has three terminals, with the center terminal representing the sliding arm. This type of variable resistor is usually furnished with a long shaft which may be cut off to the length desired.

Another type of variable resistor is shown in the upper right of Fig. 3-3. This variable resistor has a short slotted arm. Such resistors are often found in circuits where the resistance value need only be adjusted occasionally for balancing the circuit. Since continuous manual variation is not necessary, a screwdriver slot is provided for adjustments when required. These resistors are often used in high-fidelity amplifiers for hum balancing, as more fully described in the section on bias methods (Chapter 15).

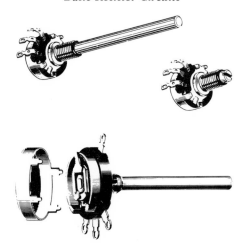

Fig. 3-3. Variable resistors. (Courtesy International Resistance Co.)

The variable resistor at the bottom center of Fig. 3-3 shows the rear cover removed, thus exposing the sliding contact arm and the resistance strip. This is a wire-wound resistor. The internal appearance of the carbon type would be similar, except that a flat circular strip of carbon-coated paper or fiber would be used. The additional terminal shown at the top is a fixed tap sometimes utilized for "bass compensation," as discussed in Chapter 15.

Variable resistors (such as those illustrated in Fig. 3-3) are often provided with a switch arrangement, so that the unit can be combined with an "on-off" switch. The switch is fastened to the back of the control, and a hole in the back cover of the variable resistor allows the variable arm of the resistor to trip the switch mechanism. The switch mechanism is insulated from the resistor, and is actually a completely separate circuit.

The manner in which resistors are indicated in electronic diagrams is shown in Fig. 3-4. The number of points in the zigzag formation is unimportant and is left to the draftsman's decision. A fixed resistor is shown at the top of the drawing. The two lower drawings show how a variable resistor may be designated.

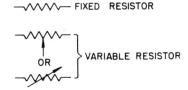

Fig. 3-4. Symbols for resistors.

Variable resistors are sometimes referred to as *rheostats* or *potentiometers*. A rheostat is usually the term used when a wire-wound variable resistor is employed for controlling the amount of voltage applied to a

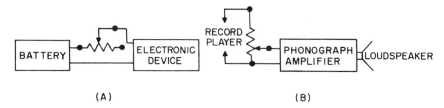

(A)   (B)

Fig. 3-5. (A) Use of variable resistor as rheostat (B) Use of variable resistor as potentiometer.

circuit or electronic device. In most instances, only the variable arm terminal and one outside terminal are employed. When such a resistor is placed in series with the current flow, as shown in Fig. 3-5(A), the amount of voltage drop which occurs across the variable resistor can be regulated by moving the variable arm. With a higher resistance value, a larger voltage drop develops across the rheostat, and less voltage is applied to the terminating circuit or electronic device. Since a higher resistance also decreases the series current, a reduction in output voltage occurs. When the variable arm is adjusted so that the series rheostat has less resistance, more current flows to the output circuit and a larger voltage drop occurs across it. With less resistance in the rheostat, output voltage will increase, and a smaller voltage drop develops across the variable resistor.

A potentiometer is usually employed for controlling signal levels, and in most instances a low wattage unit is chosen. The two outside terminals, as well as the variable arm terminal, are used. When the two outside terminals are connected to a voltage source, the amount of output voltage is a function of the setting of the variable arm furnishing such voltage as shown in Fig. 3-5(B).

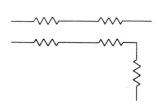

Fig. 3-6. Symbols for series resistors.

When two or more resistors are joined together, they are drawn as indicated in Fig. 3-6. Resistors may be combined in three ways: in series, in parallel, or in series-parallel. When a number of resistors, or a combination of resistors and other components such as coils are interconnected in one drawing, the latter is referred to as a *schematic*. The resistor combinations shown in Fig. 3-6 are wired in series.

RESISTORS IN SERIES

When resistors are wired up in series, the total circuit resistance increases, because each resistor contributes opposition to the circuit's current flow. Thus, if a 10-ohm resistor is placed in series with another 10-ohm resistor, the total resistance contributed by the two is 20 ohms, double what one resistor offers in ohmic opposition. Similarly, if three 10-ohm resistors are in series, the total resistance is 30 ohms. Hence, the formula for resistors in series indicates a simple additive process:

$$\text{Total Resistance} = R_1 + R_2 + R_3 + R_4 + \ldots R_n \qquad (3\text{-}1)$$

Figure 3-7 illustrates the principles of series resistors as applied to resistors of 4 ohms, 8 ohms, and 3 ohms. The total resistance of the circuit is, therefore 15 ohms $(4 + 8 + 3 = 15)$.

As shown, a current-measuring meter inserted in the series circuit indicates that 2 amperes of current is flowing. Also, since the three resistors are connected to a 30-volt battery, it is evident that the 30 volts must be present across the *combination* of resistors. Ohm's law proves this, because if the total resistance is 15 ohms, and the current is 2 amperes, then $E = IR = 2 \times 15 = 30$ volts. Because the individual

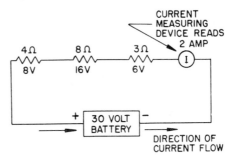

Fig. 3-7. Series circuit showing current measuring devices.

resistors have different values, *the amount of voltage across each* resistor differs. Across the 4-ohm resistor, there is a drop of 8 volts (2 amperes multiplied by 4 ohms). Across the 8-ohm resistor, there is a drop of 16 volts, and across the 3-ohm resistor a drop of 6 volts exists. When these individual voltages are added together, they will equal the total voltage previously calculated.

Current	$\times$	Resistance	$=$	Voltage
2	$\times$	4	$=$	8
2	$\times$	8	$=$	16
2	$\times$	3	$=$	6
2	$\times$	15	$=$	30

Total current in this example is 2 amperes. Because the resistors are in series, the amount of current at any point in the circuit is the same. It must be remembered that current is a measure of the amount of electron flow past a given point for a certain time interval. This amount would not change unless the applied pressure (voltage) or the resistance value (ohms) changes. Thus, current is always the same through any portion of a given series circuit, though the voltage across an individual resistor is proportional to the resistance value. In a series circuit, it is necessary only to solve for the current through *any one* of the several resistors to get the *current* value for the *entire* circuit.

Once the total resistance value has been found, we could prove the validity of the meter reading of Fig. 3-7 by Ohm's law.

$$I = \frac{E}{R} = \frac{30}{15} = 2 \text{ amperes}$$

Once two values are known, other unit values can be found by using appropriate Ohm's law equations. For Fig. 3-7, the power dissipated in each resistor, as well as total power, can be solved by use of the formula I^2R.

Current²	×	Resistance	=	Wattage
4	×	4	=	16
4	×	8	=	32
4	×	3	=	12
4	×	15	=	60

Additional proof can be had by utilizing any of the formulas previously given. Thus, if the voltage is to be calculated from the power and resistance in the circuit, we would employ the formula $E = \sqrt{PR}$. Since the power previously calculated is 60 watts, and the total resistance 15 ohms, the following calculation would be performed:

$$PR = 15 \times 60 = 900$$

$$E = \sqrt{PR} = \sqrt{900} = 30 \text{ volts}$$

While current in any part of a series circuit is the same as in any other part of the circuit, it must be remembered that the current depends on the amount of resistance as well as voltage. If *either* the resistance or the voltage in a circuit is changed, the former current value will also change. Thus, if the same values of resistors are employed as in Fig. 3-7, but twice the voltage is applied across them, as shown in Fig. 3-8, a new value of current results. This new current value can be calculated by using the current formula $(I = E/R)$. Thus, the new voltage value of 60, divided by the total resistance of 15, equals 4 amperes, showing that, when the voltage is doubled, the current also doubles. In the circuit shown in Fig. 3-8, the new value of current (4 amperes) is the same in any part of the circuit. To calculate the new voltage drops across each resistor we will apply the voltage formula $(E = IR)$.

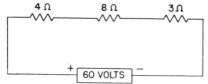

Fig. 3-8. Series circuit with 60-v battery

Hence, across the 4-ohm resistor there is now 16 volts, because we are multiplying 4 amperes times 4 ohms of resistance. The same calculation is applied to the other resistors:

Current	×	Resistance	=	Voltage
4	×	4	=	16
4	×	8	=	32
4	×	3	=	12
4	×	15	=	60

If the wattage across each resistor is recalculated, it is found that the wattage has now increased by four. Since the wattage is equal to the I^2R, the new value of current (4 ohms) is multiplied by itself to give a product of 16. This number is now used to multiply the ohmic value of each resistance, which gives a new set of wattage values:

Current²	×	Resistance	=	Wattage
16	×	4	=	64
16	×	8	=	128
16	×	3	=	48
16	×	15	=	240

Note that the wattage for each resistor is now *four times* as great as it was. In consequence, the total wattage is also four times the 60 watts previously shown.

Proof can again be obtained by utilizing any one of the formulas previously given. Using $E = \sqrt{PR}$, multiply the 240 watts by the total resistance, 15 ohms. This gives a value of 3,600. The square root of 3,600 is 60, indicating that the voltage, which produces 240 watts for a total resistance of 15 ohms, equals 60 volts.

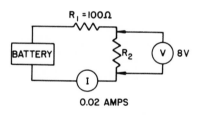

Fig. 3-9. Measurement of voltage and current in a circuit.

Ohm's law can also be employed to find the total battery voltage, if the latter is not known, or to calculate the value of a resistance, if the voltage drop across the resistance and the current through it are known. Figure 3-9, shows a typical problem of this type. Here, the value of the Resistor R_1 is given as 100 ohms, but the value of resistor R_2 is unknown. The voltage drop across R_2 is 8 volts, and a current-indicating device shows that 0.02 ampere is flowing in the circuit. The problem consists in solving for the resistance value of R_2, as well as for the total voltage.

The value of R_2 is solved as follows:

$$R_2 = \frac{E}{I} = \frac{8}{0.02} = 400 \text{ ohms}$$

After the resistance of R_2 has been ascertained, the total resistance is known, since it is the sum of the two resistors, and equals 500 ohms. The total voltage is now:

$$0.02 \times 500 = 10 \text{ volts}$$

Another method for finding the total voltage is to solve for the voltage across resistor R_1, as follows:

$$E_{R_1} = IR = 0.02 \times 100 = 2 \text{ volts}$$

The total voltage in a series circuit is the sum of the voltage drops; hence the total voltage for Fig. 3-9 equals eight plus two, and is therefore 10 volts, as established earlier.

CELLS IN SERIES

When more voltage is required than is available from a single cell, two or more cells are wired in series. This procedure is followed in the manufacture of batteries, where a number of cells are connected together to procure the necessary voltage. Thus, a 4.5-volt battery is constructed by employing three 1.5-volt cells. When cells or batteries are connected in series, the positive terminal of one unit connects to the negative of the other.

The symbol for the single cell is shown in Fig. 3-10(A), and two cells

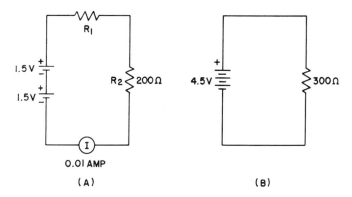

Fig. 3-10. Cells in series.

are shown wired in series. The total voltage is 3. The symbol for a battery is usually an expansion of the single cell drawing, as shown in (B), though often the symbols shown at (A) are used interchangeably for either the cell or battery. Total voltage must be observed when calculating unit values of circuits. At (A) for instance, the voltage drop across R_2 is

$$E = IR = 0.01 \times 200 = 2 \text{ volts}$$

Since total battery voltage is 3, the obvious voltage drop across R_1 is 1 volt. Resistance value is, therefore

$$R = \frac{E}{I} = \frac{1}{0.01} = 100 \text{ ohms}$$

Thus, total resistance is 300 ohms. Note that the circuit at (B) also has 300 ohms of resistance. However, because of increased voltage, its current is higher. $I = {}^{4.5}\!/_{300} = 0.015$ ampere.

RESISTORS IN PARALLEL

Resistors may also be placed in parallel, as shown in Fig. 3-11. Here, two 8-ohm resistors are in parallel with a 32-volt source. When resistors are in parallel, the total voltage appears across each resistor.

The total value of resistance can be solved by the following formula:

$$R_{\text{Total}} = \frac{R_1 R_2}{R_1 + R_2} \qquad (3\text{-}2)$$

When this formula is utilized for Fig. 3-11, the total resistance found is 4 ohms: the two resistances are multiplied together and their product, 64, is divided by the sum of the two resistances, 16. (Another formula can be used for solving the total resistance of resistors in parallel, as shown later in this chapter. When only two parallel resistors are involved, however, the formula given above is more convenient.)

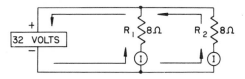

Fig. 3-11. Parallel circuit showing direction of current flow.

Since the two resistors are equal in value, each one will have the same amount of current flowing through it. Because the two resistors are placed across the power source, the current divides, and the current through the first resistor is $E/R = 32/8 = 4$ amperes. Since the second resistor also draws 4 amperes, the two parallel resistors draw a total of 8 amperes.

In solving for the total wattage utilized by the two resistors, the following calculation is used:

$$P = I^2R = (8 \times 8)4 = 64 \times 4 = 256 \text{ watts}$$

The wattage dissipated by each single resistor can also be calculated by the same equation. When the two wattages are added together, their sum equals the total wattage.

$$P \text{ in } R_1 = 16 \times 8 = 128 \text{ watts for } R_1$$
$$P \text{ in } R_2 = 16 \times 8 = 128 \text{ watts for } R_2$$
$$\overline{256 \text{ watts}}$$

In many branches of electronics, the values of current are often in fractional amperes, and fractional values are also encountered in wattages. In consequence, the terms *milliamperes* and *milliwatts* are frequently utilized. A typical parallel-resistor circuit, where a fractional value of current is involved, is shown in Fig. 3-12. Let us assume that it is neces-

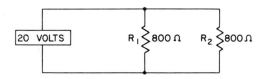

Fig. 3-12. Parallel resistors of equal value.

sary to calculate the total current in *milliamperes,* and the total power in *milliwatts.* The total current is found by dividing the voltage value (20 volts) by the total value of resistance. Using the formula for parallel resistors previously given, the total resistance value is

$$\frac{800 \times 800}{800 + 800} = \frac{640,000}{1,600} = 400 \text{ ohms}$$

Using the voltage value (20) and the total resistance value (400), the amount of current flow is found as follows:

$$I = \frac{E}{R} = \frac{20}{400} = 0.05 \text{ ampere (or 50 ma)}$$

The total power consumed in this circuit can be found by using any one of the several formulas given earlier. The most convenient is $P = EI$.

$$P_{\text{Total}} = 20 \times 0.05 = 1 \text{ watt (or 1,000 mw)}$$

Parallel resistors are, in many instances, dissimilar in value. A typical circuit of this type is shown in Fig. 3-13. The current through the first

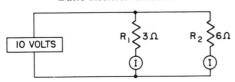

Fig. 3-13. Parallel resistors of unequal values.

resistor is established by the voltage (10) divided by the resistance (3), which indicates that approximately 3.33 amperes flows through R_1. A similar calculation for the second resistor indicates that approximately 1.666 amperes flows through this resistor. Total current flow is found by dividing the voltage (10 volts) by the total resistance. In this instance, the total resistance [which may be found by using Formula (3-2)], is 2 ohms. Thus, when the 10 volt value is divided by the 2 ohm value of resistance, the total current flow is found to be 5 amperes. (*Note:* when two or more resistors are placed in parallel, the total resistance is always *less than the value of the lowest valued resistor.*) Since additional resistors are shunting the lowest value resistor, additional paths for current are provided, and thus the total resistance is reduced below the ohmic value of the lowest value resistor in the parallel circuit.

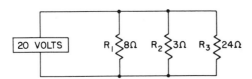

Fig. 3-14. Parallel circuit with three resistors.

When more than two resistors are placed in parallel, Formula (3-3) can be employed to find the total value of resistance.

$$R_{\text{Total}} = \cfrac{1}{\cfrac{1}{R_1} + \cfrac{1}{R_2} + \cfrac{1}{R_3} + \cdots \cfrac{1}{R_n}} \qquad (3\text{-}3)$$

A typical circuit of this kind is shown in Fig. 3-14. Utilizing the previous formula, the calculation for the total resistance is as follows:

$$R_T = \frac{1}{\frac{1}{8} + \frac{1}{3} + \frac{1}{24}} = \frac{1}{\frac{3}{24} + \frac{8}{24} + \frac{1}{24}}$$

$$= \frac{1}{\frac{12}{24}} = \frac{24}{12} = 2 \text{ ohms}$$

Here, the resistance values are placed into the formula, as shown, giving a reciprocal function of $\frac{1}{8} + \frac{1}{3} + \frac{1}{24}$. The least common denominator is 24, and the other fractional values of ⅛ and ⅓ are consequently converted to the common denominator. This gives us ³⁄₂₄, ⁸⁄₂₄, and ¹⁄₂₄. When these fractions are added together, their sum is ¹²⁄₂₄. Since a reciprocal function is involved, the ¹²⁄₂₄ can be inverted and divided. When this is done, the total ohmic value is shown to be 2 ohms. In accordance with the statements made earlier, this result is verified, because the total resistance value indicated is less than that of the smallest resistor in the parallel circuit. If the calculation had indicated a resistance value equal to or in excess of the lowest resistor in the circuit, this would have shown that the calculation was in error.

Once the total resistance has been found, the total current can again be calculated by dividing the total voltage by the total resistance. Since 20 volts are indicated, and a total resistance of 2 ohms has been found, the total current for Fig. 3-14 equals 10 amperes.

The current through each individual resistive branch of the parallel resistor circuit shown in Fig. 3-14 can also be calculated on the basis of the voltage across the resistor (20 volts) divided by the resistance value.

Since the values of the individual resistors are fixed, the total resistance established by the parallel resistor combination will also be fixed, regardless of the voltage applied. Thus, if the voltage for the circuit shown in Fig. 3-14 is increased to 40 volts, the current through each resistor doubles, and the total current becomes 20 amperes. Total resistance is then equal to

$$\frac{40 \text{ volts}}{20 \text{ amperes}} = 2 \text{ ohms}$$

This is the same total resistance value obtained when the problem was solved on the basis of 20 volts applied.

Equation (3-3) need not be used if both the total current and the voltage are given. For Fig. 3-14, let us assume that the voltage is 50 volts, and the total current is 25 amperes Since $R = E/I$, the calculation is simple, and indicates that the total resistance is 2 ohms. If, however, the individual resistance values were not given, each resistor would have to be calculated on the basis of the current flowing through it and the voltage across it.

If the resistance values are given as shown in Fig. 3-14, but the voltage is not given, the voltage can be measured before calculation. If total resistance is to be solved for, a voltage can be *assumed* and the current through each resistor calculated. Total resistance would then be obtained by dividing the assumed voltage by the total calculated current. This will give the correct total resistance of the circuit, since the resistance values remain fixed, regardless of voltage. The assumed voltage may be far removed from the correct voltage, but the total resistance value procured will be accurate. Since, however, the voltage is an assumed value, the *individual* currents through the resistors will be *incorrect,* because they are based on a false voltage.

As an illustration of this process, let us suppose that it is necessary to know the total resistance of the circuit shown in Fig. 3-14, but that there is no ready means for measuring the voltage. In such an instance, assume the total voltage is 48 volts. Current through the resistors will then be

$$I_{R1} = \frac{48}{8} = 6$$

$$I_{R2} = \frac{48}{3} = 16$$

$$I_{R3} = \frac{48}{24} = 2$$

Total current = 24 amperes

Since $R_{\text{Total}} = E/I$, the problem becomes

$$R_{\text{Total}} = \frac{\text{Assumed voltage}}{\text{Total current}} = \frac{48}{24} = 2 \text{ ohms}$$

CELLS IN PARALLEL

When cells are placed in parallel, as shown in Fig. 3-15(A), the available current increases, but the output voltage remains the same as for a single cell. The amount of current which is drawn from a battery depends on the value of the resistor placed across it. As the resistance value is

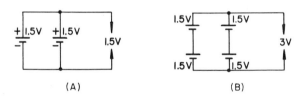

Fig. 3-15. Batteries in series and parallel combinations.

lowered, more current is drawn from a battery. As more and more current is drawn, the load on the battery increases, and the excessive amount of current flow may overheat the battery or damage it. At the point where overheating occurs, the battery is considered to be partially shorted. A complete short is the condition where a length of wire is placed directly across the battery terminals. Unless the wire is extremely thin, a section of copper or aluminum wire has such a low resistance that it would permit the maximum amount of current to flow which the battery is capable of delivering. Since the only resistance would be the low internal resistance of the battery, the excessive current flow through this internal resistance would cause the battery to heat up. The result would be a damaged battery.

When constructing batteries which must be able to provide higher currents than a simple cell, additional cells are placed in parallel with the original cell, as shown in Fig. 3-15(A). On the other hand, a parallel arrangement can also be utilized to extend the life of a battery. Thus, if the load resistance is such that a single cell would not be overloaded in terms of current drawn, an additional cell can be placed in parallel, and the two cells virtually double the life of the battery system and reduce replacement intervals. The amount of current drawn from the combination for a given load resistance would still be the same, since the *voltage* of the parallel arrangement shown at (A) has not been increased.

If it is necessary to increase the voltage available from a battery, as well as provide for higher available current, the arrangement ·shown in Fig. 3-15(B) can be employed. Here, four cells are used in a series-parellel combination. This grouping would furnish twice the voltage obtainable from a single cell, with an increase in the available current because of the parallel arrangement. If the load resistor placed across the battery is 500 ohms, the amount of current flowing in the circuit would be 0.006 amperes, or 6 ma. It is this 500-ohm resistance value, in conjunction with the 3 volts, which determines the current flow, and not the particular battery arrangement.

SERIES AND PARALLEL COMBINATIONS

A series string of cells can be placed in parallel with another series string, as shown in Fig. 3-16, to provide both increased voltage and greater available current. The combination shown in Fig. 3-16 consists of six 1.5-volt cells—three cells in series forming each string, and the two strings of series circuits connected in parallel. The three 1.5-volt cells in series raise the voltage to a total of 4.5 volts, while a parallel combination of the two series strings will provide greater current without overload than the single series section could give. Such a combination is designed for two reasons: higher voltage, and greater available current.

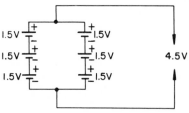

Fig. 3-16. Series-parallel battery combinations.

CURRENT CAPACITY OF WIRE

It was mentioned earlier that fixed and variable resistors are formed by using materials such as carbon composition or special alloy wire. Such resistors are utilized when it becomes necessary to increase opposition to current flow in order to reduce voltages or signals. There are occasions, however, when it is desirable to have *high conductivity,* such as in the interconnections of the various components of electronic devices, in forming circuits. Thus, the hookup wire used between electronic parts must have a very low resistance (high conductivity). To keep resistance so low that it does not affect circuit function, copper wire is usually employed, because of its inherent low resistance as compared to other metallic conductors. Thin wire and long lengths, however, will increase resistance even in copper wire, and hence such factors must be considered in selecting wire of suitable size to carry current with no appreciable loss.

Wire with a larger cross-sectional area can carry more current than wire with a smaller cross-sectional area, just as a larger waterpipe will permit a greater amount of water to flow past a given point during a certain time interval. In electronics, it is usual to find interconnecting circuit wires having cross sections of only a fraction of an inch in diameter. Hence, it is standard practice to designate wire diameters in units equal to *one-thousandth* of an inch. The name of this measure is the *mil*. Because the most common type of wire is round, the cross-sectional area of round wire has been assigned a unit of area known as the *circular mil,* and this is shown in Fig. 3-17(A), where it is compared to the square mil. With the

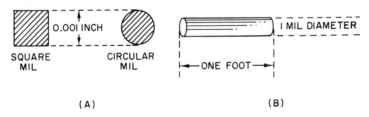

Fig. 3-17. The circular mil of wire.

diameter in mils, the circular mil is found by simply squaring the diameter. Thus, if a diameter is 2 mils (0.002 inch), the circular mil area is $2 \times 2 = 4$ circular mils.

In the United States, a standard of reference with respect to copper wire sizes has been established, known as the American Wire Gauge, where gauge numbers have been assigned to wires of various diameters. The higher numbers, such as 30, 35, or 40, refer to very thin wire, while the lower numbers, 18, 12, 10, refer to progressively thicker wire, ranging down to below zero, where several zeros are used to indicate very thick wire, such as 0000. The larger sizes (starting from approximately #18 and increasing in wire size to #0000) are used for carrying large amounts of current, such as in home and factory wiring, industrial electronic applications, and the feed wires from electric plants. Hookup wire used for electronic circuits having only milliamperes of current flowing through them usually consists of wire sizes from #22 to #28, or smaller diameter wire, depending on how many milliamperes of current will flow. On the other hand, wire to various tube filaments may have to carry several amperes of current, in which case appropriate wire sizes range from #18 to #20. A table giving the ratings of copper wire for sizes usually encountered in electronic circuitry is given in the Appendix.

In this wire table, the ohmic value of the wire of any specific gauge is given in terms of a 1000-foot length. This is based on the standard unit of wire size known as the *circular mil foot* illustrated in Fig. 3-17(B). As shown, a wire having a cross sectional area of one circular mil and a length of one foot is referred to as a *mil foot,* or *circular mil foot* of wire.

Knowing the gauge number, reference can be made to the table in the Appendix for the resistivity of copper wire. For instance, size 20 wire has an ohmic resistance of 10.35 per 1,000 feet. Hence, 2,000 feet would have twice the resistance (20.7 ohms), while 500 feet would have only half the resistance (5.175 ohms).

REVIEW QUESTIONS

1. What determines the wattage rating of a resistor?

2. Define the terms *rheostat* and *potentiometer.*

3. A circuit consists of three resistors in a series, each having a different value from the others. With a given voltage source, is the current the same through each resistor? Explain why.

4. In a parallel resistor circuit, is the current through each resistor the same when each resistor is different in ohmic value from the others? Explain why the current is the same or different.

5. Briefly explain the difference, with respect to voltage drop across the individual resistors, between a series circuit and a parallel circuit.

6. How is the ohmic value of the total resistance calculated in a parallel resistor circuit?

7. In a parallel resistive network, is the total resistance always lower or always higher than the lowest value resistor employed? Explain.

8. Show how two resistors, each of different value, can consume a similar amount of energy in watts.

9. When two batteries are placed in series, what happens with respect to the available voltage and current?

10. What is the principal advantage of placing batteries in parallel?

11. Explain how a combination of batteries can be employed to provide both higher voltage and greater current.

12. What factors determine the current-carrying capacity of wire?

13. What happens when a high current is made to flow through a high-resistance wire?

PRACTICAL PROBLEMS

Note: Draw a diagram of the circuit of each problem, to gain practice in schematic work, and to aid in visualizing each problem.

1. A 60-watt lamp bulb is operated at 120 volts. What current flows through the lamp? On the basis of the calculated current, what is the resistance of the bulb?

2. In a television receiver, two resistors are in series. The first resistor (R_1) has a voltage drop of 200 across it. The second resistor (R_2) has a drop of 50 volts across it. Current in the circuit is 20 millamperes (0.02 amperes). What is the value of each resistor? What is the total resistance?

3. In Problem 2, what wattage is dissipated by each resistor?

4. Across a 300-volt power supply, in an electronic device, there are four resistors in series. Resistor values are 20,000, 5,000, 4,500, and 500. What is the current, in milliamperes, which flows through this network?

5. In a radio there are three resistors in series: R_1 has a 1.5-volt drop across it; R_2 has a 3-volt drop across it, and R_3 has an 0.6-volt drop across it. Resistor R_3 is 20 ohms. What is the current in the circuit, and what are the resistance values of R_1 and of R_2?

6. In a transmitter, a resistor has burned out, and the exact value was not available immediately for replacement purposes. The technician replaced the resistor with a 30,000-ohm resistor in parallel with a 60,000-ohm resistor. What was the value of the original resistor? If there is a voltage of 1,000 across the parallel resistor circuit, what is the total current flowing through the two resistors in combination?

7. Across a power source, there are three parallel resistors as follows: R_1 or 2,000 ohms, R_2 or 500 ohms, and R_3 or 1,000 ohms. The power source is 150 volts. What is the current through each resistor? What is the total current? What is the total resistance?

8. Calculate Problem 7 on the basis of an assumed voltage of 300 volts. Under this condition, what is the calculated total resistance?

9. What is the total power dissipated in the two resistors of Problem 6?

10. What is the total power dissipated for the circuit described in Problem 7?

11. What would be the total power dissipated if the assumed voltage of 300 were the correct voltage in Problem 8?

12. Two resistors, R_1 and R_2 are in parallel. Resistor R_2 has a 20-volt drop across it and a current through it of 2 amperes. The total current drawn by both resistors equals 6 amperes. What are the values of R_1, R_2, and total resistance?

13. In what manner must a group of 1.5-volt cells be combined to obtain 22.5 volts?

14. Six batteries of 4.5 volts each were wired as in Fig. 3–16. What is the total voltage of the combination?

4

CIRCUIT
ANALYSIS
(D-C)

INTRODUCTION

To understand how electronic circuits function, it is necessary to acquire a good foundation in basic procedures used to analyze circuits. Series and parallel resistor combinations, as well as other components discussed later, can usually be reduced to simple equivalent circuits to aid the analysis. When a circuit which appears complex has been reduced to a simple equivalent, mathematical procedures are applied to find unit values of current, voltage, resistance, and power. Certain theorems are also applied on occasion to help understand circuit make-up. This chapter applies basic principles of circuit analysis to d-c resistor circuits composed of series, parallel, and series-parallel combinations. Initially, Ohm's law calculations are shown, and then some of the fundamental theorems used in more advanced circuit analysis are introduced.

SERIES-PARALLEL COMBINATIONS

In many electronic circuits, series and parallel resistors are combined to perform specific tasks. One of the basic combination circuits of this type is shown in Fig. 4-1(A). Here, resistor R_1 is in parallel with the series branch R_2 and R_3. Since the total value of resistors in series is found by adding their ohmic values, the series section at Fig. 4-1(A) is equal to 250 ohms. Thus, the equivalent circuit would be as shown at Fig. 4-1(B), where a 62.5-ohm resistor is in parallel with a 250-ohm resistor. The 4-volt power source (either a battery or a generator of electric power) would be across both resistors.

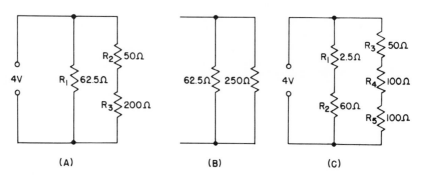

(A)   (B)   (c)

Fig. 4-1. Series-parallel circuits.

The series circuit could also consist of the resistors shown in Fig. 4-1(C), where two series strings are in parallel. The first series string of two resistors is equal to 62.5 ohms. The second series string is equal to 250 ohms. Thus, the circuit shown at (C) would draw the same amount of current as that shown at (A) or (B), and the equivalent circuit for C is also the one shown in B.

Once the individual ohmic values of the series branch resistors have been added together, the circuit can be assumed to be a simplified equivalent, such as shown in (B). Now, the formula for calculating the total resistance (R_T) of a parallel circuit is again utilized. Solving for the two resistors shown in (B) produces the following result:

$$R_T = \frac{1}{4/250 + 1/250} = \frac{1}{5/250} = \frac{250}{5} = 50 \text{ ohms}$$

If it were now necessary to solve for total current (I_T), this would be done by the Ohm's law

$$I_T = \frac{E}{R} = \frac{4}{50} = 0.08 \text{ amperes}$$

If it is desired to know the current in each branch, it then becomes necessary to solve for the current through the 62.5-ohm resistance, based on the fact that 4 volts appears across it. Since the voltage in a parallel circuit is the same across each parallel branch, the current for the second resistor would also be solved on the basis of the 4 volts.

I through first string $= 4/62.5 = 0.064$ amperes
I through second string $= 4/250 = 0.016$ amperes
$$I_T = \overline{0.080} \text{ amperes}$$

Another typical series-parallel combination is shown in Fig. 4-2(A). Here again, the resistances are reduced to the most simple resistance values

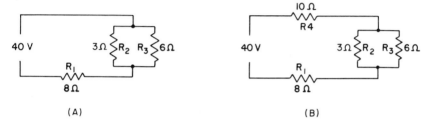

Fig. 4-2. Series-parallel combination.

for ease in obtaining total values. In this instance, the method for solving begins with the calculation of the total value of parallel resistors. Because the resistors in the parallel branch are dissimilar in value, the standard formula for solving parallel resistors would be utilized, as shown below:

$$R_{\text{Parallel}} = \frac{1}{\frac{1}{3} + \frac{1}{6}} = \frac{1}{\frac{3}{6}} = \frac{6}{3} = 2 \text{ ohms}$$

(Again note that the total resistance in a parallel circuit is always less than the lowest ohmic value of resistance in the parallel circuit.)

Total resistance in the circuit shown in Fig. 4-2(A) would now be obtained by adding the 8-ohm series resistor R_1 to the sum of the parallel branch, which is 2 ohms.

$$R_T = 8 + 2 = 10 \text{ ohms}$$

The total current for this circuit is equal to the total voltage (40) divided by the total resistance.

$$I_T = \frac{40}{10} = 4 \text{ amperes}$$

The voltage across the single 8-ohm resistor, R_1, and the voltage across the parallel branch are solved for next.

$$E_{R_1} = 4 \times 8 = 32 \text{ volts}$$
$$E_{\text{Parallel}} = 4 \times 2 = 8 \text{ volts}$$
$$(E_T = 32 + 8 = 40 \text{ volts})$$

Current through the 8-ohm resistor R_1 is equal to 4 amperes, since the total current of the circuit must flow through this series resistor. This total current will, however, divide at the parallel branch, since more current will flow through the 3-ohm resistor than through the 6-ohm resistor. To solve for the currents through each resistor (R_2 *and* R_3), divide the voltage across the parallel branch (8 volts, as found in the last example) by the individual resistor values.

$$I_{R2} = \frac{8}{3} = 2.666 \text{ amperes}$$

$$I_{R2} = \frac{8}{6} = 1.333 \text{ amperes}$$

$$I_T = \overline{3.999} \text{ (or 4) amperes}$$

Another series resistor could be placed in the circuit, as shown in Fig. 4-2(B). Here, a 10-ohm resistor (R_4) has been added to the circuit. Since the parallel combinations equals 2 ohms, and the R_1 resistor equals 8

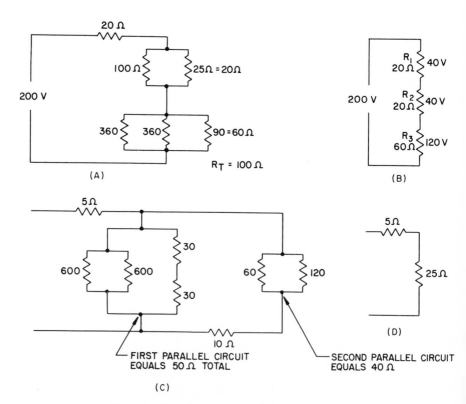

Fig. 4-3. Complex series-parallel resistor circuits.

ohms, to give a total of 10 ohms, the additional R_4 resistor gives a grand total resistance of 20 ohms. The resistance has been doubled, so that the current will now be only one-half of the former value. The individual currents through R_2 and R_3 will be decreased proportionately.

A still more complex type of series-parallel combination circuit is shown in Fig. 4-3(A). Here again, in solving, the parallel branches are reduced to equivalent single resistive values, and then are considered to be in series with each other. Thus, the total resistance of the lower parallel branch is calculated on the basis of the formula, and found to be 60 ohms. The parallel branch above it is equal to 20 ohms, and the two parallel branches are also in series with a single 20-ohm resistor. This circuit is equivalent to that shown in Fig. 4-3(B), which is a simple one having two resistors of 20 ohms each and one resistor of 60 ohms, each in series with the other, for a total of 100 ohms.

Since voltages across the resistors of a series circuit are proportionate to the resistance values, the individual voltage drops can be solved for on a *proportionate* basis.

20% voltage across $R_1 =$ 40 volts
20% voltage across top parallel $=$ 40 volts
60% voltage across other parallel $=$ 120 volts
Total voltage, $E_T = \overline{200}$ volts

or

$$I = \frac{E}{R} = \frac{200}{100} = 2 \text{ amperes}$$
$$E_{R_1} = IR = 2 \times 20 = 40 \text{ volts}$$

As shown in (B), this circuit provides 40 volts across the first 20-ohm resistor, 40 volts across the second, and 120 volts across the lower 60-ohm resistor. Total current, as given by these calculations, is equal to 2 amperes.

Instead of finding the voltage drops by using the proportionate drops based on resistance values, the individual voltage drop across each resistor can be calculated by multiplying the resistance value by the current through the resistor (see last example). Since the total current is 2 amperes, this same current is flowing through each resistor. Thus, to find the voltage across R_1, we would multiply the 20 ohms by 2 amperes, which would result in a voltage drop of 40 volts. The same is done for R_2, again resulting in 40 volts. For R_3, multiply the 60 ohms by the 2 amperes to get a voltage drop of 120.

Another complex series-parallel circuit combination is shown in Fig. 4-3(C). Again, the individual parallel circuits are solved to give a single resistance value. In this case, the first parallel circuit, composed of two 600-ohm resistors in parallel, indicates that these two resistors would give a single resistance of 300 ohms. This opposition is in parallel with two series resistors of 30 ohms each, or 60 ohms. Using 300 as the common denominator, the total resistance value of the first parallel circuit at (C) is indicated as being 50 ohms.

$$\frac{1}{\frac{1}{300} + \frac{5}{300}} = \frac{300}{6} = 50 \text{ ohms (for first parallel combination)}$$

The second parallel circuit has a total resistance of 40 ohms. This circuit, however, has another resistor of 10 ohms in series with it, which means that a total of 50 ohms is shunting the first parallel circuit. Thus, since both the first and the second parallel circuits each represent a total of 50 ohms, again solve for the single resistance value of these two parallel combinations. As two 50-ohm resistors in parallel equal 25 ohms, the two parallel branches (plus the 10-ohm resistor in series with the second parallel branch) can be represented by a single resistor of 25 ohms. Since this single resistor of 25 ohms is also in series with a 5-ohm resistor (as shown in Fig. 4-3(D)), the total resistance is 30 ohms for this circuit.

PRACTICAL APPLICATIONS

Equation (3-3) for finding the total resistance of several resistors in parallel can be employed in reverse order, when it is necessary to find what two resistors would have the same value as a single resistor. A typical problem is illustrated in Fig. 4-4(A), where a cathode resistor of 60 ohms

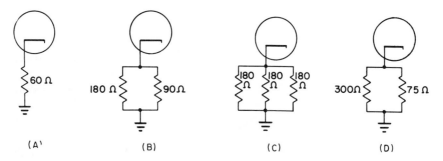

Fig. 4-4. Cathode resistor combinations.

is indicated. Let us suppose that this resistor needs to be replaced, but that no other 60-ohm unit is available. In such an instance, two 120-ohm resistors can be placed in a parallel arrangement to give the desired 60 ohms. Assume, however, that only dissimilar resistors were available— what combination would give 60 ohms?

The '60' can arbitrarily be multiplied by any number, to find what resistors in parallel will still give 60 ohms. Suppose the 60 were multiplied by 3 to give 180. Since 3 was used to multiply the 60, we would have $\frac{3}{180}$, or $\frac{1}{180} + \frac{2}{180}$. In reciprocal expressions, these would become $\frac{180}{1} + \frac{180}{2}$. The former expression of 180 divided by 1 becomes 180, which is one value of resistor to be used. The second expression becomes 180 divided by 2, which equals 90. This is the second resistor to be used. Thus, a 180-ohm unit in parallel with 90 ohms, as shown in Fig. 4-4(B), would give 60 ohms. This can be proved by using the standard formula for parallel circuits on these 180- and 60-ohm resistors (the reverse of the procedure just undertaken).

Since we had $\frac{3}{180}$ as the basis for our analysis, we could have stated this as $\frac{1}{180} + \frac{1}{180} + \frac{1}{180}$, which upon inversion would have indicated that three parallel resistors, each of 180 ohms, could also have been employed to obtain the necessary 60 ohms, as shown in Fig. 4-4(C).

If these resistors had not been available, we could have multiplied 60 by 5 to get another set of values. This could have been set down as $\frac{1}{300} + \frac{4}{300}$, a total of $\frac{5}{300}$. Inverting the first expression gives $\frac{300}{1}$, which indicates 300 ohms for one of the required resistors. The second expression, when inverted, is $\frac{300}{4}$; therefore, 75 ohms are required for the second parallel resistor for both to furnish a total of 60 ohms, as shown in Fig. 4-4(D). Two additional examples of the foregoing method follow.

Example: What two values of resistors in parallel can be used to give a total of 12 ohms?

Solution: Multiply 12 ohms by some other number, for instance 5: $12 \times 5 = 60$, or $\frac{5}{60}$, which can be split up into $\frac{1}{60}$ and $\frac{4}{60}$. When these terms are inverted to $\frac{60}{1}$ and $\frac{60}{4}$, we find that one resistor should have a value of 60 ohms and the other a value of 15 ohms.

Example: What three values of resistors can be employed to give 6 ohms when the resistors are in parallel?

Solution: $6 \times 3 = 18$, or $\frac{3}{18}$; inverting to $\frac{18}{3}$, we find that three 18-ohm resistors can be used. (If two resistors were asked for, values of 9 and 18 ohms would suffice.)

KIRCHHOFF'S LAWS

Gustav Kirchhoff (1824-1887), the German scientist, formulated two important laws concerning electric circuits. These are known as *Kirchhoff's Laws,* and may be stated as follows:

1. The current (or sum of currents) flowing into any junction of an electric circuit is equal to the current (or sum of currents) flowing out of that junction.

2. The power source voltage (or sum of such voltages) around any closed circuit is equal to the sum of the voltage drops across the resistances around the same circuit.

The first law, also known as the *current law,* is often stated as "the *algebraic* sum of all currents at any point in a circuit is *zero.*" Thus, at a certain point, the current flowing toward the point has an opposite direction to that of the current flowing away from that point (one positive, the other negative). Hence, the algebraic sum indicates zero from the standpoint of analysis, even though a definite amount of current flows.

The second law, also known as the *voltage* law, is stated as "the algebraic sum of all the voltages around the circuit is zero." Consider, for instance, the circuit shown in Fig. 4-5(A). Starting at point *x,* and going in the direction of current flow, mark down the voltages encountered, giving them a polarity as indicated by the first polarity found in either a battery or a resistor. For Fig. 4-5, the first unit is the battery, and this is set down as +50. The next unit is the 20-ohm resistor, and because the voltage drop across this is *R* times *I,* it is set down as −20*I*. The next voltage drop is across a 5-ohm resistor, and this is set down as −5*I,* bringing us back to the starting point *x.* We now have

$$50 - 20I - 5I = 0 \quad \text{or} \quad 50 - 25I = 0$$

By algebraic processes, we solve for *I* and find that $I = 2$ amperes.

For most of the simple circuits, Ohm's law provides a more direct and easy method for solving unknowns, and hence Kirchhoff's laws are not usually employed unless the circuit is much more complex. In Fig. 4-5(A), for instance, the current can be found by $I = E/R = 50/(20 + 5)$ = 2 amperes.

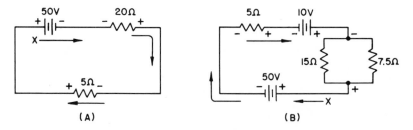

Fig. 4-5. Analysis using Kirchhoff's law.

When two power sources are in the series circuit, as shown in Fig. 4-5(B), one will oppose the other if the source of electrons from the negative terminal of one battery faces the negative terminal of the other battery. Thus, if one battery is 50 volts and is opposed by another of 10 volts, the resultant total battery potential is only $50 - 10 = 40$ volts. This is proved by applying Kirchhoff's voltage law, again starting at any point and continuing once around the circuit. Starting at x, for instance, (with the parallel branch reduced to its single resistance value) gives

$$50 - 5I - 10 - 5I = 0$$
$$40 - 10I = 0$$
$$I = 4 \text{ amperes}$$

By Ohm's law also, $I = E/R = {}^{40}\!/_{10} = 4$ amperes, because the 50-volt battery is opposed by the 10-volt, giving a total of 40 volts, and the total resistance is 5 ohms + 5 ohms = 10 ohms.

Both Ohm's law and Kirchhoff's law can be used, one to prove out the other, in circuit analysis. Either law can also be used to verify the results obtained from meter readings.

THEVENIN'S THEOREM

The characteristics of a circuit can be analyzed by voltage and current readings even though the components are not readily accessible. One method is by use of *Thévenin's theorem,* which states essentially that

a given network, with constant voltages and resistance produces a current flow in the load resistor equal to that which flows if the load resistor were applied across an equivalent circuit which has (a) an internal resistance measured at the terminals of the circuit with the voltage source replaced by its equivalent internal resistance; (b) a voltage at the terminals equal to that existing in the original circuit after removal of the load resistor.

If circuit components are not accessible for measurement, it is as though the circuit were completely enclosed in a container (a box, for instance) and two or more terminals are the only available points for circuit analysis. The box concept is often encountered in circuit design analysis, and is usually referred to as a *black box* when discussing this method of evaluating circuit characteristics.

The load resistor mentioned in the theorem can be an actual resistor or some other network combination of components representative of a resistive load. As an example of the application of Thévenin's theorem, a network of resistors with a battery is shown in Fig. 4-6(A) with the load resistance removed from terminal T_C and T_D. Applying a meter to these terminals to read voltage, a value of 30 volts is obtained. This occurs because the meter reads the voltage drop across R_2 only. Be-

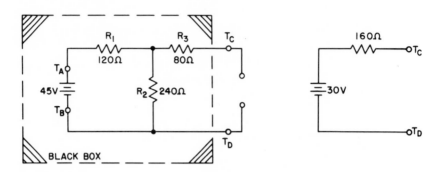

Fig. 4-6. Applying Thévenin's theorem.

cause of the open circuit, no current flows through R_3 and hence no voltage drop occurs across it. (The assumption here is the voltmeter has such a high resistance that the terminals T_C and T_D are still a virtual open circuit.)

The values in the black box are given in Fig. 4-6, and we can prove that the voltmeter would read 30 volts by Ohm's law. In actual circuit analysis of this type, however, we would not, of course, know the internal unit values of voltages and resistances.

$$I = \frac{E}{R} = \frac{45}{120 + 240} = 0.125 \text{ ampere}$$

Knowing the current flow through R_1 and R_2, the voltage drop across R_2 is found.

$$E = IR = 0.125 \times 240 = 30 \text{ volts}$$

The voltmeter is now removed and an ammeter placed across terminals T_C and T_D. The ammeter, having almost zero resistance, (see next chapter) acts as a short across the output terminals and would read 0.1875 ampere. This can also be proved by Ohm's law. With the terminals closed, R_2 and R_3 are in shunt (parallel circuit) with a total resistance value of 60 ohms.

$$\frac{240 \times 80}{240 + 80} = 60 \text{ ohms}$$

This 60-ohm value is added to that of R_1, 120 ohms, for a total of 180 ohms. Now, total current is

$$I = \frac{E}{R} = \frac{45}{180} = 0.25 \text{ ampere}$$

Of this 0.25-ampere current, only one-third as much current flows through R_2 as through R_3, because of the higher R_2 value.

$$I \text{ through } R_2 = 0.0625$$
$$I \text{ through } R_3 = \underline{0.1875}$$
$$I_T = \overline{0.2500}$$

Once current through the shorted terminals is known, the *equivalent* circuit resistance can be found.

$$R = \frac{E}{I} = \frac{30}{0.1875} = 160 \text{ ohms}$$

Hence, the *equivalent* voltage and resistance forms an equivalent circuit as shown in Fig. 4-6(B). With these values we can ascertain the amount of current flowing through any load resistor applied across the two terminals, as well as the voltage drop which would occur and the power consumed by the load resistance. If, for instance, a load resistance of 140 ohms were placed across T_C and T_D, we would solve for load current in the equivalent circuit by the following formula:

$$I_L = \frac{E}{R_e + R_L} \qquad (4\text{-}1)$$

where R_e is the equivalent circuit resistance

R_L is the value of the applied resistor

Using Equation (4-1) for the values in Fig. 4-6, we have

$$\frac{30}{160 + 140} = \frac{30}{300} = 0.1 \text{ ampere}$$

Proving Thévenin's theorem by Ohm's law does, of course, lengthen the process. In actual practice a voltmeter is applied initially for the voltage reading, and next an ammeter for current. Dividing the voltage by the current immediately gives the equivalent circuit resistance. The latter, when applied to Equation (4-1) indicates the load current for any value of load resistance.

If, in Fig. 4-6, the battery were outside the black box, we would have a four-terminal network, with input terminals T_A and T_B available in addition to the output terminals T_C and T_D. Now, if the battery were removed and the terminals T_A and T_B shorted, the process would be simplified. Next, a resistance-reading meter (ohmmeter) is placed across the output terminals and the resistance read directly. The value for Fig. 4-6 would again be 160 ohms. (With the input terminals shorted, R_1 shunts R_2 for a total resistance value of 80 ohms. With this value in series with R_3, the total resistance is again 160 ohms.) If the battery has an appreciable internal resistance, this should be indicated in the calculations, and the T_A and T_B terminals not shorted, but replaced with the equivalent internal battery resistance. Similarly, with the first procedure, the battery resistance would have to be included as part of the R_1 resistance.

NORTON'S THEOREM

Norton's theorem is based on a source voltage producing a *constant current* as opposed to the *constant voltage* theorem of Thévenin. The impedance of the equivalent circuit is considered to be in parallel with the load resistance. Other than this difference, Norton's theorem also states that any resistive-voltage network can be replaced by a single voltage and resistance as an equivalent.

To show that the same solution is obtained with Norton's theorem, Fig. 4-6 is again used.

Initially, T_C and T_D are shorted, which places R_3 in shunt with R_2 for resistance of 60 ohms. When this is added to the 120-ohm resistor, a total of 180 ohms is the result. Circuit current is, therefore

$$I_c = \frac{45}{180} = 0.25 \text{ ampere}$$

With an ammeter used as the shorting component, the current would read 0.1875 ampere. This can be proved by Ohm's law or by considering proportionate values. Since 0.25 ampere is the total current, this value divides across the parallel network of R_2 and R_3. Since R_3 is one-third the value of R_2, it will have three times the current flow through it. Now the resistance is determined at T_C and T_D by the same method employed for Thévenin's theorem. The battery is removed and battery terminals T_A and T_B are shorted. Again the resistance value will be found to be 160 ohms. Current through the load resistor is found by the following equation involving circuit resistance (R_c) and the load resistance (R_L):

$$I_L = I_c \times \frac{R_c}{R_c + R_L} \qquad (4\text{-}2)$$

If the same value load resistance is used as for the example with Thévenin's theorem, we have the same current value obtained with Thévenin.

$$I_L = 0.1875 \times \frac{160}{160 + 140} = 0.1 \text{ ampere}$$

REVIEW QUESTIONS

1. Draw a circuit with a single resistor in series with a parallel branch having two resistors each. Assign an ohmic value to each resistor and show the calculation for total resistance.

2. For the circuit drawing in the preceding question, assign a battery potential across the network, and calculate the voltage drop across each resistor, on the basis of the applied voltage.

3. Briefly explain how the formula for finding the total resistance in parallel can be employed in reverse order for finding what individual values two resistors must have so that their combination will provide the same value as a single resistor.

4. Give an example of using two resistors in series to provide the same ohmic value as a single resistor.

5. Show how three resistors can be used in series to provide the same ohmic value as a single resistor.

6. Give a typical example of using two resistors in parallel to provide the same ohmic value as a single resistor.

7. Give a typical example of employing three resistors in parallel to provide the same ohmic value as a single resistor.

8. What two important laws of circuit analysis did Kirchhoff formulate?

9. What theorem applies to a constant voltage network?

10. What theorem applies to a constant current network?

11. What is the *black box* concept?

12. Of what value is Norton's theorem?

PRACTICAL PROBLEMS

Note: Draw a diagram of the circuit of each problem. This will give you practice in schematic work and aid you in visualizing each problem.

1. In an electronic circuit, a resistor R_1 of 100 ohms is in series with two parallel resistors. The latter, designated R_2 and R_3, are 600 ohms each. The voltage applied to the network is 800 volts. What is the total resistance, and what is the voltage drop across each resistor?

2. A 700-ohm resistor R_1 had in series with it a parallel resistor circuit composed of a 600-ohm resistor R_2 shunted by a 300-ohm resistor R_3. Also in series with this parallel combination was another resistor R_4 having a value of 100 ohms. The voltage measured across the R_4 resistor was 50. What is the total current, total resistance, and the total voltage applied to the complete circuit?

3. In the cathode circuit of a vacuum tube, a 100-ohm resistor burned out. This value of resistance is not immediately available. What resistor can be placed in parallel with a 500-ohm resistor on hand to obtain a resistance value equal to the original 100-ohm resistor?

4. Give three values of resistance which can be used in parallel to produce a total of 26 ohms.

5. In a voltage-divider network, there is an applied voltage of 80, and the circuit consists of two parallel resistors, one having a value of 12.5 ohms, and the other having a value of 50 ohms. In series with this parallel circuit is another parallel circuit having two resistors of 36 ohms and 18 ohms. From the second parallel circuit, a single 18-ohm resistor completes the circuit to the voltage source. What is the total resistance value, and what is the voltage drop across the 18-ohm resistor?

6. For the circuit shown at Fig. 4–7 use Thévenin's theorem and solve for the equivalent circuit resistance R_e and I_L, using a load resistance value of 3,422 ohms.

7. For Fig. 4–7 solve for I_L using Norton's theorem, and an R_L of 3,422 ohms.

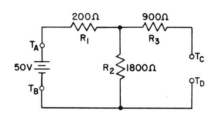

Fig. 4-7. Circuit for Problem 6.

5

D-C

MEASUREMENTS

INTRODUCTION

Values of current, voltage, resistance, and wattage in various electronic circuits are measured by specially designed instruments which have dials calibrated to indicate the unit values of the quantities being measured. The meter which measures current is known as an *ammeter*. When fractional values of current are to be measured, a *milliammeter* is employed. For measuring voltage, a *voltmeter* is used, which has several ranges for measuring low, intermediate, or high voltages. Meters are also available for measuring resistance values and wattages. There are also combination meters which are capable of reading voltages, currents, and resistances, as more fully described in Chapter 22.

In order to provide a particular meter with the ability to make measurements over a useful range of values, it is necessary to employ series and parallel resistor combinations based on principles given in this and the previous chapters. The basic meter movement involves a permanent magnet, and a moving coil, as well as electromagnetic fields (as more fully discussed in subsequent chapters). This chapter is concerned with the basic principles of extending meter ranges by use of resistors.

THE AMMETER

When an ammeter is used for measuring current, it is necessary for the current *to flow through* the meter. Thus, an ammeter is connected in *series* with the circuit in which the current is to be measured. For this reason, the ammeter must have a low d-c resistance so that the meter will not offer opposition to the current flow in the circuit. If the ammeter has any appreciable resistance, it will decrease the current flow of the circuit, and an accurate reading of the amount of current which flows in the circuit without the meter will not be obtainable. Hence, the ammeter must be constructed using wire having such a low resistance that its effect on the circuit is negligible. The same factor of low internal resistance also applies to milliammeters. For electronic work involving receivers, recording equipment, and the like, where low currents are present, the milliammeter finds greater usefulness than the ammeter. In transmitting and industrial electronic circuits, or in other such devices where high power is encountered, ammeters must be employed.

A basic ammeter or milliammeter employs a needle indicator that has a deflection proportional to the current flowing through the instrument, up to a maximum needle deflection. Hence, if the maximum needle deflection is one milliampere, lesser currents will appear as a fraction of that value and the meter will read that amount as a maximum. For increasing the range of such an instrument, parallel resistors are shunted across the meter movement. For each such parallel resistor, an additional scale must be provided on the meter to read the current flow within the range provided by the shunt resistor. In commercial types, a rotary switch with a number of terminals is used for convenience in selecting the proper shunt resistor and, hence, the range desired.

Figure 5-1 shows the circuit of a typical milliammeter. If the switch is in an open position, the milliammeter will read current values up to one milliampere when the test probes are placed in series with the circuit to

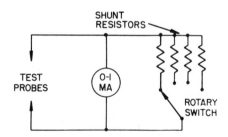

Fig. 5-1. Basic milliameter circuit.

be measured. Since an ammeter must be placed *in series* with the circuit, the latter must be opened for insertion of the meter.

The ranges established by the resistors are determined by the internal resistance of the meter. The following formula is employed for calculating the value of the shunt resistor required for full scale deflection.

$$R_s = \frac{R_m}{(N-1)}$$ (5-1)

where R_s = the value of the shunt
R_m = the meter resistance
N = the value of the number by which the scale is to be increased

Thus, if a 0-1 milliammeter with an internal R of 100 ohms is to have a maximum current reading of 5 milliamperes, the formula would be used as follows:

$$R_s = \frac{100}{5-1} = 25 \text{ ohms}$$

Hence, a 25-ohm resistor, in shunt with the meter, would permit current readings up to 5 milliamperes.

THE GALVANOMETER

Another type of current-reading meter is that known as the *galvanometer*. This instrument is primarily a laboratory device with the zero reading at the center of the meter dial permitting observation of proportional changes of current flow either in the negative or positive direction. Usually the galvanometer is not intended to read the actual amount of current flow, but only relative proportions of positive or negative polarity. The instrument finds greatest usage in the bridge circuits described later.

THE VOLTMETER

A voltmeter is employed for measuring the voltage drop *across* a resistor or some other component of a circuit. For this reason, the voltmeter is *not* placed in series with the resistor or other component, but *across* it. Since the voltmeter is shunted across the place where voltage is to be read, the meter should have a high internal resistance so that it will not behave as a low-shunt resistor. If the meter resistance is low, some of the current flowing into the resistor (or other component across which voltage is to be measured) will branch into the meter and upset true voltage readings.

Voltmeters are constructed by using a basic milliammeter, plus a series resistance, to reduce the current flowing through the meter to a value within its range. The ohmic value of the external resistor will establish the range of the voltmeter.

If the 0-1 milliammeter is placed across a circuit to be measured instead of in series with it, the milliammeter acts as a voltmeter, though it will be a very low resistance type that is capable of measuring only fractional voltage values. If the milliammeter has 100 ohms of internal resistance, it is evident that 0.1 volt will cause full needle deflection, since voltage is a function of the maximum current (0.001 ampere) times the resistance (100 ohms). If a voltage range of 5 volts is desired, then 4.9 volts must develop across the external series resistor, and 0.1 volt across the meter resistance, to give a total voltage drop of 5 volts. This 5-volt potential would cause the meter to deflect fully, because the meter movement would have 0.1 volt applied to it, which would cause one milliampere of current to flow through the 100-ohm internal resistance of the meter coil. Since one milliampere of current is the maximum which may flow through the meter, higher voltage scales would require the series resistors always to have all but 0.1 volt of the total voltage across them. Thus, if the maximum voltage which is to be read is 500 volts, 499.9 volts must drop across the series external resistor, so that again only 0.1 volt is applied to the internal meter movement. Figure 5-2 illustrates the basic voltmeter circuit. The various resistors are again selected by a rotary switch. The resistors are also referred to as *multipliers*. The following formula can be used to calculate the value of the series resistors for a desired voltage range :

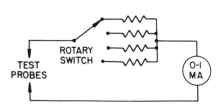

Fig. 5-2. Basic voltmeter circuit.

$$R_s = R_m (N - 1) \tag{5-2}$$

where R_s = the value of the series resistor (multiplier)
R_m = the resistance of the meter
N = the value of the number by which the scale *is to be increased*

As an example, assume the meter is to read 5 volts full scale. To apply Equation (5-2) it is necessary to determine the value of N. To do this, divide the desired full scale reading by the voltage necessary to deflect the meter fully. Thus, 5 volts divided by 0.1 equals 50. The number 50 is then placed in the formula and, when solved, it indicates that the required resistance for a full 5-volt deflection is 4,900 ohms.

$$R_s = 100(50 - 1) = 4,900 \text{ ohms}$$

The required value of the multiplier needed for a certain voltage scale can also be found by using Ohm's law to solve for total resistance. Since 5 volts is the maximum scale deflection, and 0.001 is the maximum current in amperes which will flow in the series circuit composed of the resistor and meter, the total resistance indicated is 5,000 ohms.

$$R_T = \frac{5}{0.001} = 5,000$$

Because the meter resistance is known to be 100, however, this value must be subtracted from the above figure of 5,000 to get the required series resistance (4,900 ohms) which must be used for a maximum scale reading of 5 volts.

In the foregoing, the external resistor was 4,900 ohms and the internal resistance 100 ohms, which provided a 5,000-ohm total resistance for a 5-volt scale. It will be found, with an 0-1 milliampere meter, that one volt full scale would require 900 ohms plus 100 ohms for the meter, or a total of 1,000 ohms. Hence, the meter has an internal resistance of *1,000 ohms per volt* of full scale deflection.

Such a meter will have some influence on the circuit when voltages are read, because the internal resistance is rather low. Most of the inexpensive meters use 1-milliampere meter movements (with internal *R* values ranging from 25 to 100 ohms) as the basis for the voltmeter. Higher internal resistances can be obtained by using a more sensitive milliammeter. For instance, some 20-microampere meters provide 50,000 ohms per volt, and thus affect

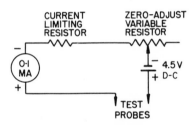

Fig. 5-3. Basic high range ohmmeter.

the circuit much less, in terms of current shunting, than the 1,000-ohm-per-volt meter. Other voltmeters are available which have internal resistances of one megohm or higher, such as the vacuum-tube voltmeters described in Chapter 22.

THE OHMMETER

The ohmmeter measures the ohmic value of resistors by employing a voltage source within the meter cabinet, and measuring the amount of current flow in the circuit formed by the resistance to be measured and the meter circuit. The ohmmeter is usually incorporated in the same housing with voltmeters, as more fully described in Chapter 22. A typical ohmmeter circuit is shown in Fig. 5-3. Again, as with meters discussed earlier, a 0-1 milliammeter can be used as the basic meter movement. Two resistors are placed in series with the meter, one being a fixed resistor to limit the current within the range desired, and the other a variable resistor so that the meter needle can be adjusted for a zero-ohm reading. A voltage source from flashlight cells in series is usually employed, as shown. When the test probes are shorted together, the ohmmeter circuit is closed, and current from the battery will flow through the meter and resistors. The variable resistor is then adjusted so that the needle deflects fully (indicating 1 milliampere of current flow within the meter). Since the test probes are to be placed across the resistor to be measured, it is obvious that, when the test probes are shorted together, a condition of zero resistance is present. Because the needle deflects to full scale, however, the ohmmeter scale must indicate *full needle deflection as zero ohms.*

Open test probes indicate an infinite resistance and because the ammeter circuit is also opened, the needle moves to the left. Thus, zero resistance is shown at the right side of the scale, and increasing resistance toward the left, with maximum resistance at the extreme left position of the needle.

When the test probes are placed across a resistor, the amount of current flow will be inversely proportional to the ohmic value of the resistor. Hence, a high value resistor permits less current flow than a low value resistor. The meter scale is calibrated to indicate such ohmic values.

Since the meter scale is calibrated on the basis of the current values in the meter circuit, the accuracy of the device is also dependent on the voltage source. Besides, as the battery ages and its voltage declines, it will be necessary to readjust the variable resistor for zero-ohm reading when the test leads are shorted together.

WHEATSTONE BRIDGE

The Wheatstone bridge is a method of employing resistor combinations in a so-called "balanced bridge" arrangement, for finding the value of any resistor whose resistance is unknown. The Wheatstone bridge principle can also be applied to finding the values of coils and other components, as more fully described later. It is named after Sir Charles Wheatstone (1802-1875), the English physicist who first stressed the importance of this balanced circuit.

The Wheatstone bridge principle is based on the polarities which are established in a resistive network similar to that shown in Fig. 5-4(A). Here are four resistors, each having a value of 50 ohms, and the potential

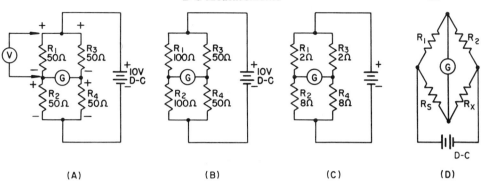

Fig. 5-4. Characteristics of resistive bridge.

applied across the network is 10 volts. Under these conditions, there is a 5-volt drop across each resistor. If a voltmeter is placed across resistor R_1, as shown, the plus test probe of the voltmeter would be put to the top of R_1, and the minus probe of the voltmeter to the bottom of R_1. If the voltage is to be read across resistor R_2, the voltmeter is moved down, and the plus probe applied to the top of R_2 and the minus probe to the bottom of R_2.

It is obvious, from the foregoing, that the center junction of R_1 and R_2 is either plus or minus, depending on whether the measurement is taken from across R_1 or R_2. (It must be remembered that polarity is relative. A plus polarity, for instance, by itself has no meaning. Such a polarity is plus only with respect to some minus potential.)

An inspection of the circuit consisting of R_3 and R_4 indicates that the center junction of these two resistors is also *either* plus or minus, *depending on whether reference is made to the top resistor or the bottom.* If a sensitive current-indicating device, such as the galvanometer (G), is placed across the two junctions, as shown, there is no reading, because the potential difference at the junction of R_1 and R_2 is identical with the potential difference which exists at the junction of R_3 and R_4. Since the polarities are identical, there is no *voltage difference* between these two points.

This principle of a balanced circuit is the basis for forming a Wheatstone bridge. It is logical, if R_2 is of a value different from the other resistors, that the zero potential difference between the two junctions will no longer exist, and a current flow is then established between these two points.

Another condition can be set up, as shown in Fig. 5-4(B). Here, even though resistors R_1 and R_2 are of a different value from resistors R_3 and R_4, a balanced circuit is still obtained. The voltage drop across each group of resistors in a parallel circuit is the same, even though the individual resistors have different ohmic values. Therefore, across R_1 and R_2 in combination, the voltage drop is still 10 volts (5 volts across each resistor), even though the total resistance is 200 ohms. Similarly, there is also a voltage drop of 10 volts across R_3 and R_4, even though this total resistance is only one-half that of the other branch. Therefore, halfway down each branch the voltage drop will be identical, and across these two junctions no potential difference exists.

The circuit arrangement shown at (C) will also function as a balanced bridge network, since the voltage drop across the upper resistors will be 2 volts, and the drop across the two lower resistors will be 8 volts. Again, across the junctions there is no potential difference.

The bridge circuit is usually illustrated as shown in Fig. 5-4(D). For measurement of an unknown resistance, the resistors marked R_1 and R_2 are of a fixed value. Resistor R_s is the *standard* or known value which is employed to determine the unknown value of R_X. The formula can be solved on the basis of the following formula:

$$R_X = R_s \ \frac{R_2}{R_1} \tag{5-3}$$

The unknown resistor is placed in the circuit shown at (D) at R_X, and the resistor R_s is varied until the bridge balances. The difference in ohmic value between R_2 and R_1 (if any) is then multiplied by the value of the known resistance so as to find the unknown. The variable resistor employed for R_s would have to be calibrated in terms of resistance variation. Instead of having a variable resistor for R_s, various resistors of known value can be placed into the circuit at R_s until the bridge is balanced, as indicated by a zero reading on the galvanometer. (A galvanometer, with its zero indication at the *center* of the scale, will read an unbalance in either the minus or plus polarity direction).

THE DECIBEL

In addition to methods for measuring unit values of current, voltage, etc. in electronics, a means for *comparing* power, voltage, or current levels is also available. This system is based on a value known as the *decibel*. Because the decibel involves *comparisons* between powers, voltages, or currents, the decibel is not, therefore, a unit *measurement*. The decibel value is based on the manner in which the human ear hears sounds of different intensities.

The human ear responds to changes in sound intensity in logarithmic fashion. (A summary of the theory of logarithms, plus tables, will be found in the Appendix. Reference should be made to this section if the subject matter is new to the reader, or if a review of the principles is indicated.) Hence, the ear is much more responsive to changes in low intensity sound levels than high intensity sound levels. Thus, for practical purposes, a means for comparing power changes in audio and electronics should also be based on logarithms. For this reason, the word decibel is used to indicate the change in volume level which occurs when the average ear is barely able to perceive a difference in a gradually changing sound amplitude.

The decibel is one-tenth of a bel, the unit expression being named after Alexander Graham Bell (1847-1922), the famed American scientist and inventor. The decibel is abbreviated as db and, as mentioned, is used as a comparison between sound power, voltage, or current levels, and not as a definite unit of measurement such as wattage.

Mathematically, the decibel is a function of the following expression:

$$10 \log \frac{P_2}{P_1} \qquad (5\text{-}4)$$

Thus, the ratio of two powers is taken and the logarithm (see Appendix) of this ratio is multiplied by ten. Ordinarily, however, the mathematical expression need not be used if one simply remembers that a *doubling* of power represents *three decibels*. Thus, if the power output from an audio amplifier is 2 watts, and the volume control is turned up to produce 4 watts, the change in decibels is three. Because this is a unit of comparison, however, the 3 decibels would only indicate that the power had been doubled, but would not express the *amounts* of power involved. Thus, if a public address system were delivering 10 watts and this were increased to 20 watts, the difference would also be 3 decibels. When there is an increase in power, this represents *plus* decibels. If there is a decrease in power, the expression would be *minus* decibels. If, for instance, a phonograph had an output of 8 watts and this output were reduced to 4 watts, it would represent a change of minus 3 decibels.

If the power of a device is increased 10 times, the difference in decibels would also be equal to 10. Thus, if sound power were increased from 1 watt to 2, this would represent 3 decibels. If the 2 watts were now increased to 4, it would represent another 3 decibels. Decibel increases are *additive*. Thus, the change in power from 1 to 4 watts would be equal to 6 decibels. If the power is increased from 4 watts to 8 (double again), another 3 decibels would be added, to indicate a total change of 9 decibels, etc. Because the decibel represents a multiplication of the logarithm of power ratio by 10, any power ratio of 10 would be equal to 10 decibels, while a power ratio of 100 would be equal to 20 decibels, 1,000 to 30 decibels, 10,000 to 40 decibels, etc.

The decibel expression is also used in reference to voltage and current changes, though in such instances a doubling of either the voltage or current would represent 6 decibels instead of 3. Assume, for instance, that a resistor of 5 ohms has a voltage drop of 10 volts across it. According to Ohm's law, the voltage divided by the current would indicate that two amperes of current is flowing through this resistor. Hence, multiplying the voltage (10) by the current (2) shows that 20 watts of power is being consumed by the resistor. If the voltage across the resistor is now doubled, it would represent a 6-decibel difference, since a voltage or current doubling is equivalent to a 6-decibel change. The proof of this is given when the amount of power is calculated, on the basis of the voltage change. Since the voltage was doubled, the current through the resistor would now be 4 amperes (20 volts divided by 5 ohms); hence, the power is now

$$P = EI = 20 \times 4 = 80 \text{ watts}$$

Since the power dissipated in the resistor is now 80 watts, as compared to the former 20-watt value, a power change of 6 decibels has occurred. This is the case because a change from 20 watts to 40 watts would be 3 decibels, and a change from 40 watts to 80 watts would be *3 decibels* more—a total of 6 decibels.

Similarly, consider the case of

$$R = 10 \text{ ohms}$$
$$I = 5 \text{ amperes}$$
$$P = I^2R = 25 \times 10 = 250 \text{ watts}$$

Now, if the current is doubled to become 10 amperes, again a 6-decibel difference would occur. If the current is doubled to become 10 amperes the power would be:

$$P = I^2R = 100 \times 10 = 1,000$$

In terms of wattage, the following decibel change is evident, when we compare the original 250 watts to the new value of 1,000 watts:

$$
\begin{array}{r}
250 \text{ watts to } 500 \text{ watts} = 3 \text{ decibels} \\
500 \text{ watts to } 1,000 \text{ watts} = 3 \text{ decibels} \\
\hline
\text{Total} = 6 \text{ decibels}
\end{array}
$$

Reference levels have been established on occasion to simplify analysis of power or voltage changes. In telephone work, a zero level of 0.006 watt had been commonly used as a reference. This was originally chosen because the 0.006 watt (6 milliwatts) was the output power of a vacuum tube often used in telephone repeaters. Thus, if a certain unit was designated as plus 10 db, it meant that it had ten times the output of the so-called telephone repeater tube of 6 milliwatts. This level has also been used by several amplifier companies as a reference level.

REVIEW QUESTIONS

1. Briefly explain how the ranges of ammeters and voltmeters can be extended.

2. Describe a galvanometer.

3. Define *meter sensitivity*.

4. What are the circuit principles of an ohmmeter?

5. Briefly describe the principles of the Wheatstone bridge.

6. How can the decibel value of a power change be ascertained easily when the change in power is a multiple of 2?

7. How is a current change rated in decibels?

8. Does a change from 2 amperes to 4 amperes have the same decibel value as a change from 60 volts to 120 volts.

PRACTICAL PROBLEMS

1. A 0–20 microammeter has a d–c resistance of 2,000 ohms. What voltage is required to deflect the meter needle to full scale?

2. A 0–50 microammeter requires 0.1 volt for full scale deflection. What is the meter resistance?

3. A meter has a maximum current reading of 5 milliamperes, but a maximum reading of 6 milliamperes is required. What must be the value of the shunting resistor if the basic 0–1 milliammeter movement has an internal resistance of 100 ohms?

4. A voltmeter, reading 5 volts full scale, has a series resistor of 4,900 ohms. The basic meter movement is 0–1 milliampere at 100 ohms. What must be the value of a new series resistor to change the meter to 50 volts full scale?

5. For the Wheatstone bridge circuit shown at Fig. 5–4(D), what is the value of the unknown resistor, when R_1 is equal to 1,000 ohms, R_2 is equal to 2,000 ohms, and R_s, the standard or known resistor, has a value of 4,000 ohms?

6. A phonograph amplifier with 5 watts of maximum output power has been rewired into a high-fidelity system having an output of 20 watts. By how many decibels has the converted unit been increased in power, as compared to the original one?

7. A television station, during repairs, reduced its power to one-tenth of its former value. What was the approximate decibel difference when the power was reduced?

8. The voltage across a resistor was increased from 2.5 volts to 20 volts. What is the decibel difference?

9. In an industrial control amplifier the power was increased from 6 watts to 18 watts. What is the decibel difference?

10. In a radar system the voltage across a resistor dropped from 23.4 to 7.8 volts. What is the decibel change which occurred?

6

INDUCTORS
AND
CAPACITORS

INTRODUCTION

Besides resistors, two other circuit components widely used in electronics are the inductor and the capacitor. The inductor (coil) finds applications in filter circuits, transformers, and other electronic circuits and devices. The capacitor (also referred to as a condenser) is employed for signal bypass purposes, filtering, signal transfer, and other uses as described later. Both the capacitor and inductor are capable of storing energy, and in combination form many important circuits. The characteristics of these two items in relation to direct current are reviewed in this chapter. The effects of alternating current and practical applications are discussed in Chapter 8.

ELECTROMAGNETISM

Oersted, while demonstrating electric principles to a class of students, noticed that a magnetized needle was deflected each time it was brought near a current-carrying wire. The needle, instead of being attracted or repelled, assumed a position which was perpendicular to the wire. This accidental discovery led to the recognition of the link between magnetism and electricity, and proved that current flow through a conductor sets up, about the conductor, fields which have characteristics *identical with the fields surrounding a permanent bar magnet.*

The magnetic field around a current-carrying wire is illustrated in Fig. 6-1. Separate circular sections are shown; though actually there are

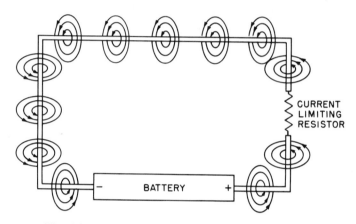

Fig. 6-1. Magnetic field around current-carrying wire.

no gaps along the wire, and the fields exist along the entire length of the wire. The electron flow through the wire causes an alignment of the electron spin of the individual atoms in the conductor thus magnetizing the metal, as discussed earlier with respect to the magnetization of iron. The field intensity is greatest at the wire.

The strength of the magnetic field (H), in oersteds, can be found at any point on a straight conductor by the following formula:

$$H = \frac{2I}{10d} \qquad (6\text{-}1)$$

where I is the current in amperes
d is the distance from the conuductor in centimeters.

From the foregoing formula, it is obvious that the field strength around a straight conductor is proportional only to the current flow through the conductor (for a fixed distance from the conductor). Hence, if the battery voltage for the circuit shown in Fig. 6-1 were increased, more current would flow, and the field intensity would also increase.

The direction of the magnetic lines of force are related to the direction of current flow. If the battery terminals are reversed, the direction of the magnetic lines of force shown in Fig. 6-1 will also change direction. With respect to the direction of the magnetic field and the direction of current flow, either can be ascertained, if the other is known, by use of the

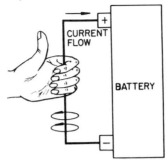

Fig. 6-2. Application of left-hand rule.

left-hand rule illustrated in Fig. 6-2. If the direction of the current flow is known (as indicated by the battery terminal polarities), grasp the wire with the left hand so that the thumb points in the same direction as the current flow. When this is done, the fingers will point in the *direction of the magnetic field*. Knowing the direction of the magnetic lines of the field, the wire is grasped so that the fingers point in the direction of the field, and the thumb will then indicate the direction of current flow.

MAGNETIC FIELDS AROUND A COIL

Coils are formed by wire loops, and a simple coil can be constructed by wrapping wire around a tube of cardboard, with each turn of wire

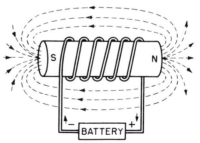

Fig. 6-3. Magnetic fields of coil.

placed next to (or near) the previous turn. (The term *solenoid* is also applied to a coil, particularly if the latter has a length greater than its radius.) In industry, a variety of coils (and transformers) are used, as discussed and illustrated more fully in Chapter 8. For this introductory explanation, however, assume a simple coil has been formed and voltage is applied, as shown in Fig. 6-3. When current flows through the coil, the individual fields of the turns combine to form an *electromagnet* with characteristics similar to a bar magnet. Hence, the coil will have a north and south pole, as shown in Fig. 6-3, and is capable of attracting magnetic materials, or repelling or attracting a similar coil (or bar magnet).

Fig. 6-4 indicates how the individual turns of the coil act to combine

(A)   (B)

Fig. 6-4. Combined fields of turns of coil.

the fields and form an electromagnet. Figure 6-4(A) shows the cross-sectional areas of two of the wire turns forming the coil. With a separation between the wires, as shown, the individual fields have the same direction, since the current flow through each turn of wire is also of like direction. When the fields are brought together, as would be the case with close-wound wire, the fields, though in the same direction, oppose each other between the turns of wire and tend to neutralize each other. Hence, with a number of closely-spaced turns of wire, as shown in Fig. 6-3(B), the outer portions of

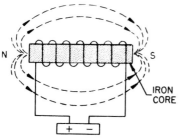

Fig. 6-5. Increasing magnetic lines of force in a coil by use of metal core.

the individual fields combine, as shown, increasing the total field *parallel with the coil length*. In consequence, the magnetic fields are established to form an electromagnet.

The left-hand rule also applies to a coil. If the left hand grasps the coil so that the fingers point in the direction of current flow, the thumb will point to the coil's *north pole*. For the coil shown in Fig. 6-2, the left hand is laid palm over the coil with fingers pointing up-ward in the direction of current flow. The thumb then points to the north pole of the coil.

When a soft-iron core is inserted into the coil, as shown in Fig. 6-5, the magnetic lines of the field are increased greatly, forming a more power-ful electromagnet. The field intensity does not increase (unless the current flow through the coil were made to increase), but the increase in magnetic lines is caused by magnetization of the iron core. The central core, be-coming magnetized, produces fields of its own which are added to the lines of the coil, resulting in increased field strength. The iron, with its high permeability, provides for increased conductivity of the magnetc flux through the core with the result that a more definite pole area is created at the ends of the coil. In practical applications, iron and other metal cores are used extensively, as more fully detailed in Chapter 8.

In coils such as shown in Figs. 6-3 and 6-5, the magnetic fields exist only while current is flowing through the coil. Current, on the other hand, flows because of the applied electric pressure (voltage). Hence, the creation of the magnetic fields is caused by what is termed *magnetomotive force* (mmf), just as current flow in a resistive circuit is caused by electromotive force (emf). Magnetomotive force, however, not only can be derived from current flow, but may also be in the form of a magnetized external unit, such as a magnet or another electromagnet. The unit of magnetomotive force is the *gilbert,* named after William Gilbert (1540-1603), the English researcher in magnetism.

Increasing the number of turns in a coil adds to the strength of the magnetizing force, over and above what is obtained when the current is increased. Hence, the equation of magnetomotive force, in gilberts, is expressed as follows:

$$\text{Magnetomotive force } (F) = 1.256NI \tag{6-2}$$

where 1.256 is 0.4 pi (π)
N is the number of turns of wire
I is the current in amperes

A gilbert may also be defined as the magnetomotive force required to produce a flux of one maxwell in a magnetic circuit in which the reluctance is one unit. The product NI (number of turns times current) is also known as the *ampere turns.* As with Ohm's law for electric circuits, the relationships between flux, reluctance, (see Chapter 2) and magnetomotive force in magnetic circuits are expressed by the equations

$$F = \phi \mathcal{R}, \qquad \phi = \frac{F}{\mathcal{R}}, \qquad \mathcal{R} = \frac{F}{\phi} \tag{6-3}$$

THE HYSTERESIS LOOP

Cores used in practical coils consist of a variety of materials, including soft iron sheets, powdered iron, silicon steel, and a crystal-metallic substance known as ferrite (the latter finding use as antenna cores and in special core applications in high-frequency techniques and computer systems). Practical considerations of core materials are covered in Chapter 8 and other subsequent chapters. The core characteristics are based, however, on the laws of magnetism and, hence, their fundamental aspects are discussed in the present chapter.

When current is made to flow through a coil such as the one in Fig. 6-5, the soft iron core becomes magnetized, and the magnetic characteristics set up in the individual atoms are aligned as discussed previously. If the battery is removed, however, the current flow through the coil stops, and the magnetic domains of the iron tend to assume a random arrangement again. Some alignment remains, however, because of the retentivity of the material. The slight magnetism which remains in the core material is known as *residual magnetism*. When the magnetizing force is plotted on a graph against the flux density, the residual magnetic characteristics of the core material are clearly indicated.

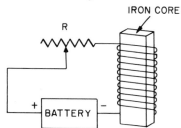

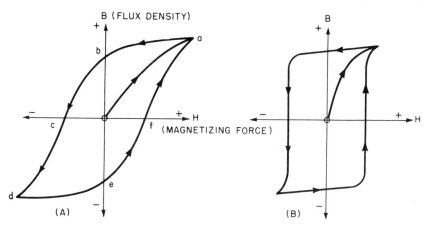

Fig. 6-6. Circuit for varying flux density.

A circuit for varying the flux density is shown in Fig. 6-6. A coil is wound around a soft iron bar and is connected to a battery, as shown. A variable resistor R is used, so that the voltage impressed on the coil can be varied from zero to the maximum produced by the battery. As the voltage is increased, current flow through the coil increases, and the magnetizing force (H) thus produced is graphed along a horizontal axis, as shown in Fig. 6-7(A). The flux density (B) created is graphed along

Fig. 6-7. Hysteresis loops (ordinary magnetic material vs ferrite).

the vertical axis, as shown. With zero battery voltage (and hence zero current), the iron bar is in an unmagnetized state, and the representation on the graph is at the zero point of interesection between the vertical and horizontal axes.

When the resistor *R* in Fig. 6-6 is varied to apply voltage to the coil, current flow occurs, and the magnetizing force is applied to the core. One oersted of magnetizing force produces one gauss of flux density and, as the current flow through the coil increases, flux density rises from zero toward the point marked *a* on the graph. As the current through the coil increases, the flux density eventually reaches point *a* (the leveling off region). An additional increase of the magnetizing force no longer increases flux density, and the state known as core *saturation* has been reached. If the magnetizing force (by virtue of the current through the coil) is now decreased, it will be found that the flux density will not decline along the initial upward curve, but now retraces along the line *a* to *b*. Thus, when the magnetizing force is zero (no current through the coil), flux density still exists (indicating residual magnetism in the core). As can be seen from the graph, the flux density *B lags* behind the magnetizing force *H,* and this lag characteristic is known as *hysteresis* (from the Greek verb *hysterein:* "to be behind, to lag"). The graph of the hysteresis of the core material is known as a *hysteresis curve* or *hysteresis loop,* or also as a *B-H curve.*

In order to decrease the residual magnetism (flux density) to zero, it would be necessary to *reverse* the battery shown in Fig. 6-6, so as to change the polarity of the magnetizing force. Applying such reversed magnetizing force to the core (from zero to *c* in Fig. 6-7), will bring the flux density back to zero. The magnetizing force used to bring the flux density to zero again is known as the *coercive force.*

If the reverse-polarity magnetizing force is increased by an addiitonal amount, the curve of flux density goes from *c* to *d* as shown. Once more, decreasing the magnetizing force to zero brings the flux density to the point *e,* which again represents a residual magnetism. To bring the residual section of the curve to zero, the polarity of the magnetizing force must be reversed, as before, to create the necessary coercive force. Increasing the magnetizing force again brings the curve to point *a,* and the ferromagnetic core has gone through a complete magnetic cycle. In order to rid the core of the residual magnetism, the core would have to be demagnetized by subjecting it to a strong external a-c field of the type subsequently described. (Coils used to demagnetize cores are known as *degaussing coils,* and are utilized on occasion to rid tape recording heads, or other devices, of residual magnetism, in such cases where its effects on electronic processes would be harmful.)

The shape of the hysteresis loop obtained depends on the type of material, with a higher permeability material producing a narrower curve than a lower permeability material, for a given magnetizing force. Ferrite material has a hysteresis loop which is almost rectangular, as shown in Fig. 6-7(B). Here, removal of the magnetizing force results in only a slight change in the flux density of the core material. When the reverse-polarity magnetizing force reaches a critical value, there is a more abrupt decline of the curve than is the case with the loop shown at (A). The rectangular loop is useful when it becomes necessary to switch the magnetic state rather abruptly, as is the case of switching and gating systems discussed later.

ELECTROMAGNETIC INDUCTION

Michael Faraday (1791-1867), the English scientist, discovered in 1831 that electric energy can be induced from one circuit to another by utilizing magnetic lines of force. This principle is illustrated in Fig. 6-8,

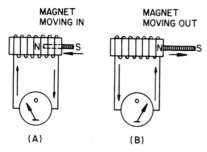

Fig. 6-8. Conductor cutting lines of force.

(A)   (B)

showing that when a conductor is moved through a magnetic field, a difference of potential is set up between the ends of the conductor, and an electromotive force is induced. This voltage exists only *during* the time when the conductor is in *motion* through the magnetic field. Thus, the current flow caused by the voltage is also present only during the time when the conductor cuts the lines of force by movement. The current which is caused to flow is known as *induced current.*

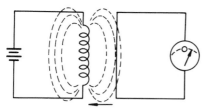

Fig. 6-9. Effects of magnet with respect to coil.

The conductor can remain stationary and the lines of force can be shifted, so that they will cut across the conductor. When this is done, an electromotive force is again induced. Thus, it is evident that the voltage may be induced in a conductor by *moving the conductor* through magnetic lines of force, or by *moving the source* of the magnetic lines of force so that they cut across the conductor.

A permanent magnet can be used, as shown in Fig. 6-9, and the conductor may be a coil. When the magnet is moved into the coil, the meter reading will be in one direction, as shown in Fig. 6-9(A). When the magnet is removed, however, the meter needle will deflect in the other direction, as in Fig. 6-9(B). As the electric field cuts through the stationary conductor, the induced current establishes another magnetic field across the conductor. The relationship between the magnetic lines of force around the conductor and those of the magnetic field which induces the voltage were observed by Heinrich Lenz (1804-1865), the German physicist. In 1834, he established the law which now bears his name, *Lenz's law.*

An induced current set up by the relative motion of a conductor and a magnetic field always flows in such a direction as to form a magnetic field which opposes the motion.

This law is also illustrated in Fig. 6-9(A) and (B) with the magnet and coil. As the north pole of the magnet is inserted into the core area of a coil, the magnetic lines of force of the magnet cut across the conductor (the wires of the coil), and the induced voltage starts a current flow in the coil, which causes the needle of the meter to deflect. The direction of the meter needle movement shows that the current flow is in the direction indicated by the arrows. The left-hand rule indicates that the electromagnet formed by the coil has its north pole at the end which faces the north pole of the bar magnet. Since two like poles repel each other, energy must be imparted to the magnet in order to overcome the repulsion existing between the north poles. After the magnet has been inserted within the coil, there will be no more induced voltage and current flow will cease since no movement is present and, thus, the lines of force will not be cut. Under this condition, the meter needle will drop to zero.

As the bar magnet is removed, its electromagnetic lines of force again cut across the conductor wires of the coil, and the induced voltage again causes an induced current to flow. The current flow, in this instance, is opposite to the current flow which was established when the magnet was inserted within the coil. The meter needle now deflects in the other direction to indicate a change of polarity with respect to the voltage and, thus, shows a current flow opposite to the former flow. Now, the left end of the *coil* becomes the south pole, and thus attracts the north pole of the *magnet.* This holding characteristic must be overcome by energy applied during the removal of the magnet from within the coil. (A magnet which produces a stronger magnetic field permits more lines of force to be cut within a certain time interval. The magnitude of the induced voltage is proportional to the number of magnetic lines of force which are cut by the conductor per second. To induce an electromotive force (emf) of 1 volt, 100,000,000 magnetic lines of force must be cut per second.)

The induced voltage can also be increased by increasing the *speed* with which the magnetic lines of force cut the conductor, or *increasing the number of conductors* which are cut. The latter process involves increasing the number of turns of wire in the coil.

Because of the induction characteristics, a coil is often referred to as an *inductor* or *inductance*. With a steady d-c flowing through a coil, however, the fields represented by the magnetic lines of force remain at a fixed distance from the wire. The magnetic lines of force represent *stored energy,* and if the applied voltage is removed, the lines of force collapse back into the wire, returning the energy to the latter. An inductor with d-c flowing through it behaves just as a resistor, with only the resistance of the wire offering opposition to the flow of d-c. In practical applications, a-c is used and its effect on coil characteristics differs radically from that of d-c. These factors are discussed in Chapter 8, where unit values, series and parallel connections, and other related data are covered.

CHARACTERISTICS OF CAPACITORS

A capacitor is formed when two conductors are brought within close proximity to each other without touching. In such an instance, air would be the medium of separation between two such conductors, and the air thus acts as an insulator. Other types of insulation can also be employed, such as mica, paper, ceramic, and plastic. The insulation between the two conductors which form a capacity is called the *dielectric*. Capacitors take many forms, some utilizing metal plates for the conducting surfaces, while others use metal foil. The various commercial types of capacitors are discussed in greater detail later. A capacitor effect is also formed between two wires which are close together, or between a length of wire and another metal surface, such as the circuit chassis. Such capacity effects are often undesirable and provisions must be made for reducing their unwanted effects in circuitry. The capacitors which are *desired* are usually of the physical type specifically designed for applications in electronic circuits. The discussion which follows is primarily concerned with the capacitors deliberately formed by metal plates or foil. Subsequent discussions will treat the capacities formed inadvertently by circuit wiring.

Typical capacitor symbols are shown in Fig. 6-10. At (A) is the standard symbol for a fixed-value capacitor. At (B) is shown a polarized capacitor—one where the correct polarity must be observed. At (C) is the older capacitor symbol which is still encountered in some manufacturers' circuits and electronic literature. Newer symbols will be used in this text.

The charging characteristics of a capacitor are shown in Fig. 6-10(D). Here, a battery and a switch are connected in series with a single capacitor,

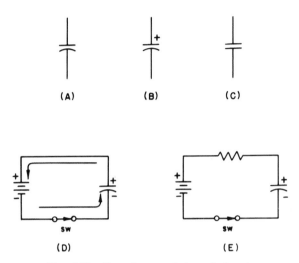

Fig. 6-10. Capacitor symbols and charging.

as shown. When the switch is closed, electrons flow from the negative side of the battery, and at the same time electrons flow into the positive terminal. The electron flow from the negative battery terminal places electrons on the lower plate of the capacitor, and such an accumulation of electrons, beyond the normal amount which would exist on this plate, creates a negative charge here. The electrons drawn into the positive side of the battery from the upper plate of the capacitor create a deficiency of electrons and, thus, the upper capacitor plate becomes positively charged.

At the instant when the switch is closed, a large amount of electrons flow, and very little voltage is required. As electrons crowd on the lower plate, however, electromotive force is required to force additional electrons on to it and, in consequence, there will be a sharp rise of voltage across the capacitor. When the voltage across the capacitor reaches the battery voltage, no more electrons can be forced on the lower plate, nor drawn away from the upper plate, and current flow to the capacitor ceases. The capacitor is now said to be *charged,* and a stable condition exists wherein the applied voltage is constant and current flow is zero.

If a resistor is placed in series with the capacitor shown in Fig. 6-10(D), there will be a delay in the charging rate of the capacitor, since the resistor offers opposition to the flow of current. The effect of the resistor in the circuit, with respect to the charging rate of the capacitor, is known as the *time constant,* as more fully explained later.

The dielectric of the capacitor has considerable influence on the *amount* of electrons which can be stored, and hence on the *charge* which can be placed on the capacitor. The reason for this is indicated in Fig. 6-11. Here, the capacitor has been charged, so that its upper plate has an excessive amount of electrons (a negative charge), while the lower plate has a deficiency of electrons (a positive charge). The electrostatic fields of these two charges cut across the dielectric (insulator), and influence the planetary electrons of the atoms forming the dielectric material. Because an insulator has a minimum of free electrons which can be set in motion, the electrostatic fields of the charges on the plates will distort the orbit of the planetary electrons, but will not remove them from such an orbit. The negative plate of the capacitor will repel the negative electrons near it in the dielectric, while the positive plate will attract the electrons which lie near it in the dielectric. Thus, the planetary atomic orbits are *distorted,* as shown in Fig. 6-11.

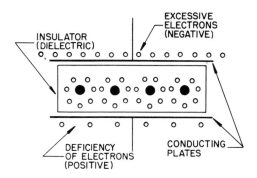

Fig. 6-11. Electron placement in charged capacitor.

Each orbital distorted atom is referred to as an *electric dipole* or *induced dipole* and as such is comparable to the atoms or magnetic dipoles which exist in magnetized material, as previously explained. In the capacitor, the induced dipoles of the dielectric material are aligned symmetrically by the electrostatic lines of force, as shown in Fig. 6-11, just as the magnetic domains and electron spins in magnetic material are symmetrically aligned. When symmetrically-aligned induced dipoles are created in the dielectric, the latter is also referred to as being *polarized.* When the charge on the capacitor is removed, the electrostatic fields collapse and the atoms are no longer distorted.

In a charged capacitor, the atomic distortion created in the dielectric material by the electrostatic lines of force will create an additional electrostatic field which opposes the original field around the charged plates and tends to neutralize them. Hence, additional electrons can be forced on to the negative plate and more can be drawn away from the positive side. In such a manner, the dielectric is influential in increasing the storage capacity of the unit. The degree to which the capacity can be increased by the dielectric depends on the nature of the dielectric. Air has the least influence in increasing capacity and, hence, the *dielectric constant* of air is assigned the numeral one. All other materials thus have a higher dielectric constant and a greater influence toward increasing the ability of the capacitor to assume a greater charge. Glass, for instance, has a dielectric constant of from six to nine, and mica from six to seven.

Since the amount of charge is also dependent on how many electrons can be forced on the negative plate and how many can be drawn from the positive plate, the amount of charge is also influenced by the *area* of the conducting plates of the capacitor. A larger area means that more electrons can be accommodated by the negative plate, and that more free electrons are available for withdrawal from the positive plate. Another factor which affects the amount of charge is the *spacing* between the capacitor plates. The closer the plates, foil, or other conductive material of the capacitor, the larger the capacity. A closer spacing of the plates means that the electrostatic fields of the negative and positive charges have a greater influence on the dielectric. Thus, the opposing fields of the dielectric have a greater influence on increasing capacity.

The unit of capacity is the *farad,* named after the eminent British scientist, Michael Faraday. A farad is the capacity to store one coulomb of charge at the emf of 1 volt. The equivalent of a coulomb, as mentioned earlier, is

$$1 \text{ Coulomb} = 6.28 \times 10^{18} \text{ electrons} \qquad (6\text{-}4)$$

From this definition of a coulomb, the formula for capacity can be stated as follows:

$$C \text{ (in farads)} = Q \text{ (coulombs)} = E \text{ (volts)} \qquad (6\text{-}5)$$

The farad, however, represents too large a capacity for use in electronics. The amount of capacity employed in ordinary electronic circuits is expressed in millionths of a farad, and such capacitors are rated in microfarads or micromicrofarads. As an example, a capacity may be rated as 2 microfarads, which means that it is two-millionths of a farad. Another capacitor may be represented as having 20 micromicrofarads, or twenty-millionths of a microfarad.

CAPACITORS IN SERIES AND PARALLEL

When capacitors are placed in series, the total capacity will be decreased. Hence, a formula for series capacitors is

$$C_T = \cfrac{1}{\cfrac{1}{C_1} + \cfrac{1}{C_2} + \cfrac{1}{C_3} + \ldots \cfrac{1}{C_n}} \qquad (6\text{-}6)$$

When capacitors are connected in parallel, each additional capacitor placed in parallel adds more capacity, since more plate area is also available for the withdrawal of electrons from the positive plates. The formula for parallel capacitors thus indicates simple addition of the individual capacities.

$$C_T = C_1 + C_2 + C_3 + \ldots C_n \qquad (6\text{-}7)$$

In Fig. 6-12(A) three capacitors are shown in series across a battery. The electron flow from the negative side of the battery causes an accumula-

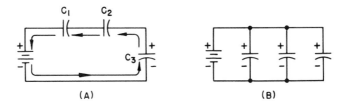

Fig. 6-12. Voltage distribution in capacitor circuits.

tion of electrons on the lower plate of C_3, and thus produces a negative charge. Electron flow into the battery from capacitor C_1 places a positive charge on the plate nearest the positive terminal of the battery. Electrons moving away from the upper plate of C_3 place the latter at a positive potential, and these electrons flow to the right-hand plate of C_2 and produce a negative charge. The electrons on the left-hand plate of C_2 leave, and hence the latter is charged at a positive polarity and these electrons accumulate on the right-hand plate of C_1 producing negative polarity. Thus, the voltage drops around this series circuit resemble the voltage drops which would occur across several resistors in series.

In Fig. 6-12(B) a parallel arrangement of capacitors is shown. Here, the voltage drops are similar to resistors in parallel; that is, each capacitor has across it the source voltage, regardless of the individual capacitor value.

TIME CONSTANT

The time constant of a circuit is a calculation used to find the charging rate of a capacitor (or a coil) when a series resistor is in the circuit. The time constant of a resistance-capacitance circuit has for its symbol *RC*, which is the algebraic expression of resistance multiplied by capacitance, with the resistance value in ohms and the capacity value expressed in farads. For coils, the symbol *L/R* gives the time constant of the inductance value in henrys divided by the resistance value in ohms. Because coils are used primarily with a-c, their characteristics with respect to time constants are discussed in Chapter 8. The following discussion covers the *RC* time constants.

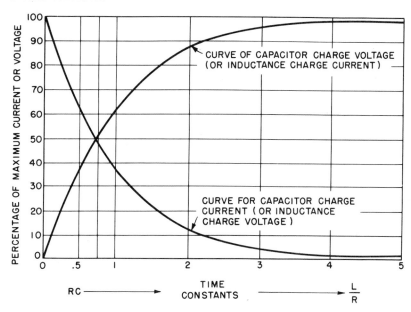

Fig. 6-13. Universal time constant chart.

The chart in Fig. 6-13 shows the percentages of maximum voltage or current for any particular time constant. Hence, the two curves shown on the time constant chart represent the changes of values which occur upon application of voltage and current to coils and capacitors. The curves rise in an exponential manner; that is, they ascend with a sharply changing amplitude initially, and then the rate of change gradually tapers off.

The curve which has its beginning at the lower left-hand corner at zero, represents the voltage rise in a capacitor upon application of energy to a circuit composed of a capacitor and a resistor in series. This curve is also representative of the inductive current in a coil. Thus, the lower left-hand curve indicates the rise time of the voltage as the capacitor is being charged or the current rise time in an inductance. The curve which has its beginning at the upper left, starts at maximum amplitude, and represents the capacitor charge current when voltage is first applied, and also the inductance charge voltage. The upper curve thus shows that capacitor current flow starts at a maximum when voltage is first applied to the *RC* circuit. It also shows that the capacitor current flow gradually decreases as the voltage across the capacitor rises. In an inductance, the voltage is maximum initially, and current starts from zero and rises as shown.

The usefulness of the time constant and the chart (also known as the *Universal Time Constant Chart*) is that charging rates of capacitors (and current rises in coils) can be found readily. The time constant of an *RC* circuit is the time required to charge the capacitor to approximately 63% of its final voltage level. Hence, the time constant *in seconds* for a capacitor (in an *RC* circuit) to reach 63% of full value is found by multiplying the resistance value by the capacity value.

Thus, if a 3-megohm resistor is in series with a capacitor of 5 microfarads, and a 100-volt source is used, the time constant (*RC*) equals

$$3,000,000 \times 0.000005 = 15 \text{ seconds}$$

Hence, it would take 15 seconds for the capacitor to charge to 63% of 100 volts, or 63 volts. Since the current to the capacitor decreases inversely as the voltage increases, the current after 15 seconds would be 37% of the initial amount of current at the time the circuit is closed and the capacitor begins to charge.

If a capacitor of 0.04 microfarad is in series with a 5,000-ohm resistor, the time constant would be

$$0.04 \times 5,000 = 200 \text{ microseconds}$$

This indicates that the capacitor will be charged to 63% of its full value in 200 microseconds. After five time constants have elapsed, the capacitor is considered to be fully charged with zero current flow. The time constant calculation can also be employed to ascertain the time it takes to discharge a capacitor to 37% of its charged value.

CHARGE AND DISCHARGE FACTORS

If a capacitor has been charged with a battery, the latter can be removed and the capacitor will retain the charge for an indefinite period, unless some internal leakage exists. In the latter instance, the electric energy stored in the charged plates will leak across the insulator and, eventually, there will be as many electrons on one plate as on the other. When the latter state is reached, no potential difference exists, and the charge is no longer present. With a good quality capacitor having a minimum of leakage, the charge may last for hours or for days. If the leads from the capacitor are touched together, as shown in Fig. 6-14(A), the capacitor will discharge, since a path is now provided for the accumulated electrons on the negative plate to flow to the positive side where a deficiency exists and where electrons are demanded. This shorting together of the leads discharges the capacitor and neutralizes the effect of an excessive amount of electrons on one plate with respect to the other. If a resistor is placed in series with the discharge path, as shown in Fig. 6-14(B), the rate of discharge will be slowed down and the time constant (RC) is again a factor. As discussed earlier, this calculation will give the amount of discharge (63%) which occurs in one second.

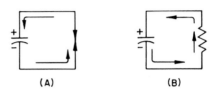

Fig. 6-14. Capacitor discharge.

If an excessive amount of voltage is employed when placing a charge across a capacitor, the electrostatic fields will be so great that the insulation will be punctured, and the capacitor will have an internal short. When the latter occurs, the accumulated electrons on the negative plate will rush through the puncture and discharge the capacitor. Since the insulation has been punctured, the resultant short will also appear across the battery, because it will permit an excessive amount of electrons to flow *through* the capacitor.

Note that in the foregoing discussion of capacitor discharge, the discharge path is opposite to the charging path, and that the electrons, in order to discharge, must flow in the direction opposite to that which they followed when the capacitor was being charged. If an ammeter were placed in series with a capacitor being charged, the needle would swing in one direction and, after a full charge had been reached, would drop back to zero. If the capacitor were now discharged, the ammeter needle would swing in the opposite direction, indicating the reversal of electrons during the discharge process. Thus, the charge and discharge of the capacitor exhibits the properties of a-c, insofar as the ammeter is concerned, since the ammeter needle swings in one direction and then in the other, indicating a plus and a minus polarity.

REVIEW QUESTIONS

1. Give the unit for the strength of a magnetic field, and explain how this strength can be ascertained when the current in amperes and the distance from the conductor are known.

2. (a) Briefly explain what is meant by the left-hand rule for finding the direction of current flow in a conductor.
(b) Explain how the left-hand rule is also applied with respect to finding the north pole of an electromagnet.

3. Briefly explain what is meant by magnetomotive force and show how this value in gilberts can be found by use of a formula.

4. Briefly explain what is meant by residual magnetism and draw a typical hysteresis curve.

5. Given a conductor and a magnetic field, explain how an electromotive force may be induced into the conductor.

6. If the ends of a coil are attached to a current-reading meter, explain what occurs when a magnet is inserted into the coil and then removed.

7. In your own words, explain what is meant by Lenz's law.

8. What factors determine the amplitude of induced voltage?

9. Briefly explain how the dielectric of a capacitor contributes to total capacitance.

10. Define a *farad*.

11. When capacitors are placed in series, is the equation for total capacitance similar to that for series resistors or parallel resistors?

12. Explain briefly what is meant by the *time constant* of a circuit.

13. What may occur when an excessive amount of voltage is impressed across a capacitor?

14. Compared to the charge path of a capacitor, in what direction is the *discharge* path?

PRACTICAL PROBLEMS

1. A single conductor had 22.5 milliamperes of current flowing through it. What is the strength (H) of the magnetic field in oersteds at 1.5 centimeters from the wire?

2. What is the magnetomotive force in gilberts of a single-layer coil with an air core if the number of turns is 50 and the current flow is 50 milliamperes?

3. If the number of turns in Problem 2 were increased to 100 and the current doubled, what would be the resultant magnetomotive force in gilberts?

4. In a single-layer coil the *ampere turns* equalled 40. What is the magnetomotive force in gilberts?

5. An inductor had 300 turns of wire and 2 milliamperes of current flow through it. What is the magnetomotive force in gilberts?

6. In a laboratory power supply, three capacitors were placed in series to increase their voltage-handling capability. If the capacitors had a value of 90 microfarads, 45 microfarads and 30 microfarads, what is the total capacitance?

7. In an electronic tracking system, two capacitors were in parallel, one having a capacity of 0.001 microfarad and the other 0.002. An additional capacitor of 0.047 was added in parallel. What is the total capacitance?

8. In a signal switching circuit a 0.003-microfarad capacitor was in series with a 5-megohm resistor. What is the time constant in seconds?

9. In a high-fidelity system a 0.02-microfarad capacitor has in series with it a 3,000-ohm resistor. An emf of 200 volts is impressed across this circuit. What is the time in microseconds for the capacitor to reach full charge?

10. A resistor, placed across a capacitor, discharged the latter to 94.5 volts in one (time constant). What was the full charge voltage on the capacitor?

7

ALTERNATING
CURRENT
(A-C)

INTRODUCTION

In all types of electric and electronic applications, both the direct and the alternating currents are used extensively. Direct current is primarily used to furnish power for transistors and vacuum tubes so these can bring signals up to a sufficient amplitude for practical employment. Alternating currents are those present in the power mains, and the transmitted carrier signals which arrive at receivers are alternating-current types. Alternating current is also used for furnishing power to the filaments of tubes (as discussed later), and frequently it is necessary to convert alternating current to direct current for specific applications. The basic factors relating to this important subject are covered in this chapter.

A-C CHARACTERISTICS

Alternating current is abbreviated a-c (also used as an adjective to describe alternating voltage). It has become common practice to refer to alternating voltage as a-c voltage. Actually this is a redundant description, since a-c voltage means "alternating-current voltage." Popular usage, however, has held to this term and for this reason it will be employed hereafter.

The insertion of a magnet into a coil, as described in the preceding chapter, actually produces a-c. Prior to the movement of the magnet into the coil, zero voltage exists. As the magnet approaches the inductor, the induced energy builds up from zero to a maximum value. When the magnet is withdrawn, voltage again builds up, but now it is of opposite polarity. After the magnet is withdrawn, the induced voltage (and current) again drops to zero.

The *waveform* of voltage induced across the inductor has a characteristic as shown in Fig. 7-1. The gradual rise of amplitude from zero to maximum, with its subsequent decline to zero represents one-half of an a-c wave. The rise to maximum again in the opposite direction and thence to zero again is the second half of the a-c wave. The two combined form a *sinewave*. The induced voltage of sinewave form also creates an induced current flow which has a waveshape similar to that of the voltage. The respective

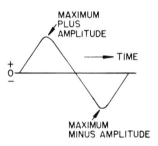

Fig. 7-1. Sinewave of a-c.

amplitudes of the current and voltage may differ depending on the internal resistance of the coil, the number of magnetic lines of force of the magnet, and the coil turns. Both current and voltage waveshapes, however, are sinusoidal.

GENERATION OF A-C

There are a number of methods for generating a-c; the most common form used is the *generator*. This device utilizes the inductive principles discussed earlier, where a conductor rotates to cut magnetic lines of force. The basic form of a generator is shown in Fig. 7-2. Here, a horseshoe type of permanent magnet is used in conjunction with a wire loop. The wire loop is between the north and south poles of the permanent magnet and, thus, is within the highly concentrated magnetic lines of force existing between the pole pieces. The wire loop of the generator has its ends terminating at collector rings, so that the loop can be rotated while the ends still make electric contact with the collector rings. Two so-called *brushes* are utilized, which are formed of a composition having a carbon base, and thus capable of conducting electricity. These brushes make physical contact with the collector rings and slide along them as the latter are rotated.

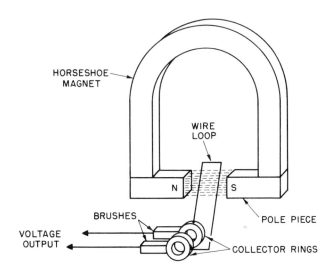

Fig. 7-2. Basic generator.

The brushes are connected to the output terminals of the generator. In actual generators, instead of the single wire loop shown in Fig. 7-2, a number of turns are used to form a coil which rotates within the magnetic lines of force. The rotating coil section is known as an *armature*.

The manner in which this simple device illustrated in Fig. 7-2 generates a-c is shown in Fig. 7-3. When the armature coil is in a vertical position, as shown in Fig. 7-3(A), the least number of lines of force are intercepted. If the coil is stationary, no voltage is induced into the coil and, hence, none appears at the collector rings and output terminals. As the coil is rotated, as shown in (B), the rotation causes the coil to assume a horizontal plane and, as it enters such a horizontal plane, it cuts more and more lines of force and, consequently, a greater voltage is induced into the coil and at the output terminals. As the coil is rotated, it again moves toward a vertical position and, as it leaves the horizontal position, the voltage which is induced still has the same polarity and the current flow is in the same direction, but it now diminishes and decreases to zero when the coil again assumes a vertical position. This rotation of the coil has now produced *one-half* of the sinewave form previously mentioned, because the coil loop has made *one-half turn*. Each conductor of the loop is now in a reversed position with respect to its starting position. As the coil is once more made to rotate toward a horizontal plane, the electro-

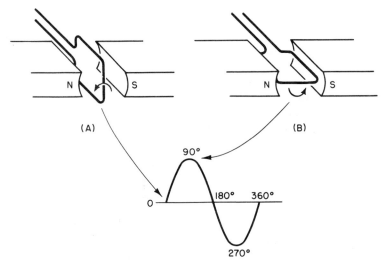

Fig. 7-3. Function of a basic generator.

motive force is again induced and gradually increases in amplitude from zero to a maximum, but with an opposite polarity than previously. During the last quarter turn of the coil, the voltage decreases from a maximum negative value back to zero, at which point the coil conductors will have assumed their original positions. If the shaft of the generator is connected to a motor, so that the armature coil is rotated at a rapid rate, an alternating current will be generated, where the positive and negative voltage peaks are produced in rapid succession.

CHARACTERISTICS OF A-C

When the a-c waveform initially begins at zero and reaches maximum, then drops to zero again, this portion of the sinewave is known as an *alternation*. The sinewave form shown in Fig. 7-1 has, therefore, two alternations. Since the third alternation would be identical to the first, and subsequent alternations would be repetitions of the initial two, *any two successive alternations are called a cycle*. Thus, one cycle of a-c may be represented as Fig. 7-4(A), where the first alternation is negative, or one cycle may be in the form shown in Fig 7-4(B) where the first alternation is positive. The next two alternations which follow a cycle would be another cycle, since the waveform would be repeated.

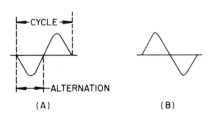

Fig. 7-4. Terms applied to an a-c sine-wave.

The *frequency* of an a-c wave-form is determined by the *number of cycles which occur per second*. The frequency commonly used in the power mains is 60 cycles per second (cps). Because there are 60 cycles of a-c occurring each second, there are 120 *alternations* per second. Since the armature coil of the generator must make a complete revolution to produce one cycle, the armature coil rotates through 360 degrees. The relative degrees of rotation of the armature, versus the sine-waveform produced, is shown in Fig. 7-3. Reference to this illustration makes it clear that maximum values of voltage (or current) are reached at the 90-degree point of the first alternation, and at the 270-degree point of the second alternation. Zero points are reached at zero degrees, 180 degrees, and 360 degrees.

Battery voltages are of a steady-state value under normal conditions and, if a resistor is placed across the battery, a fixed value of current flows. In a-c, however, the values of voltage and current are always changing, starting at zero, rising, then declining again. Hence, for one cycle of a-c, the average value would be zero, because the positive amplitude at its peak value is equal to the negative peak value amplitude, and these equal and opposite polarity values would cancel in terms of an average value. The term *average value,* however, usually refers to approximately one-half of the peak amplitude of an alternation, and is equivalent to 0.636 times the maximum or peak amplitude. The average value is encountered in rectification and pulse work, but, in general, a more commonly encountered value is the *effective value.*

The effective value is also known as the *root-mean-square* value (rms) and is equal to 0.707 times the maximum or peak value. The term "root-mean-square" is derived from the fact that its calculation is based on adding the instantaneous current values which have been squared, and dividing this sum by the number of instantaneous values taken. The effective value is, therefore, equal to the square root of the average of the instantaneous values.

The effective value of a-c is equivalent to the value of d-c required to do the same amount of work. Thus, if a light bulb is designed for 110 volts rms (effective value), it would mean that this 110-volt a-c bulb would light as brightly and consume as much power when used at 110 volts d-c. Thus, the effective value is the commonly indicated value given to the power mains furnishing a-c to the homes, and it is also the value generally read by the average a-c voltmeter.

If the effective value is known, the peak value of the a-c waveform may be found by multiplying the effective value by 1.41. This figure, 1.41, is approximately equal to the square root of 2. Thus, it is evident that the effective voltage is equal to the peak voltage divided by the square root of 2. The 110 volts of a-c supplied by the power mains consequently has a peak amplitude of 155 volts. Since the peak amplitudes are present only for short intervals, they will not perform the same amount of work which could be furnished if this peak voltage were maintained constantly. The effective value, therefore, is equal to the same d-c value which would have to be utilized to perform the same amount of work.

PHASE

In the a-c generators previously discussed, reference was made to induced voltages and induced currents. If a resistor is placed across the wires at the output of the armature coil, both the voltage and current would start simultaneously, and both would reach their positive amplitudes at the same time, as well as their respective zero and negative amplitudes. When the voltage and current peaks, and zero points, coincide in time, the voltage and current are said to be *in phase*. Under some circuit conditions, however, the voltage and current may not reach peak values at the same time, and when this is the case, the current and voltage are referred to as being *out of phase*. In Fig. 7-5(A), the voltage and current

(A) (B)

Fig. 7-5. Voltage and current phase relationships.

are shown in phase, while in Fig. 7-5(B) an out-of-phase condition is indicated. Relative amplitudes of voltage and current in (A) may differ, since current could be higher than voltage, or vice versa. Relative amplitudes have no bearing on phase, however.

The out-of-phase condition shown in (B) indicates that the voltage reaches its maximum 90 degrees ahead of the current maximum. Under this condition, the voltage also reaches zero 90 degrees ahead of the time when the current reaches zero. The voltage is said to *lead* the current by 90 degrees, or it can also be stated that, under this condition, the current is *lagging* the voltage by 90 degrees. In other words, the phase angle (the difference in degrees between voltage and current) is equivalent to 90 degrees. The symbol for the phase angle is the Greek letter theta represented by the symbol θ. Sometimes the lower case phi (ϕ) is also used.

PRACTICAL GENERATOR

The basic a-c generator illustrated earlier in Fig. 7-2 indicates the fundamental principles of operation. In actual practice, however, the a-c generators are more complex and efficient, and instead of a single loop of wire, coils are wound around the armature frame. Also, additional coils are utilized to form an electromagnet of considerable strength to produce a high power a-c output. The coils which produce the magnetic fields are referred to as *field coils* and are supplied with d-c from an external source. A typical commercial generator of this type is shown in Fig. 7-6.

In the basic generator discussed earlier, the armature was the rotating

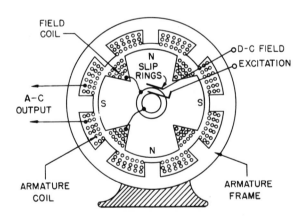

Fig. 7-6. Practical a-c generator.

element and the magnetic fields produced by the magnet surrounded the armature. As the armature rotated, the coil cut the stationary lines of force. As discussed in Chapter 6, however, the magnetic fields could be moved and induction would still be established. Thus, in an a-c generator, the armature coils can be kept stationary and the field coils rotated so that their magnetic lines of force move and cut across the armature coil to produce a-c. Thus, in practical applications the a-c generators mostly use rotating fields because of the simplicity of design. Also, the slip rings no longer need to carry the high amplitude currents which the generator furnishes the load.

As shown in Fig. 7-6, the center cylindrical section (a laminated metal drum) has appropriate slots for accomodating the field coils. This center section has four poles and the field coils are in series, with the two terminals connected to the slip rings. The d-c field voltage (excitation) is applied to these two collector rings by carbon brushes which slide over the collector rings as the center field-coil section rotates. The armature, which is now stationary, has its individual coils also connected in series, with the a-c which is generated produced at the output terminals as shown. Such a generator is a single-phase type, and it generates a single a-c waveform. The 110-120-volt a-c found in the homes is the single-phase, 60-cps variety furnished with a two-wire line. When 240-volt a-c is furnished to homes, a three-wire line is used, with one conductor representing the ground wire. Either of the other wires, with respect to the ground wire, would furnish 120 volts. This type a-c is still *single phase,* however, and must not be confused with the three-phase commercial type discussed next.

THREE-PHASE A-C

In industrial plants and in many commercial applications where large motors must be operated and high-power furnished to other equipment, the common type of a-c is the three-phase as distinguished from the single-phase furnished to residential areas by the power mains. (Two-phase is only used on rare occasions for specific industrial applications.) The three-phase generator has the armature coils divided into three sections as shown in Fig. 7-7(A) (this generator also employs a stationary armature as does the commercial-type generator previously discussed). Thus, the armature coils, regardless of their number, are grouped into sets so arranged that the induced voltage for one set of coils differs from the others by a third of a cycle (120 degrees). Such a generator is termed a *polyphase* type, since it has more than one phase of a-c.

With the armature coils divided into three sections, six terminals are available as shown at (A). By wiring the coils as shown at (B) or (C), however, the number of terminals is reduced to three, as shown. The connection shown at (B) is known as *delta,* since it resembles the Greek letter positioned sideways. At (C) the so-called *star* or *Y* connections are shown. (This is sometimes called the *Wye* type.) The delta and Y windings can also be employed on transformers, with either serving as the primary or secondary. Similarly, a delta generator (or transformer secondary) can feed a Y load, or vice-versa. At (C) is shown a Y winding feeding a delta load composed of resistors R_1, R_2 and R_3. This load could consist of a motor specifically designed for three-phase operation. The load, represented by the three resistors, is a balanced type; that is, each resistance value is identical to the others.

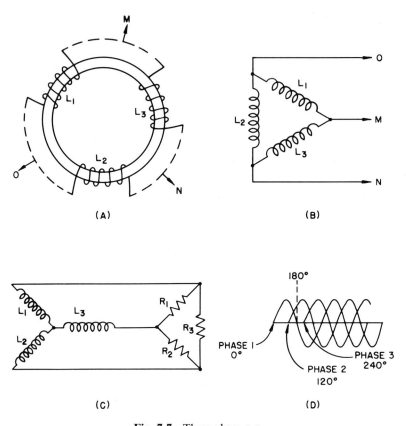

(A)   (B)

(C)   (D)

Fig. 7-7. Three-phase a-c.

The three signal waveforms produced are shown at (D). Since one complete cycle (two alternations) of a-c takes in 360 degrees, one alternation takes 180 degrees as shown. For the three-phase a-c, phase 2 is displaced with respect to phase 1 by 120 degrees (one-third cycle), and phase 3 is displaced by 240 degrees with respect to phase 1 (and by 120 degrees with respect to phase 2). With three-phase a-c, current at any instant may be flowing out of one wire and returning through the other two. At another instant, the current flows through two wires and returns through the third.

In the distribution of power to industry, a neutral (ground) wire is often used with the three-phase system as illustrated in Fig. 7-8. Such a

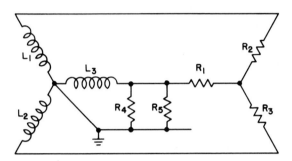

Fig. 7-8. Three-phase four-wire system.

wire is connected to the junction of the Y winding as shown and constitutes what is known as a *three-phase, four-wire* system. The neutral wire permits single-phase a-c to be obtained from the three-phase system. If, for instance, each of the inductors shown in Fig. 7-8 has a 120-volt drop across it, this voltage is obtained with respect to the neutral wire and any one of the other wires. For the system shown in Fig. 7-8, the voltage drop across L_3 is utilized to furnish 120 volts *single-phase* to the load circuits R_4 and R_5. These may be electric fans, heaters, or other devices requiring only 120-volt single-phase a-c. At the same time, a balanced load (R_1, R_2 and R_3) is furnished the three-phase a-c as shown.

REVIEW QUESTIONS

1. Draw a sinewave and label the alternations, the peak amplitudes, and the time base.

2. Define the words *generator* and *armature*.

3. Explain how a generator produces a-c.

4. Explain what is meant by the *effective* value of a-c, and indicate what percentage of the peak value this represents.

5. Explain what is meant by the *average* value of a-c, and indicate what percentage of the peak value this represents.

6. Draw two waveforms, and identify one as *current* and the other as *voltage*. Show the voltage with approximately twice the amplitude of the current, with the voltage *leading* the current by 90 degrees.

7. Repeat Problem 6, but show the current *leading* by 45 degrees.

8. If the peak a-c power is 155 volts, what is the root-mean-square value, and which value (peak or rms) is equal to the same d-c voltage which would have to be utilized for equivalent electric power?

9. If the effective value of a voltage is known, how may the peak voltage be found?

10. Why do a-c generators employ rotating field coils?

11. Draw a schematic of a three-phase delta generator winding connected to a Y-type balanced load circuit.

12. Explain what is meant by a four-wire, three-phase system.

PRACTICAL PROBLEMS

1. An electric light bulb is used in a 32-volt d-c system. What effective value of a-c voltage is necessary to have this bulb light as brightly as it does on d-c?

2. In a public address amplifier circuit there is a 300 peak sinewave à-c voltage drop across a resistor. What value of voltage will an rms type of a-c voltmeter read?

3. In a certain community the a-c power mains gave a reading of 125 volts rms. What was the peak value of this voltage?

4. What is the effective value of the sinewave voltage of a-c power main system when the peak voltage is 340?

5. In an industrial control circuit two resistors are in series with a sinewave a-c source of 200 volts rms. Only one resistor is readily accessible and this has 50 volts (effective value) across it. What is the *peak* voltage which appears across the other resistor?

6. In the schematic of a radar system a pure sinewave is shown having a voltage value from the minus peak of one alternation to the plus peak of the next alternation (peak-to-peak) of 126 volts. What is. the rms value of this a-c voltage?

7. In a four-wire, three-phrase system, 240 volts rms appears across each inductance of a delta winding. What is the peak value of the voltage impressed across the load resistor connected between the neutral wire and one of the other output terminals?

8

REACTANCE
AND
IMPEDANCE

INTRODUCTION

When a-c flows through a coil, in contrast to d-c, the magnetic lines of force are constantly building up and collapsing, and this action produces a changing field. Thus, when current starts to flow in one turn of the coil, the build-up of the magnetic lines of force which represent a changing voltage amplitude will induce a voltage into the next turn. As described earlier, the induced voltage causes a current to flow, which opposes the initial current. Thus, an opposing current is built up in the adjacent turn, which tends to reduce the initial flow of current which was established through the coil by the voltage applied.

This same opposition factor occurs throughout the coil, that is, as the changing fields induce voltages and currents in adjacent turns, a counter-electromotive force is developed by virtue of the *new* magnetic lines of force generated in adjacent turns. The induced emf always opposes the applied electromotive force of the coil and, for this reason, it is known as *back-electromotive force (back-emf)*, and also as *counterelectromotive force*. The characteristic of a coil which relates to such a *counter-emf* and

120

represents opposition to a change of current is known as the *inductance* of the coil. The counter-emf is established during the time when the applied a-c is building up, and also occurs after the a-c peak voltage has been reached, when the latter starts to decline. As the magnetic fields decline, the collapsing field again cuts across adjacent coil turns, thus inducing an electromotive force which is opposite in polarity to the applied voltage.

The unit for inductance is called the *henry,* named after the American scientist Joseph Henry (1797-1878). The unit of inductance also relates to the principle known as Lenz's law, (mentioned earlier in Chapter 6) which may be stated as follows:

When a changing current is caused to flow through a coil by applying a voltage, the magnetic lines of force produced by the current establish an induced voltage which opposes the changing current which produced it.

Thus, an inductance is *that property of a circuit that opposes any change in the amount of applied current.*

The henry is the amount of inductance present in a coil when a current change of 1 ampere per second produces an induced voltage of 1 volt. (The henry is often employed in fractional expressions such as millihenry, which is one-thousandth of a henry, and microhenry, which is one-millionth of a henry.) The symbol used for inductance is L, and the symbol for henry is the small letter h.

A resistor will oppose the flow of a-c just as it does d-c. In addition to the resistance of a coil, however, opposition to a-c flow is also produced by the coil's inductance. The opposition to the a-c which is present in an inductance is called *inductive reactance.* The symbol for reactance is X, and for inductive reactance the symbol becomes X_L.

The nature of inductive reactance is similar to the manner in which resistance offers opposition to electric flow; hence, the inductive reactance of a coil has for its unit value the ohm, which is also used for resistance. Resistance, however, will not only offer opposition to the flow of either d-c or a-c, but utilizes some of the energy and dissipates it in the form of heat. Inductive reactance, on the other hand, *does not* consume electric energy, even though it opposes current flow. Actually, electric energy is *stored* in the magnetic field of the coil, and when opposition is offered to the current flow, the current is reduced, but the unused energy is returned to the voltage source. Thus, while inductive reactance is an indication of the amount of opposition to the current flow, and hence indicates the current decrease which results by virtue of such reactance, it is not used to calculate the power consumed in the coil.

The inductive reactance can be calculated by Ohm's law, and the formula is similar to that used in solving d-c problems. These formulas can be set down as follows:

$$X_L = \frac{E}{I}, \qquad I = \frac{E}{X_L}, \qquad E = IX_L \qquad (8\text{-}1)$$

When no resistance is present in the coil, there is a 90-degree phase angle between the applied a-c voltage and the current flow through an inductance. This phase difference, (with voltage leading) also indicates that no power is consumed, because when the voltage is at its peak, the current flow at that instance is zero.

The inductive *reactance* which is established in a coil depends on the *amplitude* of the *induced* voltage. The latter, in turn, depends on the amount of inductance in henrys (or fraction of a henry), as well as the rate of change of the a-c. The rate of change, of course, depends on frequency, and for this reason determines the rate at which the current (and hence the magnetic field) is changed. Thus, the amount of inductive reactance can also be calculated by the following formula, which takes the foregoing factors into consideration:

$$X_L = 2\,\pi f L \qquad (8\text{-}2)$$

Here, f relates to the frequency (in cycles per second) of the a-c applied to the coil, while L refers to the inductance of the coil (in henrys). The symbol shown between the numeral 2 and the letter f is the Greek letter *pi*. The approximate value of pi is 3.1416.

ANGULAR VELOCITY

In a-c calculations, the expression "two pi" is used extensively. *Pi* multiplied by 2 is approximately 6.28, and this value is used in conjunction with the frequency and inductance value for solving inductive reactance, without knowledge of the current or voltage values. Reference to Fig. 8-1 will help clarify the usage of two pi.

If the radius were bent around the circumference, as shown in Fig. 8-1(A), and if another line were drawn as shown by the dotted line, which is a second radius, it would be found that the angle between these two radius lines would equal approximately 57.3 degrees. This angle, which is established when the radius is bent around the circumference once, is known as the *radian*. Since one radian is created each time the radius is bent around the circumference, in a 360-degree circle there will be 6.28 radians, just as 6.28 radius lines can be laid around the circumference without overlapping.

If a circle is drawn such as shown in Fig. 8-1(B), and if it is assumed

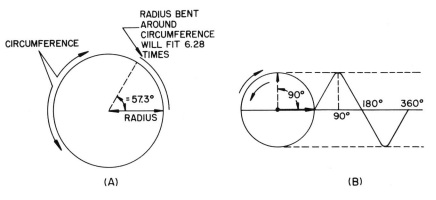

Fig. 8-1. Relative degrees in a-c waveform.

that this is a wheel which rotates in a *clockwise* direction, as indicated by the arrow, an additional representation can be made of the manner in which a-c functions and of the characteristics which it presents. If a radius line is drawn horizontally in the circle, as shown in Fig. 8-1(B), and if this radius line revolves *counterclockwise,* a clear understanding of the relation of frequency and velocity to reactance can be gained. Assume that if the wheel (circle) rotates *clockwise* once through 360 degrees, the horizontal radius line also makes a complete revolution, but in a *counterclockwise* direction. Thus, if the circle is rotated once, assume that a gear mechanism automatically turns the radius line completely around once in a direction opposite to that of the circle. If a marker were now fastened to the arrow point of the radius line, it would be found that, for a complete rotation of the circle, the radius line would draw a sine-waveform, such as shown in Fig. 8-1(B). This is a *vector* representation of the a-c characteristics. The radius is now called a *vector arm,* since it will draw out a complete sinewave during a counterclockwise rotation of the arm while the circle rotates for one complete revolution in a clockwise direction. Thus, if the vector arm moves counterclockwise until it is vertical, it will represent an angular change of 90 degrees in the circle, and at the same time will draw one-half of an alternation, or 90 degrees of the sinewave.

The speed with which the circle rotates is directly related to the frequency of the sinewave, in cycles per second. Since the vector arm, in its vertical position, represents the maximum amplitude of the sinewave produced, this arm also represents *instantaneous* values of a sinewave for positions other than the vertical. Thus, if the vector arm is at a 45-degree angle with respect to the horizontal zero reference line, it will indicate the instantaneous voltage at the 45-degree point (or instantanous current of the sinewave), since the vector arm at 45 degrees will be above the zero reference line by the amount of voltage or current representing the instantaneous value.

The angular velocity of a vector arm as it rotates indicates the change of degrees as well as the amplitude, and hence it is also an indication of the velocity of the sinewave. Thus, the expression $2\pi f$ is known as the *angular velocity*. Since 2π is equal to 6.28, the angular velocity may also be written 6.28f. When the angular velocity is multiplied by the inductance value in henrys, the value of the inductive reactance is found.

As shown in Fig. 8-1, 6.28 radians equals 360 degrees. Because a radian is 57.3 degrees, and because this represents the angle between the extremes of the radius laid along the circumference, 6.28 times the radius would indicate the complete circumference, and thus 6.28 radians equals 360 degrees. Here, basic principles of trigonometry are obviously utilized, and this branch of mathematics is useful in analyzing and understanding electronc circuits. Ratios and right-angle factors are given in the appendix for reference.

INSTANTANEOUS VALUES

Since the vector line, or radius, has a length equal to the peak or maximum value of either voltage or current, the *instantaneous value* can be ascertained if the *angle* of the vector line with respect to the zero voltage line is known. The instantaneous value of either voltage or current indicates the value of such voltage or current which prevails at the instant when the vector arm is considered to be at one place, and thus has a definite angle with respect to the zero line. If the maximum value of a voltage or current is then multiplied by the *sine* of the angle, the instantaneous value of the voltage or current will be ascertained. The formula for finding the instantaneous values of either the voltage or the current is

$$e = E \sin \theta \quad \text{or} \quad i = I \sin \theta \qquad (8\text{-}5)$$

where e or i is the instantaneous value

E or I is the maximum (peak) value

θ is the angle formed by the vector (radius) and the zero (horizontal) line.

The application of this simple formula is shown in Fig. 8-2. At (A), the vector line is shown at an incline of 45 degrees with respect to the zero voltage line. If the vector arm represents 50 volts, this potential is multiplied by the sine of the angle. The sine of a 45-degree angle is 0.707. Hence, if the 50 volts of peak value is multiplied by 0.707, the result will be 35 volts.

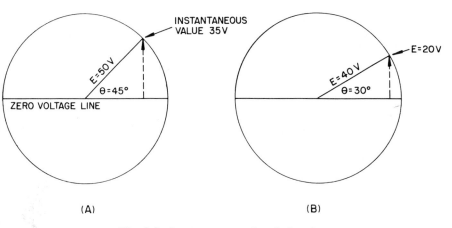

Fig. 8-2. Instantaneous value designations.

At (B) is another instance, where the peak voltage is 40 volts and the angle of incline is 30 degrees. Here, the sine of the 30-degree angle is 0.5, and when the 40 volts is multiplied by the sine of the angle, we find that the instantaneous value of the voltage is 20 volts.

The voltage representations in Fig. 8-2 could also be current values, and the methods for solving the instantaneous value would still apply. Note that, at the 30-degree angle at (B), the instantaneous value is exactly one-half of the peak value.

Example: The maximum value of an a-c voltage is 200. What is its value at the 135-degree vector angle?

Solution:

sin 135 degrees = 0.707 (same as 45 degrees)
0.707 × 200 = 141.4 volts instantaneous value

Often, voltage and current in an a-c circuit are not in phase. This occurs when an inductance or a capacitance is present. As previously mentioned, an inductance will cause the voltage to lead the current by 90 degrees. A capacity will cause the current to lead the voltage by 90 degrees. Combinations of these two, or when both factors are used in conjunction with a resistor, may cause other differences than 90 degrees, as more fully explained later in this chapter. When, however, either the voltage or the current lags, the instantaneous values can still be ascertained by finding the degrees of difference in the angle between voltage and current. The formulas for finding the instantaneous values under such a condition are as follows:

Current lagging: $\qquad i = I \sin (\theta - \phi)$ (8-6) where θ is the phase of voltage

ϕ (phi) is the phase difference between E and I, or angle of current lag.

Voltage lagging: $i = I \sin (\theta + \phi)$ (8-7)

Example: In a circuit having an inductance and resistance, the current lags the voltage by 60 degrees. The maximum value of the current is 25 milliamperes. What is the instantaneous value of the current, when the voltage is at the 90-degree vector angle?

Solution:

$$i = I \sin (\theta - \phi)$$
$$= I \sin (90° - 60°)$$
$$= 25 \times \sin 30°$$
$$= 25 \times 0.5 = 12.5 \text{ milliamperes}$$

The solving for instantaneous values does not have as much application, in practical work, as does the solving of peak values, effective values, etc. There are occasions, however, when a knowledge of the basic principles of instantaneous values will be helpful, and the foregoing explanations illustrate the mathematical factors which relate to a-c theory.

POWER FACTOR

The formula for calculating the power for instantaneous values is similar to the formula for d-c where $P = EI$:

$$P_{\text{inst}} = E_{\text{inst}} \times I_{\text{inst}} \tag{8-8}$$

When solving for power, where effective values of voltage and current are employed, the formula can still be used, provided that the voltage and current are in phase. When current or voltage are out of phase, however, there are occasions during the cycle when the current is negative while the voltage is positive, or vice versa. During such times when voltage and current have opposing polarities, the power consumed by the load circuit would be zero, since the power would be returned to the generator. When current and voltage are only slightly out of phase, some power is used, depending on the degree of phase difference. Thus, less power would be consumed by the load than would seem to be indicated by use of the formula. Actually, the formula would only indicate the *apparent* power. The *true* power in such instances would be less. The ratio of the *true* power to the *apparent* power for out-of-phase effective values of voltage and current, is known as the *power factor*. Thus, power factor may be solved by the following formula:

$$\text{Power factor} = \frac{\text{True power}}{\text{Apparent power}} \tag{8-9}$$

This ratio can be expressed as a percentage, or as a fractional value. Thus, the power factor can be 25%, or one-fourth of the apparent power. When effective values of voltage and current are employed where there is no phase difference between the two, the apparent power is then equal to the true power. The actual power consumed by the load is equal to the product of the voltage multiplied by the current, times the cosine of the angle between the current and the voltage. In the form of a formula, this becomes

$$P = EI \cos \theta \qquad (8\text{-}10)$$

The value of *the cosine of the angle is equivalent to the power factor* because, when current is in phase with the voltage the angle is zero and hence the power factor would be the cosine of zero degrees, or one. (See the trigonometric table of ratios in the Appendix.) If a 90-degree phase difference exists between current and voltage, the power factor is the cosine of 90 degrees, which is zero, indicating no power is consumed because EI times zero equals zero. Hence, it is readily apparent that an in-phase E and I delivers maximum power to the load resistance, but if the power factor is less than one (such as 0.8 or 0.6), only a portion of the voltage and current values produce actual power. Since only the true power shows all energy which performs work, it is necessary to ascertain such true power by considering the difference in the phase angle between voltage and current, as discussed more fully later in this chapter.

The power factor of a circuit can be ascertained practically by taking meter readings, or calculated mathematically when the voltage, current, and the wattage of a circuit are known.

IMPEDANCE

For simplicity, it was assumed that the coils discussed earlier had no resistance, only inductance. Actually, however, all coils have some resistance. Since lengths of wire have resistance, it follows that coils formed by wire will also have some resistance, the amount depending on the wire size, the number of turns, and the composition of the wire. If copper wire is used, and the wire diameter is large, a coil of only a few turns would have such a low resistance that the resistance effect on circuit function could be ignored. However, if the coil has more than just a negligible resistance, the latter will alter the angle of phase difference which would exist without such coil resistance.

When a resistance is present in the inductance, it will decrease the angle of current lag to less than 90 degrees. The amount by which such a phase difference is reduced depends on the *time constant* of the circuit.

(See Fig. 6-13). Depending on the amount of resistance present, there will be delay with respect to the amount of time required for the current to attain 63% of maximum. The time constant (t) of an *LC* circuit can be calculated on the basis of the following formula:

$$t = \frac{L}{R} \qquad (8\text{-}11)$$

where *L* is in henrys and *R* is in ohms.

The difference in lead and lag will determine the actual amount of power consumed by the coil. When a coil has more internal resistance than another, more power is consumed. If the coil is a pure inductance and has no resistance, there would be a 90-degree current lag. The 90-degree phase difference would provide a cosine of zero, as shown on the table of trigonometric values in the appendix. With a cosine of zero, the product of the voltage times the current would always be zero, when multiplied by a zero representing the cosine of the angle. (Assume that the voltage is 5 and the current is 2 amperes. The apparent power would be 10 watts, but the actual and true power would be zero.)

On the other hand, if a pure resistance were present (without inductance) and the same formula used, the *cosine* of the angle would be one, since the *angle* is zero. Thus, 5 volts multiplied by 2 amperes equals 10 watts. When this product is multiplied by one (representing the cosine of zero angle), it would still give 10 watts for the power. Thus, when the cosine of the angle is one, the apparent power is also the true power.

If an inductance and a resistance are present, where the resistance causes the 90-degree angle to change to a 45-degree angle, the cosine of this angle would be 0.707. Now, when the formula is applied, the true power is derived as follows:

$$EI \cos \theta = 5 \times 2 \times 0.707 = 7.07 \text{ watts}$$

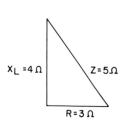

Fig. 8-3. Impedance triangle.

When a resistance is present, the opposition to the current flow is no longer simple reactance or resistance. Rather, a new term must be employed to represent the condition where a combination of resistance and reactance is present. This term is *impedance*. The symbol for impedance is the capital letter *Z*. Since impedance is a function of the angle between zero and 90 degrees, it can be set down as a right-triangle function, as represented in Fig. 8-3. Thus, if the inductive reactance is 4 ohms and the resistance is 3 ohms, the angle shown would be less than 90 degrees and, therefore, the impedance would be proportional to the hypotenuse marked *Z* in Fig. 8-3. The electric formula for this hypotenuse calculation is as follows:

$$Z = \sqrt{R^2 + X_L^2} \qquad (8\text{-}12)$$

Thus, the calculation for Fig. 8-3 would be

$$Z = \sqrt{4^2 + 3^2} = \sqrt{16 + 9} = \sqrt{25} = 5 \text{ ohms}$$

Thus, when reactance and resistance are involved, the reactance and resistance values cannot be added together for total opposition. If this had been done in the previous example, it would have indicated a value of 7 ohms for the opposition instead of the *true* value of 5 ohms.

The resistance of the coil can be represented schematically, as shown in

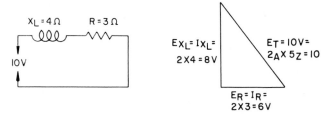

Fig. 8-4. Impedance triangle using voltages.

Fig. 8-4. Here, the coil resistance is indicated as a series resistor, for the purposes of calculation. The same schematic would also represent a coil with negligible resistance, but in series with a fixed resistance value. The total current for the circuit in Fig. 8-4 can still be calculated by using Ohm's law.

$$I = \frac{E}{Z} = \frac{10}{5} = 2 \text{ amperes}$$

The same calculation holds true for finding the voltage drop across the resistor.

$$E_{X_L} = IX_L = 2 \times 4 = 8 \text{ volts across } X_L$$
$$E_R = IR = 2 \times 3 = 6 \text{ volts across R}$$

Total voltage can be found by multiplying the value of total current by the value of the impedance.

$$E_T = IZ = 2 \times 5 = 10 \text{ volts}$$

The voltage drops across the individual units of inductance and resistance would be proportional to the respective values of the latter. Thus, if 2 amperes of current flow in the circuit, multiply the 4 ohms of inductive reactance by two to get the voltage drop across the inductance. The same multiplication factor of 2 amperes will also apply to the resistance. Thus, the voltage drop across inductive reactance differs with respect to the voltage drop across the resistance by the factor established by the multiplier two. This is shown in Fig. 8-4, where 8 volts is indicated as dropping across X_L, and 6 volts across R. This can be solved by the next formula:

$$E_T = \sqrt{E_R{}^2 + E_{X_L}{}^2} = \sqrt{6^2 + 8^2} = \sqrt{36 + 64}$$
$$= \sqrt{100} = 10 \text{ volts}$$

Thus, the total voltage in a *series* circuit composed of reactance and resistance can be solved by the vector formula, in similar fashion to the solving for total impedance.

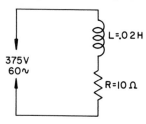

Fig. 8-5. Series circuit, inductance and resistance.

The previous circuit can be made more complex, if the inductance *reactance* is not known beforehand. If, for instance, only the *inductance* in henrys were given, as shown in Fig. 8-5, the initial calculation would consist in first solving for the amount of inductive reactance, and then applying the answer to the vector formula for finding total impedance. The inductive reactance amounts to 7.5 ohms, and this brings the impedance to 12.5 ohms.

$$X_L = 2\pi fL = 6.28 \times 60 \times 0.02 = 7.5 \text{ ohms}$$
$$Z = \sqrt{10^2 + 7.5^2} = \sqrt{100 + 56.25}$$
$$= \sqrt{156.25} = 12.5 \text{ ohms}$$

Once the ohmic value of the total impedance is known, the current flow through the circuit can be found by applying Ohm's law.

$$I = \frac{E}{Z} = \frac{375}{12.5} = 30 \text{ amperes}$$

If several series resistors are in the circuit, the total resistance is the sum of the individual resistor values.

PARALLEL REACTANCE AND RESISTANCE COMBINATIONS

When a resistor shunts a coil in parallel, as illustrated in Fig. 8-6, Equation (8-12) does not apply. In a parellel circuit, the voltage drop across each unit is the same, but the currents differ. For this reason, the calculation of impedance necessitates the calculation of total current. In order to find the total current, the current through the resistor and the current through the inductance must first be found, again using Ohm's law.

$$I_R = \frac{E}{R} = \frac{24}{4} = 6 \text{ amperes}$$

$$I_{X_L} = \frac{E}{X_L} = \frac{24}{3} = 8 \text{ amperes}$$

Once the currents through the individual units have been found, the total current must be calculated by vector addition.

$$I_T = \sqrt{I_R^2 + I_{X_L}^2} = \sqrt{6^2 + 8^2}$$
$$= \sqrt{36 + 64} = \sqrt{100} = 10 \text{ amperes}$$

$$Z = \frac{E}{I} = \frac{24}{10} = 2.4 \text{ ohms}$$

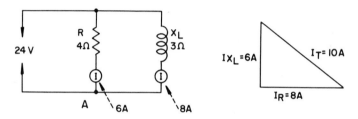

Fig. 8-6. Parallel circuit with current triangle.

From the foregoing, the total current was found to be 10 amperes, as proved by vector addition, and not 14 amperes, which would be the case if simple addition of currents were involved as for resistors. Once the total current has been found, the impedance can be ascertained by utilizing Ohm's law to give 2.4 ohms, as shown in the last example, for the circuit in Fig. 8-6. The vector diagram of the individual currents and the resultant total current, as represented by the hypotenuse, is also shown in Fig. 8-6.

When the values of resistance and reactance are known in a parallel circuit, the impedance can be ascertained, even though the source voltage value is unknown. The respective resistance and reactance values remain unchangd for various voltages impressed across them, though the current flow through each component will change for a change in applied voltage. Thus, impedance can be calculated by *assuming* a voltage, and then solving for the current through the resistor and the current through the reactance. The vector sum of the currents will give the total current which would flow for the particular voltage impressed, and the impedance can then be found by dividing the assumed voltage by the total current.

As an illustration, suppose the voltage across the circuit shown in Fig.

8-6 is unknown. Assuming a 72-volt source, the individual currents would solve as follows:

$$I_R = \frac{72}{4} = 18 \text{ amperes}$$

$$I_{X_L} = \frac{72}{3} = 24 \text{ amperes}$$

The vector calculation for total current would then be

$$I_T = \sqrt{18^2 + 24^2} = \sqrt{324 + 576}$$
$$= \sqrt{900}$$
$$= 30 \text{ amperes}$$

Now, when the assumed voltage is divided by the calculated current, the result indicates that the impedance is 2.4 ohms, the same value obtained when the calculation was performed with a 24-volt source:

$$Z = \frac{E}{I} = \frac{72}{30} = 2.4 \text{ ohms}$$

While an assumed voltage can be used to calculate the total impedance, in actual practice such an impedance will be present only if the applied voltage is of the proper frequency. *Because a particular frequency had to be used initially to obtain a specific reactance value, any a-c voltage which is actually applied would thus have to be of the proper frequency.* For purposes of calculations, however, the frequency factor can be ignored, because it is automatically taken care of, as proved by the foregoing illustration.

If several parallel resistors are employed, as shown at the left of Fig. 8-7, the current through each resistor can be found initially and then added together. The total resistive current (18 amperes) must then be used with the inductive current (1.2 ampere) in the vector addition to find total current. Instead of this procedure, however, the total resistance can be solved for and total resistance current calculated.

The inductive reactance of several inductors in parallel is calculated by

Fig. 8-7. Parallel circuits composed of inductance and resistance.

the same formula used for parallel resistors. Thus, as shown at the right of Fig. 8-7, if the first inductance has 10 ohms of reactance and the second inductance also has a reactance of 10 ohms, the parallel combination gives a total inductive reactance of 5 ohms. Therefore, in a circuit composed of a number of parallel resistors plus a number of shunt parallel inductors, the total inductive current as well as the total resistive current must first be found, and then applied to the vector addition of such currents. Once the total current has been established, the impedance can be found by simply dividing the total voltage by the total current.

PRACTICAL FACTORS (COILS)

So far in this chapter, the coils illustrated were of the air-core type, that is, they had no metallic cores. Coils are considered to have an air core even though wound on some supporting coil form, since the latter has virtually no effect on the characteristics of the coil. In practical schematic drawings, an air-core coil is indicated by a series of loops, omitting from the symbol for the coil whatever coil form, if any, is employed.

The air-core inductances find application as radio-frequency *choke coils* in FM, TV, and other communications-type short-wave receivers, as well as in the corresponding transmitters. A choke coil is usually placed in series with the power supply voltage feed line, for signal isolation purposes. Since the radio-frequency (R-F) choke is designed to provide a high-inductive reactance for the frequencies of the signals involved in the circuit, the choke offers opposition to such energy, and prevents it from leaking away from the circuits and into the power source. Such energy leakage represents a loss and, hence, the signals must be confined to their circuits as much as possible.

Metallic cores, while increasing the inductance of a coil and improving efficiency, give rise to hysteresis and eddy-current losses, which must be minimized. Hysteresis losses are due to the rapid magnetization and demagnetization of the core when a-c is applied to the coil. The cyclic changes in a-c involve a constant reversal of the field intensity polarity by a reversal of the magnetizing force, as would be the case if the hysteresis loop (Fig. 6-7) were made to change from one polarity to the other in quick succession. The rapid shift in the electron spin of the atoms making up the element generates heat, just as would be the case with a resistive loss which expends power. Hysteresis losses are reduced by using magnetic core material of better quality.

Eddy current losses are set up by circulating currents within the core material, which are caused by lines of force cutting across the conductor in such a direction as to induce a voltage in the conductor. The currents which are created do not follow any well-defined path and, hence, are termed "eddy" currents. Eddy current losses are reduced by using a core made up of thin sheets of metal, known as *laminations*. Laminations break up the solid core structure, and reduce the effects of eddy currents and heat loss factors. During the manufacturing process, the laminations are heated so that they oxidize. The oxidized laminations thus have some insulating properties for additional isolation of the individual laminations. (Varnish is also used on occasion for insulating purposes with respect to core laminations.) The laminated cores do not help reduce the hysteresis losses mentioned earlier.

Soft-iron or silicon-steel laminated cores are used for coils which operate with low-frequency signals (such as the 60-cps line voltage or audio signals from about 30 cps to 20,000 cps). At higher frequencies, such as those involved in the radio-broadcast spectrum (550 to 1,600 kilocycles), as well as the short-wave frequencies above the radio-broadcast band, powdered metal or ferrite is used for coil cores, as detailed for the transformers discussed later in this chapter.

Symbols for various coils are shown in Fig. 8-8. At (B), an iron-core

(A)   (B)   (C)   (D)   (E)   (F)

Fig. 8-8. Symbols for inductance, showing variety of cores.

coil is shown, with the core indicated by two or three parallel lines (or dashed lines as at (C). A coil having a movable iron core, so that the inductance can be varied over a given range, is shown as (D) and (E). Either a single or a double arrow may be employed. A coil in which the inductance is variable, by virtue of a portion of the coil wound on a movable form is shown at (F).

Some typical commercial inductances are illustrated in Fig. 8-9. An R-F choke consisting of three individual coils linked together to provide the necessary inductive reactance is shown at (A). A nonmagnetic material is usually utilized as the supporting form. The coil shown at (B) has no core or coil form, and is usually wound with a sufficiently heavy wire (size 18 or 20) to be self-supporting. At (C) is shown a typical filter choke. Note that the core has three legs with the coil around the center leg. With this type of core, the laminations extend all around the core, for greater effectiveness in increasing inductance. The coil shown at (D) is of the type employed as the antenna in portable radios. It is wound over a ferrite core, for high permeability and efficiency. At (E), two coils are employed in conjunction with a horseshoe-type magnet and a metal diaphragm, which make up the internal structure of an earphone.

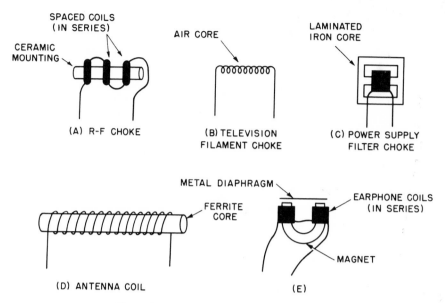

Fig. 8-9. Typical commercial inductances.

THE TRANSFORMER

When two coils are brought into close proximity, so that the magnetic lines of force of one coil link with those of the other, as shown in Fig. 8-10(A), the device is known as a *transformer*. A transformer usually

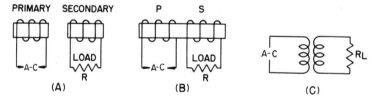

Fig. 8-10. Basic transformers.

consists of a primary winding, to which the a-c energy is applied, and a secondary winding. The a-c energy can be the 60-cycle, 110 volts derived from the power mains, or it can be in the form of audio- or radio-frequency signal energy. With a-c applied to the primary, a voltage is induced into the secondary, and a current flow will occur if the secondary is a closed circuit as shown in Fig. 8-10(A). The induced voltage is generated by the magnetic lines of force cutting the coil turns of the secondary winding.

Thus, energy is also drawn from the primary winding, and this is the energy which is dissipated in wattage across the load resistor. The only other resistance which would consume energy in a circuit of this type is the internal resistance of the coil windings. As mentioned earlier, coil reactance does not consume power.

Transformers are extensively used in all electric and electronic applications. Transformers are employed in instances where it is necessary to have a higher voltage than is available from a given a-c source, or in such cases where it is desirable to convert an existing a-c voltage to one of lower value. A transformer is also useful to couple the signal energy in one amplifier stage to that of another amplifier stage. In such an application, the transformer will isolate any d-c between the circuits, since a transformer will not pass d-c. As d-c does not produce a changing magnetic field which can cut across the secondary windings, it cannot induce a voltage into the secondary winding. Transformers are also useful for impedance matching, as more fully discussed later in this chapter.

While voltage is proportional to the number of turns, the available current is inversely proportional to the number of turns. As current availability is increased, voltage is decreased, and vice-versa. The power delivered by the secondary is equal to the power drawn from the a-c source only when the secondary winding is wound around or over the primary winding. This is known as *tight coupling* or *overcoupling,* and all the lines of force cut both the primary and secondary coils. In such a transformer of good design, efficiency as high as 95% can be obtained.

When the primary and secondary windings are wound closely together, so that the magnetic lines of each are linked (coupled), the total inductance depends on the individual inductances of the primary and secondary, as well as the *mutual inductance.* The latter represents the inductance established when the lines of force of one coil are permitted to cut across the turns of the coupled coil. Mutual inductance is defined as follows: *When a-c of 1 ampere in the primary induces 1 volt of a-c in the secondary, the two inductances have a mutual inductance of 1 henry.* The formula, when all magnetic lines of the primary cut the secondary (such is the case with an iron core transformer, where one coil layer is wound over the other), is as follows:

$$M = \sqrt{L_1 L_2} \qquad\qquad (8\text{-}13)$$

where M is the mutual inductance, (when magnetic lines of force link both coils).

In coils such as shown in Fig. 8-10(A) and (B), the secondary can be spaced some distance from the primary. In this case, the coupling is known as a "loose coupling." Degrees of coupling have a pronounced effect on the amount of energy supplied to the secondary; this factor is discussed more fully in Chapter 10 when resonant circuits employing transformers are studied.

If loose coupling is employed (where all the lines of force of the primary *do not* cut through the secondary winding), the degree of coupling known as the *"coefficient of coupling"* (k) must be taken into consideration. The formula for mutual inductance now becomes

$$M = k \sqrt{L_1 L_2} \qquad (8\text{-}14)$$

where k is the coefficient of coupling.

The coefficient of coupling actually represents the *percentage* of coupling. Thus, if only one-fourth the lines of force of the primary intercept the secondary windings, the coefficient of coupling is 25%. The formula for the coefficient of coupling is

$$k = \frac{M}{\sqrt{L_1 L_2}} \qquad (8\text{-}15)$$

PRACTICAL FACTORS (TRANSFORMERS)

The transformer shown in Fig. 8-10(A) and (B) can be represented as shown in (C). The schematic does not indicate on what form the coils are wound; it simply indicates that some nonmagnetic material is used, such as cardboard, plastic, rubber, etc., as a support for the coil forms. Neither does the schematic representation indicate the *degree* of coupling. The number of turns, the degree of coupling, and other related data, would have to be supplied in the text material which explains the schematic.

If an iron core is provided, the schematic representation of the transformer is as shown in Fig. 8-11. The usual practice is for the left winding to represent the transformer primary, and the right winding the secondary. On occasion, however, the transformer may be drawn with the primary toward the top of the page and the secondary toward the bottom, or vice-versa (as though Fig. 8-11 were turned on its side). If the secondary has considerably fewer turns than the primary, the transformer would be represented schematically as shown in the second drawing of Fig. 8-11. The latter is known as a *step-down* transformer, because the reduced number of turns in the secondary will "step down" whatever potential exists across the primary. If the primary has less turns than the secondary, the drawing would be a reverse image of that shown in the second part of Fig. 8-11

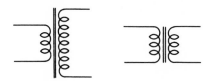

Fig. 8-11. Iron-core transformer symbols.

to represent a *step-up* transformer. This is because it will "step up" the voltage to a higher level than exists across the primary. When several secondary windings are present, they are shown schematically as in Fig. 8-12, again drawing them to the right of the primary winding.

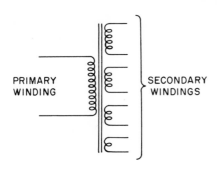

A transformer, with or without a core, can also be formed as shown in Fig. 8-13. Here, a continuous winding is employed, which has a tap somewhere along the windings. This tap forms a junction with one a-c input lead and one side of a load resistor. The a-c voltage is thus applied across one portion of this transformer, at (A) and (B). Since the

Fig. 8-12. Transformer with four secondary windings.

lines of force, as generated in the winding from (A) to (B), will cut across the winding from (B) to (C), the section from (B) to (C) represents the secondary, and it is across this section that the load resistor, or any other device which receives the energy, is connected. This type of transformer is known as an *autotransformer*.

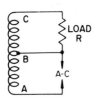

Various metal-core transformers are shown in Fig. 8-14. At (A) is shown the type of transformer used in power supplies of electronic devices. This type of transformer is utilized to increase the power main a-c to a higher voltage, for conversion to d-c, as more fully explained in Chapter 14 on Power Supplies. An additional secondary winding is also employed to reduce the line voltage to a lower value, for application to the filaments

Fig. 8-13. Autotransformer.

of vacuum tubes. In such a transformer, the primary and secondaries are wound over each other.

Figure 8-14(B) shows a typical audio output transformer using a laminated metal core. The audio signals are impressed on the primary, and a low-voltage secondary is used for application to the loudspeaker. Such a transformer provides a match between the impedance of the vacuum tube or transistor circuit and the loudspeaker impedance. Some audio output transformers employ several secondary windings, as shown at (C), so that the audio amplifier may be matched to any one of several speaker impedances. All the foregoing transformers employ a laminated iron core, as shown in Fig. 8-14(D). These laminations are usually E-shaped and when the arms of the E sections are interleaved, they form the transformer core. Both the audio and power transformers are often encased in a heavy metal shield to minimize stray fields.

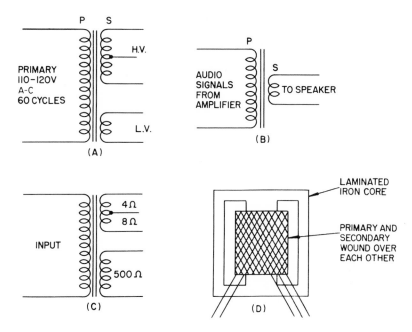

Fig. 8-14. Types of iron-core transformers.

A transformer not only has the ability to step up or step down voltages, but is also frequently used to provide an impedance match between two circuits. The turns ratio necessary to secure an impedance match can be calculated by use of the following:

$$\text{Turns ratio} = \sqrt{\frac{Z_1}{Z_2}} \qquad (8\text{-}16)$$

Typical air-core and variable-core transformers are shown in Fig. 8-15. The air-core types find primary usage in R-F amplifier stages of communications equipment. The proper symbol designation is shown in Fig. 8-15(A), and this coil may consist of a single layer such as shown at (B), or a bunch-wound type coil as at (C). The efficiency and permeability of the air-core transformers can be increased by using a core, just as with the lower-frequency types discussed earlier. In R-F amplifier circuits, the core consists of a circular "slug" of ferrite or powdered iron, which has been so shaped by using a binder material. Such a core is usually variable and can be adjusted to change its position with respect to the coil. By thus varying the transformer permeability it can be "tuned," as more fully described in Chapter 10.

The symbol for a variable-core transformer is shown in Fig. 8-15(D).

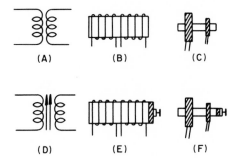

Fig. 8-15. Air-core and iron-core transformers.

Again, as with the air-core types, this may consist of a single-layer transformer, as shown at (E), or bunch-wound as at (F).

COILS IN SERIES AND PARALLEL

Coils can also be linked together by wire, without linking the magnetic lines of force which surround each coil. Two or more coils can thus be joined in series, as shown in Fig. 8-16(A). When such coils are strung in series, with sufficient separation so that the magnetic lines of force do not intercept adjacent coils, the total inductance is the sum of the individual inductances, which is expressed mathematically in the following equation:

$$L_T = L_1 + L_2 + L_3 + \ldots L_n \qquad (8\text{-}17)$$

Coils can also be placed in parallel, as shown in Fig. 8-16(B); again, they must be sufficiently separated so that the magnetic lines of force of one coil do not link with the others. The total inductance, in such an instance, is given by the formula:

$$L_T = \cfrac{1}{\cfrac{1}{L_1} + \cfrac{1}{L_2} + \cfrac{1}{L_3} + \ldots \cfrac{1}{L_N}} \qquad (8\text{-}18)$$

It will be noted that the calculations for total inductance of coils in series or in parallel are similar to the calculations for resistors in series or in parallel. The sum of the individual inductances gives the total inductance at Fig. 8-16(A), in similar fashion as the sum of individual resistances is used to calculate the total resistance in a resistive circuit. Similarly, parallel inductances, as at (B), are solved on the basis of the reciprocal function as with parallel resistors.

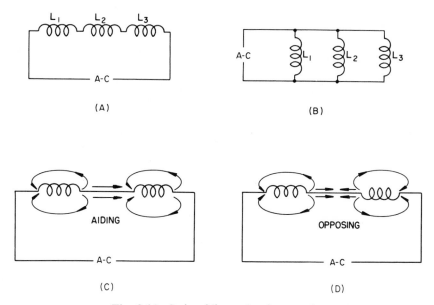

Fig. 8-16. Series aiding and series opposing.

If the coils shown in Fig. 8-16(A) are close together, so that linkage exists between the lines of force and adjacent coils, the mutual inductance which is established must be taken into consideration in order to solve for total inductance. Thus, the individual inductances of the coils are added together, and to this sum is added a factor consisting of twice the mutual inductance. The formula is as follows:

$$L_T \text{ (series aiding)} = L_1 + L_2 + 2M \qquad (8\text{-}19)$$

where M is the mutual inductance. (See Equation (8-13).)

Formula (8-19) and the other equations use the henry as unit of inductance and, for two or more coils, the sum of the individual inductances must be added to the product of twice the mutual inductance, as shown. This formula indicates the condition known as *series aiding*. This occurs when all the coils are wound in the same direction so that the lines of force can aid each other, as shown at Fig. 8-16(C). If one coil is wound in opposite direction to the other, as shown at (D), the circuit is known as *series opposing*. The formula for calculating total inductance in the series-opposing circuit is as follows:

$$L_T \text{ (series opposing)} = L_1 + L_2 - 2M \qquad (8\text{-}20)$$

SHIELDING

Coils and transformers, as previously mentioned, have a high order of magnetic lines of force surrounding them. Such magnetic lines of force can cause undesired effects in nearby circuits or circuit components because of unwanted coupling. To minimize this condition to the point where it is negligible, a metal container known as a *shield* is employed.

For transformers and coils handling low frequencies (power line a-c or audio), steel or iron shields are usually utilized. These are more effective in intercepting the magnetic lines of force which surround the coil or transformer, and the magnetic lines of force of the latter induce into the shield an emf, since the latter acts as a single-turn coil or closed circuit. Hence, current flows through the shield and sets up a magnetic field which tends to oppose the original magnetic field of a coil. Thus, a shield is effective in minimizing the effects of the fields of the coil or transformer on other devices. A shield is placed as close to the coil or transformer as possible in order to conserve space. When this is done, however, other undesired effects may be created, since the losses introduced by the shield may be severe. *Capacity* effects are also present, as more fully discussed later in this chapter.

Shields which are utilized for coils and transformers handling high frequencies are usually made of aluminum, copper, brass, or some other nonmagnetic material of this type. These shields are more effective for the rapid rate of change encountered for signals in the high-frequency (VHF-UHF, etc.) ranges.

EFFECTS OF A-C ON CAPACITORS

In Chapter 6, reference was made to the use of a battery for charging a capacitor. If, instead of a battery, an a-c source were employed, the first alternation of the cycle would cause current to flow in one direction and charge the capacitor. This is indicated at Fig. 8-17(A), which represents the first alternation as a positive one. The capacitor is charged, with the bottom plate negative and the top plate positive. At the second alternation, as shown, the top plate becomes negatively charged, and the bottom plate positively charged. Thus the charge on the capacitor is completely

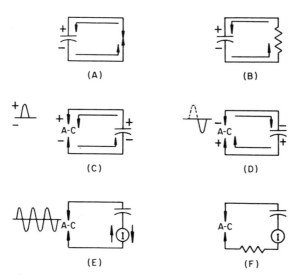

Fig. 8-17. Effect of a-c on capacitor.

reversed for each alternation of an a-c cycle. Also, the second alternation discharges the capacitor before charging it with the reverse polarity.

At (C), the same circuit is shown with an a-c ammeter placed in series with the capacitor. An *a-c ammeter* will indicate the *amount* of a-c flowing in a circuit by means of a needle moving up to the proper level of current indication *and remaining there*. In other words, an a-c ammeter needle does not swing back and forth for the negative and positive polarity changes, but moves in the same direction for either a negative or a positive current. Thus, the rapid rate of change in the a-c at (C) would cause current to flow in both directions through the ammeter, but the ammeter needle would remain in a fixed position to indicate the amount of such current. If the ammeter alone were visible, and not the remainder of the circuit, the current reading of the ammeter would only indicate that a certain amount of current is flowing in the circuit, but there would be no indication regarding whether or not a capacitor or a resistor offered opposition to the current. Thus, inspection of the ammeter alone would *seem* to indicate that a closed circuit exists for the current, and that the current flows through the ammeter and around to the voltage source and then reverses itself. This condition does not really exist, but is only made to appear so by the capacitor. Electrons flow to one plate, and away from the other. When the current is reversed electrons again flow, but in opposite direction. *Actually, current does not flow through a capacitor.*

If a resistor is placed in series with a capacitor, as shown in Fig. 8-17(D), the current flow is reduced, and such current would flow *through the resistor,* but only *to and from the capacitor.*

CAPACITIVE REACTANCE

Since the physical make-up of a capacitor (consisting of such factors as plate area, spacing, dielectric constant, etc.) affects the capacity value of the unit, the amount of current flow to and from the capacitor is thus influenced by such factors. A smaller capacitor will permit less current flow to and from it and, hence, the ammeter reading of current will be lower. A larger capacitor allows more current flow to and from its plates, and hence the ammeter indicates a higher current reading. Obviously, then, the capacitor is a limiting factor with respect to the current, and such a limiting factor or virtual opposition to a-c flow is known as *capacitive reactance.* As with inductive reactance, no power is consumed by the opposition offered by capacitive reactance, and the latter only serves to limit the amount of a-c flow. Reference to the time-constant chart shown in Fig. 6-13 indicates that, as the capacitor is being charged, current flow starts from a high level and declines, but voltage starts from a low level and increases. With a-c applied to the capacitor, there is a consistent reversal of polarity across the capacitor and, in consequence, there is always a 90-degree phase difference between voltage and current. As with the inductances, no power is consumed in a pure capacity because $P = EI$ cos ϕ, and with a 90-degree angle, the cosine is zero, and hence power is zero. In a capacitor, the current *leads* the voltage by 90 degrees.

With capacitive reactance, as with inductive reactance, consideration must be given to the angular velocity of the a-c, as well as to the capacity in farads of the capacitor. An inductance tends to oppose a change of current, while a capacitance tends to oppose a change of voltage. For this reason, capacitive reactance functions inversely to inductive reactance and the formula is

$$X_C = \frac{1}{6.28fC} \qquad (8\text{-}21)$$

Thus, the frequency (f) in cps and the value of capacity (C) in farads will determine the amount of capacitive reactance, and also the current flow. If the voltage drop across the capacitor is measured, as well as the current flow, Ohm's law can be used to determine the value of the capacitive reactance. Similarly, if the voltage drop across the capacitor is known, as well as the capacitive reactance of the capacitor, Ohm's law can be used to find the amount of current flow, without the need for measurement with an ammeter. Ohm's law can also be utilized to find the voltage drop, as well as the impedance, as shown in Equation (8-22):

$$X_C = \frac{E}{I}, \qquad I = \frac{E}{X_C}, \qquad E = IX_C, \qquad Z = \frac{E}{I} \qquad (8\text{-}22)$$

A typical example of a series circuit is composed of a resistor and a capacitor, as shown in Fig. 8-18(A). Here, a 4-ohm resistor is in series with a capacitor having a capacitive reactance of 3 ohms. The vector representation of this circuit is shown in Fig. 8-18 (B). As with inductive reactance in series with a resistor, the opposition to the flow of a-c in a circuit composed of a resistor and a capacitor is no longer either resistance or reactance alone, but impedance. Since the resistive component is at right angles to the reactive component, we solve for impedance, using a formula similar to the one employed for inductive reactance.

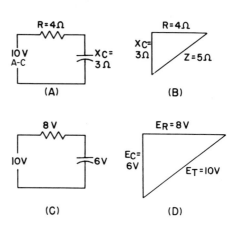

Fig. 8-18. Series resistor-capacitor circuit and impedance triangle.

$$Z = \sqrt{R^2 + X_C{}^2} \qquad (8\text{-}23)$$

As shown at (B), the impedance for this circuit is 5 ohms, and by Ohm's law we find the current flow equals 2 amperes. As with the series circuits employing an inductance and a resistor, the series circuit composed of a capacitor and a resistor will have, across the individual components, voltage drops of values determined by the current flowing in the circuit. Because current is the same throughout a series circuit, each resistance value and reactance value is multiplied by the current, and their product indicates the voltage across each component as shown in Fig. 8-18(C). If these voltage values are known, but the applied voltage to the circuit is unknown, the total voltage can be found by use of the formula

$$E_T = \sqrt{E_R{}^2 + E_C{}^2} \qquad (8\text{-}24)$$

and, as shown at (D), this equals 10 volts.

The power factor of the circuit can also be ascertained, and would indicate the true power consumed by the circuit. The angle of the vector representation shown at (D) can be ascertained by solving for the tangent of the angle, and then using the trigonometric table in the Appendix. The tangent can be solved by dividing the side opposite by the side adjacent, as shown in the top triangle of Fig. 8-19. Thus, the tangent of the angle shown at Fig. 8-18(D) can be found, and the cosine, as well as the angle (θ) can be ascertained from the table, as follows:

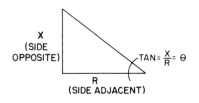

$$\tan = \frac{6}{8} = 0.75$$

$$\cos = 0.7986$$

$$\theta = 37 \text{ degrees}$$

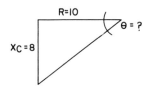

Fig. 8-19. Solving for tangent.

Using trigonometry, the impedance can also be found without the necessity for calculating by the formulas previously given. Since the cosine of an angle is the ratio of the side adjacent to the hypotenuse, the value of the side adjacent can be divided by the cosine to obtain the hypotenuse, as follows:

$$\text{Side adjacent} = 8$$
$$\text{Cosine} = 0.7986$$

and

$$Z \text{ (hy)} = \frac{8}{0.7986} = 10 \text{ ohms}$$

The tangent and the cosine functions of a right triangle are applicable whether an inductive reactance or a capacitive reactance is present. Thus, at the lower triangle of Fig. 8-19, the following calculation would be used, regardless of whether the 8 ohms represented capacitive reactance or inductive reactance:

$$\tan \theta = \frac{X}{R} = \frac{8}{10} = 0.8$$

and, from the table, θ = approximately 39 degrees.

When capacitors and resistors are in parallel, the method of solving for impedance is similar to that used for inductors in parallel. Initially, the current in each branch is calculated on the basis of the amount of voltage across the reactance divided by the value of the reactance. When the individual currents are known, the value of total current is found by:

$$I_T = \sqrt{I_R{}^2 + I_{X_C}{}^2} \qquad (8\text{-}25)$$

The impedance is then calculated by dividing the value of the voltage source by the value of total current obtained from Equation (8-25).

A typical problem involving a capacitor and parallel resistance is shown in Fig. 8-20. Here, two series resistors shunt a capacitor, and the problem is to calculate the total impedance of the circuit.

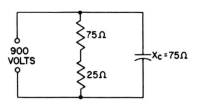

Initially, the current through the resistive branch should be found. This is done by dividing the voltage by the resitance, and the latter equals 100 ohms. Thus, the current flow through the resistive branch is 9 amperes.

Fig. 8-20. Capacity shunted by series resistor circuit.

The same voltage exists across the capacitor, and when this is divided by the capacitive reactance, the current is found to be 12 amperes. Total current is the vector sum of the individual currents, and is found as follows:

$$I_T = \sqrt{9^2 + 12^2} = \sqrt{81 + 144} = \sqrt{225} = 15 \text{ amperes}$$

This indicates that 15 amperes of current flows to the parallel resistive-capacitive network. Impedance can then be calculated by Ohm's law, as follows:

$$Z = \frac{E}{I} = \frac{900}{15} = 60 \text{ ohms}$$

As with parallel circuits using inductance, as discussed earlier in this chapter, the impedance can be obtained even if the voltage across the network is unknown. In Fig. 8-20, for instance, suppose the voltage were unknown. Any voltage can be assumed, and the current through the resistive and capacitive branches solved. (These will be false currents, but will be proportional to the opposition offered, and hence will yield accurate calculation of impedance.) Thus, if 1,800 volts is assumed, the current through the resistance would be equal to the assumed voltage divided by 100 ohms, and would therefore be 18 amperes. The current value for the capacitive reactance equals 24 amperes. Vector calculation for total current gives 30 amperes. Dividing 1,800 volts by 30 amperes results in an impedance value of 60 ohms (the correct value).

It must be remembered, however, that this assumption of a source voltage only applies if *reactance* is known. If the reactance is unknown, it must be calculated, based on the value of capacity and the frequency of the a-c voltage. Once the particular reactance is found for the specific frequency used, the assumption of any voltage value will provide the right answer, since the known reactance was derived for a particular frequency.

COMMERCIAL CAPACITORS

There are four basic types of capacitors used in electronics: mica, ceramic, paper, and electrolytic. All these are *fixed* capacitors; that is, their capacity cannot be varied and each capacitor has a value which was established in the design by the manufacturer. The value of the capacitor is stamped on the larger capacitors, but the smaller mica and ceramic capacitors have their value marked on them by a color code. (See Appendix.)

Paper and electrolytic capacitors have the voltage as well as the capacitive value marked on them. The voltage rating is the maximum voltage which can safely be applied across the capacitor without danger of internal arcing and damage resulting from a short circuit. Electrolytic capacitors sometimes have two voltage ratings printed on the housing. One of these ratings is known as the *peak voltage,* and refers to the maximum *short application* voltage which the capacitor can withstand. The other voltage rating is the *working voltage.* Two ratings are preferable because of the voltage variations encountered by these capacitors when used in power supplies, where the voltage rises to a high value (peak) when first turned on, but drops to a "working" value after the tubes of the receiver, transmitter, or other electronic device, warm up and draw current. Thus, the peak voltage rating of a capacitor is the voltage which can be impressed on the capacitor for a short interval only, while the working voltage is the maximum under which the capacitor can operate continuously without danger of breakdown.

Mica and ceramic capacitors are the smallest-value units, with values ranging from 20 to 500 micromicrofarads (0.0005 microfarad). These capacitors are used to couple and bypass high-frequency signals. For coupling and bypass purposes for lower-frequency signals, as well as audio-frequency signals, paper capacitors are employed, having values ranging as high as 0.5 microfarad. The paper, ceramic, and mica capacitors are illustrated, in that order, in Fig. 8-21.

Electrolytic capacitors are used primarily for low-frequency signal bypassing, and also as filters in power supplies. Electrolytic capacitors have polarity markings, and must not be connected into the circuit in opposition to the manner in which they are marked or serious damage will result. Electrolytic capacitors have an electrolyte of oxide or chemical composition, and will pass current in one direction, but very little current in the other (that is, they have a high resistance in one direction and low resistance in the other). Thus, particular attention must be paid to the polarities of electrolytic capacitors. Some paper capacitors are marked to indicate

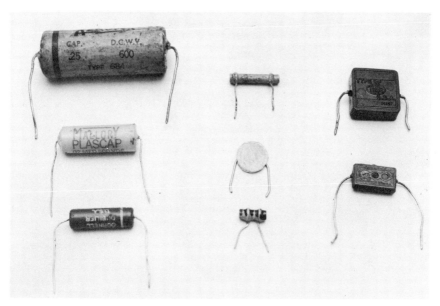

Fig. 8-21. Paper, ceramic and mica capacitors.

the lead which should go to the chassis, since it is connected to the outer foil of the capacitor and, hence, will act as a shield. Reversal will not cause damage, but may impair circuit function. Reversal of an electrolytic capacitor, however, will cause high current leakage and short-circuit conditions. Typical electrolytic capacitors are shown in Fig. 8-22. Some are available in cardboard containers, while others have a metal can for shielding purposes. In some types of capacitor, the shield container can be used as the negative section. In other capacitors, the negative and positive terminals are brought from the capacitor and isolated from the shield. The black wire is usually the negative lead, while the red wire is the positive lead in electrolytics.

When a capacitor is needed in circuit applications where a higher voltage is present than that for which a particular capacitor is rated, two such capacitors can be placed in series to double their operating value. Thus if two 600-volt paper capacitors are placed in series, the combination can withstand 1,200 volts. When capacitors are placed in series, however, the total capacity is reduced. When two or more capacitors are placed in series for higher voltage applications, each should have the same capacity value. Thus, two 0.04-microfarad paper capacitors can be placed in series, and the resultant capacity will be 0.02 microfarad. The same combining can be done with electrolytic capacitors. Two capacitors of 8 microfarads

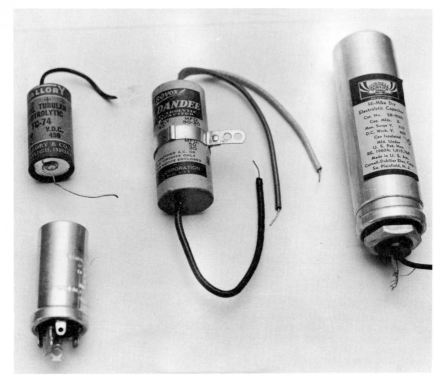

Fig. 8-22. Electrolytic capacitors.

each can be placed in series with the result that they form a single capacity of 4 microfarads, but the voltage rating is double over each capacitor. Since electrolytic capacitors having individual capacity values of 100 microfarads are available, no difficulty is experienced in getting adequate capacity for filtering purposes when it is necessary to place capacitors in series to withstand higher voltages.

Capacitors can also be placed in parallel, for increased capacity. Two 8-microfarad capacitors, for instance, will be valued at 16 microfarads when placed in parallel. The parallel combination, however, does not increase the voltage rating. Thus, two or three 400-volt capacitors in parallel will still have a 400-volt rating.

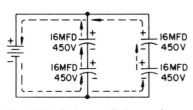

Fig. 8-23. Series-parallel capacitors.

Capacitors can be put in series-parallel combination, as shown in Fig. 8-23. Here, each capacitor has a value

Fig. 8-24

of 16 microfarads, and each is rated at 450 volts. Since two 450-volt capacitors in series will equal a voltage rating of 900 volts, the combination will withstand the latter voltage. Two 16-microfarad capacitors in series equal 8 microfarads. Since there are two branches, each having a total value of 8 microfarads, the total capacity represented by the four capacitors equals 16 microfarads.

Variable capacitors, like the ones shown in Fig. 8-24, are employed for tuning purposes in receivers. The small variable capacitors are employed for high-frequency work, or for compensating for slight differences in larger capacities. The large variable capacitors are used for tuning purposes, as more fully described in subsequent chapters.

Variable capacitors have a set of stationary plates and a set of variable plates. The variable plates mesh with the stationary plates to a degree established by rotating the shaft. Air is the insulating dielectric utilized between the stationary and the rotating plates. The stationary plates are called the *stator* of the variable capacitor, and the rotating plates are referred to as the *rotor*. Variable capacitors can be ganged, as shown in Fig. 8-24, so that control can be obtained over several circuits. The schematic representation of a single variable capacitor is shown in Fig. 8-25(A). The arrow identifies the variable arm, or rotor

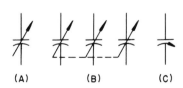

(A) (B) (C)

Fig. 8-25. Variable capacitor symbols.

of the capacitor (the rotor is usually placed at ground potential). When two or more capacitors are ganged together to permit simultaneous tuning, the ganging linkage is indicated schematically as shown at (B) by the dotted line section. The older representation for the variable capacitor is as shown at (C) with the curved arrow indicating the variable portion.

UNDESIRED CAPACITANCES

As previously mentioned, a capacity can be established between any two conductors separated by an insulation. Thus, small capacity values exist between the hookup wire and adjacent wiring, or the chassis of an electronic device. While such capacities are extremely small in value, they can have a low shunt reactance at higher frequencies. Thus, the higher the frequency, the lower the capacitive reactance and, hence, the greater the amount of signal energy which may be shunted, instead of transferred to the desired points. To minimize such *stray* or *shunt* capacitances, short leads are utilized at high frequencies, and these leads are carefully spaced away from each other. The proper positioning of hookup wires in electronic devices is known as *lead dress*.

A coil or a transformer also has a considerable amount of internal capacity established between adjacent turns, and also between adjacent layers of wire. Since each turn of wire is insulated from the adjacent turn, the insulation material acts as a dielectric, and the wires behave as miniature capacitor plates. Such capacity in a transformer is known as *distributed capacity,* and represents another possible high-frequency signal loss. The higher the signal frequencies, the lower is the capacitive reactance they will encounter in the distributed capacity of a coil or transformer. Thus, a low value of capacitive reactance caused by distributed capacities has a considerable shunting effect on high-frequency signals.

The distributed capacity in a coil also alters its inductive characteristics, since the coil is no longer a pure inductance, but now consists of inductance and capacity. Hence, the opposition to the flow of a-c energy must be calculated on the basis of the impedance established by the distributed capacity, the inductance, and whatever resistance exists in the length of wire used in the coil section. (Combinations of *L, C,* and *R* are discussed more fully in the next chapter.)

When coils are shielded so that the magnetic fields of one coil do not interfere with those of an adjacent coil, the effects of capacity also influence circuit behavior. Because the metal shield is at ground potential, any capacity between the shield and the wire of the coil provides a shunt capacity; this shunting effect of some of the signal energy is particularly pronounced at the higher signal frequencies, because, with increasing frequency, the capacitive reactance decreases and offers less opposition to the transfer of signal energy. Even with adequate spacing between the coil and the shield, the capacity effects at higher frequencies must be considered during design.

MEASUREMENT OF L AND C

The inductance of a coil, in henrys, or the value of capacitors, in microfarads, can be ascertained by utilizing the bridge circuit principle discussed in Chapter 5, and illustrated in Fig. 5-4 for resistance measurements. For measurements of L and C, however, an a-c source must be available, as shown in Fig. 8-26. The inductive circuit shown at (A)

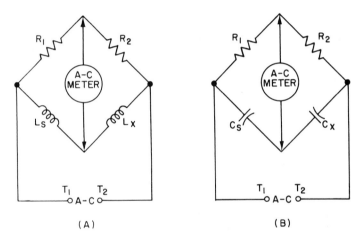

Fig. 8-26. Wheatstone bridges for measuring **L** and **C**.

functions similarly to the resistive type discussed in Chapter 5, except that a-c voltage drops develop across the respective reactances of L_s and L_x (the standard and the unknown inductance). Instead of a galvanometer, an a-c reading device must be used. For the circuit at (B), the a-c voltage drops develop across the capacitive reactances of the standard capacitor C_s and the unknown capacitor C_x. For the inductive circuit, the unknown is found by multiplying the value of the standard inductance L_s by the ratio R_2/R_1, when the bridge is balanced. For the capacitive circuit, C_x is found by multiplying the value of the standard capacitor C_s by the ratio R_1/R_2, when bridge balance is achieved.

The formulas for the two bridge circuits differ because capacitive reactance acts inversely to inductive reactance. Even though the bridge balance is achieved by virtue of the voltage drops which occur across the resistances and reactances, the reading procured indicates the value of inductance and capacity. As an example, assume that for the circuit shown in Fig. 8-26(A), resistor R_1 has a value of 5 ohms and R_2 has a value of 10 ohms. The standard inductance L_s has a value of 2.5 henrys. The value of the unknown inductance L_X is then found by use of Equation (8-26) which indicates a value of 5 henrys:

$$\frac{R_2}{R_1} L_s = L_X$$

$$\frac{10}{5}\, 2.5 = 5 \tag{8-26}$$

COMPARISON OF R, C, AND L VALUES

For comparison purposes, the calculations of total values of resistance, inductance, capacity and reactance are listed by categories. These will aid in understanding the characteristics involved in series and parallel systems, and will also be invaluable for review purposes.

TOTAL VALUE OBTAINED BY SIMPLE ADDITION

Resistance of resistors in series
Voltage of batteries in series
Inductance of coils in series (not coupled)
Inductance reactance of coils in series (not coupled)
Capacitive reactance of capacitors in series
Capacity of capacitors in parallel
Current of resistors in parallel

TOTAL VALUE OBTAINED BY USING RECIPROCAL FORMULA

Resistance of resistors in parallel
Capacity of capacitors in series
Capacitive reactance of capacitors in parallel
Inductive reactance of coils in parallel (not coupled)
Inductance of coils in parallel (not coupled)

TOTAL VALUE OBTAINED BY VECTOR CALCULATION

Impedance of inductance and resistance in series
Impedance of capacitance and resistance in series

Voltage across circuit composed of inductance and resistance in series
Voltage across circuit composed of capacitance and resistance in series
Current of a circuit composed of capacity and resistance in parallel
Current of a circuit composed of inductance and resistance in parallel

REVIEW QUESTIONS

1. If the frequency of the a-c across an inductance is increased, does the inductive reactance increase or decrease? Explain your answer.

2. Briefly explain what is meant by the angular velocity.

3. Briefly explain why the cosine of the angle of lead or lag between voltage and current must be employed in calculating true power.

4. What is the formula for finding the impedance of a circuit composed of a series resistor and inductance?

5. Explain how the impedance can also be found by using trigonometric relations of cosine, hypotenuse, etc.

6. In a circuit composed of a resistor and an inductor in parallel, what method can be employed for calculating the impedance of the circuit?

7. Where are R-F chokes commonly employed?

8. A parallel circuit contains a known value of resistance and a known value of inductive reactives. Values of voltage and current are unknown. What process can be employed for finding the impedance?

9. Briefly explain what causes hysteresis and eddy current losses. How may such losses be minimized?

10. Briefly explain what is meant by mutual inductance.

11. If a-c of 10 volts is applied to the primary of a transformer and 220 volts is read across the secondary, what is the turns ratio of the transformer?

12. If three coils, each having a reactance of 30 ohms, are placed in parallel, what is the total reactance?

13. Briefly explain the necessity for shielding coils and transformers in some applications.

14. How does the addition of a capacitor to a resistive circuit alter the opposition to current flow?

15. Briefly explain what physical factors contribute to the specific capacity of a capacitor.

16. If the *frequency* of an a-c signal across a capacitor decreases, why does the capacitive reactance increase? How does this differ from a frequency decrease of an a-c signal across an inductance?

17. If two resistors and a capacitor are in parallel, explain what method can be employed for calculating the total impedance of the circuit.

18. (a) What are the two most common applications for mica and paper capacitors?
(b) What are the two most common applications for electrolytic capacitors?

19. Why are losses in circuit wiring and in a coil increased as the signal *frequency* is increased.

20. Of inductance or capacitance, which tends to oppose a voltage change, and which tends to oppose a current change?

PRACTICAL PROBLEMS

Note: Draw a diagram of the circuit of each problem, to gain practice in schematic work, and to aid in visualizing each problem.

1. What is the inductive reactance of a power supply filter coil having an inductance of 20 henrys and operated on a frequency of 60 cycles?

2. In an electronic circuit, the current lags the voltage by 40 degrees. The current at maximum value is 50 milliamperes. What is the instantaneous value of the current at the 60-degree phase of the voltage?

3. In a circuit composed of an inductance and a resistance, there is a 45-degree phase difference. If the voltage source is 200 volts, and the current flow 50 milliamperes, what is the true power used?

4. A resistor of 10 ohms is in series with an inductance having a reactance of 7.5 ohms. What is the impedance?

5. What is the total inductive reactance if two coils are in a series circuit (not coupled) and one coil has a reactance of 720 ohms, while the other has an inductance of 50 millihenrys. The frequency at which the circuit is operated is 20 kilocycles.

6. In a series circuit composed of a coil and a resistor, there is a 24-volt drop across the resistor, and an 18-volt drop across the coil. What is the total voltage applied across the two?

7. In a parallel circuit consisting of a 24-ohm resistor and an inductance having a reactance of 32 ohms, what is the impedance of the circuit?

8. In a parallel circuit composed of a resistor shunted by an inductance, the current through the resistor is 36 milliamperes and the current through the inductor is 48 milliamperes. If the impressed voltage on the circuit is 210 volts, what is the impedance?

9. A transformer primary has 32 millihenrys of inductance, and the secondary has 2 millihenrys of inductance. All the magnetic lines of force of the primary cut the secondary. Under these conditions, what is the mutual inductance?

10. A transformer must match the impedance of a 4-ohm speaker to a circuit impedance of 14,400 ohms. What must be the turns ratio of the transformer?

11. An electronic circuit contained three inductors which were sufficiently separated so their lines of force did not interact. The inductance values were 39 millihenries, 19.5 millihenries, 13 millihenries. What is the total inductance?

12. In an industrial control system, two coils were in series aiding. One coil had an inductance of 2 millihenrys and the other 13 millihenrys, with a coefficient of coupling (k) of 0.2. What is the total inductance?

13. An electronic circuit contains a 250-micromicrofarad capacitor in series with a 100,000 ohm resistor, connected to a source voltage of 100. How long will it take the capacitor to charge to 63 volts after the switch is closed?

14. In a high-fidelity audio amplifier, two capacitors are in series, each rated at 16 microfarads, 300 working volts. What is the total capacity and the working voltage of the combination?

15. In a power supply of an electronic device, there are two capacitors in parallel, one rated at 8 microfarads and the other at 16 microfarads. Each capacitor is designed for a maximum of 450 working volts. What is the total capacity and the working voltage of the combination?

16. In a transistor amplifier circuit, a certain capacitor should have no more than 5 ohms of reactance when a signal having a frequency of 5,000 cps is impressed across it. If the capacitor is rated at 30 microfarads, does it have a low enough capacitive reactance? What is the reactance value?

17. A particular tone control circuit consists of a resistor of 360 ohms in series with a capacitor which has a reactance of 480 ohms at 300 cps. The total impedance is not to exceed 500 ohms. Is this condition satisfied? What is the impedance?

18. In a specific amplifier, a screen grid bypass capacitor of 0.06 microfarad should be used. There are available three capacitors, two of 0.02 microfarad, and one of 0.05 microfarad. In what combination will these provide the necessary 0.06 microfarad?

19. In an electronic circuit composed of a resistance in series with a capacitor, an a-c meter is placed across the resistance, and a reading of 84 volts is

indicated. The voltage at the source indicates 105 volts across the series circuit. What voltage appears across the capacitor? What is the power consumed if the current is 20 milliamperes (0.02 amperes)?

20. In an electronic control circuit a resistor is in series with a capacitor. The resistor has a value of 1,260 ohms and has a 25.2-volt drop across it. The capacitor has an 18.9-volt drop across it. What is the total voltage, total current, and impedance?

21. In a transistor circuit of a computer, a resistor is in parallel with a capacitor. An a-c milliammeter placed in series with the resistor reads 408 milliamperes, but when placed in series with the capacitor, the meter reads 544 milliamperes. What is the total current? If the impressed voltage is 136, what is the impedance?

22. A bridge circuit such as shown in Fig. 9–14(B) was balanced when $R_1 = 2,000$ ohms, $R_2 = 1,500$ ohms, and C_s was 16 microfarads. What is the value of the C_X capacitor which is being tested?

23. If a bridge circuit such as shown in Fig. 9–14(A) had the same resistor values as in Problem 10 and was balanced when the inductance L_s has a value of 16 henrys, what would be the value of L_X?

9

CIRCUIT
ANALYSIS
(A-C)

INTRODUCTION

As discussed in the previous chapter, an inductance affects circuit characteristics by introducing a 90-degree phase difference between current and voltage, with voltage leading. A capacitor, on the other hand, also causes a 90-degree phase difference, except that current leads the voltage. Since the reactances established by inductance and capacity are opposite in their effect, a circuit which contains both an inductance and a capacitor will have a total reactance which is proportional to the difference between the two reactances. Such a difference, when combined vectorally with circuit resistances, indicates the impedance. In this chapter, circuits are analyzed which contain L, C, and R in various combinations generally encountered in electronics.

SERIES L-C CIRCUITS

When an inductor and capacitor are placed in series with a resistor as shown in Fig. 9-1(A), the vector representation is as shown at (B).

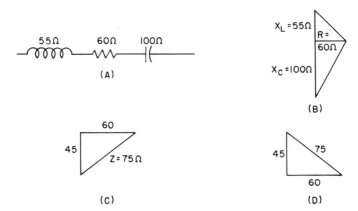

Fig. 9-1. Vector triangles for **L-C-R** circuits.

The opposite effects of X_L and X_C cancel, and the total reactance is, therefore

$$100 - 55 = 45 \text{ ohms}$$

Because the capacitive reactance is greater than the inductive reactance, the circuit will be predominantly capacitive, with the remaining 45 ohms representing capacitive reactance. Thus, the vector diagram would now be as shown in Fig. 9-1(C). If the vector triangle is drawn to proportion, the hypotenuse length would indicate an impedance of 75 ohms.

Had the inductive reactance been 55 ohms, and the capacitive reactance 100 ohms (opposite to the foregoing example), the lower value of capacitive reactance would have been subtracted from the higher value of inductive reactance, and the vector representation would then be as shown at Fig. 9-1(D), where the same impedance prevailed, except that the circuit is now predominantly inductive, since some of the later reactance remained after subtracting from it the capacitive reactance. The Formula (8-12) previously given for impedance can now be expressed as follows:

$$Z = \sqrt{R^2 + (X_L - X_C)^2} \qquad (9\text{-}1)$$

This is the usual form in which the formula is indicated in textbooks, though a variation of this formula could be expressed as

$$Z = \sqrt{R^2 + (X_C - X_L)^2} \qquad (9\text{-}2)$$

Either formula can be used, because the parenthetical expression simply indicates that the sum representing the *difference* between the two reactances is squared.

Individual voltage drops across the reactances will still be a function of the amount of such reactances multiplied by the current flow through each of them. The voltages across the individual reactances may reach high values, but, since there is a difference in the phase angle between voltage and current, the total voltage is still the vector sum of the individual

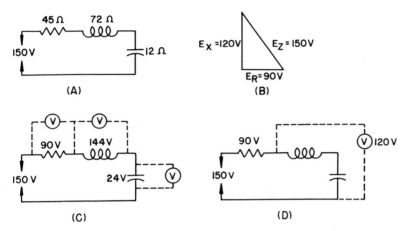

Fig. 9-2. Series impedance circuits and voltage triangle.

voltages. This is illustrated in Fig. 9-2(A). The total impedance is found by Equation (9-1) as follows:

$$Z = \sqrt{45^2 + (72 - 12)^2}$$
$$= \sqrt{2{,}025 + 3{,}600}$$
$$= \sqrt{5{,}625}$$
$$= 75 \text{ ohms.}$$

Since current is equal to voltage divided by impedance, the value of the current can be solved, and the voltage drops indicated across each circuit component.

$$I = \frac{E}{Z} = \frac{150}{75} = 2 \text{ amperes}$$
$$E_R = 2 \times 45 = 90$$
$$E_{X_L} = 2 \times 72 = 144$$
$$E_{X_C} = 2 \times 12 = 24$$

Here, the *additive* sum of the voltages would *exceed the source voltage* by a considerable amount, but actually the sum of the voltages is a function of the vector formula.

$$E_T = \sqrt{E_R^2 + (E_{X_L} - E_{X_C})^2} \qquad (9\text{-}3)$$

This formula takes into consideration the vector sum of the voltages and is similar to the impedance formula, since the voltage across the lower reactance is subtracted from the voltage across the higher reactance. Thus, the total voltage in this instance will again equal the voltage indicated at Fig. 9-2(A). The vector representation of the voltage drops across the various components is shown in Fig. 9-2(B). The voltage across the reactive component is 120 volts, since the 24-volt drop across the capacitive reactance must be subtracted from the 144 volts across the inductive component. Since there is a 90-volt drop across the resistance, the vector calculation indicates that the voltage across the impedance is 150 volts.

If an a-c voltmeter were placed across the individual components of the circuit shown in Fig. 9-2(A), the voltages indicated at (C) would be read. If a voltmeter were now placed across the inductive and capacitive reactances, as shown at Fig. 9-2(D), the total voltage read by the meter would only be 120 volts, because the 24 volts across the capacitive reactance opposes and cancels out its equivalent portion of the 144 volts across the inductive reactance.

Because $E = IX$, there are instances where the voltage drop across a reactance exceeds the source voltage. This would seem to indicate that more power is generated in the circuit than at the source, but the actual voltage across the total reactance will be the difference between the

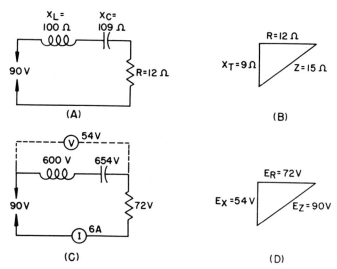

Fig. 9-3. Series impedance circuits and impedance triangles.

various voltages. This is indicated in the circuit shown at Fig. 9-3(A). The total *reactance* is only 9 ohms, as shown by the vector diagram in Fig. 9-3 (B). Solving for current and voltage drops across the individual components, however, indicates the following:

$$I = \frac{90}{15} = 6 \text{ amperes}$$

$$E_{X_L} = 6 \times 100 = 600 \text{ volts}$$
$$E_{X_C} = 6 \times 109 = 654 \text{ volts}$$
$$E_R = 6 \times 12 = 72 \text{ volts}$$

Thus, the voltage drops around the circuit are as shown in (C), where the individual voltages across the inductive reactance and the capacitive reactance each exceeds the source voltage of 90 volts. As shown at (C), however, an a-c voltmeter across the two reactances would only indicate 54 volts, since the opposing phase differences cancel out 600 volts. Thus, a vector representation of the voltage drops across the total reactance and the resistance would again indicate 90 volts, the source voltage. This high voltage drop across an individual reactive component is useful in electronics, however, since it provides a substantially high signal voltage for the particular frequency involved.

MULTIUNIT SERIES CIRCUITS

When several inductances, capacitors, and resistors are in series, the individual inductive reactances are added together to give the total reactance, since reactances in series are additive. The additive principle also applies to the series capacitive reactances, as well as the series resistors.

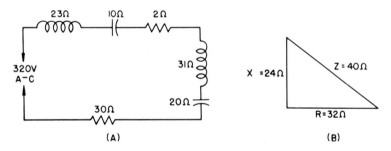

Fig. 9-4. Complex series impedance circuit.

Thus, for a circuit such as shown in Fig. 9-4(A), the individual reactances and resistances are added, and then inserted in Equation (9-1).

$$X_L = 23 + 31 = 54 \text{ ohms}$$
$$X_C = 10 + 20 = 30 \text{ ohms}$$
$$R = 2 + 30 = 32 \text{ ohms}$$
$$Z = \sqrt{32^2 + (54 - 30)^2}$$
$$= \sqrt{32^2 + 24^2} = 40 \text{ ohms}$$

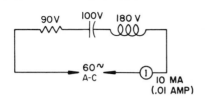

Fig. 9-5. Series impedance circuit showing voltage drops.

The vector representation of this circuit is shown at Fig. 9-4(B).

By employing appropriate formulas, it is possible to solve for various unknown values, if some known values are given. A typical example is the circuit shown in Fig. 9-5. The frequency of the source voltage is given, but the amount of voltage is not indicated. Since the current flow is shown, however, the individual resistance and reactance values can be calculated. As the frequency of the a-c is also given, the actual value of the capacity in microfarads and the inductance in henrys can be calculated. Solving for *R and X_c*:

$$R = \frac{E}{I} = \frac{90}{0.01} = 9{,}000 \text{ ohms}$$

$$X_C = \frac{100}{0.01} = 10{,}000 \text{ ohms}$$

Since we know the frequency of the a-c, we can transpose the formula for capacitive reactance, and solve for the total capacity, as follows:

$$C = \frac{1}{6.28fX_C} = \frac{1}{376.8 \times 10{,}000} = 0.26 \text{ microfarad}$$

The inductive reactance and the inductance can then be calculated in similar fashion:

$$X_L = \frac{180}{0.01} = 18{,}000 \text{ ohms}$$

$$L = \frac{X_L}{6.28f} = \frac{18{,}000}{6.28f} = \frac{18{,}000}{376.8} = 47.7 \text{ henrys}$$

Thus, from the values given in Fig. 9-5, the individual reactances, as well as capacities and inductances, can be calculated. The total voltage can also be ascertained by solving for the vector sum of the individual voltages. The phase angle can be found by calculating for the tangent (dividing the total reactance by the total resistance), and when the tangent is known, the table of trigonometric values will show the degree of the phase angle involved.

$$\tan \theta = \frac{X}{R} = \frac{180 - 100}{90} = \frac{80}{90} = 0.8888$$

$$\theta = 41 \text{ degrees (approx.)}$$

When the frequency applied to an inductance is increased, the inductive reactance also increases, as shown by the inductive reactance Equation

(8-2). Since capacitive reactance has a reciprocal function, an increase in the frequency of the a-c voltage to a capacitor will result in a decrease of capacitive reactance. When these factors are known, it is a relatively easy matter to ascertain the values of inductive reactance and capacitive reactance for frequencies double or half the given frequency. A chart can be made as follows:

freq. (cps)	X_L	X_C	X
60	18,000	10,000	8,000
120	36,000	5,000	31,000
240	72,000	2,500	69,500
30	9,000	20,000	11,000
15	4,500	40,000	35,500

In the foregoing, the frequency for the circuit of Fig. 9-5 is set down (60 cps), and the inductive reactance for this frequency (18,000 ohms) is listed, as well as the capacitive reactance (10,000 ohms). The difference between these two reactances will give the total reactance, 8,000 ohms. If this same circuit now had a 120-cycle a-c applied to it instead of a 60-cycle a-c, the inductive reactance would double and become 36,000 ohms, while the capacitive reactance would be halved and become 5,000 ohms. In the latter instance, the total reactance would be 31,000 ohms. A similar procedure can be undertaken for 240 cycles, which is double the 120-cycle frequency previously mentioned. Here again, the inductive reactance would double, and the capacitive reactance would decrease by one-half.

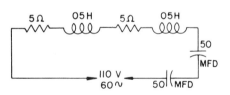

Fig. 9-6. Complex series impedance problem.

When the reactance values are not given, the solution of the problem is more lengthy, since the individual values have to be ascertained from the inductance and capacity values. A typical example of a problem of this type is shown in Fig. 9-6. Here, there are two inductances, two resistances, and two capacitors. Since both resistors have the same value, the total resistance will be 10 ohms. Inductances in series provide a total inductance which is the additive sum of the individual inductances, but for capacities in series, the total capacity will be less than any individual series capacitor. Thus, the total values of the individual components are as follows:

$$L = 0.05 + 0.05 = 0.1 \text{ henry}$$
$$R = 5 + 5 = 10 \text{ ohms}$$

$$C = \frac{50 \times 50}{50 + 50} = 25 \text{ microfarads}$$

Once these values have been ascertained, the individual reactive values are calculated, using the formulas previously given:

$$X_L = 6.28fL = 6.28 \times 60 \times 0.1$$
$$= 37.68 \text{ ohms}$$

$$X_C = \frac{1}{6.28fC}$$

$$= \frac{1}{6.28 \times 60 \times 25 \times 10^{-6}}$$

$$= \frac{1}{942 \times 10^{-5}} = \frac{10^5}{942} = 106 \text{ ohms}$$

After the individual reactive components have been ascertained, they are combined with the resistance in the usual Formula (9-1) giving the impedance in a series circuit composed of inductance, capacity, and resistance. This shows that approximately 68.6 ohms of impedance is present for the circuit shown in Fig. 9-6:

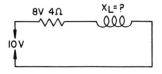

$$Z = \sqrt{100^2 + (37.68 - 106)^2}$$
$$= \sqrt{10,000 + 4,668} = 121 \text{ ohms}$$

Once the value of total impedance is known, total current is found:

Fig. 9-7. Simple series circuit with inductive reactance un-known.

$$I = \frac{E}{Z} = \frac{110}{121} = .9 \text{ amperes}$$

Knowing this value, the voltage drops across the individual components can then be calculated.

The value of unknown reactance can also be found, provided the voltage source and the voltage drop across the other components are known. A typical example is shown in the simple series circuit of Fig. 9-7, where a 4-ohm resistor is in series with an inductance whose reactance is unknown. The source voltage and the voltage drop across the resistance are known, however, and hence the current is

$$I = \frac{8}{4} = 2 \text{ amperes}$$

Once it is known that 2 amperes of current flows, the impedance can be found by dividing the total voltage value (10) by the current (2). This indicates that the impedance is 5 ohms. The vector formula for solving for the unknown reactance can now be used, as follows:

$$Z = \frac{5}{\sqrt{R^2 + X_L^2}} = \frac{5}{\sqrt{16 + X_L^2}}$$

or
$$5^2 = 25$$
$$25 - 16 = 9 \text{ ohms}$$
$$\sqrt{16} = 4 \text{ ohms for } R$$
$$\sqrt{9} = 3 \text{ ohms for } X_L$$

The value of the resistance is 4 ohms, and $4^2 = 16$. Since this 16 *plus another number* equals the square of five, it is obvious that 16 plus the unknown number equals 25. Thus, the unknown number is nine, and the square root of nine gives 3 ohms for the unknown inductive reactance.

PARALLEL L, C, AND R COMBINATIONS

The method for solving a parallel circuit composed of resistance, inductance, and capacity, is similar to the previous parallel circuits method discussed, except that the opposing factors of inductive and capacitive currents must be considered. When the total reactive current is known, a vector sum of the resistive and reactive currents is taken to find the total current. The impedance is then a function of the total voltage divided by the total current.

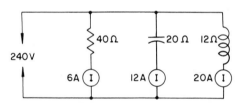

Fig. 9-8. Parallel impedance circuit giving current values with 240-volt source.

A typical example of a circuit employing resistance, inductance, and capacity in parallel is shown in Fig. 9-8. Since the a-c voltage across each component is 240 volts, the individual currents are calculated and the total current found as follows:

$$I_R = \frac{240}{40} = 6 \text{ amperes}$$

$$I_{X_C} = \frac{240}{20} = 12 \text{ amperes}$$

$$I_{X_L} = \frac{240}{12} = 20 \text{ amperes}$$

$$I_T = \sqrt{I_R^2 + (I_{X_L} - I_{X_C})^2}$$
$$= \sqrt{36 + (20 - 12)^2}$$
$$= \sqrt{36 + 64} = \sqrt{100} = 10$$

The impedance, as well as the phase angle, can then be solved as follows:

$$Z = \frac{E}{I} = \frac{240}{10} = 24 \text{ ohms}$$

$$\tan \theta = \frac{I_X}{I_R} = \frac{6}{8} = 0.7500$$

$$\theta = 37° \text{ (approx.)}$$

It is significant that the circuit of Fig. 9-8 will indicate the same impedance if the source voltage is changed. Since the current flow in each branch is proportional to the voltage divided by the opposition, the same relative proportions will hold, regardless of the source voltage. In Fig. 9-9, the same circuit is shown, except that the source voltage has now been decreased to 120 volts (one-half the original value). This will cause a proportionate decrease (by one-half) of the current through each branch. Thus, the current through the resistor is now 3 amperes, the current in the capacitive branch 6 amperes, and the current through the inductive branch 10 amperes. Solving for I and Z:

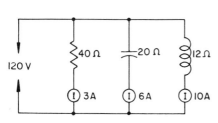

Fig. 9-9. Circuit of Fig. 9-8 with 120-volt source.

$$I = \sqrt{9 + 16} = \sqrt{25} = 5 \text{ amperes}$$

$$Z = \frac{120}{5} = 24 \text{ ohms}$$

Thus, in a parallel circuit such as shown in Fig. 9-9, where the reactive and resistance values are given, the total impedance can be found by assuming a source voltage and calculating on the basis of the total current, using the vector form, and solving for impedance by dividing the assumed voltage by the calculated current. (It must be emphasized that the current values thus derived will hold only for the voltage used in the calculation, as in previous discussions of parallel circuits in Chapter 8. The current values will change for different source voltage values, but the calculated impedance will be the true impedance, and will be the same regardless of the value of the source voltage assumed for calculation purposes.)

When several components are in series, and such series combinations are placed in parallel with other components, the individual reactances must be added together to solve for current. A typical example of such a circuit is shown in Fig. 9-10. Here, resistors R_1 and R_2 form a series

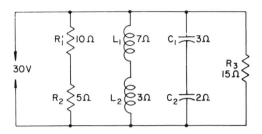

Fig. 9-10. Parallel circuit composed of series branches.

circuit and the total resistance in this branch is 15 ohms. This is paralleled by another resistor (R_3), which is 15 ohms, so that the total resistance in the circuit is now 7.5 ohms. Therefore, in order to find the total resistive current, the voltage (30) can be divided by total resistance (7.5), which indicates 4 amperes of resistive currents. Instead of this method, the current through the R_1 plus R_2 branch can be solved separately. Hence, for this combination, 30 volts divided by 15 ohms gives 2 amperes. For R_3, 2 amperes is also found, and adding the two resistive currents indicates the total resistive current is 4 amperes. The two inductive reactances of 7 ohms and 3 ohms total 10 ohms, and the current thus would be 3 amperes. Since two capacitors in series are also in the circuit, the reactances of these two units are added together (three plus two), which indicates that the current in the capacitive branch is 6 amperes (30 divided by five). To solve for total current, the individual resistive and reactive currents are set down as follows, and the total impedance is therefore 6 ohms:

$$I_T = \sqrt{4^2 + (6 - 3)^2}$$
$$= \sqrt{16 + 9} = \sqrt{25} = 5 \text{ amperes}$$
$$Z = \frac{30}{5} = 6 \text{ ohms}$$

REVIEW QUESTIONS

1. In a series circuit of resistance, inductance, and capacitance, the voltage drops across the reactances and resistances are known. How is the total voltage found?

2. In a series circuit of L, C, and R, how is the phase angle between voltage and current found?

3. (a) If the frequency and the capacitive reactives are known, what equation can be used for finding the capacitance?

(b) What formula is used for finding the capacity, if the frequency and the capacitive reactance are known?

4. What formula can be employed for finding the inductance, if the frequency and the inductive reactance are known?

5. What relationship of reactance to resistance will indicate the tangent of the phase angle?

6. How is the total current calculated, on the basis of the individual currents in the branches of a parallel circuit?

7. What formula is used for solving impedance in a parallel circuit?

8. Explain why the correct impedance can be found in some parallel circuits, even though a source voltage value is assumed.

9. Explain the method for solving for total impedance of a circuit composed of series-parallel combinations.

10. Draw a typical circuit composed of two resistors in parallel, the latter in series with an inductance and capacitor in parallel. Assign reactance and resistor values, and show calculations for solving for impedance.

PRACTICAL PROBLEMS

1. In an electronic circuit identical to that shown in Fig. 9–4, it is necessary to find the total current and the phase angle. From the values given in Fig. 9–4, make these calculations.

2. An electronic device uses the same circuit as shown in Fig. 9-5, with identical values. Calculate the a-c voltage applied to the circuit.

3. A coil in an audio filter network has an inductance of 20 henrys at 600 cps. The distributed capacity has a reactance of 50,000 ohms at 600 cps. What are the *reactances* (capacitive and inductive) at the following frequencies: (a) 150 cps; (b) 300 cps; (c) 600 cps; (d) 1,200 cps; (e) 2,400 cps?

4. An electronic device employs the series *L, C, R* circuit illustrated in Fig. 9–11. What is the impedance of this circuit?

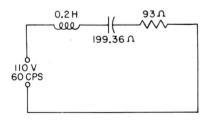

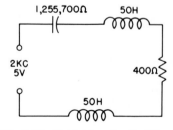

Fig. **9-11.** Illustration for Problem 9-4.

Fig. **9-12.** Illustration for Problem 9-5.

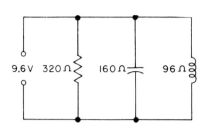

Fig. 9-13. Illustration for Problem 9-6.

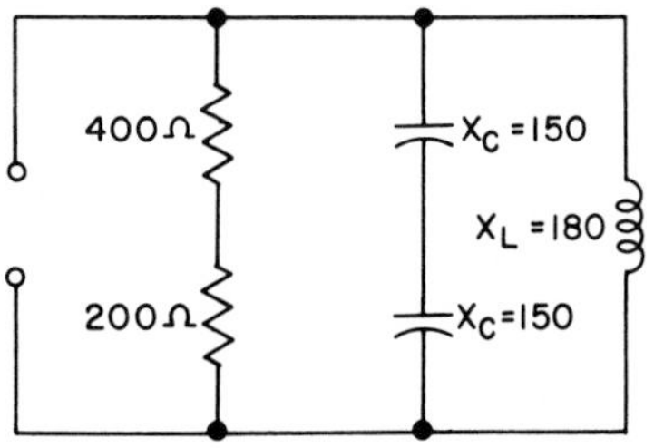

Fig. 9-14. Illustration for Problem 9-7.

5. In an electronic device using the circuit shown in Fig. 9–12, a frequency of 2 kilocycles is employed. What is the total current flow in this circuit (in milliamperes), and what is the total inductive reactance? Also, what is the total impedance which this circuit presents to the voltage source?

6. In a television receiver, the circuit shown in Fig. 9–13 is employed. When a certain frequency appears across this circuit, the opposition to current flow is as shown. What is the total current flow in milliamperes? What is the total impedance?

7. The schematic for an industrial electronic device includes the network shown in Fig. 9–14. No input voltage is given. What is the total impedance of this circuit?

10

RESONANCE

INTRODUCTION

In many electronic circuits, the inductive reactance and the capacitive reactance in a circuit are often equal in value. When this happens, the total reactance is zero, because the inductance would cause the voltage to lead by 90 degrees and the capacitor would cause the voltage to lag by 90 degrees, and these two conditions oppose each other. Hence, the voltage would neither lead nor lag the current, and the voltage and current would be in phase. This in-phase condition, when an inductance and capacitor are in the circuit, is known as *resonance*. Resonance is one of the most remarkable phenomena of electronics, since it permits the selection of desired signal frequencies while rejecting undesired ones. Thus, a resonant circuit has the ability to select specific frequencies, and is extensively used in virtually all branches of electronics. Without resonance, electronic communication as we know it today would be impossible.

Resonance can be achieved in either a series or a parallel circuit composed of inductance, capacity, and resistance. When reactances are equal, the circuit not only exhibits marked selection characteristics for a specific signal or group of signals closely clustered around the resonant frequency, but it also tends to reject signals having frequencies removed from the resonant frequency, regardless of whether such rejected signals have frequencies which lie above or below the frequency which produces resonance.

This selection characteristic is known as *selectivity,* and relates to the degree by which the circuit accepts desired signal frequencies and rejects undesired signal frequencies. The degree of selectivity is dependent on the amount of resistance present, as more fully detailed subsequently.

Signal reception, transmission, and other electronic applications which require the selection of a band of signal frequencies and the rejection of signal frequencies above and below this band, all depend on the resonance principle. Since practically all transmitting and receiving circuits which handle R-F signals employ either series or parallel resonant circuits, an understanding of the principles involved is of particular importance.

SERIES RESONANT CIRCUITS

Figure 10-1(A), shows a simple series circuit consisting of a resistor

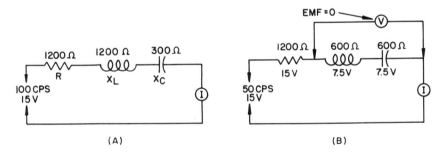

Fig. 10-1. Series resonant circuits.

of 1,200 ohms in series with an inductive reactance of 1,200 ohms and a capacitive reactance of 300 ohms. Here, the total reactance is 900 ohms (1,200 − 300) and, when this reactive value is used in conjunction with the resistive value, the impedance is equal to 1,500 ohms.

$$Z = \sqrt{1,200^2 + 900^2} = 1,500 \text{ ohms}$$

Now assume that this 15-volt, 100-cps signal is one of several signals applied to this circuit. For reference purposes, this signal is denoted as signal No. 1 and the other signals present are as follows:

15-volt signal	cps	X_L	X_C	X
No. 1	100	1,200	300	900
No. 2	200	2,400	150	2,250
No. 3	50	600	600	0
No. 4	25	300	1,200	900
No. 5	12.5	150	2,400	2,250

Since the second signal is 200 cps, the higher frequency will double the inductive reactance, and will reduce the capacitive reactance by one-half. Total reactance is now 2,250 ohms, as against 900 ohms for signal No. 1, and consequently the impedance will be still higher and less current will flow. Signal No. 3 has a frequency of 50 cps and, since this is one-half of the frequency designated for the circuit shown at Fig. 10-1(A), the inductive reactance will decrease by half and become 600 ohms, while the capacitive reactance will double and also become 600 ohms. The total *reactance* is now zero and, in consequence, the impedance is equal to the resistance only, or 1,200 ohms. Under this condition, the current flow is a function of the voltage (15 volts) divided by the impedance (1,200 ohms), and a higher current will now flow (12.5 milliamperes) than for the other signal frequencies shown in the chart. Signal No. 4 has a still lower frequency (25 cycles), which will cause the inductive reactance to decrease to a still lower value (300 ohms), and the capacitive reactance doubles again, becoming 1,200 ohms. This gives a reactance of 900 ohms, and again a higher impedance and lower current result.

For any frequency other than 50 cps, the current will be lower than 12.5 milliamperes, whether such frequency is higher or lower than 50 cps. Thus, for the circuit shown in Fig. 10-1(B), resonance is achieved at a frequency of 50 cps. Under this condition, maximum signal energy flows, since neither the inductive reactance nor the capacitive reactance offers opposition to such flow. As the inductive reactance and the capacitive reactance are equal and opposite in their function, their effects are cancelled to produce the resultant zero reactance. The voltage drop across the 1,200-ohm resistor $(I \times R)$ is 15 volts. Since neither reactance is offering effective opposition, the full source voltage will develop across the series resistor. Voltage across each reactance is a function of the current times the reactance and, therefore, amounts to 7.5 volts for each. Such voltages could be read across each unit individually, but a voltmeter across the two would read zero voltage, since at any instant the voltage drop across the inductance is 180 degrees out of phase with the voltage drop across the capacitance, and in consequence the voltage drop across the two combined is zero, as shown in Fig. 10-1(B).

At resonance, the inductive reactance is equal and opposite to the capacitive reactance.

$$6.28fL = \frac{1}{6.28fC} \qquad (10\text{-}1)$$

This gives us the following expression:

$$6.28f^2 = \frac{1}{LC} \qquad (10\text{-}2)$$

which is then converted to the following formula for finding the resonant frequency, when the values of inductance and capacitance are known:

$$f = \frac{1}{6.28 \sqrt{LC}} \qquad (10\text{-}3)$$

The formula indicates that the resonant frequency is established by definite values of inductance and capacitance, since the product of L times C is utilized. Thus, for a *specific resonance frequency,* there can be only *one product* of L times C. Since this is a *product,* however, it is obvious that various values of L and C can be used to obtain the same product. For instance, assume that L is 2 microhenrys and C is 4 microfarads, to give a product of eight. This product will produce a specific frequency even though the value of L is changed to 4 microhenrys and the capacitance is changed to 2 microfarads, since the product is still eight. Numerous other combinations of L and C to give a product of eight are possible, and the chart shown below indicates a few of these.

L	C	LC
2	4	8
4	2	8
8	1	8
0.5	16	8

Even for the same product, however, a change in the values of L and C will alter circuit selectivity as detailed in the discussion which follows. The relationship between L and C which gives a constant product for a given frequency is known as the L/C ratio, because the same product is procured for various ratios of L to C.

CIRCUIT Q

The Q of a circuit relates to the degree of selectivity realized from a combination of inductance, resistance, and capacity, and it is a figure of merit. The Q of a circuit is based on the effect which circuit resistance has on the ability of the circuit to reject frequencies on each side of the resonant frequency.

On occasion, it is desirable to have a chart of the resonant characteristics of a circuit, so that the circuit current value with respect to a particular frequency is easily seen. If the resonant frequency characteristics of a series resonant circuit are plotted, the procedure consists in measuring the current for various frequency values, starting at a frequency considerably below resonance, and gradually increasing the frequency to resonance, and then above. For each frequency which is impressed on the circuit, the value of current would be read, and a series of such points would be marked on the graph, as shown at the left of Fig. 10-2. When a line is drawn

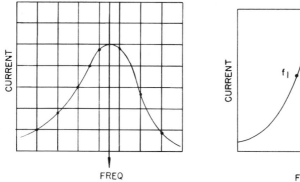 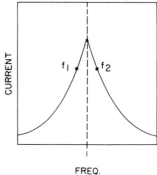

Fig. 10-2. Selectivity curves.

through all these points, a graph will be obtained which is known as the *response curve* of the series resonant circuit. As can be seen from the response curve of the left graph of Fig. 10-2, the response characteristics may be such that several frequencies clustered around the resonant frequency may produce virtually the same high current flow. Thus, the circuit is said to be broadly resonant, since it will have a high current flow for a group of frequencies, and will reject those frequencies removed from this group. Another circuit, however, may produce a response curve such as shown in the right graph of Fig. 10-2, where virtually only one frequency is resonant, and frequencies on each side of the resonant frequency produce a considerably lower current flow. This type of resonant curve has a high degree of selectivity, while the curve at the left in Fig. 10-2 has low selectivity characteristics.

The response curve of the circuit is directly affected by the value of the resistance. Such resistance can be in the form of an external resistor, or of any other resistance in the circuit, such as the resistance of the coil winding, or the leakage resistance of the capacitor. Since the variable capacitors in radio or other electronic circuits are of the air-core variable type, they have virtually no leakage resistance. The inductance, however, always has some resistance in the wire and, for this reason, the figure of merit (circuit Q) is based on the ratio of the inductive reactance to the resistance:

$$Q = \frac{X_L}{R} \qquad (10\text{-}4)$$

Thus, the greater the inductive reactance with respect to the resistance, the higher the selectivity.

The resonant bandpass of a circuit is defined as the width between two points on the graph established as 0.707 of the maximum current at resonance. Thus, the Q of the circuit is also proportional to

$$\frac{f_r}{f_2 - f_1} \qquad (10\text{-}5)$$

Since the 0.707 points of the response curve indicate the bandwidth, and since the bandwidth is proportional to the Q of the circuit, the formula above is applicable. The aforementioned frequency points are indicated on the response curve shown in the right graph of Fig. 10-2.

A series resonant circuit has a maximum amount of current flow at resonance (limited only by the resistive component of the circuit), hence the circuit will have a low impedance when the resonant frequency signal is applied to it, and higher impedance for signal frequencies either *above* *or below* resonance. The higher impedance on each side of resonance establishes a greater opposition to the current flow, and it is this higher impedance, both above and below the resonant frequency, which tends to reject signal frequencies other than the resonant frequency signal or the cluster of signals whose frequencies are near the resonant frequency.

Because the Q of the circuit is a function of the inductive reactance divided by the resistance, a higher Q can be obtained by increasing the L/C ratio (but maintaining the same product of L times C for the specific resonant frequency desired). Thus, if the inductive reactance were to be increased to obtain a higher $Q,$ it would necessitate increasing the *inductance.* An increase in inductance would, however, lower the resonant frequency and, in order to keep the same resonant frequency as before (but still raise the Q), the series capacitor value has to be decreased. The decrease in capacity must be sufficient to compensate for the increase in inductance, so that the same product of LC is maintained.

The Q of a circuit is important in establishing the degree by which a circuit will pass a group or band of signals having frequencies around the resonance point. Thus, the circuit Q establishes the amount of *bandpass* required in a particular resonant circuit, since in some applications perhaps only one signal frequency is involved, while in others several signal frequencies may be handled by the circuit. The higher Q not only narrows the bandpass, but offers a higher degree of selectivity for undesired signals having frequencies on each side of the resonant frequency, because of the steepness of the bandpass characteristic. A low-Q circuit, on the other hand, while having a much wider bandpass, also has more gradual inclines and slopes at the sides of the resonant curve, and hence the degree of selectivity is reduced. To regain the high degree of selectivity which is lost when the Q is lowered, several resonant circuits can be employed in successive stages to improve the selectivity, as more fully detailed subsequently.

In a series resonant circuit, a high Q produces a steep bandpass curve and the circuit has a lower impedance (and thus higher current) at resonance than would be the case with a circuit having a low Q. The circuit with considerable resistance in it produces a low Q.

Since the resistance in a series resonant circuit is the only current-limiting factor, and since low-Q circuits have a higher resistance than high-Q circuits, the series resonant circuits with low Q limit the current flow because of the greater resistance which is present during resonance. Even though inductive reactance is equal and opposite to capacitive reactance, and the opposite effects of the two cancel one another, the higher resistance which is left for a low-Q circuit is the current-limiting factor. With the low-Q circuit, however, the signal current at resonance is still higher than the current on each side of resonance. It is simply the *peak signal current* which has been reduced for the low-Q circuit.

There are several factors which tend to influence the amount of Q, and which must be considered in circuit design. Since the Q is a factor of the inductive reactance divided by the resistance, it would seem that the Q could be raised by simply increasing the inductance and lowering the capacity, as previously mentioned. When the inductance is raised by increasing the number of turns of the coil, however, the d-c resistance of the wire which forms the coil will be increased, since an additional length of wire is required, and thus added resistance is introduced into the circuit. The additional resistance would tend to decrease the Q. If the d-c resistance of the wire is appreciable, a larger conductor wire must be employed to reduce the d-c resistance established by the additional turns.

Another factor which must be considered when an attempt is made to raise circuit Q is the distributed capacity of an inductance. Since an inductance is composed of a number of turns of wire forming a coil, capacity will be established between adjacent turns of the wire, since each turn acts as a capacitor plate, with the dielectric composed of the insulation around the wire. Capacity is also established between successive layers of coil when multilayer inductances are employed. Since capacity increases when the conductor areas are increased, coils employing larger wire will have more distributed capacity than those using relatively thin wire. For this reason, the increase in wire diameter mentioned in the previous paragraph to reduce the d-c resistance of a coil will still act adversely on the circuit Q, since an increase in wire diameter will also mean an increase in circuit capacity. Because circuit Q is lowered with an increase in capacity (but raised with an increase in inductance), the increase in capacity of a coil employing larger wire must be compensated for by decreasing in proportion the physical capacity placed in series with the inductance.

Still another factor which affects circuit Q is the resistance encountered at very high frequencies. Such high-frequency resistance is known as *skin-effect*, and this subject will be treated more fully later.

The distributed capacity of an inductance must not only be kept at a minimum so as not to lower circuit Q, but also to prevent attenuating or diminishing signal energy. A considerable amount of distributed capacity in an inductance has the same effect as an inductance being shunted by a capacitor. Thus, the higher-frequency signal energy would find a low capacitive reactance path shunting the inductance, which would cause some loss of such signal energy. Low coil capacity is of particular importance in R-F choke coils, which are employed to isolate the signal energy present in one stage from another circuit. A choke coil is designed to have a high series inductive reactance, which will offer considerable opposition to the signal energy and prevent its leakage to circuits where it is not desired. The choke coil also preserves the signal energy contained in a circuit, and minimizes its loss by preventing leakage of such signal energy away from the circuit where it is handled. The reactance of a choke coil can be made as high as required, since inductive reactance for a certain frequency is proportional to the angular velocity multiplied by the frequency and the value of the inductance. If too high an inductive reactance is chosen, in an effort to provide maximum opposition to signal energy leakage, the distributed capacity increases, and this will nullify the effect of the high inductive reactance, since it will provide a low capacitive reactance path through the coil. Thus, choke coils are wound in a fashion which tends to decrease distributed capacity and, at the same time, a compromise must be established with respect to a minimum of capacitive reactance shunt and a maximum inductive reactance opposition.

In ultrahigh and microwave practices, resonant circuits are often established by employing physical inductances in conjunction with distributed capacities, since the high frequency involved entails only a small amount of capacity for establishing resonance. Often, the distributed capacity is already of a sufficient amount for resonance, without inclusion of an actual physical capacitor.

Series resonant circuits can be employed in filters which will pass certain frequencies and reject others. One typical example of this is shown at Fig. 10-3(A), which shows two circuits interconnected by a series

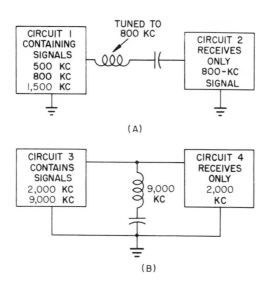

(A)

(B)

Fig. 10-3. Series circuits used as filters.

resonant circuit. Assume that the first circuit contains the following signals: 500 kilocycles, 800 kilocycles, and 1,500 kilocycles. It is necessary to transfer the desired frequency of 800 kilocycles to the second circuit, but at the same time prevent the entry into the latter circuit of the 500-kilocycle and 1,500-kilocycle signals. A convenient method for doing this is to employ a series resonant circuit to interconnect the two circuits. The series resonant circuit is tuned ot the desired frequency, 800 kilocycles, where it will have a low impedance and, hence, a maximum current flow. For the signal frequencies of 500 kilocycles and 1,500 kilocycles, however, the impedance will be considerably higher and, thus, a high opposition is established for these frequencies, and very little current will flow. Hence, the series resonant circuit will transfer the desired signal to circuit No. 2 while minimizing the undesired signals. The resonant circuit thus *couples* the second circuit to the first for the desired 800-kilocycle frequency.

The series resonant circuit is also convenient for shunting signals while permitting the *desired* signal to pass between two circuits. This is shown in Fig. 10-3(B), where a circuit containing 2,000 kilocycles and 9,000 kilocycles is coupled to the next circuit. If the 2,000-kilocycle signal is to be applied to the next circuit, but the 9,000 signal is to be kept out, the arrangement shown at (B) can be employed. Here, a shunt series resonant circuit is tuned to the *undesired* signal of 9,000 kilocycles. Resonance at this frequency means that a maximum current will flow for this signal and, hence, the 9,000-kilocycle signal will encounter a low-impedance shunt path. The *desired* signal of 2,000 kilocycles, however, will find a high impedance in the shunt series resonant circuit, and will not be shunted or diminished to any appreciable degree but will be applied to the second circuit.

A combination of the two methods can be employed, as shown in Fig. 10-4. Here, the first circuit again contains a 2,000-kilocycle signal,

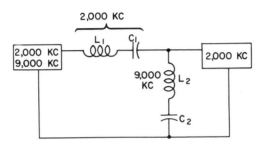

Fig. 10-4. Combination series resonant circuits used as filters.

as well as a 9,000-kilocycle signal, and only the 2,000-kilocycle signal is to be transferred to the second circuit. The series resonant circuit consisting of L_1 and C_1 is tuned to the *desired* frequency of 2,000 kilocycles and, hence, it will transfer this signal, since the resonant circuit has a low impedance for it. The impedance of L_1 and C_1 to the 9,000-kilocycle signal, however, will be high, so that little signal energy will flow. The shunt series resonant circuit composed of L_2 and C_2 is tuned to the undesired frequency of 9,000 kilocycles; it provides a low reactance shunt circuit for this frequency, and will, in effect, bypass the undesired signal and prevent little of such energy from entering the second circuit.

Series resonant circuits are seldom used for receiver tuning purposes, since the parallel resonant circuits which are discussed next are more expedient. The series circuits are, however, used to a considerable extent in filter networks of the type previously described for trapping out undesired signals from circuits, and otherwise getting rid of unwanted or spurious signals.

PARALLEL RESONANCE

When a capacitor is placed in parallel with a coil, as shown at (A) of Fig. 10-5, the circuit combination of *L* and *C* will be resonant for a

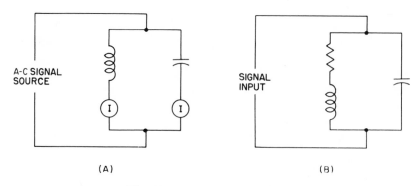

Fig. 10-5. Parallel resonant circuits.

certain frequency which causes the inductive reactance to be equal to the capacitive reactance. When a signal of resonant frequency is applied, the reactances are equal, and the current measured in the inductive branch will have the same value as that in the capacitive branch, since the same amount of voltage is applied to each component. Because these currents are equal and opposite, they would cancel out in the vector formula used for calculating total current in a parallel circuit composed of inductance, capacity, and resistance. Hence, in a parallel resonant circuit, the impedance is a function of the total voltage divided by the total resistive current:

$$Z = \frac{E}{I_R} \qquad (10\text{-}6)$$

If no physical resistor shunts the parallel resonant circuit, and assuming the coil has a negligible amount of resistance, the impedance will be very high, since the only current consumed would be by what little resistance is present in the circuit. If the inductance has an appreciable resistance, it must be represented as a series resistance, as shown at (B) of Fig. 10-5, and the circuit will become a combination of a series circuit in parallel with a capacity.

With a negligible amount of circuit resistance, the voltage drop across the parallel resonant circuit would be high, since the impedance is high. For frequencies above and below resonance, the impedance would decrease, because either the inductive reactance or the capacitive reactance would decrease below that established for resonance. This is illustrated in Fig. 10-6, where a parallel resonant circuit is shown at (A) for a signal frequency of 10,000 kilocycles. With a specific L/C ratio, the inductive reactance is 50,000 ohms and, since the circuit is resonant, the capacitive reactance is also 50,000 ohms. Despite the fact that a coil (or a capacitor) with a reactance of 50,000 ohms would normally permit current flow, the currents in the two branches are 180 degrees out of phase, and being opposite, their effects cancel out.

If the input signal frequency is now changed to 20,000 kilocycles (twice the resonant frequency), the inductive reactance becomes 100,000 ohms, since an increase in frequency will raise inductive reactance. For the 20,000-kilocycle signal, the capacitive reactance will decrease to 25,000 ohms, as shown at (B). As there is now a difference in the reactances between coil and capacitor, currents are no longer equal and opposite, and will not cancel fully. Partial cancellation occurs, since the lower current of the inductive reactance is subtracted from the higher current established by the lower capacitive reactance. The resultant current is combined with the resistive current in the vector formula for

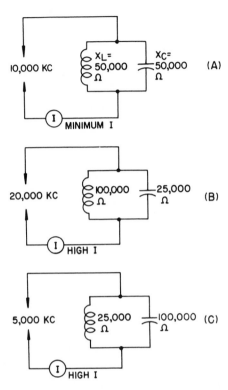

Fig. 10-6. Effect of frequency on parallel resonant circuits.

finding total current. Since a reactive current is now present, a higher circulating current results, and the ammeter will now indicate a high current flow. Impedance being a function of the voltage divided by the current, the higher current would give a lower value of impedance than for the resonant circuit in Fig. 10-6(A). The lower value of capacitive reactance for the circuit in (B) establishes the high current flow, since it now provides a low shunt reactance across the inductance. Because the capacitor is instrumental in decreasing the impedance, the circuit at (B) is now primarily capacitive. If the frequency of the circuit shown at (A) is halved to 5,000 kilocycles, as at (C), the inductive reactance shown in (A) will decrease by one-half, since a decrease in frequency means a corresponding decrease in inductive reactance. Hence, the inductive reactance for the circuit in (C) is now 25,000 ohms.

The *decrease* of signal frequency from that in (A) will cause the capacitive reactance of the circuit at (C) to increase to 100,000 ohms, since a decrease in signal frequency raises capacitive reactance. Again, as with the circuit shown at (B), the off-resonance condition increases the current flow and lowers the impedance. As the inductive reactance has now decreased, it becomes the shunting factor which increases current, hence the circuit shown at (C) is predominantly an inductive circuit.

From the foregoing, it is evident that parallel resonant circuits act in opposite fashion to series resonant circuits. In a series circuit at resonance, the impedance for the signal frequency which establishes resonance is low, and signal current is high. In a parallel resonant circuit, the impedance for the signal frequency which establishes resonance is high, while the signal current is low.

The high impedance of a parallel resonant circuit decreases the resonant frequency signal current flow to and from the signal source, but establishes a large voltage drop for the signal. For signals having frequencies either above or below the resonant frequency, circuit impedance is low. Thus, even though undesired signals are present in the circuit they would develop only a low value voltage drop across the parallel resonant circuit.

At resonance, a parallel resonant circuit acts as a storage device and, assuming negligible resistance, the signal energy is interchanged between the inductance and the capacity, at a rate corresponding to the frequency of the incoming signal. This interchange of energy would continue even though the signal source were removed, since the capacitor would become charged by the signal energy and would discharge such energy into the coil. The collapsing field of the inductance would establish a back emf which would recharge the capacitor. Since the resonant frequency potential established the initial full charge, no more signal energy will be accepted by the circuit. This is similar to the charging of a capacitor by a certain potential. Once the capacitor is charged, current flow ceases, since, for a given emf and a fixed value of capacity, only a specific charge can be established. A specific charge is also placed across the capacitor in the parallel resonant circuit, except that the energy flows back and forth from capacitor to coil. Such an energy would continue the interchange indefinitely, but for the fact that the signal energy would eventually be consumed by whatever resistance is in the circuit. The characteristic of energy exchange in a resonant circuit is known as the *flywheel* effect, and is more fully discussed in Chapter 17.

The formula for ascertaining the frequency, when the values of the inductance and capacity are known, is similar to the formula employed for the series resonant circuit.

$$f = \frac{1}{6.28\sqrt{LC}} \qquad (10\text{-}7)$$

Because frequencies in *kilocycles* are encountered often, however, the following formula can be employed, which gives the answer directly in kilocycles rather than in cycles.

$$f(kc) = \frac{0.159}{\sqrt{LC}} \tag{10-8}$$

In circuits where wide ranges of signals are encountered, it is necessary to increase the bandpass characteristics of a resonant circuit, by adding a physical shunting resistor across the circuit, to broaden the range of frequencies handled, as shown in Fig. 10-7. As such a resistor shunts the high impedance circuit, it will lower the impedance in proportion to its own value. A resistor having a very high resistance will have little effect on lowering the impedance, while a lower resistor will have an appreciable effect. In wideband circuits of this type, the circuit Q is proportional to the resistance divided by either the inductive reactance or the capacitive reactance. Since each of these reactances is the same at resonance, it is immaterial which is employed. Also, since the amount of such shunt resistance will determine the amount of impedance, the formula can be expressed as

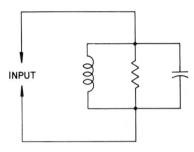

Fig. 10-7. Resonant circuit with shunting resistance.

$$Q = \frac{Z}{X} \tag{10-9}$$

TUNED CIRCUIT TRANSFORMERS

Parallel resonant circuits are used extensively to couple the various circuits of R-F signal generators, R-F amplifiers, filter networks and similar R-F sections. This is usually done through a transformer arrangement, by coupling the inductance of one parallel resonant circuit to the inductance of a second parallel resonant circuit, as shown in Fig. 10-8(A). Since the inductances generate magnetic lines of force, as previously explained, the placement of a second coil in close proximity to the first coil causes the former to intercept the signal energy present in the first resonant circuit. Because the coupling is by virtue of the magnetic fields of the inductances, it cannot be truly considered as the coupling of one parallel circuit to

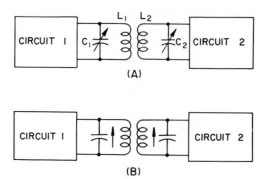

Fig. 10-8. Parallel resonant circuits form coupling transformers.

another, since the individual capacitors of the parallel circuits are not coupled together, but only the inductances. For this reason, the transfer of energy from L_1, which forms the primary of the transformer, to L_2, which forms the secondary, must be considered equivalent to a series circuit. The induced voltage will cause the current to flow, which again is subject to the characteristics of the second parallel resonant circuit, composed of L_2 and C_3.

Variable capacitors can be utilized, as shown in Fig. 10-8(A), so that the individual stages can be tuned to resonance. Another method for tuning is to employ metallic slugs which are moved in and out of the core of the coils. As previously mentioned, the core affects permeability, and hence will change the inductance of a coil. When the core is inserted entirely into the coil, a high inductance results, which will decrease as the core is gradually removed from the coil.

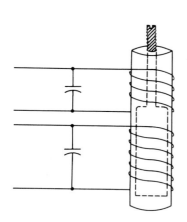

When a variable core is used for tuning purposes, an arrow is often placed beside each coil, as shown in Fig. 10-8(B). Since both coils are wound on a single form, as shown in Fig. 10-9, a single metallic slug is sometimes utilized, so that both the primary and secondary resonant circuits can be tuned simultaneously. The factors relating to the characteristics of such devices are covered more fully in subsequent discussions.

Fig. 10-9. Iron-core slug for tuning purposes.

The degree of coupling, or how much the two coils are brought together, affects the bandpass characteristics of the circuits, as well as the amplitude of the signal transferred. As mentioned earlier in the discussion on transformers, when two coils are coupled as closely together as possible, such coupling is known as *overcoupling,* or *tight* coupling. Under this condition, the loading effect of one coil on the other decreases the Q of the combined circuits to a considerable extent, and has a pronounced influence on the impedance of the parallel resonant circuits. At the resonant frequency, the impedance decreases, but is still high on each side of the resonant frequency, as shown in Fig. 10-10. Thus, a double-hump resonant curve is produced when overcoupling is employed.

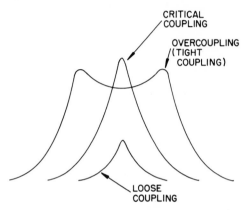

Fig. 10-10. Effects of the degree of coupling in transformers.

If the inductors are spaced some distance apart (loose coupling), but still sufficiently close so that some energy is transferred, not all the magnetic lines of force generated by the primary coil will be intercepted by the secondary coil, and considerably less signal energy is transferred than would be the case with overcoupling. Since there is less loading effect from one inductance to the other, the bandpass characteristics are narrow, and selectivity is good, as shown in Fig. 10-10. At some point between loose coupling and tight coupling, the condition known as *critical* coupling exists. At this point, there will be a maximum transfer of signal energy from one parallel resonant circuit to the other with much sharper selectivity, as shown in Fig. 10-10.

The factors relating to the coefficient of coupling also apply for the coupling of parallel resonant circuits in transformer arrangement.

PARALLEL FILTER SYSTEMS

As with the series resonant circuits previously discussed in this chapter, the parallel resonant circuits can also be employed as filter devices. If, for instance, a circuit contains a signal frequency of 5,000 kilocycles, and an undesired signal of 10,000 kilocycles, as shown at Fig. 10-11(A) (circuit

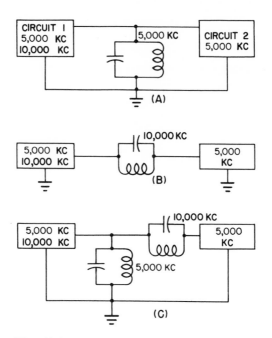

Fig. 10-11. Parallel resonant circuits employed as filters.

No. 1), the undesired 10,000-kilocycle signal can be shunted by a parallel resonant combination employed as shown, so that only the 5,000-kilocycle desired signal reaches the second circuit. The parallel resonant circuit is tuned to 5,000 kilocycles (the desired signal) and, hence, the high impedance will prevent the desired signal from being shunted across circuit No. 2. Since the 10,000-kilocycle signal will not produce the same high impedance in the parallel resonant circuit which the 5,000-kilocycle resonant frequency produces, the lower impedance will have a shunting effect on the 10,000-kilocycle signal.

A similar arrangement can be made, as shown in Fig. 10-11(B), where a parallel resonant circuit is placed in series between the two circuits. This parallel resonant circuit is tuned to 10,000 kilocycles (the undesired signal) and, hence, offers a high opposition to it, because of the high impedance. Since the desired frequency of 5,000 kilocycles does not find resonance in the capacitor-inductance combination, the low impedance resulting for the 5,000-kilocycle signal permits transfer of this desired signal. For more effective filtering of the undesired signal, a combination of the two aforementioned methods can be employed as shown at Fig. 10-11(C). The parallel combination which is in series between circuits No. 1 and No. 2 is tuned to 10,000 kilocycles and, hence, offers a high impedance to the undesired frequency, while the shunt parallel-resonant section is tuned to 5,000 kilocycles and, thus, offers a low impedance shunt path for the 10,000-kilocycle undesired signal. The combination of the two filter circuit arrangements is more effective than either of the methods shown at (A) or (B).

Combinations of series and parallel resonant circuits can also be used for filtering purposes. In Fig. 10-11(C), for instance, the 10,000-kilocycle parallel circuit could be replaced with a series resonant circuit tuned to 5,000 kilocycles. The series circuit would have a low impedance for the desired 5,000-kilocycle signal and would pass it while offering a high impedance for the undesired 10,000-kilocycle signal.

APPLIED MATHEMATICS

In electronics, the Greek letter ω (lower case omega) is used as a symbol for the *product* of the angular velocity (6.28) multiplied by the signal frequency:

$$\omega = 6.28f \qquad (10\text{-}10)$$

Thus, the symbol ω is a convenient way to express $6.28f$. Typical derivations of formulas employing this symbol are as follows:

Since $X_L = X_C$ at resonance

$$X_L - X_C = 0$$

$$\omega L - \frac{1}{\omega C} = 0 \qquad (10\text{-}11)$$

$$\omega^2 = \frac{1}{LC} \left(6.28f^2 = \frac{1}{LC} \right) \qquad (10\text{-}12)$$

$$LC = \frac{1}{\omega^2} \qquad (10\text{-}13)$$

$$f = \frac{1}{6.28 \sqrt{LC}} \qquad (10\text{-}7)$$

Thus, the product of L times C is a function of $1/\omega^2$. Also ω times the inductance is, therefore, an expression for the inductive reactance. A study of the foregoing will help in solving typical problems.

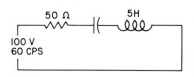

Fig. 10-12. Calculation of capacity in series resonant circuit.

As an example, consider the circuit shown in Fig. 10-12. Here, a 100-volt 60-cycle signal source is applied to a series circuit consisting of a 50-ohm resistor in series with an unknown capacitor and an inductance of 5 henrys. The problem is to find both the inductive and capacitive reactances at resonance (60 cycles), as well as the total current and the voltage drop across each component. The inductive reactance is found by multiplying ω by 5 henrys, which gives 1,884 ohms. Since the circuit is at resonance, the capacitive reactance would be of the same value. Total current is a function of the voltage divided by the impedance, and since the impedance at resonance is established by the resistance, the current is 2 amperes, as follows:

$$I_T = \frac{E}{R} = \frac{100}{50} = 2 \text{ amperes}$$

Once the current value is known, the voltage across the individual components is a function of the current multiplied by the resistance or reactance. The following calculations show these values:

$$E_R = IR = 2 \times 50 = 100 \text{ volts}$$
$$E_L = IX_L = 2 \times 1,884 = 3,768 \text{ volts}$$
$$E_c = IX_C = 2 \times 1,884 = 3,768 \text{ volts}$$

This indicates that the voltage drop across the resistor is 100 volts, with 3,768 volts across each reactance. As previously explained, the individual voltage drops across the components in a circuit composed of *L, C,* and *R,* may sometimes exceed the source voltage. The *total voltage across the inductor and capacitor, however, is zero, since the voltages are of opposite phase and their combined effects cancel.*

Since the inductive reactance oppose the capacitive reactance in a resonant circuit, the voltage and current will again be in phase, so that, when solving for power, the apparent power becomes the true power. Because there is no phase angle, the power for the circuit shown in Fig. 10-12 would be calculated as follows:

$$P = EI = 2 \times 100 = 200 \text{ watts}$$

FREQUENCY EFFECTS ON *L, C,* AND *R*

Component	Effect of Frequency	
	Increase	Decrease
Resistance (*R*)	None	None
Capacitance (*C*)	None	None
Capacitive reactance (*X_C*)	Lowers X_C	Raises X_C
Inductance (*L*)	None	None
Inductive reactance (*X_L*)	Raises X_L	Lowers X_L
Series capacitor-resistor combination (*Z*)	Lowers Z	Raises Z
Series inductance-resistor combination (*Z*)	Raises Z	Lowers Z
Parallel capacitor-resistor combination (*Z*)	Lowers Z	Raises Z
Parallel inductance-resistor combination (*Z*)	Raises Z	Lowers Z
Series resonance (*Z*)	Raises Z	Raises Z
Parallel resonance (*Z*)	Lowers Z	Lowers Z

REVIEW QUESTIONS

1. Compare the impedance and current relationships with respect to parallel resonant and series resonant circuits.

2. Briefly explain what is meant by the *Q* of a resonant circuit.

3. Briefly explain what effect distributive capacity has on circuit *Q*.

4. If the product of *L* times *C* is known, what formula can be used for solving for the resonant frequency of the circuit?

5. What is the phase angle between voltage and current in a series resonant circuit? In a parallel resonant circuit?

6. Briefly explain the type of bandpass characteristics obtained from over-coupling coils, as well as when using critical coupling for coils.

7. Designate the *type* of series resonant filter circuit you would employ to transfer a 40-megacycle signal from one stage to another, while minimizing the transfer of a 100-megacycle signal.

8. Designate the *type* of parallel resonant filter circuit you would employ to transfer a 60-kilocycle signal to a subsequent stage, while minimizing the transfer of a 300-kilocycle signal.

9. Indicate a combination of series and parallel circuits which would effectively filter out a 200-megacycle signal from a subsequent stage, while permitting the coupling of a 50-megacycle signal.

10. Explain two methods which can be employed to tune the primary and secondary circuits of an R-F transformer.

11. What precautions must be taken to design an effective choke coil which will isolate a signal frequency and prevent its leakage to other circuits?

12. Explain what the Greek letter omega (ω) represents in electronics, and give a typical example of its use in a formula.

PRACTICAL PROBLEMS

1. If an electronic device utilizes the resonant circuit shown in Fig. 10–13, what is the total current flow in *milliamperes?* Also solve for the power consumed. What is the value of the inductive reactance at resonance? What is the value of inductive reactance at 180 cps?

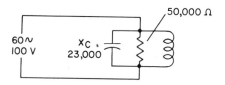

Fig. 10-13. Illustration for Problem 10-1.

2. What is the Q of a series resonant circuit if the capacitive reactance is 2,000 ohms and the resistance is 10 ohms? If the resistance value is 100 ohms, what is the Q? Which resistor reduces the selectivity of the circuit the least?

3. In an industrial control circuit an undesired resonance effect is secured because of the presence of inductance and capacity. If LC is equal to 0.0001, what is the resonant frequency which must be eliminated?

4. In a test instrument, a series circuit is employed which has a resistance of 200 ohms, a capacitive reactance of 4,000 ohms, and an inductive reactance of 250 ohms when used at 1,000 kilocycles. At what frequency is this circuit resonant?

5. The filter network used in a short wave transmitter is similar to that shown in Fig. 10-11(C). The 5,000-kilocycle parallel resonant circuit was replaced by a *series* resonant circuit. To what frequency must the latter be tuned?

6. An R-F choke has an inductive reactance of 50,000 ohms at 20 megacycles, but the distributed capacity provides a shunt reactance of 25,000 ohms. At what frequency would X_C be eight times higher than X_L?

7. In an industrial circuit for automation, it was found that the product of L (in microhenries) and C (in microfarads) was 0.0253, producing an undesired resonant effect. What is the frequency of the resonant circuit thus formed?

8. An electronic signal filter had a series resonant circuit in which the product of L (in microhenries) and C (in microfarads) was 0.0704. What is the resonant frequency? What is the frequency of the signal which is applied to the load, if the input to the filter consists of signals having the following frequencies (in *kilocycles*): 100, 300, 600, 900, 1,200?

9. The product of L (in microhenries) and C (in microfarads) was found to be 0.225 in a control circuit. What is the value of $(6.28 \times f)^2$ and what is the frequency of the resonant circuit thus formed?

Part **2**

Principles of
Electronics

11

VACUUM TUBES

INTRODUCTION

Vacuum tubes are extensively employed in virtually all branches of electronics. Their importance stems from their ability to perform any of the several functions of rectification, detection, amplification, voltage regulation, signal gating, and oscillation. In addition they form photoelectric devices, picture and oscilloscope screens, and display devices in computers. Hence they have found wide applications in electronic computers, control systems, electronic organs, all types of transmitters and receivers, and in various other allied branches of the electronic industry.

In recent years, many of the functions of the vacuum tube have been duplicated by the *transistor,* as more fully described in Chapter 13. While the transistor is a tiny device, when compared in size to its vacuum tube counterpart, and takes much less power to perform similar functions, the vacuum tube will always be employed in certain branches of electronics, since it is capable of handling greater amounts of power than the simple transistor. While the transistor has a limited power handling range, the vacuum tube can be designed to handle either microwatts of power, by making the tube extremely small, or it can be made to handle thousands of watts of power, by increasing tube size and using water-cooled types.

Thus, vacuum tube sizes range from extremely small types utilized in portable or high-frequency electronic equipment, to the huge sizes employed in high-powered radio and television transmitting stations.

Applications for vacuum tubes are numerous, since there is such a variety available in terms of design and functional characteristics. Thus, differences in internal structures and arrangements of the components which make up the vacuum tube produce the great variety of types for special circuit applications to meet specific needs.

THERMIONIC EMISSION

As mentioned in the first two chapters, a conductor has an atomic characteristic which permits the free movement of electrons, since some of the latter are not so rigidly bound to the limits of the nuclear orbit that they cannot be removed from such an orbit. If such a conductor is heated, the velocity of the electrons revolving around the nuclear orbit increases, and this acceleration imparts to the electrons sufficient kinetic energy so that they leave the orbital influence of the atomic structure. When many electrons leave their atomic orbit, they can escape beyond the surface of the conductor material. The free electrons form a cloud of electrons around the conducting surface, and create what is referred to as a *space charge*. Since this cloud is composed of free electrons which have left their central orbit, such electrons can be readily pulled entirely away from the influence of the conductor material, by subjecting the electrons to a positive electric charge which will attract the negative charge representative of the electrons. Thus, a continuous flow of electrons can be established from a conducting surface to some other surface having a plus charge. This method of procuring electrons by a heating process is known as *thermionic emission* (from the word *thermal,* referring to heat), and is the basic operating principle of a vacuum tube.

The famed American inventor Thomas A. Edison (1847-1931) observed this thermionic emission phenomenon during research on incandescent lamps. Edison was experimenting with methods for extending the life of the incandescent lamp filament. During such experiments, a metal plate was installed within the lamp envelope. The plate was placed near the filament, for the purpose of absorbing heat from the latter, in an effort to extend its useful life through temperature reduction. Edison connected a galvanometer in series with the positive terminal of the battery supplying electric energy to the filament. The galvanometer indicated that, in the circuit which had been formed, there was a current flow between the filament of the incandescent lamp and the metal plate. This is known as the *Edison effect,* and though its discoverer recorded the phenomenon (1883), he attached no particular significance to it and considered it as a mere laboratory curiosity.

Before the turn of the twentieth century the noted English electrical engineer J. A. Fleming (1847-1945) conducted extensive experiments with the so-called Edison effect, and in 1905 patented the *Fleming valve.* This valve, or tube, was the forerunner of the modern vacuum tube. The original Fleming valve contained a filament wire and metal plate within a glass envelope, with most of the air pumped out to form a partial vacuum. Such a simple tube type is now referred to as a diode.

THE DIODE

Since the development of the diode by Fleming, numerous elements have been added to the device to form the many varieties of tubes currently in use. However, the simple plate and filament arrangement originally patented by Fleming still finds extensive use in industrial electronics, radio, television receiver, transmitter, and other such applications. The simple diode is shown schematically in Fig. 11-1(A), where the circle represents the glass or metal envelope of the vacuum tube. The plate and the lead extending from it are usually drawn at the top of the circle, as shown, while the filament which is heated from an electric source is at the lower part. Such a tube can also be illustrated schematically as shown at (B), where the plate is a simple horizontal line.

The element within a vacuum tube which is the source of electrons is known as the *cathode.* The element within the tube which has a positive charge placed on it, and which attracts and receives the electrons emitted by the cathode is known as the *anode.* Thus, the filament at Fig. 11-1(A) is also the cathode, while the plate is the anode. Vacuum tubes are also designed in which the filament itself is not utilized for the cathode, but

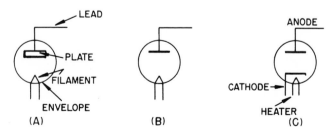

Fig. 11-1. Diode vacuum-tube symbols.

acts only as a heater. A separate cathode element is employed in such tubes, and the heater filament is placed sufficiently close to the cathode so that the heater will raise the temperature of the cathode to the point where it will emit electrons. This type of tube is shown at (C) of Fig. 11-1 and is known as an *indirectly-heated* tube, as opposed to the *directly-heated* tube shown at (A) of Fig. 11-1. Both these types are diodes, since only one cathode and one anode are employed. Thus, the term *diode,* used to represent a two-element tube, refers to the cathode and anode elements, regardless of whether a directly-heated or indirectly-heated type is employed.

Cathodes can be made of either tungsten or thoriated tungsten. Other cathodes are oxide-coated, and still others belong to the cylindrical type of cathodes employed in cathode ray tubes, which have a deposit of barium oxide capable of producing a large amount of free electrons.

The tungsten-type cathodes are primarily employed in heavy duty industrial electronic equipment, in transmitting for radio and television, and in other application where tube filaments must emit a considerable amount of electrons and, thus, must be brought to a very high temperature. Tungsten filaments are operated at approximately 2,500 degrees Kelvin. (Kelvin measurements can be converted to centigrade degrees by adding 273 to the Kelvin designation.) Such temperatures range above 4,000 degrees Fahrenheit.

Thoriated tungsten cathodes are composed of pure tungsten to which has been added some thorium oxide. The addition of the thorium increases thermionic emission to a considerable degree over that of the pure tungsten filament types. Such a thoriated tungsten filament, while more efficient, is more subject to damage by overloading. Overloading will cause an evaporation of the thorium layer when the emission limits are exceeded, and, in consequence, the efficiency will decline. Thoriated tungsten filaments are operated at approximately 1,900 degrees Kelvin.

The oxide-coated filament is formed by coating the conductor with barium or strontium oxides. The conductor which forms the filament is usually a nickel-alloy wire. Oxide-coated filaments produce a high order of thermionic emission with temperatures much lower as compared with the other filament types. For temperatures as low as 1,150 degrees Kelvin, the oxide-coated filaments offer a high emission efficiency and, for that reason, are extensively used in applications where a high amount of filament power is not required. Thus, the oxide-coated type of emitters are employed in high-fidelity audio systems, in radio, frequency-modulation, and television receivers, and in other generally low-powered electronic applications.

The two types of cathodes, the directly heated and indirectly heated, are shown at (A) and (B) of Fig. 11-2. Figure 11-2(A) represents the directly-heated type, consisting of a wire filament to which the electric energy is applied at the two terminals at the bottom. The filament is shaped in the form of the inverted letter V (or on occasion, the inverted letter W), and is supported by one or two wire loops at the top. The indirectly-heated type consists of a spiral heater element and a cathode metal sleeve structure. The

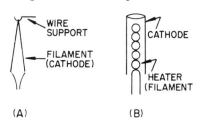

Fig. 11-2. Filament sections of vacuum tubes.

latter is coated with an emitting material such as the barium oxide previously mentioned. The cathode is insulated from the heater by an asbestos sleeve.

In its elementary form, the application of potentials to a diode vacuum tube is as shown in the simple circuit of Fig. 11-3. A battery, or other voltage source, is connected to the filament wires to heat them to incandescence and thus liberate electrons. The anode is connected to a resistor placed in series with another battery. The resistor is referred to as the load resistor (R_L), since the signal energy handled by the diode will appear across this resistor, as more fully described later.

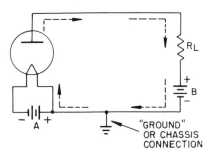

Fig. 11-3. Current flow in diode vacuum-tube circuit.

The cathode-filament battery or power source is known as the *A* battery or *A* voltage, while the anode potential is supplied from a *B* voltage source or a *B* battery. The polarity of the *B* battery must be such that the plate of the tube is *positive* with respect to its cathode. In order to achieve this result, the negative terminal of the *B* battery must be connected to the filament source, so that the electrons which leave the filament will have a complete return path to the plate, down through the load resistor and battery, and thence back to the filament, as shown by the dashed arrows in Fig. 11-3. The *ground* or *chassis* connection which is shown simply indicates that the chassis of the electronic device is employed for interconnecting the current path from the bottom of one battery to the filament and *A* battery connections.

In modern electronic references, the word *ground* indicates only a common chassis connection, where the chassis is used to interconnect a number of points which would have a common connecting wire.

For Fig. 11-3 the amount of *I* which flows depends on the applied *E* and the circuit resistance. With a low value of plate voltage, very little current flows from the filament to the plate and through the load resistor. As the plate voltage is increased, however, there is also an increase in current, up to the point where the condition known as *saturation* occurs.

Saturation is the highest value of plate current which will flow, regardless of an increase in plate voltage. At saturation, all the electrons which are emitted by the cathode are drawn to the plate. For plate voltages below the saturation point, plate current is correspondingly lower, which indicates that not all of the electrons emitted by the cathode are reaching the anode.

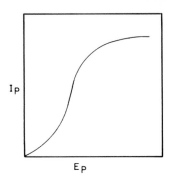

Ip

Ep

Fig. 11-4. Graph of plate current versus plate voltage in diode.

When electrons are emitted by a cathode structure, the loose and free electrons form a cloud around the cathode, as previously mentioned. This space-charge cloud forms a negative group of electrons which set up an electrostatic field. The latter tends to repel other electrons coming from the cathode structure. For low values of plate voltage, the anode does not have sufficient drawing power to attract all the electrons or to pull electrons away from the cathode and through the space charge. Only those electrons which initially have sufficient kinetic energy to overcome the space charge barrier reach the plate to contribute to current flow. With an increase in anode voltage, however, the electrostatic force exerted by the rising anode potential exerts a greater influence on the electrons and, thus, has a greater effect on overcoming the space charge.

With a fixed plate potential and an increase in cathode temperature, a curve for the plate voltage would be obtained similar to that shown in Fig. 11-4. The saturation is also reached for an increase in cathode temperature, and such *temperature saturation* is the limit at which the cathode is able to emit electrons.

An increase in plate potential above the point where current saturation occurs, will increase the *velocity* of the electrons and cause them to strike the plate with a greater impact, but the amount of electrons reaching the plate will not increase.

RECTIFICATION

The diode is useful as a *rectifier* and, in this application, it exhibits the ability of converting a-c to d-c. Thus, in such instances where it is necessary to obtain d-c when only an a-c source is available, the diode tube is employed. Specific applications include the conversion of the a-c power found in homes to the necessary d-c for radio and television receivers, as more fully detailed in Chapter 14 (Power Supplies).

Another application for the diode is *detection,* in which the diode is employed to obtain the audio or television signal components from the modulated carrier wave. This process is more fully detailed in Chapter 18 (Modulation and Demodulation).

Both the detection and rectification processes are essentially similar to their basic function. Both take advantage of the fact that current flow in a diode tube is only in one direction; i.e., from cathode to anode. If, for instance, the B battery shown in Fig. 11-3 were reversed, so that the battery would apply a negative potential to the plate, electron flow would cease, since the negative charge on the anode would repel the negative electrons which form the space charge around the heated cathode. Under such a condition, the transit of electrons from the cathode to the plate does not occur. This principle of current flowing in only one direction through a diode is utilized for detection and rectification, and a simple circuit of this type is shown in Fig. 11-5(A). When an a-c signal is applied to terminals T_1 and T_2, a negative alternation (such as the first shaded one shown) would place a negative potential at T_1 and a positive potential at T_2; hence, current would flow through the vacuum tube, as indicated by the solid arrows. This current flow would start at zero, just as the negative alternation of the a-c does, and would reach a peak value, then decline to zero again. This rising and falling current would also flow through the resistor, and cause corresponding voltages across the latter. This voltage change across the load resistor (R_L) would reproduce the first negative alternation, as shown.

The second input alternation, which is in the positive direction, would cause terminal T_1 to have a plus polarity and terminal T_2 to have a nega-

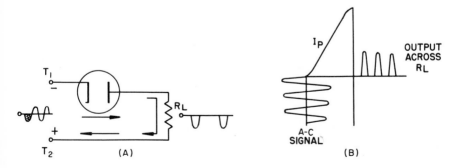

Fig. 11-5. Rectifying principle of diode.

tive polarity. Under this condition, the anode of the tube would be negative and, hence, would repel rather than attract electrons. In consequence, the tube would *not* conduct during the time interval of this second alternation across T_1 and T_2. During the *third* alternation, which is again of negative polarity like the first, the proper polarities are again applied across the diode tube, and conduction occurs again. Thus, a second negative alternation appears across the load resistor. Successive negative alternations will reappear across the load resistor in the form of *pulsating* d-c. This is graphically shown at Fig. 11-5(B), which illustrates the application of the a-c signal to the tube.

This graph represents the plate-current (I_p) rise along the vertical axis. The application of the a-c input signal is represented on the graph as extending to the point where the negative-going portion of the signal causes no current flow, while the positive-going portion of the signal will cause current flow proportionate to the emitting characteristics of the filament and the voltage of the input signal. The output across the load resistor (R_L) shows the current pulses which flow through this resistor. Such *current* variations through the load resistor will, of course, also create *voltage* variations across the load resistor, such voltage changes having waveshapes similar to the half cycles, or negative alternations. As can be seen, this is not pure d-c, but rather a pulsating d-c, which occurs only at intervals. Filter circuits, however, as described in the chapter on power supplies, are employed to smooth out the ripple and produce a d-c sufficiently free from variations for application to circuits requiring d-c.

THE TRIODE

One of the truly great advances in vacuum tubes occurred in 1906, when Dr. Lee DeForest, (1873-1961) the noted American inventor, introduced the *grid* for the vacuum tube. The grid consists of a third element added to the basic diode, and is placed between the cathode and anode. This grid, which is also known as a *control grid,* is represented schematically as shown in Fig. 11-6(A). On occasion, it may also be represented as shown at (B), where it resembles the symbol used for a resistor. The method of drawing the grid as shown in (A), however, is preferred, since it is a truer representation of the grid structure, and leads to less confusion for students. The grid is referred to as a control grid because it affects the amount of electrons which flow through the vacuum tube. The control grid is usually composed of fine mesh wires suspended across two stiff wire supports, as shown at (C). Within the grid wire are the cathode structure and the filament element, as shown at (D).

The remarkable characteristics of the control grid are due to the fact that a relatively small voltage placed on the control grid can influence and control a considerable amount of plate-current electron flow in the tube. If a negative voltage is applied to the grid, the potential will set up an electrostatic charge around the grid wires, which will repel electrons. Since the grid is placed close to the cathode structure, it has considerable influence on the amount of electrons which will flow from the cathode to the plate. If only a small negative voltage is applied to the grid, the grid charge is not sufficient to repel all the electrons leaving the cathode, and some plate current will flow. If a larger negative potential is applied to the grid structure, more electrons will be repelled. As the negative potential on the grid is increased, eventually the negative potential on the grid reaches such a value that it creates an electrostatic field of sufficient intensity to repel *all* electrons back to the cathode. Current flow within the tube then stops. This condition, where the grid potential has reached the point where it stops all current flow, is known as the tube *cutoff*. This progressive influence on decreasing current flow is shown in Fig. 11-7.

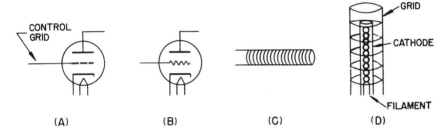

Fig. 11-6. Grid of triode.

In Fig. 11-7(A), a small negative potential is applied to the grid, and current flow, as read by a meter, may be 20 milliamperes (the amount depending on the type of tube and the value of the series load resistor). At (B), a higher negative potential is applied to the grid, and current flow has dropped to 10 milliamperes. A still higher negative potential, as in (C), repels all current and the meter now reads zero. This condition is illustrated graphically at Fig. 11-7(D), where the grid potential shown in (A) is designated by the vertical line marked "low bias." Here, a high plate current flows (20 milliamperes). For the grid voltage in (B), a correspondingly lower plate current flows, while the condition illustrated in (C) indicates no current flow along the *x* axis, which represents zero

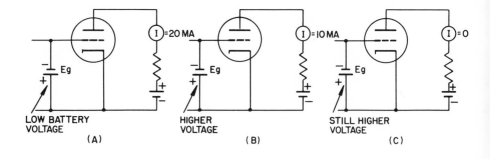

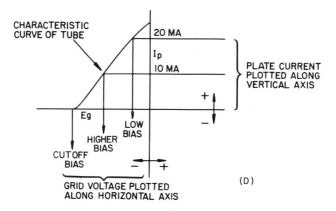

Fig. 11-7. Effects of bias on tube conduction.

on the graph. An additional increase of negative potential no longer affects current flow, because the grid voltage is beyond tube cutoff.

If the grid potential is reduced to zero, maximum current (established by the plate voltage and the value of the load resistor) flows through the tube. If the voltage at the grid is made positive instead of negative, no more current will flow, since tube saturation has been reached. Actually, plate current would decrease, for a plus voltage on the control grid would cause the latter to have an electrostatic field of such a polarity that it would attract rather than repel electrons. Under such a condition, the control grid draws electrons and, hence, grid current flows. Since such a current flow comes from the cathode structure, it would tend to decrease the saturation current level of the anode circuit.

In normal circuits employed to amplify the relatively weak signals picked up by an antenna, or the weak electric signals produced by a microphone, a fixed negative potential is applied to the grid. This fixed potential is known as *grid bias*. The grid bias may be of a value between the cutoff point of the tube and zero, as shown in graph (A) of Fig. 11-8. The bias, since it is negative and repels some electrons, would lower the current flow below the saturation level and establish a fixed value of current which

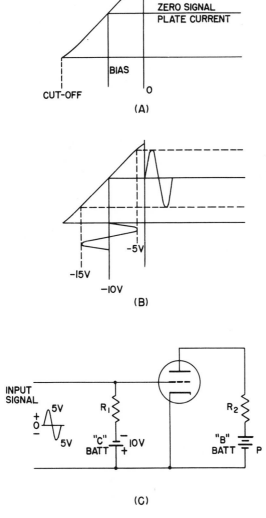

Fig. 11-8. Graph of grid-voltage change versus plate-current change.

is sometimes known as the *zero signal plate current*. When an a-c voltage is now applied to the grid circuit, such voltage will alternately add and subtract from this bias value, as shown at (B) of Fig. 11-8. The circuit representation is shown in (C), where resistor R_1 is a grid resistor placed in series with the battery or other voltage source for supplying the negative grid bias.

If a battery is used for grid bias, it is known as a *C* battery or, if another voltage source is used, it is referred to as the *C* bias potential. Resistor R_2 is the load resistor previously referred to. For convenience, the filament of the vacuum tube is not shown, since its function is only to heat the cathode and, hence, has no bearing on the signal handling characteristics of the circuit. The filament symbols are often omitted from commercial schematics of electronic devices, in such instances where the filament wiring is conventional and the circuit hook-up would be obvious to the trained technician.

The a-c voltage is representative of a signal applied to the circuit, and such a signal is impressed across the grid and cathode terminals, as shown in Fig. 11-8. The first alternation of the incoming signal, shown at Fig. 11-8(B) and (C), is of positive polarity and, therefore, decreases the bias and causes an increase in the current through the tube. If, for instance, the bias is a negative 10 volts, the positive polarity of a 5-volt a-c signal would oppose 5 volts of the negative *C* polarity, and leave only a negative 5 volts at the grid of the tube during the peak of the positive alternation. Hence, the plate current within the tube would rise and reach a peak, as shown at (B). When the input signal swings in the opposite direction to reach a negative 5 volts, this negative voltage adds to the existing negative 10 volts of bias to produce a total bias of minus 15 volts. The greater electrostatic charge now at the grid will repel more electrons, so that the plate current drops to a low value, as shown at (B). Since the plate-current change may be several hundred milliamperes or more for a small change in grid voltage, a much higher signal power and voltage develop in the plate circuit than is represented by the relatively low power, low voltage grid input signal. This control of a large amount of output power by a relatively small amount of input signal voltage is known as *amplification*. (For simplicity in basic analysis, Fig. 11-8(C) does not show coupling or bypass capacitors. The latter are, however, essential to proper signal amplification and are covered in detail in Chapter 15.)

Besides having the property of amplifying audio- and radio-frequency signals, vacuum tubes can also be used to generate fundamental radio- and audio-frequency signals in circuits known as *oscillators*. Oscillators, amplifiers, and other circuits employing vacuum tubes (as well as transistors) are more fully discussed in succeeding chapters.

CHARACTERISTICS OF A TRIODE

Information regarding the application of triode tubes, as well as the characteristics of such tubes under various voltage applications and signal intensities, can be obtained from graphs which indicate one set of conditions, when two other conditions are established. That is to say, if a certain bias and plate voltage are applied to the tube, a definite amount of current will flow. If the *grid voltage* were held *constant,* and the plate voltage were changed successively, different values of plate current would result.

Another procedure is to hold the *plate voltage constant,* while the bias on the control grid is varied. Here again, a different value of plate current would be obtained for each change of control grid bias value. Thus, sets of *characteristic curves* can be graphed, which give a visual indication of the relationship existing between grid voltage, plate voltage, and the resultant plate current. The circuit for doing this consists of the usual *C* and *B* voltage supplies, across which are placed variable resistors (potentiometers), so that the grid voltage and the plate voltage can be altered. Voltmeters and milliammeters to read voltage and current, respectively, are included in the circuit.

One set of curves which can be obtained is shown in Fig. 11-9, which gives the plate current values for various grid bias voltages and plate voltages. Another set of curves, known as the plate current-grid voltage

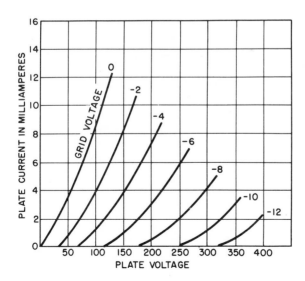

Fig. 11-9. Plate voltage-plate current curves.

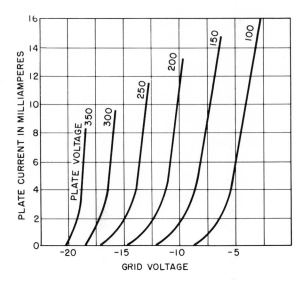

Fig. 11-10. Plate current-grid voltage curves.

curves, is shown in Fig. 11-10. This indicates the plate current values for changes of grid voltage and different values of plate voltage. The plate current-plate voltage curves are obtained by maintaining a fixed-bias value and taking the current reading while changing plate voltages. When a set of points has been established and a line drawn through these points, the various current changes for one value of fixed bias will be obtained, to indicate the effect of plate voltage changes. The plate current-grid voltage curves are obtained by keeping the plate voltage constant and changing the grid voltage to obtain various values of plate current. This procedure establishes one plate-voltage curve. The plate voltage is then changed to a new value and held at this value, while the grid bias is again varied to obtain new plate-current readings. The manner in which such curves are utilized is indicated in the discussions which follow.

AMPLIFICATION FACTOR

The *amplification factor* of a tube indicates the ratio of a plate voltage change to a grid voltage change, with the plate current held constant. This relationship may be set down as follows:

$$\mu = \frac{dE_{\text{p}}}{dE_{\text{g}}} \bigg| I_{\text{p}} \text{ constant} \qquad (11\text{-}1)$$

Here, mu (μ) is the amplification factor of a tube, and the small letter

d indicates a change [as an alternative the Greek letter delta (Δ) is often employed]. Thus, the amplification factor is an indication of the tube's ability to amplify an *a-c signal*. Hence, it represents a *dynamic* characteristic, rather than a *static* characteristic, as is the case for the plate voltage-plate current and plate current-grid voltage curves. As can be seen from the formula just given, if a small voltage change on the grid produces a correspondingly large plate-voltage change, the amplification of the tube is high. The formula indicates that the plate current is held constant, but this refers to the d-c. During the actual amplification process, the small change of grid voltage, which produces a large change of plate voltage, would also produce a change of plate current from the value established by the d-c power supply.

The amplification factor of a tube depends on the tube design, and consists of such factors as element spacing and closeness of the grid to the cathode, as well as closeness of the mesh of the grid structure. When a smaller change of plate voltage occurs for a given grid voltage change, a lower amplification factor is indicated. Thus, the ability of a tube to amplify a signal is referred to as the amplification factor of the tube.

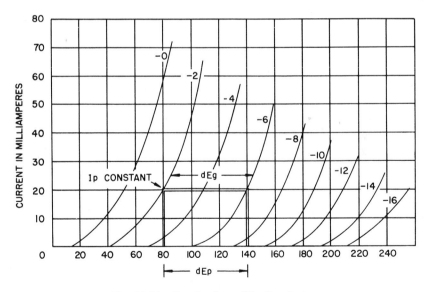

Fig. 11-11. Graph of amplification factor.

The amplification factor of a tube can be ascertained from the static characteristic curves of the tube. A typical example can be provided from an inspection of Fig. 11-11. Since the amplification factor of a tube is found by dividing a change in plate voltage (with constant current) by a grid-voltage change, these variables can be obtained from the graph of Fig. 11-11. Assume that the plate-voltage change is that which is indicated between the two double vertical lines shown, 80 volts and 140 volts. This would give a change of 60 volts. Using the 20-milliampere horizontal line as the constant current reference, the bias voltages between the plate voltage changes are ascertained. As shown in Fig. 11-11, the two bias points are 2 volts and 6 volts, giving a 4-volt change. The amplification factor, when the voltage *changes* are substituted in the formula, is 15, as shown below:

$$\mu = \frac{140 - 80}{6 - 2} = \frac{60}{4} = 15$$

Another tube characteristic is the *plate resistance* (r_p). This indicates the opposition to the a-c signal current flow between the cathode and anode of a tube. The plate resistance is not a measurement of the plate voltage divided by the plate current in the absence of a signal, but rather the opposition encountered for a *change* of plate voltage and a *change* of plate current. It is the ratio of a plate-voltage change to a plate-current change, with the grid voltage held constant. The formula is expressed as follows:

$$r_p = \frac{dE_p}{dI_p} \bigg| E_g \text{ constant} \qquad (11\text{-}2)$$

Thus, the plate resistance relates to the dynamic resistance characteristics of a tube and, for this reason, it is sometimes known as the *a-c plate resistance* or *dynamic plate resistance*. The plate resistance solved by the formula given above produces an answer in ohms.

As an example, consider again the graph of Fig. 11-11. To hold E_g constant, *one* bias line is chosen. Assume the bias line -4 volts is used. A plate voltage change is then selected, and could be from 100 volts to 130 volts. This represents a 30-volt change. For the 100-volt point on the -4 bias line, the current is approximately 15 milliamperes, and for the 130-volt point the current is approximately 45 milliamperes (a current change of 30 milliamperes, or 0.030 amperes). Setting these changes down gives

$$r_p = \frac{30}{0.030} = 1,000 \text{ ohms}$$

Another characteristic of a vacuum tube is the ratio of a plate-current change to a grid-voltage change, with the plate voltage held constant. This is known as the *transconductance* (g_m) of a tube, and is expressed mathematically as

$$g_m = \frac{dI_p}{dE_g} \bigg| \qquad (11\text{-}3)$$

The transconductance is an approximate figure of merit for the tube, and indicates the amount of signal current change which is produced for a given plate voltage change. The transconductance is also referred to on occasion as the *mutual conductance* of a tube, and is a reciprocal function of the plate resistance. The formula solves for the unit quantity expressed in mhos. (It will be noted that a mho is the word *ohm* spelled backwards.)

Using Fig. 11-11 again, an example of finding the transconductance is provided by choosing a constant plate voltage, such as 120. A current change can then be chosen, as from 5 milliamperes to 32 milliamperes, because these current values occur exactly where the −6 and −4 bias lines intercept the 120-volt vertical line. Thus, the transconductance is

$$g_m = \frac{0.027}{2} = 0.0135 \text{ mho (or 13,500 micromhos)}$$

The relationships between plate resistance, transconductance, and amplification factor are

$$g_m = \frac{\mu}{r_p} \qquad \mu = g_m r_p \qquad (11\text{-}4)$$

In triode tubes, the plate resistance may vary from a low value of a few hundred ohms to several thousand ohms. The transconductance is usually designated in micromho values, and may be equal to several thousand micromhos for the average triode tube. The amplification factor for triode tubes usually does not exceed 100, and in most instances ranges between 5 and 50.

Generally, in triode tubes where only the grid arrangement is altered to change the amplification factor of a tube, the plate resistance is related to the amplification factor. If the grid structure has a coarser mesh, it will have less influence on the electron flow and, hence, the amplification factor will be lowered. In such a tube, the plate resistance is also at a lower value than would be the case if the grid structure were finer. A more closely-meshed grid structure enables the grid to have a greater influence on the electron flow, so that the amplification factor and the plate resistance are increased.

In Fig. 11-12(A), a simplified form of signal-voltage triode amplifier stage is shown. The input signal is applied across the grid and cathode circuit. As previously stated, the input signal will alternately increase and decrease the negative grid bias. Such an a-c signal can consist of electrically equivalent audio voltages, or other signal energy which must be amplified. The *plus* alternation of the signal decreases bias and, hence, current flow *increases*. Since current flow through the tube is in the direction shown by the arrows, the voltage drop across the load resistor will have a minus polarity at the anode side of the resistor. Therefore, a negative voltage drop exists across the load resistor. The increase in plate-current flow through the anode circuit (because of the plus alternation on the grid) will also increase the voltage drop across the load resistor. Since this is a *negative-going* voltage drop, the *increase* in potential would have to be represented as a *decrease* in the negative-polarity direction, as shown in Fig. 11-12(B).

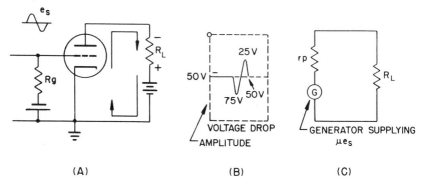

(A)   (B)   (C)

Fig. 11-12. Amplification process.

In Fig. 11-12, it is assumed that the voltage drop caused by the power supply across the load resistance is 50 volts. An increase in plate current may cause a 75-volt negative signal to develop across the load resistor, as shown in (B). When the incoming grid signal is at the midpoint between two alternations, the grid signal voltage at that instant is zero and, in consequence, the bias on the tube is not altered from its original fixed value. Thus, the plate current returns to its normal value, and the voltage drop across the load resistor also returns to its normal 50-volt value. During a negative signal alternation at the grid of the tube, less current flows, because the bias has been increased. Less current flow through the load resistor would decrease the negative voltage drop to a 25-volt value. When the input signal negative alternation again reaches zero, the normal grid bias brings the voltage drop across the load resistor back to 50 volts, as shown in (B). Thus, an a-c type of signal is reproduced in the plate circuit, though it is not a true a-c signal, since it still has a d-c component. Because, however, the signal varies above and below a middle point reference line, this signal has a-c characteristics and can be converted to a pure a-c signal by coupling it to a next stage, via either a coupling capacitor or a transformer. (Only the a-c signal component will be transferred, since d-c does not go through either a capacitor or a transformer.)

The signal input (e_s) shown in (A) may have an amplitude of only a fraction of a volt, yet could cause the generation of a 25-volt signal, as shown in (B). (Actually, this is a 50-volt signal, when considered from the peak of one alternation to the peak of the next. Insofar as the a-c component goes, however, the minus 50-volt zero-signal reference line is considered as zero. Thus, as in all a-c voltage discussions, the a-c signal has a peak value measured from zero to one alternation peak, or an *effective* value of 0.707 times the peak voltage.)

For the reasons outlined above, there is a 180-degree phase difference between the input signal and the output signal of this single-stage amplifier. Thus, the amplified signal (μ_{es}) is 180 degrees out of phase with the grid input signal. This factor is of considerable importance in many electronic circuits where the relative polarity of a signal must be ascertained. This is particularly true of video detectors and amplifiers in television receivers.

The circuit at (A) can be redrawn in a more basic form, to show the electric characteristics, as at Fig. 11-12(C). Here, the cathode-anode sections of the tube are considered as a generator, since in combination they generate an amplified version of the type of signal applied to the grid input. Because the plate and cathode circuits are instrumental in establishing a voltage drop across the load resistor, a representation of the tube as a generator for supplying the amplified signal energy is in order. Since all tubes have some internal plate resistance, the plate resistance of the tube shown at (C) has been designated as a series resistor, with the generator supplying the amplified signal energy output. Obviously, current flow through the tube will develop ·a voltage drop across the plate resistance, as well as the load resistance. The changing current, representative of the a-c signal, will therefore cause an a-c signal voltage drop across r_p and R_L. Thus, the full amplification factor at which a tube is rated cannot be realized across R_L, since part of the signal voltage will develop across the internal resistance. If the load resistor has the same value as the plate resistor, the maximum amount of *power* will be transferred, but the *signal voltage* obtained across the load resistor will not be at a maximum. As the value of the load resistor is increased over the value of the plate resistance, a proportionately greater voltage will be developed across the load resistor. In general practice (as more fully detailed later), the load resistor is never made more than three times the internal plate resistance. Such being the case, no more than approximately 75 per cent of the rated amplification factor of the tube is realized.

TETRODES

The tetrode tube has four signal-active elements, as compared with three for the triode. In the tetrode, an additional grid is added, as shown in Fig. 11-13. This additional grid is placed between the anode and the control grid, and is known as a *screen grid*. The screen grid is usually placed at *signal ground* by use of a bypass capacitor. Thus, the screen grid acts as an isolation factor between the anode (output) circuit of the amplifier and the input (grid) circuit.

The desirability for isolation comes about because of the existence of tube capacities. Such interelectrode capacities in a triode occur between the cathode and grid, between the grid and the plate, and between the plate and the cathode. Since these capacities have a measurable reactance, signal voltage drops occur across such reactances and, thus, some of the amplified signal energy in the anode circuit is coupled to the input circuit, with the consequence that undesirable effects are created. The screen grid, however, isolates the output circuit from the input circuit by establishing an electrostatic shield between them.

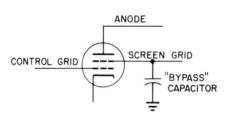

Fig. 11-13. Tetrode tube.

The screen grid is operated at a plus d-c potential and, hence, is also instrumental in accelerating the electron flow from cathode to plate. Since the screen grid acts as an electrostatic shield between the anode and the grid (as well as between the anode and the cathode), the electron emission from the cathode is influenced only to a very slight degree by changes of plate voltage. Thus, the screen grid element of the tube establishes a condition where the electron emission is influenced almost entirely by the control-grid and screen-grid voltages. Since the ratio of plate-voltage change with respect to plate-current change is now increased, the plate resistance of a tetrode is much higher than for a triode.

The amplification factor for a tetrode is also much higher, since the ratio of a larger plate voltage to the grid voltage change is greater. The positive screen grid diverts some of the electrons which would normally flow to the plate. These diverted electrons flow through the screen circuit and become the screen-grid current. Because some of the electrons which would normally flow to the plate are diverted, the transconductance is usually lower in a tetrode than in a triode.

If electrons strike a metal object with a high velocity, the impact of the arriving electrons will knock off other electrons from the metal plate. This condition is known as *secondary emission*. (The *primary* emission is the source of electrons from the cathode. The release of additional electrons because of the impact of the original electrons is a secondary emission process.) X-rays can be generated by the secondary emission process, because they are formed by having a high velocity electron beam strike a metallic object; the electrons which are deflected from the plate form the high-frequency X-rays. In ordinary vacuum tubes, the velocity of the electrons is not sufficiently high to produce measurable amounts of X-rays. In television picture tubes, however, X-rays are produced when anode voltages higher than about 15,000 volts are used.

Secondary emission characteristics are present in a tetrode when the screen grid potential is higher than the plate potential. The higher *screen grid* potential increases the velocity of the electron stream, and the lower *plate voltage* does not offer sufficient attraction to bring back the electrons which are knocked off. In consequence, such electrons which are knocked off the plate are attracted to the more highly positive screen grid. If the screen grid voltage is held constant, and the plate voltage is gradually increased, the electrons reach a higher velocity and the screen grid current increases, because of the absorption of secondary emission electrons. This characteristic is shown in Fig. 11-14, where the initial rise of current is indicated for low plate voltage. The current can rise gradually, because the velocity of the electrons arriving at the plate is not great enough to dislodge secondary electrons. Once the plate voltage has reached a value equal to or higher than the screen grid potential, the amount of secondary emission electrons is decreased at a rapid rate. In Fig. 11-14, the point where the current line levels out is where the plate voltage is sufficiently higher than the screen grid voltage and, hence, attracts the secondary electrons knocked off by the electron stream. This attraction on the secondary-emission electrons occurs because the plate now exerts a much greater attractive force than the screen grid. Hence, all secondary emission electrons which are dislodged are immediately returned to the anode of the tetrode tube.

The tetrode tube is still used in some electronic circuit applications, though this tube has been generally superseded by the five-element *pentode* type described next.

THE PENTODE

To minimize the effects of undesirable secondary emission from the plate, such as is encountered in tetrode tubes, an additional grid is added in the pentode tube. This additional grid lies between the screen grid and the anode of the tube, as shown in Fig. 11-15. The additional grid is known as the *suppressor grid,* and is in the same form as the screen grid and the control grid, i.e., it is a spirally-wound wire mesh affair.

The suppressor grid is more coarse in structure than either the screen grid or the control grid. This coarse structure minimizes the influence of the suppressor grid on the primary electron flow. The suppressor grid, however, is usually connected to the cathode. In some pentodes, the suppressor grid is connected to the cathode within the tube, while in other pentode types the suppressor grid terminal is brought out of the tube so that it can be connected externally to the cathode or to ground, as shown in Fig. 11-15(A) and (B).

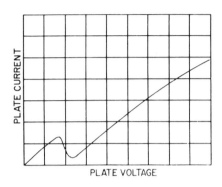

Fig. 11-14. Tetrode characteristics.

When the suppressor grid is thus placed at signal-ground potential, it has a negative polarity with respect to the anode. Hence, when electrons strike the anode with sufficient velocity to dislodge secondary-emission electrons, the latter will be driven back to the anode, because of the repelling force of the electrostatic charges established by the negative potential on the suppressor grid (like poles repel). Thus, the suppressor grid will effectively repel secondary-emission electrons and prevent their reaching the screen grid, even though the screen potential may be somewhat higher than the anode potential.

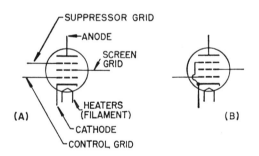

Fig. 11-15. Pentode vacuum-tube symbols.

The pentode tube has a higher plate resistance than triodes and tetrodes, and the amplification factor as well as the transconductance is also higher than for triodes and tetrodes.

The characteristic curves for pentodes differ from those for triodes and tetrodes, as shown in Fig. 11-16. For the plate current-plate voltage curves, there is a sharp rise of plate current during an increase in plate voltage from zero to approximately 20 volts. After that, however, a plate voltage increase would cause little change in the plate current. During low plate voltages, the anode does not have sufficient attraction for the

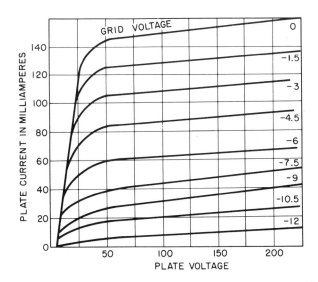

Fig. 11-16. Pentode-tube characteristic curves.

electrons to overcome the negative electrostatic barrier established by the cathode-connected suppressor grid. At such low anode voltages, a suppressor grid becomes a repelling factor and, thus, the screen grid, which is the first positive potential encountered by the electrons, will attract the electrons, so that greater screen grid current will flow, but anode current will be low. As the anode voltage is raised, however, it will overcome the barrier established by the suppressor grid, and the increased velocity of the electrons, established by virtue of the plus screen grid, assures a virtually constant current with only a slight rise for increasing voltage. For a change of control grid signal voltage, however, a considerable change is established with respect to voltage amplification and,

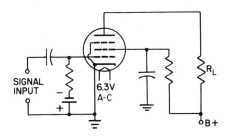

Fig. 11-17. Pentode amplifier with fixed battery bias.

hence, the amplification factor (mu) of the tube is considerably higher.

A typical amplifier circuit for the pentode tube is shown in Fig. 11-17. The screen grid contains the usual screen voltage-dropping resistor and bypass capacitor, and the suppressor grid can be grounded directly to the chassis or to the cathode. As with the tetrode, the screen grid is placed at *signal ground,* to establish an electrostatic shield between the control grid input circuit and the anode output circuit of the amplifier. The signal grounding of the screen grid also prevents signal voltage variations across the screen voltage-dropping resistor. If signal voltage variations were permitted across the screen-dropping resistor, the latter would share the functions of the load resistor. When the latter occurs, gain declines because in an ordinary pentode tube, there is a fixed value of transconductance. This means that, for a given grid input signal voltage change, there is a corresponding plate signal current change. Because the current flow in a tetrode or pentode tube flows to the screen grid of the tube as well as to the anode, it is evident that, if the signal current changes were also permitted to enter the screen-grid circuit, there would be a division of *signal current* within the tube, just as current divides in a parallel resistive circuit. Since the transconductance of the tube establishes a fixed value of such signal current, a division of this current between the screen resistor and plate load resistor would mean that a maximum amount of signal current no longer flows through the load resistor, because the screen resistor is sharing some of this signal current. Because the output signal is taken from across the load resistor only, and not from the combination load resistor and screen resistor, any reduction in the signal current through the load resistor would alter the amplification of the tube.

Pentode vacuum tubes can be employed in amplifier circuits for producing either signal voltage amplification or power amplification. In either application, the pentode has a high degree of efficiency, and can be employed for either audio or R-F signal voltages. The disadvantage of the pentode, as compared to the triode, is that the pentode has a higher harmonic distortion than the triode, as more fully discussed later.

VARIABLE-MU OR REMOTE CUTOFF TUBES

There are two basic types of pentode tubes: the sharp cutoff and the remote cutoff. The sharp cutoff tube is one in which an increase in the negative bias potential soon causes the grid to become so negative that it repels all electrons from the cathode, and none reach the anode. Since the amplification factor of such a tube is fairly constant for changes of grid bias, the sharp cutoff tube is also known as the *constant-mu* tube.

There are occasions when it is desirable to have a tube which does not have a sharp cutoff characteristic. When such is the case, a tube known as the *variable-mu* tube is utilized. The variable-mu tube has a specially constructed control grid structure. The pitch of the grid wires is constructed differently from an ordinary grid: the grid wires are given greater spacing around the midpoint than at the ends. This is shown in Fig. 11-18(A). Such a grid structure still permits varying the current flow by changing grid bias. As the grid bias is increased, less current flows, just as with an ordinary grid, except that at high negative potentials the grid is unable to cause a complete cessation of current flow, because of the wide spacing of the grid wires. The wide spacing still permits electrons to go through the grid structure and reach the anode, at negative grid potentials which normally would cause tube cutoff. This is in contrast to the sharp cutoff tube, where the spirally wound control-grid wires are spaced equally and much closer together. In the latter type of grid wire, the negative grid potential has a greater influence on the electrons emanating from the cathode, and an increase of negative potential finally results in complete current cutoff, as previously mentioned. With the variable-mu tube, however, the characteristics are as shown in Fig. 11-18(B). Here, low values of bias have a much greater effect on current flow than higher values of bias. As the bias is increased, it has less effect on current flow,

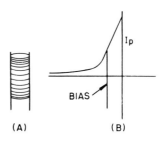

Fig. 11-18. Remote cutoff grid and characteristics.

as can be seen from the gradual incline of the characteristic curve of the tube. In such a tube, the amplification factor varies with each change in grid bias voltage. Hence, the designation *variable-mu* or *remote cutoff tube*. The tube is also known as a *super-control tube*.

The variable-mu tube is used extensively in radio, FM, and television receivers where special measures are taken to vary the bias of the tube for different levels of signals which arrive at the receiver. Such bias changes are useful, since they prevent overloading from strong stations, and also increase the amplification factor of the tube for weak stations. In radio receivers, the process is known as *automatic volume control;* in television receivers, the picture contrast is also controlled by variable-mu tubes, and here the circuit is known as *automatic gain control*. The abbreviation for automatic volume control is avc, and for automatic gain control agc. These two systems are discussed more fully in subsequent chapters.

BEAM-POWER TUBES

Pentodes, like triodes and tetrodes, are designed for use as either signal voltage amplifiers or signal power amplifiers. An improvement over the pentode power amplifier is a tube known as the *beam-power tube*. This tube type has a special internal construction which reduces the harmonic distortion below that generated in pentodes and tetrodes. (Harmonic distortion is discussed more fully in Chapter 15.) The beam-power tube also permits greater power handling with higher transconductance. This tube, however, has an amplification factor which is lower than the pentode-type tubes, though higher than triodes, since most of the latter do not have an amplification factor in excess of 100. The plate resistance of the beam power tube is also lower than that of the pentode types, but higher than in triodes.

The advantages in low distortion and power handling ability of the beam power tube are due to the special construction involved. This is shown at Fig. 11-19(A), where the internal electrodes are exposed. The

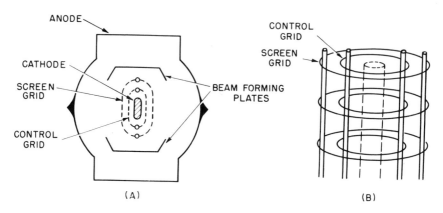

Fig. 11-19. Beam-power tube construction.

control-grid and screen-grid wires have the same pitch, and the individual wires of the control-grid are aligned with the individual screen-grid wires so that they are virtually parallel with each other, as shown in (B). This alignment of grid wires causes the electrons to form into layers as they leave the cathode structure. The cathode structure is flat and cylindrical, and the control-grid and screen-grid wires form an oval around the cathode. Thus, most of the electrons emanate from two sides of the cathode structure, since the latter has its greatest surface area on the flat sides.

Special beam-forming plates are placed at each side of the oval grid structures, as shown at Fig. 11-19(A), and these plates are internally connected to the cathode. Thus, the beam-forming plates have electrostatic fields which are at a negative potential with respect to the anode. These electrostatic fields repel electrons and form the electron stream into a beam. For this reason, the alignment of the control-grid and screen-grid wires causes the beam to leave the cathode in layers, and the beam-forming plates concentrate the stream into a narrow path. The result is that the electron beam is virtually focused to the plate in a concentrated beam, hence the name *beam-power tube*. Thus, the concentrated beam and its increased velocity result in greater power output, as well as in a high degree of efficiency and low harmonic distortion. The beam-forming plates, since they are also connected to the cathode, act as suppressor grids in the tetrode beam-power type tubes. For this reason, they reduce the effects of secondary emission which would otherwise result.

Because of their many advantages, beam-power tubes are extensively employed in final audio-power amplifier stages of transmitters and receivers, public address systems, tape recorders, industrial control circuits, automation systems, and in other electronic applications. Typical beam-power tubes include the 6V6, 6L6, 6CD6, 12BQ6, 17DQ6A, among many others.

MULTIELECTRODE TUBES

There are a number of tube types other than those previously discussed; they consist mostly of tubes with additional grids, or combinations of several different tube types contained in one envelope.

The multielement type tubes find primary applications in superhetero-

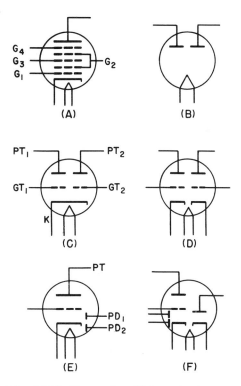

Fig. 11-20. Types of multielement tubes.

dyne receivers, as more fully discussed in subsequent chapters. In such receivers, the multielement tube consists of the mixer or pentagrid converter tube, as shown at Fig. 11-20(A). Such a tube contains five grids and is capable of mixing an R-F signal applied to one of its grids with a signal generated by an oscillator and applied to another of its grids. A dual-grid element (G2) shields the two input sources and isolates the input and output sections. Specific applications and function are described more fully later. Typical pentagrid converter tubes are the 6SA7, 6BA7, and 6BE6. The latter two are miniature types for use in television receivers, while the 6SA7 is usually employed in radio receivers.

When two or more tubes can be combined in a single envelope without interaction between the stages attached to such tubes, considerable space is saved in electronic devices and, of course, a smaller total number of tubes is required. Hence, numerous tube types are available which contain two or more diodes or triodes in a single-tube envelope. A typical one is shown in Fig. 11-20(B), which illustrates the dual diode used for full-wave rectification in power supplies of radio and television receivers, the application of which is more fully discussed later. A typical dual diode is the 5Y4G tube.

Another typical combination of two tubes in one envelope is shown in (C), where two triodes are contained in the same envelope. Here, a single cathode furnishes electrons for both plates of the dual triode. Letter and number symbols are used to identify the elements which are related to the individual tubes. For instance, the grid for triode No. 1 in Fig. 11-20(C) is marked GT1, and the associated anode for this grid is marked PT1. The second diode section grid is marked GT2, and its associated anode is marked PT2. A typical tube of this type is the 6N7, which is a high-mu twin-power triode.

Another twin-triode tube is shown in Fig. 11-20(D), but here a separate cathode is used for each tube, in contrast to the single cathode for the tube shown in (C). A typical tube of the type shown in (D) is the 6SN7, which is a medium-mu twin triode.

A tube which contains two diodes and a high-mu triode is shown in Fig. 11-20 (E). Here, the plate of the triode is marked PT, and the plate for diode No. 1 is marked PD1, while the plate for the second diode is marked PD2. A typical tube of this type is the 6SQ7, formerly used as a combined detector and audio amplifier in radios, or the 6AT6 miniature type, which has found some application in television receivers.

A tube which contains three diodes as well as a high-mu triode is the 6S8GT, shown in Fig. 11-20(F). This tube has often been used in combination FM and AM receivers, where it combines the detector for the FM signals with the detector for the AM signals, and also contains the first audio amplifier tube.

Some special tubes of this type have been named *Compactrons* because they form a *compact* assembly to save space. Compactrons include the 12AL11 which serves as a dual pentode audio-detector and output audio amplifier; the 33GY7 which is a pentode-diode; and the 17JZ8 triode-pentode, as well as others.

Other special-purpose tubes are also employed in electronics, including the "magic-eye" tube, in receivers, which helps the station tuning process by closing when the tuning is correct, or in test equipment. Other special-purpose tubes are the cathode-ray tubes used in television receivers and oscilloscopes. Both of the foregoing tubes use a phosphor coating which will glow when struck by an electron beam, as more fully detailed in Chapters 21 and 22.

PHYSICAL CHARACTERISTICS

Tubes are available in glass or metal envelopes, and typical types are illustrated in Fig. 11-21. The metal-envelope tubes are shown at the left,

Fig. 11-21. Typical metal and glass tubes.

and such types are self-shielding. The metal envelope is connected to one of the base pins, so that the latter can be grounded to the chassis, thus effectively using the metal envelope as a shield. Glass types are shown at the right and bottom of Fig. 11-21. The right two are larger-sized tubes used in radio and audio-amplifier applications, while the bottom glass type is the miniature tube especially suitable for high-frequency electronic applications. Some tubes have caps at the top, for either grid or plate connections, to avoid bringing these connections out from the base in applications which might cause hum, arcing, or other undesirable effects.

TYPICAL TUBE BASES

There are a number of tubes on the market, and since some are simple diodes, while others are complex multielement tubes or tubes containing diodes and triodes in one envelope, there are a variety of tube bases encountered in practical electronic applications. The tube base contains the prongs which are internally connected to the various tube elements, and the prongs fit into appropriate tube sockets. Since the socket and not the tube is wired to the circuit, the tube can be easily removed and replaced.

Tube manuals indicate the socket connections for a particular tube and give the particular tube prong numbers involved. The socket connections shown in tube manuals are the *bottom view,* and the numbering system starts at the left and goes in a clockwise direction.

Some tubes incorporate what is known as an *octal base,* which consists of eight equally-spaced tube pins, each pin being the same size as the other. The center of the tube base contains a base extension or extrusion, and this has a ribbed section which acts as a key, as shown in Fig. 11-22(A). Since this key is actually an extension of the tube base, it is

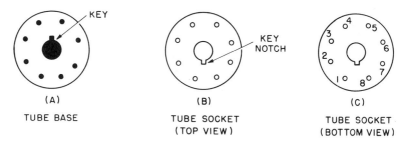

(A)	(B)	(C)
TUBE BASE	TUBE SOCKET (TOP VIEW)	TUBE SOCKET (BOTTOM VIEW)

Fig. 11-22. Octal socket keys and prong hole numbering.

composed of the same insulating material. The key, with its ribbed section, fits into a notch in the socket, shown in Fig. 11-22(B), and centers the tube exactly into the socket. Thus, the octal tube can be placed in its socket just by pressing the tube down and rotating it until the key fits into the notch. After this, the tube is pushed into place and all the tube base pins fit into the proper socket holes. Since all such octal type tubes do not employ eight elements, some of the tube pins are omitted, when not necessary. Pin No. 1 starts at the left of the key notch, as shown in Fig. 11-22(C). The socket holes are then numbered consecutively, regardless of whether or not some of the tube pins are missing. Typical tube sockets are shown in Fig. 11-23, with the octal-type socket shown at the left.

Fig. 11-23. Typical tube sockets.

Another type of the tube base (encountered less) is the *loctal* base. In such a tube, the pins extending from the base are smaller in diameter than in the octal types. The base itself is metal, and each pin protrudes through a small hole in the metal. Each pin is, of course, insulated from the metal base. The centering pin and key are again an extension of the base, but are of metal, in this case, and have a knob shape, as shown in Fig. 11-24. The socket for the loctal tube has a clamp arrangement in the centering hole, so that, when the tube is inserted into the socket, it is held rigidly in place and cannot become loose. Such a tube was specifically designed for applications in car radios or other mobile or portable electronic equipment, where vibration may cause the tube to work loose from its socket. Some loctal tubes were, however, also employed in home radios.

With the advent of frequency modulation, television, and vhf-uhf electronic devices, the larger tube types were replaced by miniature types, so as to reduce interelectrode capacity losses and conserve space. The miniature types have no separate tube base as such, and the tube elements protrude from the bottom of the glass envelope. A typical miniature tube of this type is shown at the bottom center of Fig. 11-21. The sockets

Fig. 11-24. Base of octal tube.

for such tubes are correspondingly small and, since the tubes do not have a centering pin, a space is provided between two of the tube elements, which serves as a guide for inserting the tube into the socket. (See the two types at the left of Fig. 11-23.) Thus, the tube can be inserted only when the pins are in the proper position, since the spacing of the holes in the socket does not permit inserting the tube except in the position where the guide space also exists in the tube pins. Some tubes have seven pins, such as the 12AL5 twin diode. Other miniature tubes have nine pins, such as the 12AT7, which is a high-mu twin triode. The sockets for these two tubes are not interchangeable, and for the 12AL5 tube a special seven-hole socket must be employed, while the 12AT7 tube requires a special nine-prong socket.

TUBE NUMBERING SYSTEM

The early tubes which were brought out in the years following 1920 were numbered consecutively; for this reason, it was virtually impossible to identify the tube type from the number alone, and reference had to be made to a tube manual to identify the characteristics of a particular tube such as a 27, a 45, or an 80 tube. (These obsolete tubes are no longer listed in present-day tube manuals.)

Modern tubes are numbered so that some identification is possible, though, of course, all the information pertaining to a particular tube cannot be obtained from an inspection of the number alone. The initial digit or digits indicate the voltage applied to the heater (filament) terminals. Thus, a 6L6 tube indicates that approximately 6 volts (actually 6.3 volts) can be applied to the filaments. A 12AT7, on the other hand, is a 12-volt (actually 12.6 volts) tube with respect to the filament potential.

In some of the battery-operated tubes for portable electronic use, the number one is used for tubes which operate at 1.25 volts. This group includes the 1AC5 power pentode tube, the 1AD5 sharp cutoff pentode tube and the 1C5 power pentode. The initial numeral two, such as in the

2A3 tube, indicates that the filament voltage should be 2.5 volts. Another such tube, the 3A8-GT, has a mid-tap filament, so that the tube may be used with either a 1.4- or a 2.8-volt d-c filament supply. A similar tapped filament arrangement is also employed with the tubes designed for a-c filament applications. One such tube is the 12AU7A, which can be used with an application of either 6.3 volts or 12.6 volts to the filament. This tube is shown in Fig. 11-25. If the heater connections Nos. 4 and 5 are tied together, the combination can be used in conjunction with the center tap (pin 9) for 6.3-volt application. If used for 12.6 volts, the latter voltage is applied to pins 4 and 5. Other such tubes which take either 6.3 or 12.6 volts are the 12AV7, 12AX7, etc.

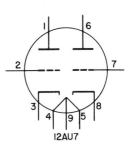

Fig. 11-25. Tube with tapped filament.

In most modern general-type tubes, one or two letters follow the initial number or numbers. Originally, these letters had specific significance, but the large number of tubes which are currently employed has required the use of so many single and double letters that it is difficult to assign a specific meaning to the particular letter employed. Consequently, reference should be made to the tube manual for an indication of whether the tube is a converter, an amplifier, or a rectifier.

The numeral which follows the letters sometimes represents the number of elements within the tube, and on other occasions indicates the useful elements or prongs employed. Consequently, not much information can be gained from the last number. Additional letters sometimes follow the last number, such as G or GT. The letter G following the tube symbol indicates "glass" and identifies the tube as having a standard-sized glass envelope. The letters GT indicate "glass-tiny," and show that a glass envelope is used having smaller dimensions than the G-type tube. Except for miniature types, modern tubes without the G or the GT following the last number are metal-envelope tubes.

From the foregoing, it is evident that the only correct tube numbering identifications are the first two numbers, which indicate the approximate heater or filament voltage, and the last two letters, which refer to the size of the glass envelope. Tubes are available which are designed for heater voltages of 25 volts, such as the 25L6 beam-power amplifier or the 25Z6 dual diode rectifier. There are also a series of tubes designed for 35-volt filaments, such as the 35A5 beam-power amplifier, or the 35W4 half-wave rectifier. Fifty-volt filament types include the 50A5 beam-power amplifier and the 50Y6-GT dual-diode rectifier. Some tubes have also been designed to take the full 115-volt a-c line source on their filaments. Such tubes include the 117Z3, which is a half-wave rectifier, the 117Z6-GT, which is a dual-diode rectifier, and the 117N7-GT, which is a combined diode rectifier and beam-power amplifier. The 117-volt filament-type tubes were popular in radios some years ago, while the 12-, 35-, and 50-volt filament tubes are still employed in some radios and television receivers. The reason for employing tubes with such high filament ratings is that such tubes can be placed in series in a proper combination, so that the total series string will accommodate the 115-volt line potential and, thus, can be fitted directly from the a-c power mains, without the necessity for employing an intervening stepdown transformer. A typical series filament string is shown in Fig. 11-26(A). The first three tubes are each designed for 12.6 volts

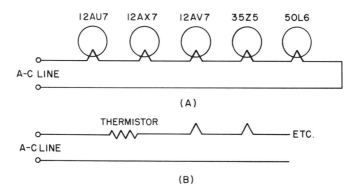

Fig. 11-26. Series filament strings.

and, hence, these three alone would take 37.8 volts. This is followed by a 35-volt tube, which brings the total voltage which these tubes can stand up to 72.8 volts. The final tube is a 50-volt filament type. The combination will operate on a line voltage of 115 volts and the tubes will not be endangered, even though the line voltage goes slightly above 120 volts.

A number of 6-volt tubes can also be placed in series with 35- or 50-volt filament tubes to form a filament circuit which can be applied directly across the 110-volt a-c line source. The only precaution which must be observed is the selection of tubes so that each tube draws the same amount of filament current as the others. Tubes rated in dissimilar filament currents cannot be employed without using shunting resistors across some of the tubes to equalize the current, since the differences in filament current required would alter the voltage drop across the tubes, so that the voltage on any particular tube might exceed that for which the tube is rated, resulting in tube failure.

When a number of 6- or 12-volt filament tubes are used in a series string, a series resistor is sometimes employed, if the individual voltage drops of the tubes do not come up to the a-c line voltage. Such a resistor is usually a negative temperature-coefficient resistor known as a *thermistor.* The latter precedes the series filament string, as shown in Fig. 11-26(B). The resistance of a thermistor decreases with an increase in temperature, and is high when the thermistor is cold. Thus, the thermistor holds down the filament current when the voltage is applied to the string, so as to minimize a voltage surge. (When tube filaments are cold, their resistance is low and, hence, an excessive amount of current may flow when the electronic device is first turned on.)

A number of electronic devices (including some television receivers) use series heater strings made up of tubes specially designed for this purpose. Such tubes permit series filament operation without the necessity for using shunt resistors across some of the tubes to equalize currents. Some series string tubes are designed for 600-milliampere filament current operation, while others have a rating of 450 milliamperes. Such tubes have identical warmup characteristics (approximately 10 seconds), so that surge voltage problems are reduced to a minimum. At the same time, the thermistor-type resistor is not needed and, if additional resistance must be placed in the series string to bring the total voltage drops up to the line voltage potential, ordinary resistors can be employed. Tubes of this type include the 3BZ6, 3AU6, 5T8, 10DE7, and others.

GAS-TYPE TUBES

In some industrial electronic applications, gas-filled tubes are used instead of the high-vacuum types. The gas employed is usually a vapor derived from mercury, neon, or argon. The characteristics of a gas-filled tube differ to a considerable extent from those of the high-vacuum type. With the gas-filled tube, the plate current increases from zero as the plate voltage rises from zero, in a fashion similar to that for the high-vacuum type. At a certain plate potential, however, (usually above 10 volts) the electrons have sufficient velocity so that, when they collide with the gas atoms, they will cause ionization. (Ionization is discussed in Chapter 1, under *Atom Bonds.*) The ionized gas neutralizes the space charge at the cathode, so that no barrier is present to limit current flow. Thus, as soon as ionization occurs, the plate-current flow reaches maximum.

The space charge is neutralized because the positive ions are attracted by the electrostatic fields of the negative cathode. Upon reaching the cathode region, the ions capture free electrons to replace those which had been lost during ionization. Thus, the space-charge electrons are constantly removed to reform the gas atoms with a consequent neutralization of the space charge.

Once ionization occurs in a gas-filled tube, the plate resistance is

Fig. 11-27. Symbol for gas-filled tube.

extremely low, because the space charge has been neutralized. Because of their characteristics, gas-filled tubes find extensive applications in commercial power supplies (as discussed in Chapter 14), where they act as highly efficient rectifiers capable of handling high power. Such diodes are not generally employed for receiver purposes, since the ionization process generates a high noise which must be filtered from the power supply. Also, unless precautions are taken, the danger of voltage breakdown and arcing is also greater for the hot-cathode gas diodes used for rectifiers.

For these reasons, high-vacuum-type rectifiers are preferred in radio and television receivers, since such rectifiers are less troublesome and do not require shielding or filtering to perform well in receivers. A typical gas-filled rectifier is shown in Fig. 11-27. The black dot within the tube circle of the symbol indicates that the tube is a gas-filled type.

Gas-filled tubes are also employed for voltage-regulation purposes, as more fully described in Chapter 14. The voltage-regulator type of gas-filled tube is of the cold-cathode type, in which ionization occurs because of the electrostatic charge built up between the cold cathode and the anode. After a certain grid potential is reached, ionization occurs and the tube conducts heavily. As with the high-vacuum diode rectifiers previously discussed, the current flow is only in one direction during tube conduction and, hence, gas diodes are suitable for rectification and voltage-regulating purposes.

THYRATRONS

Hot-cathode gas-type tubes are also available with a control electrode between the cathode and anode. The control electrode is similar to the control grid of an ordinary high-vacuum tube, but affects current flow differently. If a high negative voltage is applied to a control electrode of a gas-filled tube, and this voltage is gradually reduced, it will be found that plate-current flow starts suddenly, and immediately reaches a maximum value, once the control-electrode bias voltage is insufficient to hold the tube in a nonconducting state. Once current flow has started and the tube is ionized, the control electrode loses its control on current flow. Thus, during tube conduction, the grid bias can be increased far beyond the normal cutoff value without affecting the plate-current flow. The *plate voltage* must be *lowered* below the ionizing potential, before plate current will cease. When current flow stops, the control grid will again hold the tube in nonconduction, so long as the high negative bias voltage is maintained in the control electrode.

The reason for this conduction behavior, which differs so radically from that of the high-vacuum tube, is the presence of the positive ions which result when current starts to flow. These ions, which have a plus polarity, are attracted to the negative grid, since opposite poles attract. The positive ions surround the grid and shield its electrostatic fields. The shielding effect prevents the grid from repelling electrons and controlling current flow. As pointed out earlier, the positive ions also neutralize the space charge region at the cathode, so that the limitations normally imposed on current flow are removed.

The thyratron-type tube has internal elements as shown in Fig. 11-28(A). This tube is useful as a triggering device for electronic equipment.

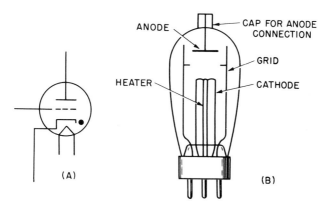

Fig. 11-28. Thyratron tube symbol and construction.

The large commercial thyratrons have a cylindrical control electrode, as shown in Fig. 11-28(B). Even with the large types employed in commercial applications, only a small grid potential is necessary to trigger the tube into sudden and high conduction. Some thyratrons use mercury vapor, whereas others use argon or hydrogen. With hydrogen a more rapid triggering action is obtained, and the sudden current rise within the tube is useful in the formation of square waves or sharp pulse spikes having an extremely rapid rise time. The usefulness of square waves is discussed more fully later. (Additional thyratron and other gas-tube types are discussed in Chapter 14.)

REVIEW QUESTIONS

1. (a) Is a tube having a filament, cathode, and anode a diode or a triode tube?

(b) Is a tube which has a filament, cathode, grid, and anode a triode or a tetrode?

2. Briefly explain what is meant by space charge.

3. Explain the purpose for the screen grid of a vacuum tube.

4. What is the purpose for the suppressor grid of a vacuum tube?

5. (a) What are the primary uses for a diode?
(b) What are the primary uses for the triode, tetrode, and pentode type tubes?

6. Briefly explain how information can be secured for plotting the type of graph shown in Fig. 11-9, which represents the characteristic curves of a typical vacuum tube.

7. Briefly explain the purpose for placing a negative d-c bias potential on the grid of a vacuum tube used for amplification of signals.

8. What methods are employed for forming the electron stream into a beam, in the beam-power amplifier tube? Explain briefly.

9. How does the *plate resistance* of a vacuum tube differ from d-c resistance?

10. What does the transconductance of a tube indicate? What is the unit value of the transconductance?

11. Briefly explain the differences between the control factors of the control grid in a vacuum tube and those of the control electrode in the thyratron type of gas-filled tube.

12. Explain why the amplification factor of a pentode is higher than that of a triode.

13. What is the difference between a variable-mu tube and a sharp cutoff type? Where is a variable-mu tube useful?

14. Briefly explain what is meant by *plate saturation*.

15. (a) What does a black dot in the schematic of a vacuum-tube signify?
(b) In a 6SQ7-GT, what does the first digit represent, and what is the significance of the final two letters?

16. (a) Briefly explain the difference between a loctal and an octal socket.
(b) What is meant by the *key*, in tubes of the loctal and octal types?

17. What are some of the applications of gas-filled tubes?

PRACTICAL PROBLEMS

1. In a design laboratory a 6W6GT tube was tested while connected to a triode (screen-grid connected to anode). With a bias of −15 volts, 100 milliamperes of plate current flowed with an anode voltage of 200. When

the grid-bias voltage was changed to -30 volts and the plate voltage raised to 310 volts, the same plate current flowed (100 milliamperes). What is the amplification factor of this tube?

2. The same tube as in Problem 1 was operated at -30-volts bias. At 200 volts on the anode, 10 milliamperes of plate current was read. At 300 volts on the anode, the plate current rose to 85 milliamperes. What was the plate resistance?

3. A 12AU7A medium-mu triode was analyzed for operation in an industrial control system. At 200 volts, the plate current was 5 milliamperes with a bias of -8 volts. When the bias was decreased to -4 volts, the plate current rose to 15 milliamperes. The plate voltage was held at a constant amplitude. What is the transconductance?

4. In the design of a vacuum tube it was found that a plate current of 45 milliamperes flowed when the plate voltage was 100 and the bias -5 volts. When the bias was changed to -10 volts, the plate voltage had to be raised to 200 to have the same 45-milliammeter plate-current flow. What was the amplification factor of this tube?

5. An amplifier tube for an audio system has the following characteristics: $I_p = 10$ milliamperes when $E_p = 90$ volts; $I_p = 2$ milliamperes when $E_p = 40$ volts. What is r_p?

6. What is the transconductance of a vacuum tube used in an electronic computer, if a change of two grid volts produces a change of plate current of 2 milliamperes?

7. In the vacuum tube graphed in Fig. 11-11, what is the plate resistance for a voltage change from 80 to 100 volts on the -2-volt bias line?

8. For the tube graphed in Fig. 11-9, calculate the transconductance for the following operating conditions:

$$E_p = 150 \text{ volts}; E_g = -4 \text{ volts}; \qquad I_p = 4 \text{ milliamperes}$$

9. What is the amplification factor of the tube graphed in Fig. 11-9 for the following operating conditions:

$$E_p = 150 \text{ volts}; E_g = -4 \text{ volts}; \qquad I_p = 4 \text{ milliamperes}$$

10. Tube No. 1 at 200 volts draws a plate current of 30 millamperes, at 2 volts of bias. At 6 volts of bias, the plate voltage must be raised to 600 volts to establish the same plate-current flow of 30 milliamperes. Tube No. 2 at 200 volts draws a plate current of 30 milliamperes at 3 volts of bias. At 6 volts of bias, however, the plate voltage must be increased to 350 volts to have the same 30 milliamperes of current flow. Which tube, No. 1 or No. 2, is a better amplifier?

12

SOLID-STATE
FUNDAMENTALS

INTRODUCTION

Solid-state diodes, triodes, and similar devices have circuit applications similar to vacuum and gas tubes, but differ radically in the manner in which they function. No cathodes, grids, or anodes are present, though comparable elements exist which perform the same tasks. The absence of a filament or heater eliminates the warmup time required in tubes, and contributes to economical operation. In addition, the solid-state units are considerably smaller than tubes with the same power-handling ratings. Because of their long life and other advantages, solid-state devices are extensively employed in numerous circuits which formerly utilized gas or vacuum tubes.

The design and function of solid-state diodes and transistors are related to their crystalline structure and atomic characteristics. Hence, the section on Atom Bonds in Chapter 1 should be reviewed, because the principles contained in this chapter are an extension of that material. The fundamental aspects of crystal diodes and transistors are covered in this chapter, and transistor circuitry is treated in Chapter 13.

THE COVALENT BOND

The covalent bonding characteristics found in hydrogen and atmospheric oxygen was discussed in Chapter 1. The covalent bond also occurs in germanium and silicon which are the building blocks for solid-state devices. Because of the crystal structures formed, the covalent bond found in carbon is closely related to the germanium and silicon bonds. In order to understand the particular binding characteristics which take place with any one of these three elements, note the outer ring valence electrons shown for each element in Fig. 12-1. In each of these elements, there are only four electrons in the outer ring.

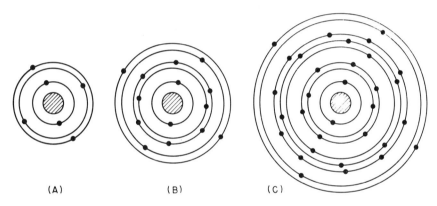

(A)   (B)   (C)

Fig. 12-1. Atoms of carbon, silicon, and germanium.

The silicon atom uses three primary rings, but only *two* subshells of the outer ring contain electrons. What would constitute the third subshell is an empty orbit. Hence, the first subshell of the outer primary shell group is completely filled with two electrons, but the second subshell requires four more electrons to fill it completely. When the various silicon atoms are brought together, there is a sharing of valence electrons by the atoms, and a crystal-lattice network is formed. The crystal is not in the cube arrangement as shown earlier in Chapter 1 for sodium chloride, but instead is of a tetrahedron arrangement as shown in Fig. 12-2. Note that the arrangement is in the form of a four-sided structure with atoms at each corner, plus an atom at the center of the structure. As shown, the central atom (indicated by the dotted outline) is surrounded by four other atoms. Each of the surrounding atoms shares one of its outer ring electrons with the central atom. Because of the crystal-lattice network, *each* atom within the structure is surrounded by four other atoms. This can be illustrated more clearly in two-dimensional forms as shown in Fig. 12-3. In this illustration only the outer ring electrons and the nucleus of

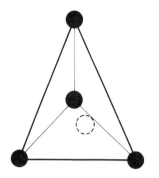

each atom are shown, for the sake of simplicity. A tight covalent bond is formed because of the sharing of valance electrons by the various atoms.

As can be seen from the illustration, the sharing of adjacent electrons by any particular atom means that each atom has eight electrons in the first two shells of the outer ring. This comes about because the electrons in the outer rings not only revolve around their own nucleus, but also revolve around the nuclei of adjacent atoms. The electrons are still rigidly bound to any particular nucleus around which they revolve, even though shared by adjacent atoms. Because of the filling up of the two outer subshells, the entire structure presents a highly stable state of an element with a considerable degree of hardness and rigidity. Such a structure does not lend itself to the carrying of electric energy by means of electric motion, because the outer ring electrons are not free but, instead, are rigidly bound in their orbital paths.

Fig. 12-2. Formation of crystal lattice.

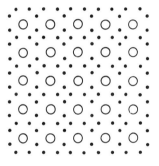

Fig. 12-3. Crystal-lattice network.

The same crystal-lattice network covalent binding described before occurs when either germanium atoms or carbon atoms are brought into close proximity. With carbon atoms, the covalent bonds produced represent the carbon crystal (diamond). Note, from Fig. 12-1, that carbon has four electrons in the second ring. Since this ring can accommodate only eight electrons (in both subshells), this means that a crystal-lattice network formed from carbon closes the entire outer shell. This condition of a completely filled outer shell forms an extremely stable and rigid bond, and this is the reason for the particular hardness and brittle characteristic of a diamond. With germanium and silicon, however, only two of the outer ring subshells are completely closed and, while this forms a stable bond and also a crystal, the fact that the outer shell is not completely filled means that the silicon and germanium bonds can be broken more easily than the carbon crystal, by the application of voltage, heat, or other energy.

For a clearer illustration of the foregoing, partial orbital shells of the three elements are shown in Fig. 12-4 and represent *valence-bound* atoms. Thus, the second primary ring of carbon is completely filled, so that the crystal carbon is extremely hard (diamond). For silicon, however, only the first two subshells of the third primary ring are filled. Although this still forms a fairly rigid bond, the fact that the third subshell is empty means a less rigid binding than occurs with carbon. With germanium, also, only two subshells of the outer ring are filled in a valence-bound atom, and again there is a less rigid bond than occurs for carbon.

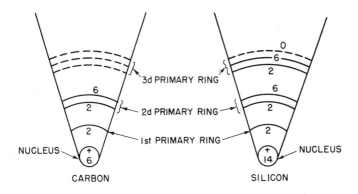

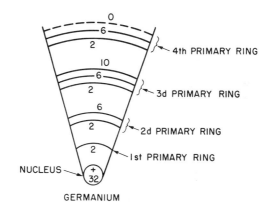

Fig. 12-4. Valence-bound atoms of carbon, silicon, and germanium crystals.

In Fig. 12-4, it will be noted that, if an effort were made to move an electron out of the outer subshell of the carbon atom, sufficient energy would have to be applied to break the valence bond and move the electron over a gap into the third primary ring. With silicon and germanium, however, only sufficient effort is necessary to bridge the space between a subshell, since the third subshell of the valence ring is empty.

Electrons nearest the nucleus are at low-energy levels, whereas those in the outer orbits are at higher energy levels. In a solid such as a crystal, the energy levels of individual atoms reform and create *bands of energy levels.* The upper bands of the germanium crystal are shown in Fig. 12-5, and consist of the valence-band energy level, the forbidden band, and the conduction energy level band. In the valence band, the electrons are tightly bound and, hence, are not free to carry current easily. The forbidden band is the gap between the conduction band and the valence band, and it is this forbidden band which must be crossed by electrons which are to be moved from the valence band to the conduction band. The latter is a band where the energy level of the electrons is sufficiently high to permit electron movement and current flow.

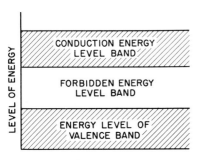

Fig. 12-5. Energy levels of an atom in a crystal-lattice network.

In an insulator, the forbidden band is so large that few electrons can be provided with sufficient energy to reach the conduction band. With the germanium or silicon crystal, however, the forbidden band is more narrow, and normal temperature ranges provide sufficient energy for the valence electrons to permit them to reach the conduction band. The number of electrons which will reach the conduction band depends on the width of the forbidden band, as well as on the amount of energy applied, either by temperature or electric pressure. (Light can also be a source of energy for electron movement, as described more fully for photoelectric devices.) Thus, these crystals are known as semiconductors. For ordinary conductors, such as copper, silver, etc., many free electrons are present at room temperatures, and the forbidden region is extremely narrow (or nonexistent), so that the valence band and the conduction band are virtually one.

CURRENT FLOW VERSUS HOLE FLOW

We have already learned that current flow in a conductor consists of an electron movement under the influence of energy pressure, such as electromotive force. This normal current flow can also occur in the case of the semiconductor, where the covalent bond has been broken and an electron of the atom moves into the conduction band. This factor of an electron leaving the valence band and moving into the conduction band creates a condition which is peculiar to transistors. This curious condition is the formation of *holes* which can, in fact, be considered as current carriers, just as electrons are carriers of current.

Figure 12-6 will help clarify the conception of holes in transistors. When

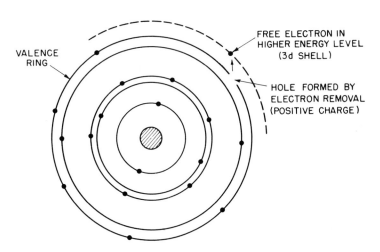

Fig. 12-6. Silicon crystal atom with energy applied to an electron.

an electron moves out of the valance band and into the conduction band, it leaves a vacancy in the atom, and the latter becomes a positive ion. Since the hole creates a positive area in the subshell from which the electron is removed, the hole can be considered as having a positive charge, just as the electron has a negative charge. The nature of the hole in the atom is such that it can sustain current flow by electron and hole movement from *one valence band to another,* without the electrons moving in the conduction band. Assume, for instance, that the free electron of the atom shown in Fig. 12-6 has moved on, leaving a positive ion. It is then quite possible for an electron from the valence band of an adjacent atom to break its bond and move into the hole in its neighboring atom. When this occurs, the atom which originally had the hole is now a *neutral* atom again, having regained the missing electron. The adjacent atom, however, now has a vacancy (hole), where the electron broke its bond and moved into the hole of the neighboring atom. Thus, even though electrons have moved along (current flow), the energy was confined to the valence bands because of the hole movement.

Figure 12-7 will aid in acquiring the concept of hole movement. Here, each numbered circle represents an electron which is going to break its covalent bond and move to a neighboring atom at the right. Note that, at (A), a hole already exists between electrons No. 5 and No. 6. As electron No. 5 moves to the right and into the hole of the adjacent atom, the

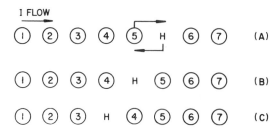

Fig. 12-7. Current flow versus hole flow in transistor.

hole (in effect) moves to the left, and now occupies the space formerly held by electron No. 5, as at (B). Next, electron No. 4 breaks its covalent bond and moves into the hole of the atom at the right, to create the condition shown at (C). Thus, it is evident that *hole flow is opposite to current flow* in the semiconductor material.

IMPURITIES

So far, our discussions have covered the factors relating to the pure germanium or silicon crystal, plus the concept of hole flow versus current flow. In the manufacture of a transistor, however, the pure crystal structure must be modified by the addition of another element, before the transistor can perform the general functions of the vacuum tube. This modification of the crystal consists in adding a controlled amount of so-called impurities to the crystal structure. There are two such impurity types utilized, one type having atoms of three valence electrons, and the other type having atoms of five valence electrons. To aid in understanding how each contributes to transistor function, each will be treated separately.

The impurities mentioned above are actually pure elements as such, and are referred to as impurities only with respect to the germanium or silicon crystal structure. Considering the germanium or silicon elements as the pure or original state, the addition of any other elements labels the latter as so-called impurities. The impurities which have three valence electrons include

Acceptor (P) impurity	*Atomic number*	*Valence electrons*
Boron	5	3
Aluminum	13	3
Gallium	31	3
Indium	49	3

These impurity elements have an important function in transistors, so that it is worthwhile to analyze their effect when they are combined with the pure crystal elements. Any one of the four impurities listed in the chart can be employed to form what are known as positive areas (referred to as *P* zones). The *P*-zone designation means that a zone within the crystal structure has been formed by the impurity, such a zone or area having a positive relationship with respect to the surrounding areas. Any one of the four listed impurities can be used, since each has only three valence electrons, even though their atomic numbers differ. This can be proved by setting up the rings and subshells in a drawing, and allocating the proper number of electrons successively from the first ring to the last subshell, in accordance with the number of electrons indicated by the atomic number. As an example, in boron, with an atomic number 5, the first primary ring is filled with its quota of two electrons, as is the first subshell of the second ring (see Fig. 12-8). Since the atomic number 5 indicates a total number of five electrons, four are used up in the first ring and first subshell of the second ring. Thus, the second subshell contains only one electron. Hence, the valence ring (outer ring) contains only three electrons.

Fig. 12-8. Boron atom (3 valence electrons).

When boron (or one of the other acceptor impurities) is inserted into a crystal-lattice network, covalent bonds are again formed, as previously seen. Now, however, the impurity atom contributes only three valance electrons to the covalent bonds which are formed. This is seen in Fig. 12-9, which again shows a crystal-lattice network which could be either germanium or silicon. For convenience, only the outer ring valence electrons are shown for each atom. Each atom is marked V3 or V4, to indicate the number of valence electrons for that particular atom.

The number of impurity atoms which are inserted is relatively small, as compared to the surrounding germanium or silicon atoms. Often, impurity atoms are inserted in the proportion of one part impurity to 10^{15} germanium or silicon atoms.

As shown in Fig. 12-9, the impurity atom, with its valence ring containing only three electrons, creates a deficiency of electrons with respect to the valence bonds which are formed. Previously, it was mentioned that each atom shares its electrons with four adjacent atoms and, in consequence, each bound atom has the equivalent of eight electrons in its valence ring. With eight electrons in the valence ring of either germanium or silicon, the two subshells of the outer ring are completely filled, as mentioned earlier, and hence a rigid bond is formed. The impurity atom, however, contributes only three electrons to the valence binding process.

Hence, the circulation and sharing of the neighboring electrons forms an *area* or *zone* which is deficient in one electron, and creates a situation equivalent to the hole previously described. Since there is one electron less in this area, it is known as a *P* zone, indicating a *positive* area. Since this atom has only three valence electrons, it has the ability to accept another electron in order to fill completely the valence ring. Hence, this impurity atom is known as an *acceptor atom.*

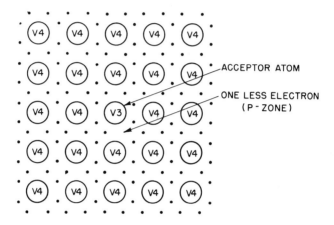

Fig. 12-9. Crystal atoms with one impurity atom added to form *P*-zone.

As mentioned previously, the existence of a hole in a crystal structure creates a situation where a valence-bound electron from an adjacent atom can move into the hole, causing another hole to appear in the atom formation which the electron has left. Thus, hole flow can constitute current flow, in a manner different from the movement of free electrons in the conduction band. It is sometimes convenient to think of the current carriers within such a structure as the holes rather than the electrons, to distinguish this type of current flow from that where free electrons in the conduction band move along to create current flow.

The impurity *atom* does not actually have a deficiency of electrons, because in its normal state it only has three valence electrons. It is only when such an atom is placed within the germanium or silicon crystal network that a deficiency exists *with respect to adjacent atoms.* When an electron moves into the hole of the *P* zone and enters the valence ring of the impurity atom, the latter becomes a negative ion. Even though the entry of an electron into the orbit of the impuriy now fills the outer two subshells completely, there is not as rigid a bond created as in the case of pure germanium or silicon atoms, because the impurity atom has an unwanted electron in its orbit. It is, therefore, relatively easy to move this electron on. How these factors are an important aspect of transistors will be covered in greater detail after the following discussion of the other type of impurity.

The second type of impurity which is utilized in transistors consists of elements having five valence electrons. Elements of this type are:

Donor (N) *impurity*	*Atomic* *number*	*Valence* *electrons*
Phosphorous	15	5
Arsenic	33	5
Antimony	51	5

In the impurities just listed, each valence ring contains five electrons, even though the atomic numbers of the impurity elements differ. Again, if the atom structure were laid out on paper, and the electrons indicated by the atomic number placed in their respective orbits, it would be found that the outer ring contains five electrons. As an example, the element phosphorus is shown in Fig. 12-10. Phosphorus has an atomic number 15; hence, in its neutral state, there are 15 electrons in orbit. As shown, the first ring contains its quota of two electrons. The second ring has two subshells, with the first subshell containing its quota of two electrons, and the second subshell six electrons, giving a total of eight. These eight electrons plus the two in the first ring, total ten electrons, leaving five for the next ring. The next ring (the third ring) can have three subshells, but only two are employed for the remaining five electrons, as shown.

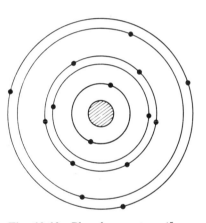

Fig. 12-10. Phosphorus atom (5 valence electrons).

Fig. 12–11 shows the crystal-lattice network, with each crystal atom marked V4 to indicate the normal four valence electrons. The impurity atom is designated V5, to indicate the impurity atom with its five valence electrons. Of the latter, however, only four valence electrons are used to form the covalent bond; hence, there is an extra electron which will be shared by adjacent *atoms*. Thus, the extra electron can be moved readily out of this zone or area, and is not needed for binding purposes. Because the impurity injects an extra electron into the area, the impurity atom is known as a *donor atom* and forms a negative zone (*N* zone), because an excess of electrons is designated as negative, while a deficiency of electrons is designated as positive.

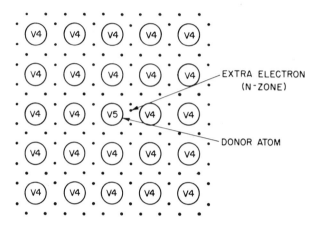

Fig. 12-11. Crystal atoms with one impurity atom added to form *N* zone.

The extra electron contributed by the donor atom is in the nature of a free electron in the conduction band. When such donor electrons carry current, the situation is similar to that which exists in copper, silver, or other conductors. Upon the application of fields generated by electromotive force, for instance, the electrons move along in succession and constitute normal current flow in the conduction band, as opposed to the current flow which exists by virtue of hole movement. As with the acceptor impurity, the donor atom is a neutral element. Hence, when an electron moves away from the donor atom, the latter becomes a positive ion.

P AND N JUNCTIONS

Heretofore, the pure state germanium and silicon crystals were discussed, and the factors involving the formation of *P* and *N* zones were also covered. When *P* and *N* crystals are joined to form a union, the junction device can be compared to the diode vacuum tube in its general characteristics. Hence, a *P-N* junction will exhibit a high resistance characteristic in one direction, and a low resistance characteristic in the other direction. The basic *triode*-type transistor is formed either by joining *P-N-P* sections (in that order), or by combining *N-P-N* sections. Initially, however, it is necessary to investigate more fully the characteristics of the simple *P-N* formation, as a basis for understanding the more complex *P-N-P* or *N-P-N* transistor function.

A *P*-type crystal, by itself, represents a neutral-state material, because the net negative charge of the electrons in any single atom is balanced by the net positive charge of the nuclei. (Even the *P*-type impurity atom, with its three valence electrons, represents an electrically neutral atom.) If there is a hole movement at the valence band, the electrons moving from one atom to the other do not disturb the electrically neutral state, since the over-all charges of the total electrons and the total nuclei still balance. With the *N*-type crystal, by itself, there is also a total and net electrically neutral state, since any movement of the free negative electrons will be counteracted by the positive nuclei.

When the *P*- and *N*-type crystals are combined, there is a countereffect of one material on the other. This effect can be considered to be produced by the attraction existing between the two regions of relative opposite polarity. Hence, *at the time of combining,* some electrons move from the *N* region to the *P* region and, also, holes move from the *P* region to the *N* region. A hole movement in one direction and an electron movement in the other, mean, of course, that current flow exists. Such hole and electron movement, however, ceases once the *P* and *N* sections have been finally joined. (The methods employed for forming junctions of *P* and *N* zones will be discussed later.)

Because the *P* and *N* crystals were in a neutral state prior to joining, the movement of holes from the *P* zone and electrons from the *N* zone means that *neither* crystal section is now electrically neutral. Since the *P* crystal lost some holes (by electrons moving in from the *N* zone), the *P* crystal now has a predominantly *negative* charge. The *N* region, on the other hand, having given up some of its electrons, now has a net *positive* charge, as compared with its former neutral state. Inasmuch as one section of the *P-N* junction has a net positive charge, and the other section a net negative charge, there is a *potential difference* between the two sections. This potential difference between the two sections means that a voltage exists, just as it would across the terminals of a cell or battery. The amplitude (voltage difference) between the two sections depends on the construction (in terms of the type of crystal and the type of impurities). This voltage is known as the *potential barrier* which exists between the two sections forming the junction. It is the influence of an *external* voltage on the potential barrier which creates the transistor function.

The external voltage (a battery or other power source) applied to a transistor or other solid-state device is known as a *bias* voltage. This term must not be confused with the grid-bias potential applied to a vacuum tube, because the transistor has no grid element as such. The various terminals of a transistor can be likened to the anode, grid, and cathode of a vacuum tube for discussion purposes, as will be shown later, but in reality the transistor does not have a grid, cathode, or anode. With the vacuum tube, as mentioned earlier, the voltage applied to the filaments is referred to as the *A* voltage. The plate-voltage supply is known as the *B* voltage or *B* power, while the grid potential is known as *C* bias. In transistors, on the other hand, the voltage is referred to as *bias,* regardless of where it is placed.

There are two types of bias potentials used for transistors. One of the bias potentials is known as *forward bias,* and this term refers to the condition established when the positive polarity of the battery is connected to the *P* region and the negative polarity of the battery is connected to the

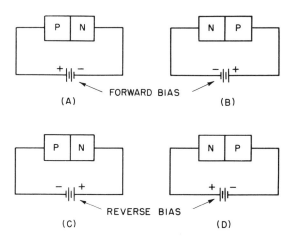

Fig. 12-12. Forward- and reverse-bias connections.

N region. The forward-bias conections can be shown as at Fig. 12–12(A) or (B). Note that, in either case, the negative terminal of the battery is connected to the negative-zone crystal, and the positive side of the battery is connected to the positive-zone crystal. The other type of bias is shown at (C) and (D) of Fig. 12–12 and is known as *reverse bias.* Here, the battery polarities are reversed with respect to the *P*-and *N*-zone polarities. In either drawing, (C) or (D), the positive battery terminal is connected to the *N*-zone crystal, while the negative terminal of the battery is connected to the *P*-zone crystal. Each type connection (forward and reverse) has a particular influence on the *P-N* junction and contributes to transistor behavior.

As mentioned earlier, the union of the *P*- and *N*-type crystals upsets the equilibrium of the electrically neutral states of the individual crystal units, with the result that the *P* crystal represents a net negative charge, and the *N* crystal a net positive charge. With forward bias, as shown at

Fig. 12–12(A) or (B), the potential barrier of the *P-N* junction is reduced, because the plus potential of the battery, when applied to the *P* zone, tends to counteract the net negative charge on the *P*-zone side of the junction. On the other hand, the forward bias of the negative battery potential applied to the *N* region counteracts the net positive charge existing there. The result of the forward bias is, therefore, that the potential barrier has been reduced and current flow occurs. Electrons now move freely from the *N* region to the *P* region, and hole flow occurs from the *P* region to the *N* region. Thus, forward bias means a lowering of the internal resistance of the junction and, consequently, less hindrance to current flow through the transistor and around the battery circuit.

When reverse bias is employed, as illustrated in Fig. 12–12(C) and (D), the polarities of the battery connections are such that the potential barrier is not reduced. With the negative terminal of the battery connection to the *P* region, the battery forces electrons into that region, while withdrawing them from the *N* region into the positive battery terminal. Because the negative terminal of the battery is connected to the *P* zone having a net negative status, it would seem that no current could flow, since opposite poles repel. Similarly, the *N* region has a net positive charge and, again, the positive battery terminal would represent an opposite and, hence, repelling factor. The battery potential, however, is made higher than the potential barrier, so that the battery has the power to force some electrons to flow against the normal barrier polarities. Also, during the combining process of the two regions, not all the holes of the *P* region were filled, nor did all the free electrons of the *N* region move to the *P* region. Hence, some holes in the *P* region and some electrons in the *N* region are still left for producing current flow. Because the potential barrier has not been completely overcome, as was the case with forward bias, the current flow which occurs in much less than for the forward bias condition, even when batteries of the same voltage are employed for both. Thus, for reverse bias, a high-resistance circuit is present, which limits current flow to a considerable extent, as compared to the amount of current which would flow for forward-bias conditions.

CRYSTAL DIODES

From the foregoing, it becomes evident that the *P-N* junction has some of the characteristics of the vacuum-tube diode. In the latter, current can flow when the plate is made positive and the cathode negative. Reversing the polarity of the applied voltage, so that the plate is made negative and the cathode positive, stops current flow. With the crystal diode *P-N* device, a similar (though not quite identical) condition exists. Current will flow in one direction with forward bias, but only a small amount of current flows when reverse bias is used. The difference in resistance (and hence in current flow) between the two conditions is, however, sufficiently great so that the crystal diode can perform many of the functions of the vacuum-tube diode in electronic circuits, as discussed and illustrated more fully in later chapters.

Fig. 12-13. Diode symbol.

The symbol for the crystal diode is shown at Fig. 12–13. The straight line at a right angle to the triangle point represents the cathode toward which electrons flow and is usually marked with a positive sign on the actual unit. The direction of electron flow is shown by the arrow below the symbol. A variety of diode crystals are utilized in industrial electronics, including the silicon, zener, and controlled rectifiers. These are described in the next two chapters and their general characteristics explained and graphed.

REVIEW QUESTIONS

1. Give three advantages of solid-state devices over vacuum tubes.

2. Briefly explain how a crystal-lattice network is formed by silicon atoms.

3. Why does a crystal-lattice network formed from carbon produce an extremely stable and rigid bond?

4. Briefly explain what is meant by bands of energy levels, and how these relate to conductors and insulators.

5. How does current flow in a conductor differ from that established by the hole carriers of current?

6. List at least three acceptor and three donor impurities. Indicate the number of valence electrons in each impurity, and specify which form P zones and which form N zones.

7. What effect does a donor impurity have on the crystal-lattice network of germanium or sìlicon?

8. What effect does an acceptor impurity have on the crystal-lattice network of germanium or silicon?

9. In a P-N junction, what occurs to make the P region have a predominantly negative charge and the N region a predominantly positive charge?

10. Briefly explain what is meant by a potential barrier in a P-N junction.

11. Briefly explain what is meant by forward and reverse bias, and illustrate these conditions by simple drawings.

12. Briefly explain what effect forward bias has on the potential barrier, and also what effect reverse bias has on the potential barrier.

13. Show the symbol for a crystal diode, and indicate the direction of current flow.

PRACTICAL PROBLEMS

Note: The following problems constitute a review of some of the material covered in earlier chapters.

1. In an electronic circuit the power dissipated in a 15,000-ohm resistor is 13.5 watts. What is the voltage drop across the resistor?

2. In a control system R_1 is in parallel with R_2; R_1 has a value of 450,000 ohms and R_2 has 1.6 milliamperes of current flow through it. If the voltage across the parallel circuit is 360, what is the total resistance of the network?

3. A 50-microampere meter having an internal resistance of 2,000 ohms is to be converted to a voltmeter with a 20-volt full-scale deflection. What must be the value of the series resistor?

4. The current through a 2,000-ohm resistor reads 50 milliamperes rms. What is the peak value of the a-c voltage drop across the resistor?

5. In a series circuit composed of a resistor and an inductance, the apparent power was given as 60 watts, and the true power as 30 watts. By what phase angle does the voltage lead the current in this circuit?

6. An inductance of 0.09 henry was placed in series with a resistor of 150,000 ohms. At what time in microseconds after voltage is applied to the circuit will the inductor current reach 63% of full value?

7. In a filter circuit an inductor with a reactance of 69 ohms was in series with a resistor of 92 ohms. What is the impedance of the circuit?

8. In an industrial electronic graphing device it was necessary to match a circuit impedance of 105,625 ohms to a scriber unit having an impedance of 25 ohms. What must be the turns ratio of the matching transformer between the circuit and the scriber?

9. A 0.05-microfarad capacitor is in series with a 200,000-ohm resistor. At what time in seconds after voltage is applied to the circuit will the voltage reach 63 % of maximum amplitude?

10. A series circuit was composed of a 40.5-ohm resistor, a capacitor having a reactance of 24 ohms, and an inductor with a 78-ohm reactance. What is the impedance of this circuit?

11. In a parallel circuit a resistor had 24 milliamperes of current flow through it, an inductor had 8 milliamperes, and an a-c meter in series with the capacitor read 26 milliamperes. If the applied voltage is 85.8, what is the impedance of the circuit? What is the total current supplied by the power source?

12. What is the Q of a series resonant circuit if the resistance is 14,500 ohms, and X_L as well as X_C each has a value of 290,000 ohms?

13. In a resonant circuit the $L \times C$ product $= 0.00282$, where L is in micro-henries and C in microfarads. What is the resonant frequency in mega-cycles?

14. In a vacuum tube a change of grid voltage from 2 to 5 caused a plate current increase of 50 milliamperes. When the plate voltage was reduced from 200 to 50, however, the current decreased by 50 milliamperes to the original value. What is the amplification factor of this tube?

15. In a vacuum-tube the plate voltage was changed from 25 volts to 100 volts, and the current changed from 1.5 milliamperes to 9 milliamperes. The grid voltage was held at a constant value. What is the plate resistance of this tube?

13

TRANSISTOR
CIRCUITS

INTRODUCTION

When utilized in appropriate circuits, transistors function in a fashion similar to vacuum tubes in their ability to amplify, generate, and process electric signals. Thus, transistors can be used in virtually all electronic circuits in which tubes were formerly employed. Because they are structurally different from tubes, however, circuits must be modified to take into consideration the impedance differences between transistors and tubes. Basic transistor circuits are analyzed in this chapter in addition to the practical factors regarding the units themselves.

TRANSISTOR TYPES

Typical transistors are shown in Fig. 13-1. Those at (A) and (B) are the smaller types which are plugged into miniature sockets or wired directly into the circuits. The larger types shown at (C) and (D) are bolted to the chassis and the flanges help dissipate the heat which is gen-

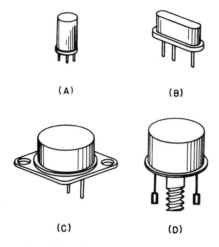

(A)   (B)

(C)   (D)

Fig. 13-1. Transistors.

erated by the higher-power transistors while in operation. The flanges are sometimes referred to as *heat sinks,* as more fully discussed later. The units are sealed against moisture and are housed in either plastic or metallic containers.

As with tubes, there is a variety of transistors. Some are designed for low-frequency signal services, others for the high frequencies, and special types are available for pulse signals, control circuits, and computer systems. Photosensitive types are also in use, as more fully discussed later.

BASIC TRANSISTOR CIRCUIT

As mentioned in Chapter 12, transistors can be formed by using *P*- and *N*-region combinations to produce either *P-N-P* transistors, or *N-P-N* transistors. In either the *P-N-P* transistor or *N-P-N* transistor, a device is formed which resembles the triode (three-element) vacuum tube in its basic characteristics, with respect to amplification or other circuit functions. The two transistor types are illustrated in Fig. 13-2 and, before a discussion is undertaken regarding the manner in which a transistor can amplify, it will be helpful to become familiar with the terms assigned to the various parts of the transistor, and with the symbol designations.

At Fig. 13-2(A), the *P-N-P* transistor is shown. This type of representation is usually utilized when discussing the transistor function, though in published literature and in circuit drawings the symbol shown at (B) or (C) is more often employed. Whether the *P-N-P* symbol is as shown in (B) or in (C) depends on the circuit drawing in which the symbol is used. Sometimes it is more convenient to use the symbol shown in (B), and at other times it is more simple to turn the symbol on its side as in (C). The arrow in the symbol represents the transistor terminal connected to a zone called the *emitter.* If the arrows point *toward* the zone, it indicates a *P*-zone, hence the transistor must be a *P-N-P* type, as shown at (A). If the arrow points away from a zone, it still indicates the emitter, but now also shows that the zone in question is an *N*-type. Thus, when the emitter arrow points away from the symbol, it shows that the transistor is an *N-P-N* type, as at (D), with the corresponding schematic symbols as in either (E) or (F).

Both the *P-N-P* and the *N-P-N* transistor have two like zones (either *P* or *N*). The other zone having the same polarity as the emitter zone is known as the *collector,* and is also represented by a slanting line. The collector lead, however, is simply a straight line, not an arrow, as shown in Fig. 13-2. The lead terminal from the middle zone is known as the *base,*

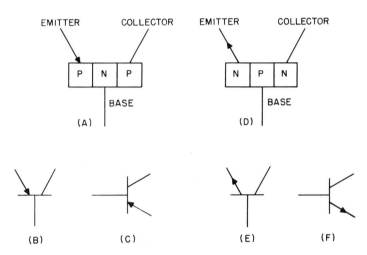

Fig. 13-2. Transistor terminals and symbols.

and is represented by a straight line at right angles to the line which represents the transistor body (the horizontal line in B or E). Generally speaking, the base of the transistor can be compared to the grid of a vacuum tube. The emitter is comparable to the cathode of a vacuum tube, while the collector may be compared to the anode (plate).

In Chapter 11, an introductory discussion of the basic amplifier was undertaken, and it was shown that the input signal is applied between the grid and cathode circuits, while the amplified output signal was developed across the plate load resistor. While only the basic circuit was discussed, such an amplifier *is* extensively used in electronics. Other amplifier types are also important, however, and they will be discussed later. For a discussion of the basic transistor amplifier, the same basic type amplifier will be covered in this chapter. Later, other types of transistor amplifiers and circuits will be illustrated and described, plus additional data given on the two fundamental types discussed in the preceding chapter as well as in this chapter.

A *P-N-P* transistor in a basic circuit is shown in Fig. 13-3. Note that the base-emitter circuit is biased in the forward direction, while the collector, with a *P* zone, has a negative polarity applied to it and, hence, is biased in the reverse direction. This method of biasing the input and output sections of a transistor circuit also applies to the *N-P-N* type, that is, the input is biased in the forward direction, and the output (collector side) is biased in the reverse direction.

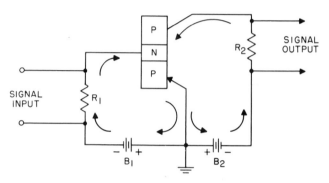

Fig. 13-3. Basic *P-N-P* grounded-emitter circuit.

Resistor R_1 is provided for purposes of accepting the input signal, while resistor R_2 is the output resistor across which the amplified version of the signal appears. Current flow for the input and output sides is indicated by solid arrows within the drawing. As shown, current from the input side battery (B_1) flows from the negative side of the battery, through R_1, and to the base of the transistor (the *N* zone). From the latter point, it flows to the emitter side and back into the battery. For the collector side, current flows from battery B_2 through resistor R_2 and to the collector. For a return to the plus side of the battery B_2, the current must flow through the center *N* zone and to the *P* zone of the emitter.

As mentioned in Chapter 12, forward bias causes current to flow rather freely, and this condition prevails at the base-emitter side of the circuit of Fig. 13-3. With current flowing from the base to the emitter, hole flow is in the opposite direction. Holes flowing from emitter to base, however, represent like charges and hence will repel each other and tend to diffuse and spread out, and some holes thus reach the collector area. (The base region is purposely made thinner than the emitter and plate sections, so that electron and current flow in the base region has a shorter distance to travel in diffusing to the collector side.)

The holes which reach the collector area are somewhat accelerated, because they have a positive charge (positive current carriers) and are attracted by the fields of the negative battery potential applied to the collector. Normally, the collector, with its reverse bias, has a high potential barrier, because the reverse-bias battery did not reduce the potential barrier, as was the case with the forward bias on the emitter side. As mentioned earlier, the barrier causes the collector *P* area to have a net negative charge, and the base *N* area to have a net positive charge. The electron flow from the base-emitter battery overcomes much of the potential barrier in that side of the circuit, thus influencing the *N* zone. The hole flow from the emitter, in diffusing toward the collector, tends to reduce the potential barrier there, because the holes are "collected" by the collector and the negative charge is reduced. Hence, the collector *P* zone tends more and more to become an acceptor area, and will thus permit an increase in current flow from the collector battery B$_2$. Thus, the hole flow to the collector area constitutes a *primary* carrier of current (sometimes referred to as a *majority* or *chief* carrier of current). Hence, in the *P-N-P* transistor, the chief carriers of current are the holes, while electron flow, in this case, is the secondary or minority carrier of current.

From the previous paragraph, it becomes obvious that the emitter hole flow influences current flow in the collector side. Thus, the hole diffusion to the collector caused a reduction in the collector barrier potential, which, expressed in another way, means that the high resistance of the barrier section was reduced, because of the effects of the hole flow set up by the current flow in the base-emitter side.

This influence on collector current flow by current and hole flow in the base-emitter side is what permits amplification to occur. Obviously, if more current were caused to flow in the base-emitter side, there would be an increase in hole flow. The increase in hole flow means that more holes reach the collector area and further reduce the potential barrier. In consequence, there would be an increase in current flow in the collector side. Conversely, if the current flow in the base-emitter side were reduced (as by a lower battery potential or a signal source), the potential barrier resistance at the collector would increase, and current flow in the collector side would decrease.

The amplifying characteristics which come about by the application of a signal to the base-emitter circuit can be understood more readily by reference to Fig. 13-4. In (A) of this figure, one alternation of an input signal is shown. Since this is a positive-going alternation, it will develop a voltage across the input resistor, as shown, with plus toward the base and negative toward the battery. Suppose the battery voltage is 4.5 and the signal voltage at its peak is 0.5. Since the signal voltage sets up across the resistor a voltage drop which opposes in polarity the battery voltage, the net voltage between base and emitter would decrease to 4 volts, from the original 4.5 volts. On the collector side, the collector battery caused a *positive* d-c voltage drop to occur across the output resistor. Because the input signal decreased the voltage between base and emitter, the current

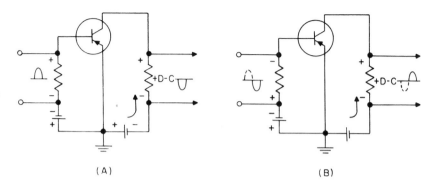

Fig. 13-4. Effect of signal on *P-N-P* circuit.

flow through the input side also decreased, and there were less holes reaching the collector. In consequence, the collector barrier resistance increased, and less current flowed through the output resistor. The reduction of collector current caused the voltage drop across the output resistor to decrease also, in step with the voltage change which occurred across the input resistor. Thus, an amplified version of the input signal appears at the output.

For the second alternation of the input signal, as shown in Fig. 13-4(B), the negative input signal alternation sets up a voltage drop of the polarity shown, with negative toward the base and positive toward the battery. This voltage now aids the battery voltage, because the voltage across the resistor is as though another battery (of lower voltage) were placed in series with the original battery. Thus, if the battery voltage is 4.5 and the signal voltage at its peak is 0.5 volts, the voltage between base and emitter would reach a 5-volt value. The increase in voltage between base and emitter increases current flow through the input side and, hence, there is an increase in hole diffusion to the collector. In consequence, collector barrier resistance decreases, and the increased current flows through the output resistor. The result of the current increase is an increase in voltage across the output resistor, as shown. (Note that there is a phase reversal between the input and output signals, as was the case with the vacuum-tube amplifier discussed in the previous chapter.)

When an *N-P-N* transistor is used to form a basic amplifier circuit, as shown in Fig. 13-5, amplification again occurs, because the collector potential barrier is again influenced by the emitter side. With the *N-P-N* transistor, however, current flow and hole flow are the reverse of what they were with the *P-N-P* type. The *N-P-N* transistor must still be biased in the forward direction at the base-emitter side, which means that a negative polarity must be applied to the *N*-zone emitter, and a positive polarity to the *P*-zone base, as shown in Fig. 13-5. The collector, on the other hand, must again be biased in reverse, that is, the collector must have a positive polarity applied to its *N*-zone, as shown. Current flow is indicated by the solid arrows within the drawing. Note that current flows toward the emitter and out of the base to the positive side of the battery. On the collector side, current flows toward the emitter, out of the collector and back to the positive terminal of the collector battery.

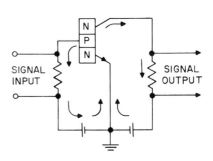

Fig. 13-5. Basic *N-P-N* grounded-emitter circuit.

For the *N-P-N* transistor, the current flow from emitter to base diffuses (like charges of electrons repel each other) and encroaches on the *N* section of the collector area, attracted by the fields set up by the positive potential of the battery applied to the collector. The collector *N* area, as mentioned earlier, has a potential barrier, with the *N* area having a positive charge, because of the holes which entered the area when the *N* and *P* zones were combined. The electron flow from the emitter, in diffusing upward and being collected by the collector section, fills up the holes in the *N* area, thus contributing to the presence of free electrons and permitting a reduction of the potential barrier. Therefore, there is an increase in current through the collector side, because of the influence of the electrons from the emitter section. For this reason, the electrons are the principal or primary current carriers in the *N-P-N* transistor, with the holes taking a secondary place and becoming minority carriers of current. If the potential difference between the base and emitter voltage is changed, there will be a change in the amount of electrons reaching the collector, and hence a change in the potential barrier and collector current flow. Thus, as with the *P-N-P* type, amplification occurs when a signal is applied to the input, because of the changes which occur in the base-emitter current.

Note that, with either the *P-N-P* or the *N-P-N* transistor, changes of base-emitter current are influential in altering the amount of current flow in the collector section. For this reason, the transistor is primarily a current-amplifying device, and hence can be considered as a power amplifier. (Such amplifiers will be discussed more fully later.) Signal voltages can, of course, also be obtained at the output, because such voltages would develop across the output resistor by virtue of the current flow through this resistor.

For the *N-P-N* transistor circuit, the signal inputs affect the collector side in a fashion similar to that described for the *P-N-P* transistor illustrated in Fig. 13-4. The *N-P-N* version is shown in Fig. 13-6. Note, how-

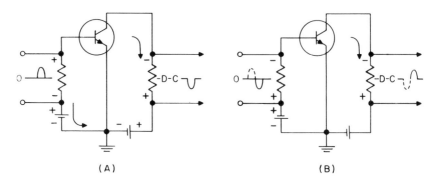

(A)   (B)

Fig. 13-6. Effect of signal on *N-P-N* circuit.

ever, that when a positive alternation is applied to the input resistor at (A), the polarity of the voltage drop across the input resistor *aids* rather than opposes the battery voltage. Also note that current flow through the output resistor is now from collector down to the positive terminal of the battery. Hence, there is a *negative* d-c voltage drop across the output resistor. Since the first alternation of the input signal aids the battery potential, there will be an increase in current flow through the base-emitter circuit and, hence, more electrons reach the collector to reduce the potential barrier. The collector current increases, causing an *increase* in the voltage drop across the output resistor (in the *negative* direction—that is, a larger negative voltage drop). Thus, there appears at the output an amplified version of the input signal. As with the *P-N-P* circuit, there is a phase reversal of the signal between input and output. The second alternation of the signal will develop an opposing voltage across the input resistor, as shown in Fig. 13-6(B), with a consequent reduction of the net voltage between base and emitter. This voltage decrease causes a current decrease, and fewer electrons reach the collector. Hence, the collector barrier is increased, and less current flows through the output resistor in the collector circuit. The decrease in current through the output resistor causes a decrease in the *negative polarity* voltage drop across the resistor (which is equivalent to a positive-going voltage change).

Fig. 13-7 shows the basic *N-P-N* transistor amplifier circuit at (A), for comparison with its vacuum-tube counterpart at (B). Coupling capacitors are used at the input and output sections to keep back the d-c part of the signal, and transfer only the a-c component. Bypass capacitors are also employed across the batteries, to prevent the signal energy from suffering losses in traveling through the battery resistance. From Fig. 13-7,

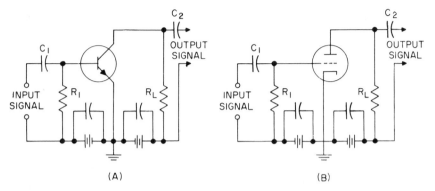

(A)   (B)

Fig. 13-7. Comparison of basic *N-P-N* transistor amplifier circuit with vacuum-tube circuit.

it is obvious that the grounded-emitter transistor amplifier compares to the grounded-cathode vacuum-tube circuit. Other types of transistor and vacuum-tube circuits will be discussed later, in the section on amplifiers.

TRANSISTOR CHARACTERISTICS

Characteristic curves for transistors can be graphed in a fashion similar to those for vacuum tubes. Changes in input voltage to the basic transistor amplifier are made, while noting the changes in the base current which occurs. Voltage is applied to the collector side, and the collector currents are graphed for various changes of base current. Collector voltages are changed and, again, collector currents are graphed with respect to base currents. The result is a graph of the characteristic curves of a transistor, as shown in Fig. 13-8. These curves relate to the basic ground emitter circuit discussed in this chapter.

As with the characteristic curves of vacuum tubes, information regarding a particular transistor can be obtained, including the current gain of a grounded-emitter amplifier circuit. Current gain in a grounded-emitter circuit is known as *beta,* and the symbol for it is the Greek letter β. Current gain, in such an instance, refers to the *signal* current gain which results by a change of signal current in the base side, with respect to the amplified version of the signal current in the collector side. As an illustration of how current gain (beta) can be found from the characteristic curves of Fig.

13-8, assume that the collector battery voltage is held at 10 volts (the battery voltage at the base side is unimportant here, since only the signal current changes in the base side need to be considered). If a signal voltage

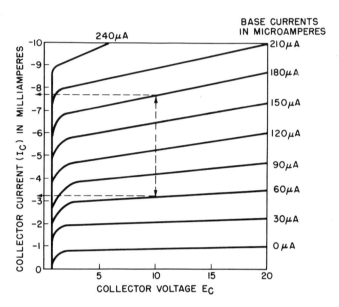

Fig. 13-8. Typical characteristic curves of transistor in grounded-emitter circuit.

is now applied to the base-emitter input of the circuit, to cause a change of base current from 60 microamperes to 180 microamperes, as shown by the vertical dotted arrow in Fig. 13-8, there will be a change of collector current from 3.25 milliamperes to 7.75 milliamperes, as shown by the horizontal dotted arrows. The formula for calculating the current gain is

$$\beta = \frac{dI_c}{dI_b} \qquad (13\text{-}1)$$

This formula indicates that current gain is equal to the change of collector current divided by a change of base current. The small letter *d* preceding each current symbol in the formula is the symbol used for a change or difference (differential); as in the formula used for vacuum tube characteristics, the Greek letter *delta* (Δ) is sometimes employed. When the values obtained from the chart in the foregoing example are set down, the formula indicates that the current gain for this particular transistor is 37.5, as follows:

$$\beta = \frac{dI_c}{dI_b} = \frac{7.75 \text{ milliamperes} - 3.25 \text{ milliamperes}}{180 \text{ microamperes} - 60 \text{ microamperes}}$$
$$= \frac{4.5 \text{ milliamperes}}{120 \text{ microamperes}} = \frac{0.0045}{0.000120} = 37.5$$

This calculation shows that the signal current in the base-emitter side is amplified 37.5 times the collector side. The relation of such current gain to power gain is covered more fully in the section on power amplifiers.

TRANSISTOR DIFFERENCES

There are several basic transistor types, which are the result of specific manufacturing processes. The earliest type of transistor was the *point contact* transistor, which was manufactured by using an *N*-type crystal slab, to which were fused the emitter and collector wires. The fusion process created *P* zones, as shown at (A) of Fig. 13-9. A base lead is attached to

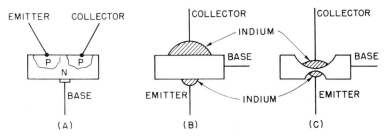

Fig. 13-9. Transistor types.

the *N* section to complete the transistor. The point contact transistor has an extremely high noise level when used in amplifier circuits and, hence, is not as suitable as other types for such purposes.

Another type of transistor is the junction transistor, which can be of either the *N-P-N* or the *P-N-P* type. Several processes are employed for forming the junction transistor. One method is by growing the basic crystal structure. The process involves the placing of a pure germanium crystal plus impurities in a high-temperature furnace. The material is melted and the basic crystal seed is withdrawn and cooled; *P* regions are formed adjacent to *N* regions and, after additional processing, the junction transistor results. Another method consists in again using a basic *N*-type slab, as with the point contact type, and placing a small portion of indium on each side, as shown in Fig. 13-9(B). The crystal slab and the indium deposits are heated at high temperatures, which causes the indium to melt and combine with the slab structure. The indium forms a chemical alloy with the N-type germanium, and P zones are then formed in the alloy area. Thus, a P-N-P transistor results. A larger deposit of indium is used for the collector side, as shown in Fig. 13-9. This type of transistor is sometimes known as an *alloy-junction* transistor. The N-P-N transistor types may also be manufactured by the alloy-junction process, using a P-type germanium crystal slab and employing an impurity element having five valence electrons, such as arsenic or antimony.

Another method utilized in the construction of transistors is the surface-barrier process. As with the alloy-junction, indium is used with respect to a basic N-type crystal slab, as shown at Fig. 13-9(C). In this process, two jets which can shoot an electrolyte into a concentrated area on both the top and bottom of the crystal are employed. A voltage is applied across the jets, so that the electrolyte can conduct current, and an etching process results, when the jets shoot the electrolyte on both sides of the crystal. This etching process eats away the center sections of the crystal, until only a thin layer remains. The polarity of the electrolyte current is then reversed, and an indium plating process begins. During the plating process, the chemical bonds between the indium and the N-type slab form a surface area which becomes the P-zone. Hence, this type of transistor is known as the surface-barrier transistor, with the potential barrier existing at the surface area of the crystal, which is chemically joined with the indium.

In addition to triode-type transistors, tetrode types are also available. For the tetrode transistor, an additional electrode is connected to the center

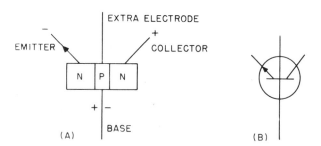

Fig. 13-10. Tetrode transistor.

P zone of an N-P-N transistor, as shown in Fig. 13-10(A). The extra electrode provides a reduction in the zone diffusion path link and, hence, the base resistance is decreased. Thus, a higher efficiency is realized and operation of the transistor at higher signal frequencies than normally would be the case is possible. The base resistance is lowered in the tetrode type, because the emitter confines electron flow in the *P*-zone section to a relatively small area close to the base contact point.

For the *N-P-N* type shown at (A), forward bias to the emitter side is applied in conventional manner, that is, a negative potential is applied to the emitter, with the base as the reference positive potential. For the collector, a positive potential is applied as shown, to provide the necessary reverse bias. The additional electrode is made slightly negative with respect to the base potential. Except for the additional voltage applied to the extra electrode, circuit connections are the same as for the other transistor circuits described in this book. The symbol for the tetrode transistor is shown at Fig. 13-10(B), and may be drawn with or without the enclosing circle, depending on the draftsman's particular choice.

Another type transistor is the so-called *field-effect* or *unipolar* transistor illustrated in Fig. 13-11. This transistor is characterized by operating at

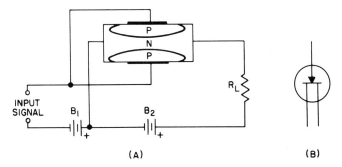

Fig. 13-11. Basic field-effect transistor amplifier.

frequencies beyond 100 megacycles and having high input and output impedances. Basically, the field-effect transistor consists of *P* and *N* junctions as with the transistors described earlier, but the operating characteristics differ somewhat from the general junction types. The primary current flow is established by battery B_2 and flows through the *N* section and through the load resistor R_L. In an *N*-type structure the current flow consists primarily of electrons, and hence these are the so-called *majority carriers* for the primary current of B_2. Battery B_1 applies a reverse bias to both *P*-zones with respect to the *N*-zone, as shown, with the negative battery terminal forming a closed circuit with the *P*-zones through the signal-applying circuit connected to the input. Thus, a sinewave signal applied to the input will increase or decrease the reverse-bias potential supplied by B_1.

When reverse bias is applied to the transistor it causes the current carriers to move away from the *P-N* junctions, leaving depleted regions.

Such *depletion regions* (lack of current carriers) now surround the junctions and extend into the *N* region, thus providing a potential barrier of the type discussed earlier in Chapter 12. Hence, the greater the encroachment of the depletion region on the *N*-zone, the less carriers will be present in this zone for current conduction. Thus, the extent of the depletion region's movement into the *N*-zone is directly established by the amplitude of the reverse-bias potential. The signal input adds and subtracts from the reverse bias, and hence moves the depletion region more and less into the *N*-zone area which serves to carry the main current. In consequence, a low-amplitude signal variation produces an amplified signal output much greater than the input signal. The *N* region can be likened to a corridor which is widened and narrowed by changes in the reverse bias, thus having a decided effect on the amount of current flow through it. The average current flow through the *N* region is limited by the potential of B_2, and the degree of impurities which were injected into the *N* crystal.

The upper input terminal connecting to the two *P* regions can be considered as the base connection, with the left *N* input acting as the emitter and the right *N* output to the load as the collector. The symbol for the field-effect transistor is shown at (B). Since the *N* region between the two *P*-zone terminals is considered as the base, the symbol represents a field-effect transistor with an *N*-type base. For the *P*-type base, the triangular area in the symbol would be reversed, as is also done with transistors to distinguish between the *P-N-P* and *N-P-N* types.

NEGATIVE-RESISTANCE UNITS

A solid-state device having *negative-resistance* characteristics is the *tunnel* diode. Unlike the silicon diodes discussed earlier, the primary application for the tunnel diode is not rectification (see Chapter 14) but amplification and rapid switching. The tunnel diode can operate at much higher signal frequencies than the ordinary transistor and has switching capabilities which are faster by a ratio of over 100 to 1.

Unlike the average transistor, the tunnel diode is not susceptible to temperature changes to the degree found in the transistor and hence remains stable for wide temperature variations. Also, the tunnel diode resists the adverse effects of nuclear radiation and hence finds important applications in this field. Radiation effects in semiconductor diodes and transistors normally consist of a change in the internal resistance and an increase in the noise level.

The term *tunnel diode* stems from the so-called "tunnel effect" which occurs between the *P-N* junction by virtue of the extremely narrow barrier area formed by the addition of impurity elements in excess of the amount normally employed for the transistor. Hence, an electric particle reaching the barrier suddenly disappears and reappears virtually instantly at the other side of the barrier. The transfer occurs at the speed of light (186,000 miles per second), in contrast to the transistor where charges move through the barrier at comparatively slow speeds. The behavior appears as though the particle "tunnels" beneath the barrier rather than penetrating it. Hence, the tunnel diode can operate at signal frequencies ranging up to thousands of megacycles.

The tunnel diode can function as an amplifier because of the negative-resistance characteristic. The latter is identical to that which occurs for a tetrode tube and a comparison of Fig. 11–14, with the graph in Fig. 13-12(A) will indicate the similarities. In the tetrode, the negative-

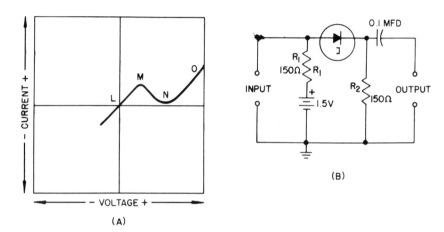

Fig. 13-12. Tunnel diode factors.

resistance occurs because of the secondary emission which results when the screen-grid potential exceeds the anode potential. The disloged electrons are attracted to the screen grid and causes a decrease in plate current, with a resultant decrease in internal tube resistance. Because this occurs for an increase in plate potential, the decreased resistance is termed *negative resistance.*

The tunnel diode, as shown in Fig. 13-12(A), will have a current rise when forward bias is applied. This current increase, however from the zero point (*L*) will soon reach the peak marked *M.* An additional voltage increase will now drop current amplitude from the *M* level to *N,* as shown. As with the tetrode tube, this decrease in current represents negative resistance because of the drop of internal resistance with an increase in applied voltage. An additional voltage increase will cause a gradual rise from *N* to *O,* as with the tetrode tube.

If a fixed forward-bias potential is applied to set an operating point between *M* and *N,* amplification characteristics are obtained. An input sinewave, for instance, will alternately add and subtract from the forward-bias value and cause a comparatively high signal-current change to occur. A basic circuit application is shown at (B). If the input signal is such that it increases the forward bias, current decreases and lowers the voltage drop across R_2, producing a negative-signal output change. For an input signal opposing the forward bias and thus reducing its amplitude, there will be a rise in current to produce a positive signal change at the output. Thus signal power amplification occurs.

Another solid-state device exhibiting negative-resistance characteristics is the *Unijunction* transistor illustrated at Fig. 13-13(A). As shown, the

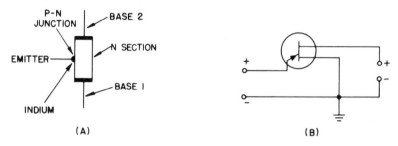

(A)   (B)

Fig. 13-13. Unijunction transistor.

transistor is formed from an N-type silicon slab to which is chemically bonded another element such as indium to form a P-N junction. The unit has two base leads and one emitter as shown, and the basic circuit showing proper voltage polarities is at Fig. 13-13(B).

When the voltage applied to the emitter is in reverse-bias form (or zero voltage), the slab acts as a conventional resistor. Because the emitter taps the crystal slab, a voltage difference exists between emitter and ground. When a forward bias is now applied to the emitter circuit, transistor characteristics are formed and the resistance of the slab between emitter and base 1 decreases, resulting in a current increase. The emitter voltage can now be decreased with a consequent current increase (negative resistance). Since a reduction of emitter potential no longer causes a decrease in base current, the unit behaves as a *thyratron* with gating characteristics. (Thyratrons are discussed fully in the next chapter.) As with other transistors, the Unijunction type can be used to form oscillator or other type circuits.

LEAD CONNECTIONS

Lead connections for various transistors vary to a considerable extent, and no set rules can be given for guidance. Three general types are shown in Fig. 13-14, however, for reference purposes and to indicate the general methods which are employed. One type, shown at (A), has two of the leads spaced closer than the third lead. The lead spaced away from the two is the collector, and the other two are the base and emitter, as shown. Another type of transistor has the leads equally spaced in a row, but a red dot is present on one side of the transistor to identify the collector side, as shown. Still another method is that shown at Fig. 13-14(C), where the leads are also equidistant, but are placed in a triangular arrangement at the bottom of the circular transistor. Here, a red dot or line again identifies the collector lead, with the base and emitter leads reading from right to left around the circle, as shown.

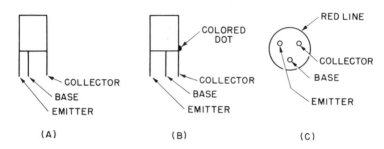

Fig. 13-14. Transistor lead identification.

As shown in Fig. 13-15, the larger transistors which handle higher power, are designed to be bolted to the chassis for heat dissipating purposes. In such cases, the transistor shell or mounting bolt forms one connection. At (A) the transistor shell is the collector, while at (B) the mounting bolt is also the collector terminal.

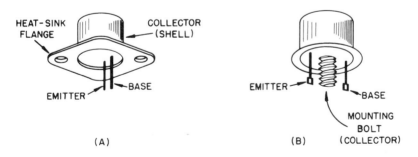

Fig. 13-15. High-power transistor leads.

The identifying (numbering) systems used for transistors vary considerably from those for tube types, and also vary among manufacturers.

Quite often, one manufacturer's numbering system will differ from another manufacturer's, even though both transistors have the same general characteristics. Transistor numbering systems usually include letters, as well as numbers, and take such forms as: 2N35, 2N44, 2N212, etc. For the proper numbering system and base connections with respect to a particular transistor, reference should be made to the manufacturer's specifications.

NETWORK PARAMETERS

In Chapter 4, resistive circuits were analyzed, using Kirchhoff, Thévenin, and Norton theorems to set up equivalent circuits. Similarly, the operational characteristics (parameters) of transistors can also be obtained by utilizing equivalent networks. The transistor can be considered as a resistive device represented as shown at Fig. 13-16(A). Here the emitter

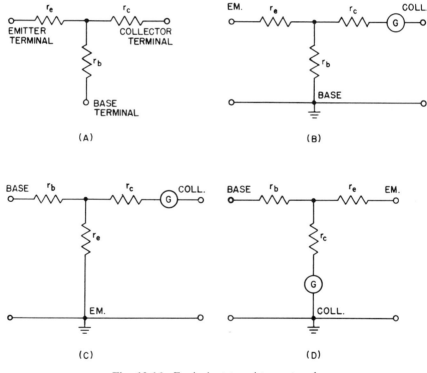

Fig. 13-16. Equivalent transistor networks.

is indicated by a resistor r_e, the base by r_b and the collector by r_c. Together they form a T-network of resistors with ohmic values such as would be obtained by making d-c measurements. Since this T-network is a *passive* type, it is not a true representation of a transistor, because such a three-resistor combination does not have amplifying characteristics. Also, the network at (A) is shown as a three-terminal device. Actually, however, a common input-output lead is present in a transistor circuit and hence the practical transistor must be represented as a four-terminal network.

The four-terminal equivalent network is shown at (B) and represents the common base (grounded base) circuit. Instead of a passive network, a generator (G) is indicated in the collector lead, making this an *active* network. Thus, the amplifying function of the transistor is indicated by the equivalent generator in the output, just as the plate-grid in a grounded-grid tube amplifier can be so shown. The grounded emitter is shown at (C).

For the grounded emitter, the generator in the output line represents the emitter-collector section, as with the cathode-plate portion of the vacuum-tube circuit. Now the left arm of the T-network is shown as r_b for the equivalent base resistance which now forms the input terminal, and r_e as the representative grounded-emitter resistance. The active network for the grounded collector is shown at (D).

The active resistance network characteristics of a transistor are a close approximation at low signal frequencies, or with d-c. At high signal frequencies, however, it becomes an impedance network because the internal capacitances, with their decreasing reactances, are influencing factors. Input and output impedances are also affected by the ohmic value of the load resistance applied to the output, as well as the resistance of the circuit or device applied to the input. Hence, for a true evaluation of circuit parameters, the internal network values must be considered in conjunction with the external networks which are applied so that maximum signal-power transfer and maximum circuit efficiency are obtained. In the discussions which follow, we will be concerned primarily with the resistive characteristics of the equivalent networks for a clearer understanding of the notation employed and the methods utilized.

As discussed in Chapter 4, for convenience in analyzing networks, it is expedient to consider the network as a black box wherein we have internal components of unknown values. To analyze the internal circuit we read voltages and currents, or apply test signals to the input and output terminals and evaluate their effects. The voltage and current measurements are also undertaken during the open circuit or short circuit of either the input or output terminals.

The four-terminal equivalent network of a triode transistor can be represented as a black box, as shown in Fig. 13-17. Here, V_1 is the input voltage, V_2 the output voltage, I_1 the input current, and I_2 the output current. The resistance parameters of the transistor so represented have

been symbolized by the so-called *R*-parameters as well as by the more widely-used *H*-parameters. Initially we will consider the *R*-type parameters, since they serve as a more solid foundation for understanding the *H*-(hybrid) types.

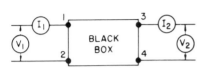

Fig. 13-17. Equivalent black-box representation.

Because $E/I = R$, the input resistance is notated as R_{11}, to identify that this R value is obtained by using the V_1 and I_1 values. Thus the first 1 of the subscript indicates V_1 voltage and the second 1 of the subscript the I_1 current. Thus, R_{11} is a measure of the resistance with the test voltage V_1 applied to the input terminals 1 and 2, with the output terminals 3 and 4 open; that is, $I_2 = 0$. Similarly, R_{21} indicates the forward transfer resistance, with the test voltage V_1 applied to the input terminals again and the ratio of V_2/I_1 taken for the R_{21} value. When the test voltage is applied to the output terminals 3 and 4 and the input terminals left open ($I_1 = 0$) we obtain

$$R_{12} = \frac{V_1}{I_2} = \text{reverse transfer resistance (feedback resistance)}$$

$$R_{22} = \frac{V_2}{I_2} = \text{output resistance}$$

From the foregoing we can derive the loop equations for the transistor network.

$$V_1 = R_{11} I_1 + R_{12} I_2 \qquad (13\text{-}2)$$
$$V_2 = R_{21} I_1 + R_{22} I_2 \qquad (13\text{-}3)$$

The amplifying ability of the transistor network relates to the mutual resistance (r_m), and current amplification is referred to as *alpha* (α). Related to the R parameters, these are:

$$r_m = R_{21} - R_{12} \qquad (13\text{-}4)$$

$$\text{alpha} = \frac{R_{21}}{R_{22}} \qquad (13\text{-}5)$$

The *r*-value relationships of (A) in Fig. 13-16 (common base) become:

$$r_e = R_{11} - R_{12} \qquad (13\text{-}6)$$
$$r_c = R_{22} - R_{21} \qquad (13\text{-}7)$$
$$r_b = R_{12} \qquad (13\text{-}8)$$

The equivalent generator voltage is equal to $I_1(R_{21} - R_{12})$. The resistive parameters can also be utilized for the dynamic characteristics of the network under signal conditions. Using the lower case delta to indicate a quantity change, and holding i_c constant, we get

$$R_{11} = \text{slope of curve } dV_e/dI_e$$
$$R_{21} = \text{slope of curve } dV_c/dI_e$$

Holding i_e constant, produces the following:

$$R_{12} = \text{slope of curve } dV_e/dI_c$$
$$R_{22} = \text{slope of curve } dV_c/dI_c$$

HYBRID (h) PARAMETERS

R parameters were obtained under open-circuit conditions, representing constant-voltage types. As discussed in Chapter 4, it is often convenient to use the constant current analysis, shorting out terminals as required. By combining the constant-voltage and constant-current approach, a more desirable type of parameter is obtained, and one favored by transistor manufacturers. The combination has led to the term *hybrid* or *h*-parameter. Thus, for our black box of Fig. 13-17, the following notations apply:

$h_{11} = V_1/I_1$ (with output terminals 3 and 4 shorted and $V_2 = 0$)

$h_{12} = V_1/V_2$ (with input terminals 1 and 2 open and $I_1 = 0$)

$h_{21} = I_2/I_1$ (with output terminals 3 and 4 shorted and $V_2 = 0$)

$h_{22} = I_2/V_2$ (with input terminals 1 and 2 open and $I_1 = 0$)

Basic calculations can be used if necessary to convert R to h or h to R. Parameter R_{11}, for instance, equal to $(h_{11}h_{22} - h_{12}h_{21})/h_{22}$. Similarly, $R_{12} = h_{12}/h_{22}$ and $R_{21} = h_{21}/h_{22}$.

Standards have been adopted for letter subscripts for easier identification of the h parameters. The first subscript designates the characteristic, i for input, o for output, f for forward transfer, and r for reverse transfer. The second subscript designates the circuit configuration, with b for common base, e for common emitter, and c for common collector. Thus, h_{11} can be indicated as h_{ib} for the input h of a common base network. Similarly h_{12} can be written as h_{rb} for reverse transfer in the common base network. This avoids the confusion which might result by simply using h_{11}, for instance, without designating whether it is in reference to common base, common emitter, or common collector. Initially the common base was used as the reference network, but the widespread usage of the common emitter circuit (comparable to the grounded cathode of tube circuits) led to the general adoption of the *h*-parameter notation with letter subscripts.

HYBRID EQUIVALENT

Figure 13-18(A) shows a basic grounded-emitter circuit. Applied to the input is the signal voltage to be amplified. This could be symbolized as e_s for *signal voltage*, or as e_g for *generator voltage*, as shown in Fig. 13-18. The resistance associated with the input signal is marked R_g. The load resistance applied to the output is indicated by the standard R_L symbol. The d-c power sources E_1 and E_2 are effectively bypassed by capacitors C_1 and C_2, hence are not part of the active parameter analysis.

The equivalent circuit for the grounded-emitter is shown at (B), with appropriate hybrid symbols with letter subscripts. The base current is indicated as i_b, and collector current as i_c. The input voltage e_g also develops across R_g, hence the actual voltage applied to the base and emitter is

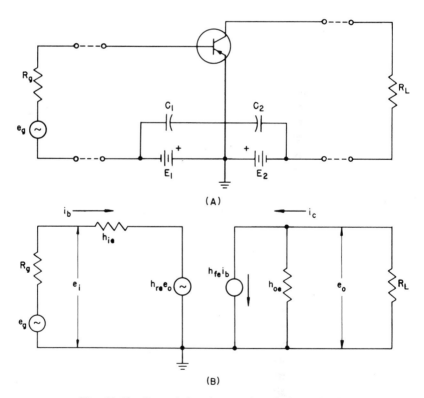

(A)

(B)

Fig. 13-18. Grounded emitter and equivalent circuit.

indicated as e_i. The output voltage across the load resistor is shown as e_o. The emitter input resistance is given as h_{ie}, and the output admittance or conductance is given as h_{oe}, measured in mhos. Note the use of the reverse-voltage transfer ratio symbol h_{re} for the emitter circuit. (In a common base this would be h_{rb}.) The forward-current ratio is designated as h_{fe}, indicating the emitter designation.

The forward current-transfer ratio h_{fe} is now i_c/i_b (with $e_o = 0$) which is the same as the Equitation (13-1) given earlier for signal current gain β (beta). Manufacturers have used A_i for signal-current gain, symbolizing current amplification. The full equation is

$$A_i = \frac{i_c}{i_b} = \frac{h_{fe}}{1 + h_{oe}\, R_L} \qquad (13\text{-}9)$$

While this equation refers to the common-emitter circuit of Fig. 13-18, it also applies to the grounded-base or grounded-collector circuits. The equation remains the same except for a change from e to b or c for the second subscript to suit the circuit configuration. Other equations used to analyze circuit parameters are also applicable to the three basic circuit systems of transistors, using the appropriate second subscript to denote emitter, base, or collector. The following example shows the application of Equation (13-9):

Example: The GE 2N508 transistor has a low-signal designation of $E_1 = 5$ volts, and $I_b = 0.1$ milliamperes. The manufacturer's h ratings are

$$h_{ie} = 2{,}800 \text{ ohms}$$
$$h_{oe} = 43 \text{ micromhos}$$
$$h_{fe} = 110$$
$$h_{re} = 7.5 \times 10^{-4}$$

Assume a load resistance of 10,000 ohms is to be used. What is the current gain?

Solution: $A_i = h_{fe}/1 + h_{oe}\, R_L$

$$= \frac{110}{1 + (43 \times 10^{-6} \times 10{,}000)} = 77$$

The input resistance R_i can be found by the following equation:

$$R_i = h_{ie} - \frac{h_{fe} h_{re} R_L}{1 + h_{oe} R_L} \qquad (13\text{-}10)$$

Using the h values given above for the 2N508 transistor, with a load resistance of 10,000 ohms, the following shows the application of Equation (13-10):

$$R_i = 2{,}800 - \frac{110 \times 7.5 \times 10^{-4} \times 10{,}000}{1 + (43 \times 10^{-6} \times 10{,}000)} = 2{,}224 \text{ ohms}$$

The signal-voltage-gain amplification of the transistor circuit is found by

$$A_e = \frac{e_o}{e_i} = \frac{1}{h_{re} - \dfrac{h_{ie}}{R_L}\left(\dfrac{1 + h_{oe}R_L}{h_{fe}}\right)} \qquad (13\text{-}11)$$

Again, using the values given for the 2N508 transistor as an example, the voltage amplification is found:

$$A_e = \frac{1}{0.00075 - \dfrac{2{,}800}{10{,}000}\left(\dfrac{1 + (43 \times 10^{-6} \times 10{,}000)}{110}\right)} = 274.$$

The power gain of the transistor circuit is found by multiplying the signal-current gain A_i by the signal-voltage gain A_e:

$$A_p = A_e A_i \qquad (13\text{-}12)$$

Applying the two values previously obtained for the transistor used as an example, we find the power gain to be

$$A_p = 274 \times 77 = 21{,}098$$

REVIEW QUESTIONS

1. In the transistor symbol, what terminal is identified by the lead with the arrow?

2. What is the significance of the arrow pointing toward the transistor symbol or away from the transistor symbol?

3. Briefly explain how amplification occurs in a transistor.

4. To what vacuum-tube amplifier does the grounded-emitter transistor circuit compare?

5. Briefly explain the difference between triode and tetrode transistors. Use simple drawings to illustrate the explanation.

6. Explain how the field-effect transistor amplifies an input signal for the circuit shown in Fig. 13-11.

7. Describe *negative resistance* as it applies to the tunnel diode and the Unijunction transistor.

8. List some of the advantages of a tunnel diode over an ordinary silicon diode or transistor.

9. Why does a tunnel diode have amplification characteristics?

10. What is the difference between an *active* and a *passive* network?

11. What are the basic differences between the R and h transistor parameters?

12. How is the transistor parameter h_{22} obtained?

13. How may h_{11} and h_{12} be written with letter subscripts?

14. To what transistor equation does h_{fe} relate?

15. What is the equation for current amplification (A_i) for a *grounded-base* transistor circuit?

16. What is the equation for input resistance (R_i) for a *grounded-collector* transistor circuit?

PRACTICAL PROBLEMS

1. In a transistor a base I change from 50 to 175 microamperes produces a collector I change from 4 to 8 milliamperes. What is the current gain?

2. In a grounded-emitter transistor circuit dI_b is 100 microamperes and dI_c is 2.5 microamperes. What is β?

3. A commercial transistor has a low-signal designation of $E_1 = 5.5$ volts and $I_b = 0.125$ milliamperes. The manufacturer's h ratings are $h_{ie} = 2,500$ ohms, $h_{oe} = 50$ micromhos, $h_{fe} = 100$, $h_{re} = 6 \times 10^{-4}$, and the recommended $R_L = 10,000$ ohms. What is the current gain (A_i)?

4. For the h values given in Problem 3, what is the value of the input resistance (R_i)?

5. For the h values given in Problem 3, what is the signal voltage amplification (A_e)?

6. For the h values given in Problem 3, what is the power gain (A_p)?

7. For the h values in Problem 3, what would be the A_i if the load resistance were changed to 5,000 ohms?

8. A transistor has the same h values as in Problem 3 except for $h_{fe} = 125$. With a 5,000-ohm load resistance, what is A_i?

14

POWER
SUPPLIES

INTRODUCTION

The various electronic devices used in industry and in the home which employ vacuum tubes, require a source of power to operate the filaments, plates, and other tube elements at their respective voltage ratings. Transistors also require a source of power, though in contrast to vacuum tubes, a less complex voltage supply is needed. Portable electronic units utilize a battery or batteries as the source of power, but in permanent or semi-permanent installations of electronic gear, generators or power supplies are employed.

Since d-c is required for vacuum tubes and transistors, operation of electronic devices without batteries makes it necessary to convert the a-c in the power mains to d-c. The most convenient method for doing this is to rectify the a-c of the power mains and use a filter system to produce d-c, as mentioned earlier. Since the power main voltages supplied to the home range between 110 to 220 volts a-c, it is necessary to alter the voltage and current properties of such a-c in order to meet the requirements of the various tube elements and circuits of transmitters, receivers, and other electronic devices.

Tube filaments which have no separate cathode, for instance, require the use of d-c, because the application of a-c causes the voltage fluctuations to mix in with the audio- or radio-frequency signal to be amplified, with the result that the 60-cycle hum would be heard in a receiver or high-fidelity amplifier, or that interfering bars would appear on the television screen. For vacuum tubes which are indirectly heated, that is, which have a separate cathode, the latter remains at fairly constant temperature and, because it is an independent circuit with respect to the filament, hum interference is reduced. Even though a-c can thus be applied directly to tubes having indirectly-heated cathodes, the a-c line voltage must be reduced below the 115 volts because some tubes require 6.3 volts, others 12.6 volts, and still others operate with filament voltages up to 50 volts a-c. Current drawn by the filaments of tubes may vary from a fraction of an ampere to several amperes. Hence, one of the duties of the power supply for a particular electronic device is to furnish the correct filament voltage while also having sufficient current available for proper operation.

Anodes and screen grid elements of vacuum tubes require a much higher voltage than used by the filaments, besides which the anodes require a d-c voltage and not an a-c. Current requirements for plates and screens of tubes, however, are much less than for the tube's filaments. Hence, an anode of a power-amplifier tube in an audio system may draw 50 to 100 milliamperes from the power supply, with a voltage ranging from 250 to 300 volts. Because of the various voltages required, it is necessary to employ some means for "stepping up" as well as dropping down the line voltage available from the a-c outlets in homes. A common method for doing this is to utilize a transformer (referred to as "power transformer") which will either step up or step down the voltage, or do both, as necessary, before rectification of the a-c.

HALF-WAVE POWER SUPPLIES

The basic principle of rectification was discussed in the early portion of Chapter 11 and illustrated in Fig. 11-5. Such a rectifier system, which utilizes every other alternation of the a-c cycle for producing d-c, is known as *half-wave* power supply, because it only employs one-half of the a-c cycle for production of d-c.

A typical commercial half-wave rectifying system, using a vacuum tube, is shown in Fig. 14-1(A). In the primary winding, the slanted arrow indicates a switch for turning the device on and off. The top secondary winding provides the necessary heater current for the rectifier tube. The secondary winding connected to the anode of the rectifier and ground provides a much higher voltage than the other windings, since this is the source of the ultimate d-c for the anodes and screen grids of the tubes. In contrast to filament windings where low voltage and high currents are necessary, the anode rectifier winding provides a high voltage with low current. For this reason, the high-voltage secondary is wound with much thinner wire, such as No. 28, No. 30, 32, or 34, while filament secondaries would be wound with No. 16, 18, or 20 wire.

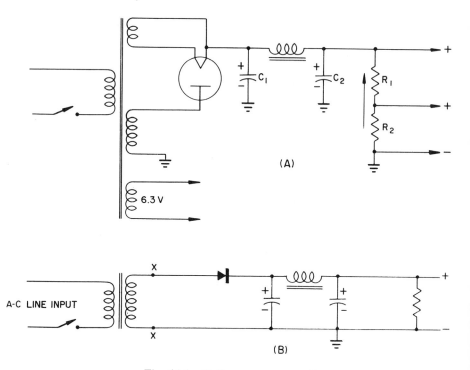

Fig. 14-1. Half-wave power supplies.

The high-voltage winding can have as many turns as required for the amount of voltage needed. In common practice, the voltage step-up is usually of the order of 200 or 300. One lead of the high-voltage winding connects to the plate, as shown in Fig. 14-1(A), while the other lead connects to ground. (It must be remembered that ground connections are simply made for the purpose of *providing interconnection between other similar voltage points.* In most transformer-type power supplies the negative section of the power supply is referred to as the *ground potential.*)

The cathode element of the rectifier is connected to a filter capacitor (C_1) and to a filter choke, as shown in (A). An additional filter capacitor is employed (C_2) for smoothing out the a-c ripple. Across the output terminals of the power supply, two resistors, R_1 and R_2, are used. The output voltage develops across these resistors. In some radios or other devices, the resistors may be dispensed with, and the positive and negative terminals are connected directly to the circuits. The resistor network is known as a *bleeder* section, since it imposes a slight current drain on the power supply, and thus helps to stabilize the output voltage. The voltage-regulating function of the bleeder resistor is explained in greater detail later in this chapter. The bleeder network can also be used as a source of lower voltages, by employing several resistors in series, or by using a single resistor with several taps. Thus, the center positive terminal shown at the output of circuit (A), in Fig. 14-1, provides a lower voltage than that obtained from the top positive terminal.

An additional secondary winding is employed (6.3 volts or higher, as required) for furnishing heater power to the tubes of the electronic device. Where a large number of tubes is used, additional secondary windings may be provided. Additional windings are, of course, necessary when other values of voltages are required, besides the voltage furnished by the single 6.3-volt secondary.

When a positive alternation appears at the rectifier anode, current flows from the ground side of the high-voltage winding and along the chassis of the power supply to the bottom of the capacitors, as well as to the bottom of the resistor R_2 in the bleeder. Since the filter capacitors have a zero charge initially, capacitor C_1 across the rectifier tube charges to a peak value of the a-c alternation. Since the peak value is calculated on the basis of 1.41 times the effective voltage, capacitor C_1 charges to a peak value of 282 volts, if the secondary is delivering a voltage of approximately 200. (The peak value will be reduced in proportion to the resistance of the rectifier. Pulses involve a calculation based on the average value, as mentioned earlier.) A charge is also placed across capacitor C_2, but such a charge has a value less than the peak voltage because the filter choke is in series with capacitor C_2 and reduces the voltage. Once the filter capacitor has been charged, current flow will occur through R_2 and R_1, and will return to the cathode of the rectifier.

During a negative alternation of the a-c voltage across the high-voltage secondary, the plate side of the winding will be negative and the cathode side positive. During this time, the tube cannot conduct. The filter capacitors are charged, however, and seek a path for discharge. Such a discharge path is provided by the bleeder network consisting of resistors R_1 and R_2. The capacitors start to discharge through the bleeder network in the direction shown by the arrow. When the supply is furnishing power to a load such as an audio amplifier or other electronic device, the discharge of the capacitor furnishes the power during the time the tube is not conducting. Eventually, of course, the capacitors would discharge completely, but while the power supply is in operation, the capacitors are fed constantly by each positive alternation, which occurs once every sixtieth of a second. During the charging cycle of the capacitors, the time constant of the circuit is short, since the tube is conducting and offers very little resistance, and the capacitors are virtually across the voltage source. When the tube does not conduct, however, the time constant of the circuit is long, because the capacitors must discharge through the bleeder (they cannot discharge through the vacuum tube, because the latter is in a nonconducting condition). Thus, very little of the charge leaks off before a new charge is placed on the capacitors. If the resistors R_1 and R_2 were made smaller, the time constant would be shortened, and the capacitors would discharge more rapidly during the intervals when the tube is not conducting. In normal operation, the bleeder resistance is made fairly high (usually between 25,000 and 50,000 ohms).

The bleeder resistor network represents a load on the power supply, since some energy is consumed as the electrons flow through the resistors. When vacuum-tube circuits or other resistors are added across the output of the power supply, additional current is consumed from the power supply (i.e., the load on the power supply is increased). Adding more circuits or resistors means that additional current is drawn from the power supply. An increase in current indicates a decrease in the value of resistance across the supply, and this is virtually what occurs, since each circuit or additional resistor placed across the bleeder network would reduce the resistance value across the plus and minus terminals. As more and more energy is drawn from the power supply, the decline of voltage across the bleeder becomes more pronounced. As extra current is drawn from the filter capacitors, the latter discharge to a lower level between alternations, and will not charge to as high a level during voltage peaks. Thus, the output of the power supply declines as the load increases (as more current is drawn). This change of voltage output with a change of current consumption is referred to as *regulation,* and will be more fully described later in this chapter.

By employing additional filtering, such as increasing the value of the filter capacitors, the sharp decline of capacitor charges can be minimized, so that the output voltage will be substantially ripple-free and becomes sufficiently smooth for application to the circuits of high fidelity systems, television or radio receivers, etc. The filter choke also minimizes ripple, because it tends to diminish the peak amplitudes of the voltage through its opposition to sudden changes of voltage. The filter choke can also be considered as a series inductance which provides a high order of inductive reactance to any ripple component. By similar analysis, the filter capacitors become a low capacitive reactance shunt for any ripple component of the output d-c voltage.

While the rectifier can be a tube with a separate cathode, a rectifier with a directly-heated cathode element is often employed. In such an instance, the filament of the rectifier also acts as a cathode, as explained earlier. There is virtually no difference in performance, since one leg of the filament will now carry the d-c rectified by the tube. The necessity for a cathode, however, arises when a single filament winding of the transformer must also furnish heater current for other tubes besides the rectified tube. In such an instance, a separate cathode is necessary to keep the high d-c voltages out of the filament circuits of other tubes.

SOLID-STATE RECTIFIERS

A typical half-wave power supply using a solid-state diode is shown in Fig. 14-1(B). In earlier devices of this type, the selenium rectifier was employed. This consisted of metal disks treated with selenium to pass current in one direction. The disks were stacked, as shown in Fig. 14-2(A), to conform to the voltage and current requirements. The selenium rectifiers have generally been replaced by the silicon diodes, which are solid-state units operating on the *P-N* and *N-P* transistor principles discussed in the preceding two chapters. The silicon diodes are smaller than the selenium type handling the same current (and with the same voltage ratings) and also have a higher forward-to-back resistance ratio. The resistance in one direction is usually in excess of 2,000 times that in the other direction, and thus very little current flow is possible in the reverse direction. With the selenium types, the much lower resistance ratio permitted some current flow in the reverse direction.

Silicon rectifiers come in various sizes, from the small units shown at

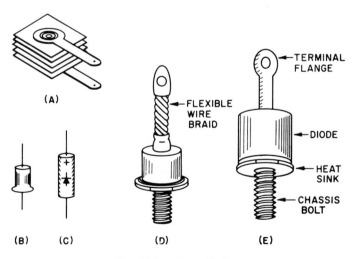

Fig. 14-2. Silicon diodes.

(B) and (C) of Fig. 14-2, to the larger types shown at (D) and (E). Those for electronic equipment in the home (tape recorders, receivers, etc.) range from current ratings of 50 milliamperes to approximately 450. For industrial applications the current ratings are in amperes. As shown at (D) and (E), a threaded terminal is provided to permit the unit to be bolted to the chassis, with the flange acting as a *heat sink*. With the flange bolted flat against the chassis the heat is absorbed by the chassis and drained away from the rectifier, in similar fashion to some of the larger power transistors.

For the circuit shown in Fig. 14-1(B), a transformer is used which steps up the voltage from the line, though the power supply is often connected directly to the line at the terminals marked X when high voltage outputs are not necessary. The operation of this power supply is similar to that of the simple half-wave type discussed earlier. During positive alternations of the input voltage, the rectifier conducts and creates pulsating d-c which is filtered so that a sufficiently smooth d-c appears at the output terminals.

FULL-WAVE POWER SUPPLIES

A full-wave power supply is one which uses both alternations of the a-c cycle, and such a power supply has several advantages over the half-wave type previously discussed. Because the filtering is easier to accomplish in the full-wave type, smaller value filter capacitors can be used, and the power supply has better regulation for changes in load. For full-wave rectification, however, a dual-diode rectifier must be employed. The two rectifiers can be separate units, or they can be combined into one, such as the full-wave rectifier vacuum tubes which have two diodes in one envelope. Only a single cathode or filament element is needed, in addition to the two anodes of the full-wave rectifier vacuum tube.

A typical full-wave rectifier circuit is shown in Fig. 14-3(A). For this type of full-wave rectification, a tapped secondary is required. The high voltage of this secondary winding is approximately twice the voltage available at the output of the power supply. This is in contrast to the half-wave type, where only a single high-voltage secondary winding is needed.

As shown in Fig. 14-3(A), one lead of the secondary connects to one of the rectifier plates (P_1), while the other end of the secondary connects to the second plate (P_2). The center tap of the transformer (CT) is the negative return to the bottom of the filter capacitors and bleeder resistor, and hence this terminal is usually grounded.

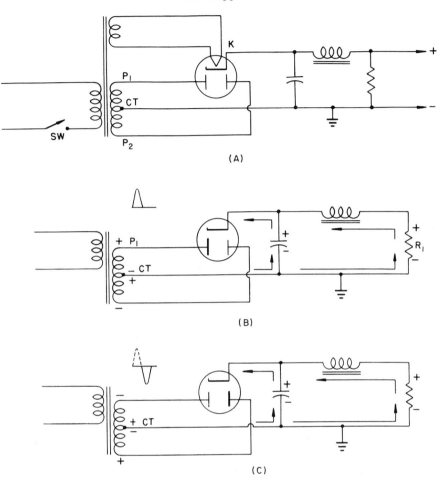

Fig. 14-3. Current flow in full-wave power supply.

The manner in which this circuit functions can be ascertained by reference to Fig. 14-3(B). When the switch is closed and a positive alternation appears across the secondary, the voltage polarity at the terminal applied to the first plate will be positive, while the polarity at the second plate (fed by the bottom of the transformer) is negative. The center tap of the secondary winding has a polarity *which depends on its relationship to either the first or second plate.* If P_1 is positive, the center tap will be negative with respect to that plate. When P_2 is negative, the center tap will be positive with respect to it. This is a common polarity relationship, as described in greater detail in earlier chapters. Under the condition illustrated in (B), therefore, plate P_1 would conduct. Since the negative terminal with respect to this P_1 plate is the center tap which connects to the cathode of the rectifier, electrons will leave the center tap and charge the filter capacitor, as in the process described for the half-wave rectifier. Current flow through the resistor R_1 is also in the direction shown by the arrows; P_2 cannot conduct, because it is negative with respect to the cathode.

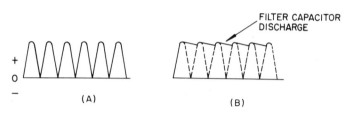

(A)   (B)

Fig. 14-4. Function of filter capacitor.

At the second alternation of the a-c across the secondary, the conditions will be established as shown in Fig. 14-3(C). Here, the second plate P_2 is conducting, because it is positive with respect to the cathode. The cathode, in turn, is connected to the center tap via a capacitor and a resistor. Thus, the cathode is negative with respect to P_2, but positive with respect to P_1. Because the first diode has minus on the plate and plus on the cathode, it is unable to conduct.

Current flow in the circuit external to the rectifier tube will again be *in the same direction as it was during the first positive alternation* illustrated in (B). Again, the capacitor is charged toward the peak value of the voltage, and will discharge across the resistor in the direction shown by the arrows. Thus, the capacitor receives a charge at a rate which is *twice* that for half-wave rectification. As shown in Fig. 14-4(A), the pulsating d-c which results has a ripple frequency of 120 cycles per second, instead of 60. As shown in Fig. 14-4(B), the discharge time between the peaks of the pulsating d-c is only half that encountered in half-wave rectification. Because of the reduced interval between peaks, the filter capacitors do not have as long a discharge time, and are more capable of maintaining a relatively high charge. At the same time, the high ripple frequency will create a higher inductive reactance in the filter choke, as well as a lower capacitive reactance in the filter capacitor. Thus, the choke is more effective in limiting voltage variations, and the capacitor is more efficient in shunting ripple components.

A more complete version of the full-wave power supply is shown in Fig. 14-5(A). Here again, a rectifier could be used which has a separate cathode, or the one illustrated can be employed, which dispenses with the cathode element. Since the chassis can be utilized as a return circuit for the current flow from the negative terminal of the supply, ground connections are shown, instead of using a continuous line to interconnect

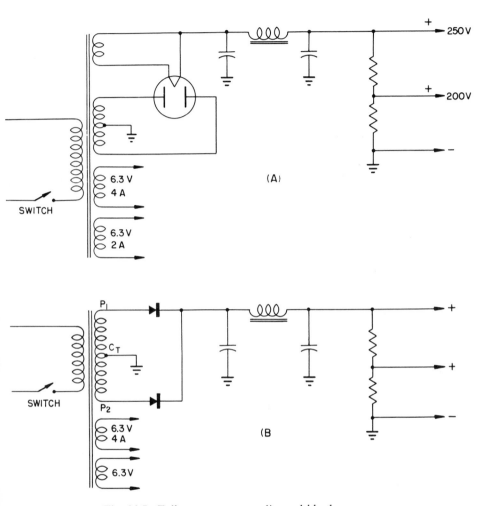

Fig. 14-5. Full-wave power supplies and bleeders.

negative points. A two-resistor bleeder is shown, for providing a voltage tap below the maximum available. The two secondary windings shown are for furnishing heater potentials to the tubes of the receiver or the tubes of some other electronic device. The first winding will deliver 6.3 volts at 4 amperes, while the second winding will deliver 6.3 volts at 2 amperes. It must be remembered that the ampere rating indicates the maximum *permissible* current which can be drawn from the secondary, and not the amount which flows, regardless of the type of tube used. Thus, the amount of current which is delivered by the first heater secondary will depend on the load imposed on it by the filaments of the tubes. Each tube which has its filament placed across the terminals of this secondary will have 6.3 volts impressed across it. As more and more tubes are placed across the secondary winding, more current is drawn. Precautions must be observed, so as not to draw more than 4 amperes from the secondary, if this is its maximum current rating. If more current is drawn than specified, the winding will overheat and may burn out. (If more voltage is impressed across the heaters of a tube than called for by the tube, the filament will burn out.)

In Fig. 14-5(B), the same circuit is shown as in (A), except that solid-state rectifiers are used in place of the vacuum-tube diode types. In contrast to the circuits shown in (A), the one in (B), which uses selenium or silicon rectifiers does not have a filament winding for the rectifier tubes. Additional filament windings can, however, be included in the transformer, for furnishing heater voltages for other tubes of the receiver or electronic device powered by this supply.

Full-wave rectification can also be secured without using a center tap in the high-voltage secondary of the power transformer. To accomplish this, however, additional rectifier units are employed. A typical circuit is shown in Fig. 14-6, and this is known as a *bridge rectifier*. Pulsating d-c is provided across the output, and must be filtered with the conventional filter circuits shown earlier.

Operation of the bridge rectifier of Fig. 14-6 is dependent on the manner in which the rectifiers are connected with respect to their polarities. When a positive alternation appears at the secondary, as shown by the first alternation (in solid lines), the top of the secondary is positive and the bottom of the secondary is negative. Under these conditions, the current flow is as shown by the solid arrows. From the bottom of the secondary terminal (negative), current flows through the silicon rectifier S_3 to the junction of S_1 and S_3. Since this current flow is in the opposite direction to

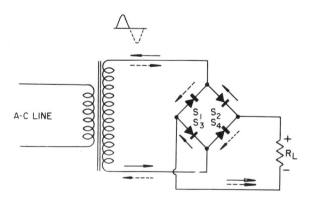

Fig. 14-6. Full-wave bridge rectifier.

what S_1 will conduct, the current cannot enter S_1 but, instead, will flow to the bottom of resistor R_L, and through this resistor to the junction of S_2 and S_4. The current then flows through S_2 to its return circuit which is the positive terminal of the secondary.

When the second alternation appears (shown by the dotted outline), the top of the secondary has a negative polarity and the bottom of the secondary has a positive polarity. Current now flows from the top negative terminal through the circuit, as shown by the dotted arrows.

VOLTAGE DOUBLING

The transformer in a power supply can be dispensed with, and greater voltage than present in the a-c line can still be procured. The voltage increase is accomplished by circuits using voltage-doubling or voltage-tripling systems. A typical transformerless power supply using the voltage-doubling principle is shown in Fig. 14-7(A). Two silicon rectifiers are shown, instead of dual-diode vacuum tube rectifiers, although two diode tubes could also be used. The voltage-doubling circuit furnishes pulsating d-c, which must be filtered for smooth d-c, by using a filter choke and capacitor, as previously detailed.

Reference to the basic voltage-doubling circuit shown in Fig. 14-7(A) will aid in understanding how this circuit functions. Initially, assume that the line voltage applied to the terminals X and Y is an alternation which applies a negative polarity to the X terminal and a plus polarity to the Y terminal. Under this condition, current will flow from the X terminal and will charge capacitor C_1 with a polarity as shown. The completion of the circuit is in such a manner that current flow is in the direction shown by the arrow. During this time, however, the diode rectifier D_2 does not permit current to flow, since it is wired into the circuit in opposite fashion to D_1. (With selenium rectifiers, a slight reverse current will flow, but this is negligible insofar as the rectifying process is concerned.)

During the next alternation of the line voltage, the X input terminal would have a positive polarity, and the Y input terminal would have a negative polarity. Under this condition, diode D_1, is in a nonconducting state. Diode D_2, however, now conducts and permits current to flow through it in the direction shown by the arrow beside D_2. This current flow from the negative Y terminal must complete its circuit back to the positive X terminal. Because C_1 has been charged by the previous alternation, however, the charge on C_1 *will combine with the a-c line voltage,* and hence, double the line voltage will appear across capacitor C_2.

An inspection of the rearranged circuit shown in (B) will help illustrate the manner in which the a-c line voltage adds to the charged capacitor.

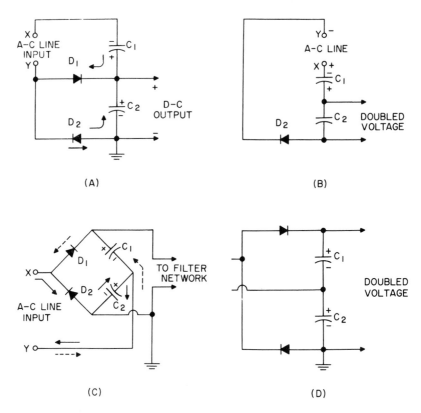

Fig. 14-7. Voltage doubling.

Here, you will note that the a-c line polarity at this instant is negative for the Y terminal and positive for the X terminal. This voltage source is in series with C_1. The latter has stored the energy from the previous alternation, and its polarity is such that its energy adds to that of the a-c line energy in charging capacitor C_2.

During the third alternation, the X terminal is again negative, and capacitor C_1 is recharged. During the fourth alternation, the line voltage and the charge on C_1 again add together to double the voltage impressed across capacitor C_2. Since the doubled voltage which is impressed across C_2 occurs for every *other* alternation, a 60-cycle hum ripple is present, and this ripple must be filtered out by the usual combination of filter capacitors and filter chokes.

Another method for voltage doubling is by use of the circuit shown in (C), where a symmetrical arrangement provides a ripple frequency of 120 cycles per second, instead of a 60-cycle ripple frequency. Hence, this circuit is equivalent to full-wave rectification and, while a ripple filter network is still necessary, the filtering requirements are less demanding than for the 60-cycle ripple frequency.

If the a-c line alternation is such that the input terminal X is negative and the input terminal Y is positive, current will flow from the X terminal in the direction shown by the solid arrows. This path of current from the X terminal includes the diode rectifier D_2 and capacitor C_2, then returns to the positive terminal Y. During this current flow, capacitor C_2 is charged, with a polarity as shown. During the next alternation, when the X terminal is positive and the Y terminal is negative, current will flow as shown by the dotted arrows. Hence, current flows from the Y terminal toward capacitor C_1, and charges the latter through the peak of the line voltage. Current continues through diode rectifier D_1 to the positive X terminal. From the foregoing, it is evident that capacitors C_1 and C_2 are charged to the peak values of the a-c line voltage during successive alternations. The d-c output voltage is taken from across the two capacitors, and hence will be approximately double that of the line voltage, because the two capacitors are effectively in series, with their polarities adding to increase total voltage. While most schematic representations of the circuit are as shown in (C), the circuit has been redrawn in (D) to indicate more clearly how the output voltage is secured from across the two charged series capacitors C_1 and C_2.

Voltage-doubling circuits of the type described usually include a resistor inserted between one lead of the a-c line and the rectifier circuit. Such a resistor, ranging between 5 ohms and 10 ohms, helps limit the peaks of the current surges. Also, when transformerless supplies of these types are used, no convenient transformer windings are available for heating the filaments of the tubes in the receiver. Hence, the heaters of the receiver tubes must be wired in series, so that they will withstand the full line voltage of 115. By wiring a number of tubes in series, each tube is furnished with its required low voltage for the filament, because the individual voltage drops across the tubes are only a fraction of the total line voltage, as discussed in Chapter 12.

VOLTAGE TRIPLING

Vacuum-tube or solid-state diodes can also be used to triple the line voltage in a voltage-tripling power supply. A typical circuit of this type is shown in Fig. 14-8, which illustrates the use of selenium, silicon, or other such rectifiers for this purpose. Diode vacuum-tube rectifiers can take the place of D_1, D_2, and D_3, without any other changes in the circuit, except that the tubes will require heater energy.

An examination of Fig. 14-8(A) will show the manner in which the circuit functions. When an alternation of the a-c input voltage is positive, terminal T_1 will be positive and terminal T_2 negative. Under this condition, electrons will leave the lower terminal (T_2), and will flow through the rectifier circuit to T_1. Since the diode rectifier (D_1) will conduct under such polarity conditions, capacitor C_1 will charge to the peak line voltage, with a polarity as shown. (Actually the charge will be somewhat less than the peak voltage, because of the resistance of D_1 and the resultant voltage drop across the latter. For simplicity, however, reference will be made to the peak-voltage charge.)

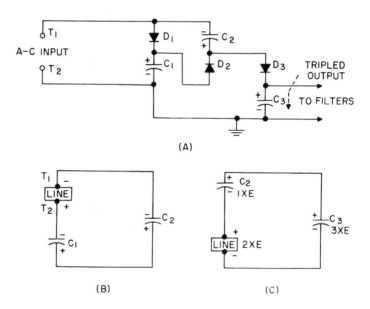

Fig. 14-8. Voltage tripling principles.

During the next alternation, when T_1 is negative and T_2 positive, the rectifier D_1 will not conduct, but D_2 will now conduct, because the proper polarity is present for it. Electrons will leave terminal T_1 and flow through D_2. It will be noted that the return path for D_2 is *via* C_1 *to terminal* T_2. Thus, the charge which is already across C_1 will add to the line voltage and place across C_2 a charge which is proportional to the line voltage added to the potential already across C_1.

This is more clearly shown in Fig. 14-8(B), where the circuit which charges C_2 has been rearranged to illustrate the principle involved. Note that, when the alternation is such that T_1 is negative and T_2 is positive, the charge on C_1 has the same polarity relationship. Consequently, the circuit can be considered as consisting of two generators (the line voltage plus the charge across C_1). This situation is similar to that of placing two batteries in series to get double the voltage. Because capacitor C_2 is across these two voltage sources, the potential which appears across C_2 will be equal to the sum of the voltage across C_1 plus the a-c line voltage.

During the next alternation, when terminal T_1 is positive and terminal T_2 is negative, the charge across C_1 is replenished but, at the same time, rectifier D_3 conducts, and charges capacitor C_3 (see Fig. 14-8(A)). When D_3 conducts, the charge across C_3 will be composed of the line voltage *plus* the existing charge across C_2. Since the charge across C_2 represents the *doubled voltage,* the latter adds to the line voltage, and the result is a triple voltage across C_3. This is shown in Fig. 14-8(C), where the circuit has been redrawn for simplicity, with the rectifier omitted, since it is in a conducting state and can be considered a closed circuit. As can be seen from this drawing, the line voltage represents one potential source in series with the potential source across C_2. The *combination* of these two voltages appears across C_3. Since C_2 has *double* the voltage, and this is added to the existing line voltage, the voltage across C_3 will be three times the normal line voltage.

In the circuit shown at (A), the lowest voltage can be obtained from across C_1. Twice the voltage can be obtained from across C_2, though in this instance the negative potential would not be at ground. A voltage output of three times the line voltage can be obtained from across C_3, though in all instances additional filtering would be necessary to reduce the ripple component to an acceptable minimum, for application to the circuits of receivers and other electronic devices.

VIBRATOR POWER SUPPLY

Portable electronic equipment, such as public address systems, receivers, portable transmitters, Geiger counters, and other electronic devices using vacuum tubes, depend on storage-type batteries for power. Storage batteries, however, furnish only enough voltage for filaments and, to secure higher B voltages, other measures must be taken. One method is to use batteries in series to acquire the necessary high voltage, but these are costly to replace and add extra weight to the portable device. Hence, special devices have been designed to supply the necessary high-voltage d-c from low-voltage batteries. With transistor devices, of course, the potentials available from single storage batteries, or similar battery types, are fully adequate for operation of the device. When vacuum tubes must be employed, however, the problem of acquiring high voltage d-c is of considerable importance.

Since a transformer will not step up d-c voltages, it is necessary to convert the d-c from the battery to equivalent a-c, so it can be stepped up to a higher voltage. This is done by interrupting the battery current flow by use of a *vibrator,* which literally breaks up the pure d-c into changing-amplitude signals in the form of pulses.

The vibrator itself consists of a vibrating reed, a vibrator coil, and contact points. This unit is housed in a metal container which shields it from the circuits of the receiver or other electronic devices operated by the power supply. Such shielding is necessary, because of the high order of interference which results from the sparking contacts of the vibrator.

NONSYNCHRONOUS TYPE

A circuit of a typical vibrator power supply is shown in Fig. 14-9. The vibrator unit is to the left of the horizontal dashed line, and is attached to

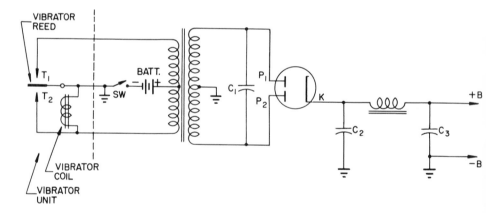

Fig. 14-9. Nonsynchronous vibrator power supply.

the primary of a transformer, as shown. The battery is in series with the center tap of the primary and with a switch (SW). When the switch is closed, it completes the circuit and places the battery potential across the vibrator coil, since a closed circuit will exist from the battery through the lower half of the primary, and then to the coil and back to the negative terminal of the battery. When current flows through the vibrator coil, a magnetic field is set up which attracts the metal vibrating reed and pulls it down to make contact with the lower terminal (T_2). At the time the vibrator reed is in contact with T_2, the vibrator *coil* is effectively *shorted out* and no longer attracts the vibrating reed. Since the vibrator reed is in the form of a springy metal extension, it will move away from T_2 and strike T_1. When the reed leaves T_2, the short is removed from across the vibrator coil, and the magnetic field again builds up and attracts the reed down again to make contact with terminal T_2. This vibrating process is repeated at a rapid rate, and thus alternately applies the battery potential to the upper and lower halves of the primary winding. The process creates a repeated reversal of the magnetic field generated by the primary winding and, therefore, induces a corresponding alternating voltage across the secondary of the transformer. The frequency of this voltage is approximately 115 cycles per second. The voltage which is induced across the transformer secondary can be any amount required, depending on the turns ratio. For the vibrator power supplies, it is stepped up to approximately 300 volts on each side of the center tap. Since this secondary voltage is equivalent to a-c, it must now be rectified, in order to convert it back to d-c. For the latter purpose, a dual-diode tube is used to provide full-wave rectification, as shown in Fig. 14-9. Since this rectified energy will be in the form of pulsating d-c, it will be necessary to use a conventional filtering network, which usually consists of two filter capacitors, as shown, in addition to a filter choke.

In vibrator supplies, a capacitor (C_1) is required across the secondary of the transformer, as shown. This capacitor is known as a *buffer* capacitor and absorbs high-voltage surges which are created by the building up and collapsing of the magnetic fields in the transformer. Thus, it is also effective in minimizing excessive sparking at the contacts of the vibrator. The value of this capacitor is rather critical, and replacement should be made only with the same value as the original.

Sometimes, an R-F choke coil is inserted in series between the cathode and the filter choke, and other chokes and capacitors are included in the system for filtering the *noise,* when this power supply is used for receivers. The vibrator unit is also mounted on rubber to absorb vibrations which might be transferred to nearby receiver tubes.

SYNCHRONOUS TYPE

Another type of vibrator power supply often used is one which does not require a rectifier tube for changing the a-c to d-c. Such a type is known as the *synchronous type* and uses an ingenious circuit which makes the center tap of the secondary transformer at all times positive in polarity with respect to ground.

While it may appear that discussion of the synchronous type should precede that of the nonsynchronous type, the latter is easier to understand and, hence, provides a better introduction to the manner in which vibrator power supplies operate.

Before undertaking an analysis of the circuit involved, reference should be made to Fig. 14-10, which reviews the principles of polarity with respect to a tapped secondary of a transformer. As shown in (A), when a positive alternation of the a-c cycle is present on the secondary, the top terminal (T_1) is positive in polarity with respect to the bottom terminal (T_3). The center tap (T_2), however, is *either positive or negative*, depending on whether it is compared with T_1 or T_3. Thus, the center terminal (T_2) is negative with respect to the top (T_1), but positive with respect to T_3. It is obvious, therefore, that T_2 cannot be considered plus or minus without making such a statement with reference to either terminal T_1 or terminal T_3. When a negative alternation appears across the secondary, as indicated in Fig. 14-10(B), T_1 is negative with respect to the positive T_3. The center tap, however, is positive with respect to T_1, but negative with respect to T_3. Ob-

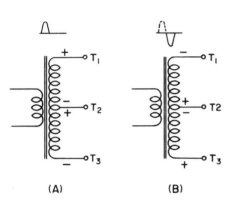

Fig. 14-10. Polarity relationships across a transformer.

viously, in either case, (A) or (B), the center tap can be *either* positive or negative, depending on which reference point is used with respect to T_1 or T_3. If this principle is understood, the factors involved in the synchronous-type power supply can be grasped more readily.

Figure 14-11 shows a typical vibrator power supply utilizing the synchronous design. The vibrator unit now has *four* contact points instead of the two used for the nonsynchronous vibrator. In Fig. 14-11, the top contacts have been marked A_1 and A_2, while the bottom contacts have been marked B_1 and B_2. A vibrator coil is still included, as with the nonsynchronous type.

During operation, contact points A_2 and B_2 function in similar manner to the contact points for the nonsynchronous type, by breaking up the d-c into equivalent a-c, so that the potentials can be stepped up, at the transformer secondary, to the required amplitude. When the vibrator reed makes contact with the top terminals (A_1 and A_2), assume that a negative alternation appears across the secondary. If this is the case, terminal C of the secondary would be negative while terminal E would be positive. Terminal D, however, would be positive with respect to C and, if the latter could be grounded *at this particular instant,* it would definitely establish the center tap (D) as positive with respect to ground. This is exactly what is done by terminal A_1. When the vibrating reed makes contact with this terminal, it automatically grounds the top of the secondary (C), because the reed itself is grounded. When the reed makes contact with the lower terminals, B_1 and B_2, a positive alternation appears across the secondary, making the top of the transformer secondary (C) positive and the bottom (E) negative. Again, the center tap (D) is positive, but now *with respect to the bottom terminal (E)*. This condition is again assured because terminal B_1 makes contact with the vibrating reed and, therefore, grounds B_1 and terminal E of the secondary. Thus, again the negative polarity is placed to ground, which in turn would make D positive with respect to E. It can now be seen that, as the reed vibrates, it alternately places the top and the bottom of the secondary at ground, at the exact moment when such a terminal is negative with respect to the center tap. Thus, the center tap is always of positive polarity with respect to ground, and the necessity for a rectifier is eliminated.

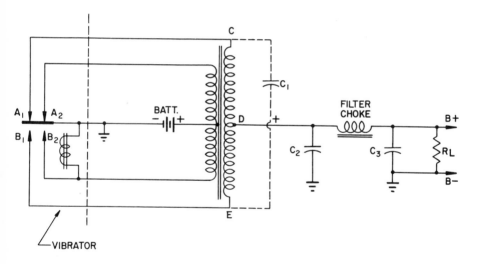

Fig. 14-11. Synchronous power supply.

The d-c thus found is still pulsating and, for this reason, it is again necessary to use a filtering circuit, in the conventional manner. A filter choke plus two filter capacitors are usually employed, as shown in Fig. 14-11.

The vibrator-type power supplies are also known as *converters* (because they *convert* d-c to a-c) and as *choppers* (because they literally "chop up" the d-c to form a signal having a-c characteristics). In some industrial applications the circuit is modified somewhat from those shown previously so that the nature of the output signal can be controlled to meet specific

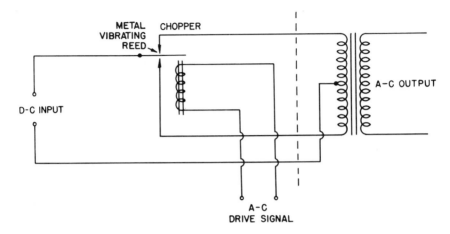

Fig. 14-12. Industrial chopper.

requirements. A typical chopper of this type is shown in Fig. 14-12. Here, the vibrator coil is supplied an a-c signal from an external source. By varying the frequency of this drive signal, the frequency of the output a-c can be adjusted as needed. Also, the d-c input signal amplitude can be changed to regulate the amount of output a-c which appears at the secondary of the transformer. As with the previously discussed vibrator supplies, the output can be rectified and filtered if needed.

Instead of the mechanical vibrators, the d-c can be converted to a-c using either vacuum tubes or transistors in circuits known as *inverters*. To understand how this is accomplished, first consider the simple circuit shown at Fig. 14-13(A). This is a neon tube flasher or "blinker" consisting of a d-c source and an RC network, as shown. When voltage is first applied, the voltage across the capacitor builds up gradually as the capacitor charges, in accordance with the time-constant factors discussed earlier in Chapter 6. Thus, the full voltage necessary to ionize the neon light is not applied immediately. When the capacitor voltage charge has reached a value sufficient to ionize the neon tube, the latter glows and conducts current. The low internal resistance during ionization shunts the capacitor and hence discharges it through the neon tube. With the capacitor discharged, the neon ionization stops and the voltage starts to build up again across the capacitor, repeating the entire process. Thus, the neon tube flashes intermittently at a rate dependent on the time constant of the resistor and capacitor.

The same principle is utilized to convert d-c to a-c in commercial inverter circuits. A typical inverter is shown at Fig. 14-13(B), with the primary of the transformer in series with the gas tube (such as a thyratron).

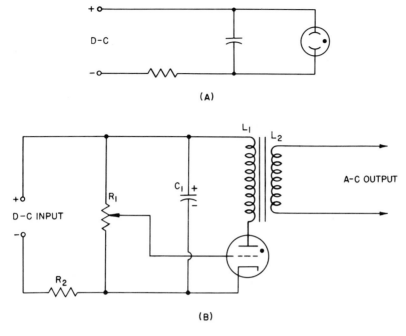

Fig. 14-13. Inverter circuit.

When d-c is first applied, the capacitor (shunting the transformer primary and the tube) prevents conduction of the tube because voltage builds up gradually across C_1 depending on the time constant of R_2 and C_1. When the voltage across the capacitor reaches a value sufficient to ionize the tube, current flows through the latter from cathode to plate and through the primary L_1 toward the positive side of the d-c input source.

The inductor L_1, in turn, opposes a change of current and the latter builds up at a rate depending on the L-R time constant. At the same time the inductor stores energy in the magnetic fields which are built up. During tube conduction the tube impedance is at a low value and the capacitor discharges through the tube. When the capacitor has discharged fully it *momentarily* acts as a short-circuit shunt across the tube and hence drops the anode potential and ionization stops. During the current rise in the transformer primary a voltage is induced across the secondary, and during the collapsing fields of the primary, the induced voltage at the secondary is of opposite polarity to that during L_1 current rise. Hence, an a-c output voltage is obtained across L_2 (the secondary winding). Resistor R_1 sets the time the tube fires. (Additional thyratron factors are given later in this chapter.)

FILTER FACTORS

There are a variety of filter circuits which can be employed for smoothing out the ripple in power supplies. The most representative types are illustrated in Fig. 14-14. At (A) is shown the choke input filter. This type consists of an iron-core choke having a value which can range from approximately 5 henrys to approximately 25 henrys. Such a choke coil is sometimes referred to as a *smoothing* choke. A single capacitor is sufficient for some power supply applications, though, when a single filter capacitor is utilized, it must be of a higher rating in terms of microfarads than filter sections utilizing several capacitors and chokes.

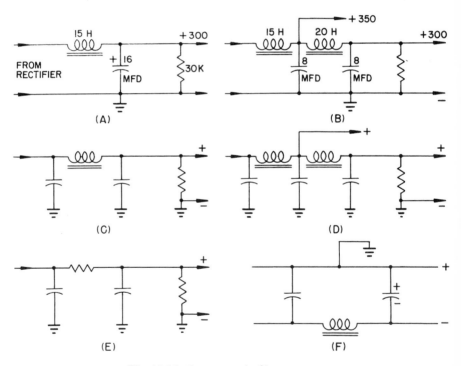

Fig. 14-14. Power-supply filter systems.

The choke input filter type provides better power supply regulation than the capacitor input type, as more fully detailed later in this chapter. The resistor shown at the output of the filter section is the bleeder resistor which also improves regulation, since there is a constant current flow through this resistor. Such a resistor can also be used as a voltage divider, as explained earlier in this chapter.

A more elaborate choke input filter section is shown in Fig. 14-14(B). This circuit has greater ability to smooth the ripple components of the rectified a-c. The first inductance shown will limit the peak values of voltage, because of its characteristics in opposing a current change such as results during pulsating d-c. The filter choke also presents a high inductive reactance to the ripple components of the rectified waveform. Similarly, the filter capacitor presents a low shunt reactance for ripple components. From the practical standpoint, however, the filter capacitors charge to peak values of voltage, and tend to maintain a constant output voltage, free from fluctuations, because of the storage characteristics of the capacitors and their ability to oppose voltage changes. With the double section filter shown in (B), the output voltage is substantially free from ripple and suitable for circuits in which the hum factor must be kept at a low level. If such a device is used for an audio-amplifier system, for instance, the output voltage can be applied to the early stages, where a minimum of ripple is desired. For the power-output amplifier stages, where amplification is low and a slight ripple is not a serious factor, the B voltage can be obtained from the junction of the two filter chokes. This arrangement also provides a higher level of voltage than is secured from the other output, because the voltage drop across the d-c resistance of the second filter choke reduces the output voltage.

The capacitor input type of filter, such as shown in Fig. 14-14(C), will provide a higher output voltage than the choke input filters, but regulation is somewhat poorer. The higher output voltage is achieved because the first filter capacitor charges to the peak value of the rectified signal waveform. When a choke input is used, the filter capacitor which follows it does not charge to as high a peak value, since the latter amplitude has been lowered and smoothed by the input-smoothing filter choke. The filter section shown in (C) utilizes two capacitors, so that the hum level is considerably lower than would be the case with the simple filter circuit shown in (A). The filter section in (C) is most commonly used in home radios or audio systems, and also in television receivers. In high-fidelity systems or in television receivers, where it is necessary to keep hum levels at a minimum, the type of filter section shown in (D) is sometimes employed. This is a capacitor input filter using a double section similar to the choke input shown in (B). The filter section in (D), however, has somewhat poorer regulation than the choke input filter, though the output voltage levels would be higher.

The most inexpensive type of filter system is that shown in (E), which uses a combination of resistance and capacitance. Here, a capacitor input filter is utilized, but the filter choke is replaced by a fixed resistor. The disadvantage of this system is that a proportionately larger voltage drop occurs across the series resistor, thus decreasing the voltage output. The cost is less, however, because the higher-priced filter choke has been replaced by a comparatively low-priced resistor.

For bias supplies, where a negative potential with respect to ground is desired, the filter section shown in (F) is often employed. Here, the positive terminal of the power supply is placed at ground potential, and the filter choke is placed in the negative lead, as shown. This procedure prevents isolation of the ground portions of the power supply, which would otherwise occur if the filter choke were to remain in the positive lead. With bias supplies, any of the other combinations of choke or capacitor input filters can be employed.

REGULATION

The amount of voltage obtainable across the output terminals of a power supply depends on the voltage produced by the secondary winding less the voltage drops which occur across the rectifier and the filter chokes. Because the amplitude of the voltage which drops across the rectifier and filter chokes depends on the amount of current flowing through these units, the voltage output of a power supply is also affected by the amount of current drawn from the unit. When a minimum of current is drawn from the power supply, the output voltage will be near its maximum value, since the voltage drops across the rectifier and filter chokes will be at a minimum. When more current is drawn from the power supply, the voltage drops across the power supply units increase and, in consequence, the output voltage is reduced. This variation of voltage output with respect to the amount of current drawn from the power supply is known as *voltage regulation,* as mentioned previously.

When the load circuit is such that its current drain from the power supply varies, voltage regulation will be poor if a capacitor input filter is used. Poorer regulation occurs because the capacitor at the input of the filter section will charge to the peak voltage of the rectified a-c, but such a peak value is impressed across the capacitor at only short time intervals because the voltage peaks of the pulsating d-c have a short duration. Thus, as more current is drawn from the power supply, the charge on the filter capacitors is drained off more rapidly than it can be replaced by the current peaks of the pulsating d-c. With the choke input filter, however, the peaks have been reduced to a lower level and, in consequence, there is less of a decline from the relatively high-peak value to the average value which results by virtue of the choke input filter.

The percentage of voltage regulation of a power supply can be expressed by the formula

$$\% \text{ voltage regulation} = \frac{\text{no-load } E - \text{full-load } E}{\text{full-load } E} \times 100$$

This formula takes into consideration the proportions of voltage increase and decrease with a change of load on a power supply. The load on a power supply would consist of the radio, amplifier, or other device attached to it, in terms of the amount of current drawn. Actually, the load on the power supply would also include any bleeder resistor which may be placed across it, since the latter would also consume power. Thus, if the voltage is 400 with no load attached to the power supply, but decreases to 300 volts under load, the calculation for the percentage of voltage regulation would be

$$\frac{400 - 300}{300} \times 100 = \frac{100}{300} \times 100 = 0.3 \times 100 = 30\%$$

This percentage would indicate the amount of regulation, and the same calculation can be utilized for each of several power supplies, in order to compare their differences in regulation. The greater the difference between the full-load and no-load voltages, the poorer the regulation of the power supply. Power supply regulation is particularly important when electronic devices are used which have a varying load; that is, when the current drawn from the power supply varies constantly. The conventional radio, FM, and television receivers usually do not require exceptionally good regulation, since the load is constant a few minutes after the receiver is turned on. When the receiver is first turned on, there is virtually no load on the power supply, since approximately 30 seconds to one minute elapse before the cathodes of the indirectly-heated vacuum tubes come up to full temperature. After the vacuum tubes are at operating temperatures, current flow is at a maximum, and a full load is impressed on the power supply. Thus, for the remaining time during which the receiver is utilized, there is virtually no load change on the power supply. Many television receivers, particularly the color types, require good voltage regulation because certain circuits are employed which depend on proper voltage relationships for good function.

There are several ways to improve the voltage regulation of a power supply. One of these is to use a choke input filter, instead of the capacitor input filter as mentioned previously. Use of an input choke results in a considerable improvement in regulation, as shown by Fig. 14-15, which is a graph of a typical rectifier tube, the 5U4, often used in public address systems, console television and high fidelity systems, etc. As shown, the regulation with a filter capacitor input is much poorer than with a choke input, for various values of plate voltage supplied from the secondary of the transformer. For a comparison of the differences, note the solid line for 400 volts of Fig. 14-15, which represents capacitor input versus the dashed line of 400 volts, which represents a choke input filter. The rectified output voltage from the filter for choke input remains substantially constant for various differences in current drawn by the load. For the solid line indicating capacitor input, however, the rectifier output voltage varies from a high value of approximately 560 volts at zero current, to less than 400 volts, with 250 milliamperes of current drawn by the load.

The ability of the choke input filter to improve regulation can be increased to a greater degree by the use of a *swinging choke* which is particularly designed to produce a considerable change in inductive value with a change in the current flow through the choke inductance. The

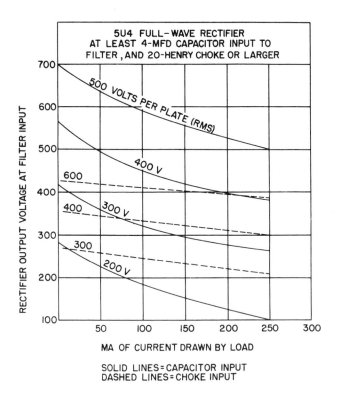

Fig. 14-15. Rectifier regulation chart.

swinging choke is also known as a *saturable reactor* because it has a change of reactance for changes of its magnetic density when operated around the saturation levels of the B-H curve. The most efficient type of swinging choke utilizes core material which produces the nearly rectangular hysteresis loop shown earlier in Fig. 6-15(B). As discussed in Chapter 6, the permeability of core material is altered by varying the intensity of the magnetizing force. A change in permeability will also change the inductance and hence the inductive reactance. The swinging choke has a high value inductance when there is little current flowing through it. With a low value of current flow the core is below the saturation level, hence permeability and inductance values are high. In some swinging chokes, the high value of the inductance is approximately 22 to 25 henrys.

With a high value inductance, the impedance of the choke is also high, and a larger voltage drop occurs across it. Because of the latter factor, the output voltage of the power supply is lower. As more current is drawn by the load circuit, the voltage output would normally tend to decrease. When more current flows through the swinging choke, however, the magnetizing force causes saturation (or near-saturation) and the inductance value may drop to a level between 5 and 10 henrys. When the inductance value drops, the series impedance decreases and the voltage drop across the choke becomes less. Hence, the output voltage of the power supply tends to rise and compensate for the drop which otherwise occurs because of the increased current drawn by the load circuit. The swinging choke is usually used as the input choke to the type of filter which was shown in Fig. 14-14(B). The swinging choke is followed by a second choke, of the ordinary smoothing variety.

Another method for improving regulation is to employ gaseous rectifiers, such as the mercury-vapor types. Because of the ionization which occurs within such tubes, the internal resistance is very low and, in consequence, there is a minimum of voltage drop across them, for either high or low values of current flow. Gaseous rectifiers are employed frequently in commercial power supplies where a high degree of voltage regulation is essential in industrial control applications or critical circuits in computers, transmitters, or other such units. Such rectifiers, however, are not suitable for receivers because of the high-frequency noise which they develop during ionization, as mentioned in Chapter 11.

Improved regulation can also be provided by use of solid-state or gaseous voltage regulator units. Typical regulator tubes of this type include the VR-105-30, VR-150-40, etc. The first number refers to the terminal voltage, and the second number is the maximum current which the tube is permitted to pass. Tubes of this type maintain the voltage of the power supply at a close constant level, even though the load on the power supply is such that the current varies considerably.

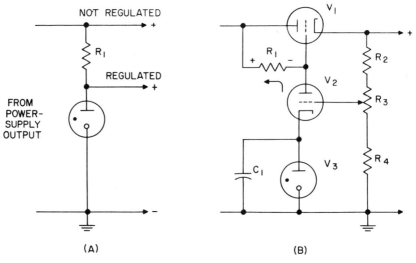

Fig. 14-16. Voltage regulators.

For a single-tube voltage regulator, the circuit shown in Fig. 14-16(A) is employed. This circuit is attached to the output from the power supply, following the filter section. Resistor R_1 is a limiting resistor, which must have a value such that, under no-load conditions, the current does not exceed the current rating of the voltage regulator tube.

The regulator tube will not only maintain a constant voltage for current variations caused by a varying load, but also for voltage variations of the a-c line. If the load current decreases, the voltage across the regulator network would tend to increase. The increase across the network causes the current through the regulator tube to rise, increasing the voltage drop across the limiting resistor. An increase in voltage drop across the latter will cause a corresponding decrease in the output voltage from the power supply. Hence, the rise in voltage, which might be caused by a line voltage increase or a load current decrease, will be compensated for by the regulator tube. On the other hand, if the voltage across the regulator network tends to decline, because of a lower a-c line voltage or because of an increase in the load current, the current through the regulator tube drops. Since the limiting resistor is in series with the regulator tube, there will be less current through the resistor and less voltage will develop across the latter. This permits the output voltage to rise and compensate for the tendency of the output voltage to drop.

A higher order of regulation and, hence, a better voltage stability may be obtained by use of a more elaborate regulating system, as shown in Fig. 14-16(B). Here, V_1 and V_2 are high-vacuum tubes, and V_3 is the gaseous voltage regulator tube. Such a system, while more elaborate than that shown in A, finds usefulness when it is necessary to maintain the output voltage variations within approximately 0.02 volt per milliampere of current flow in the system.

Both V_1 and V_2 are triode tubes, such as used in the audio amplifiers of radios or television receivers. Tube V_1 should be a power-amplifier type, while V_2 should be a voltage-amplifier tube having a fairly high amplification factor. Pentode tubes can also be employed, instead of triodes.

The regulator tube, V_3, maintains the cathode of V_2 at a constant voltage with respect to ground. Tube V_2 functions as a control tube, and obtains bias from the potentiometer R_3. The latter control permits setting the amount of the regulated voltage in the circuit.

Assume that the load on the power supply decreases and, hence, draws less current. In such an instance, the tendency would be for the voltage across the resistive network R_2, R_3, and R_4 to rise. If a voltage rise occurs, the grid of the control tube, V_2, experiences a decline in the voltage applied to it, because of the rise of voltage across resistor R_3. When the grid voltage of V_2 decreases (the grid being negative with respect to the positive output terminal of the network), there will be a current increase through V_2 and, hence, an increase in the current flow through R_1. The increased current through R_1 also increases the voltage drop across this resistor. An increase in voltage across this resistor will raise the negative potential present at the grid of V_1, so that current through the latter tube declines. The lower current through V_1 increases the plate resistance of this tube, and the voltage drop across the tube therefore rises. The rise in voltage across V_1 decreases the output voltage at the terminal marked plus.

From the foregoing, it is obvious that a change of voltage across the resistive network R_2, R_3, and R_4 varies the bias on V_2, which in turn affects the conduction of V_1. A change of voltage across the resistive network also affects the current through V_2, because of the bias change at the grid of the latter. The voltage regulator tube, by maintaining a constant cathode potential, regardless of current flow through V_2, permits the bias changes of V_2 to be the sole voltage regulating factor.

Capacitor C_1 across the voltage regulator tube minimizes the tendency for the circuit to generate audio-frequency oscillations, which sometimes occur in a circuit of this type.

ZENER VOLTAGE REGULATORS

The silicon-junction diode is used as a voltage regulator because of its unusual breakdown characteristics graphed in Fig. 14-17. When forward bias (voltage) is applied the diode behaves much like ordinary silicon (or other solid-state) diodes, though with lower internal resistance and greater current-passing characteristics as the voltage is raised. When reverse voltage of a low amplitude is applied, the resistance of the unit is high and only a few microamperes of current flow. As the reverse voltage is gradually increased only a slight conduction increase occurs. Once, however, the reverse voltage reaches a certain amplitude the internal resistance suddenly drops to a low value and current shoots up from a few microamperes to several milliamperes as shown in the lower left-hand quadrant of the graph in Fig. 14-17. Despite the sudden high amplitude current flow, the voltage drop across the diode remains practically the same as before the breakdown, making the device very useful for voltage regulation.

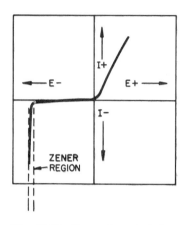

Fig. 14-17. Zener characteristics.

The reverse-voltage breakdown is not damaging to the zener diode as it would be for other diodes (solid-stage or tube). The breakdown occurs when a certain reverse-voltage amplitude is reached which is sufficient to penetrate the diode's internal semiconductor barrier, causing the unit to become a conductor in the reverse direction. After removal of the reverse voltage the internal barrier region reforms itself without damage.

The breakdown point is known as the *zener region,* as shown on the graph. The breakdown point can be closely estimated during design and manufacture by control of the internal resistivity of the silicon structure. Hence, the zener point can be set at several volts or at several hundred volts as desired. In ordinary silicon rectifiers the zener point is set sufficiently high so as to be beyond the *peak inverse voltage* (discussed later) at which the unit is rated.

A typical zener-diode voltage regulation circuit is shown at Fig. 14-18(A). Note that this is basically similar to the gas-tube regulator shown in Fig. 14-16. For the zener regulator, the value of the reverse-current limiting resistor R_1 must be chosen to hold the diode in the zener region. While operating in the zener region, the voltage drop across the diode remains constant, even though the current drawn by the load varies and would normally affect voltage regulation.

The zener diodes can also be utilized for voltage regulation of a-c as shown at Fig. 14-18(B). Here, two zener diodes are placed "back-to-back" so that each half of the a-c cycle is under control. Two separate zener diodes can be employed, or special double-ended diodes, manu-

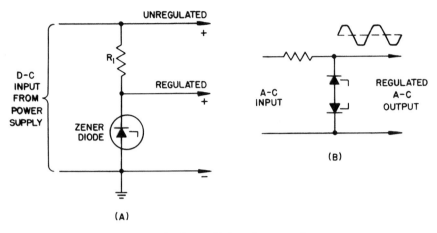

Fig. 14-18. Zener-diode voltage regulators.

factured specifically for this purpose, can be used. With separate diodes, each should have identical operating characteristics as the other. The output waveform is clipped somewhat at the peaks, as shown.

FILTER RATINGS AND VALUES

The various components in the filter section of a power supply must have the proper ratings, both in terms of the permissible voltage which can be employed on them, and in terms of their value in either capacity, resistance, or inductance. The power rating is also important in preventing burn-out.

The filter choke should have a value approaching that indicated in the previous discussions, or larger, to provide smooth and effective filtering. Also, the wires which make up the winding of a choke must have sufficient insulation and be of adequate size to carry the current consumed by the load without undue overheating. Thus, a choke coil would not only be rated in 5 or 10 henrys, but also at 100 milliamperes or 150 milliamperes. The latter ratings would indicate the maximum permissible current flow through the filter choke. An increase in either the inductance or the rated value of current is advisable to provide better smoothing action, as well as longer life.

Most filter capacitors are rated in their capacity value in microfarads, and their rating also usually includes peak voltage and working voltage. The peak voltage rating is the maximum voltage which the capacitor can be subjected to during the initial warmup of the receiver or other load. During such a time, the output from the power supply increases, and the filter capacitors would have a higher voltage than normal impressed on them. Thus, the peak voltage which occurs before load warmup must not exceed the rated peak value of the filter capacitor. When the load is drawing a normal amount of current and the voltage from the rectifiers has dropped to the value normal during operation, the voltage existing across the filter capacitors should not exceed the working voltage (WV) marked on the capacitor.

As a general rule the higher-capacity filter capacitors are preferable to the lower ones, for smoother filter action. There are occasions, however, when an increase in the value of the capacitor used as the input to the filter network may not be advisable because of inverse peak voltage effects described more fully later. Hence, a filter capacitor having a value in excess of 30 microfarads should not be employed for the input filter unless the specifications for the rectifier tube are checked initially to make sure a higher value of capacity can safely be employed. For filter capacitors which follow a filter choke, however, the higher values can be used safely for the production of a more ripple-free d-c output, and in consequence minimizing the possibility of hum modulation of the receiver or other electronic device which is fed by the power supply.

The input filter capacitor should have a voltage rating which is above the peak value of the pulsating d-c applied across it. Thus, if the transformer secondary furnishes 400 volts of a-c (rms), the peak value of such a voltage would be 1.41 times the rms value, or 564 volts. Thus, the input filter capacitor should have a *working voltage rating* in excess of 564 volts to minimize the danger of internal arcing and capacitor damage. A value of 600 volts or more is preferred.

When a single capacitor of sufficiently high voltage rating is unavailable, two filter capacitors can be wired in series to provide a voltage rating which is substantially higher than the peak value of the voltage applied across the particular capacitor. Thus, if two capacitors are placed in series and each has a 450-volt rating, the combination will withstand 900 volts. Since considerably less voltage will actually be impressed across the two in combination, they will not be subjected to overload, and will have a much longer life. When two such capacitors are utilized in series as the input capacitor of the power-supply filter, each should have the same value, and preferably the same d-c resistance, as the other, as measured on an ohmmeter. This matching of the two insures the equal distribution of voltage across each. It must be remembered, however, that if an 8-microfarad input filter capacity is desired, *two 16-microfarad* filter capacitors must be employed in series. The series circuit of two 16-microfarad capacitors will result in a total capacity of 8 microfarads.

PEAK INVERSE VOLTAGE

Generally, rectifier tubes are rated in terms of current, voltage, and peak inverse voltage. The current rating is the maximum current which is permitted to flow through the tube without causing damage. The voltage rating is the maximum voltage which may be applied safely across the anode and cathode of the tube without causing arc (voltage breakdown). The peak inverse voltage rating is the peak value of the voltage which may exist between the plate and the filament (cathode) of the rectifier during the time when the latter is not conducting. In a simple half-wave rectifier circuit without any filter section, the peak inverse voltage would simply be the product of the rms value multiplied by 1.41. Thus, if the transformer delivers 400 volts, the peak inverse voltage would be 400 times 1.41 or 564 volts. Rectifiers with the necessary filter sections, however, have different inverse peak voltage values, because of the effect of the voltage charges appearing across capacitors.

Figure 14-19(A) shows a typical half-wave rectifier system using a

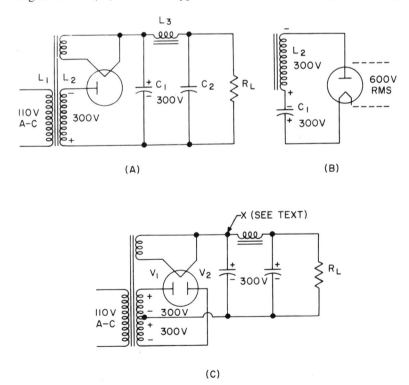

Fig. 14-19. Peak inverse voltage with capacitor input filter.

capacitor input filter. Each time the rectifier tube conducts, a charge is placed across capacitors C_1 *and* C_2, as mentioned previously in this chapter. Capacitor C_1, however, receives the full charge of the rectified voltage. As shown at (A), if the secondary of the transformer delivers 300 volts rms, capacitor C_1 is also charged to this voltage value with a polarity as indicated in the drawing. During the time the tube is not conducting, a negative potential appears at the top of the secondary winding L_2 and a positive potential appears at the lower end of this winding as shown in Fig. 14-19(A). During the time the tube is in its nonconducting state, the charge on the input capacitor is added to the voltage produced by the secondary winding. This is shown at (B), where the secondary L_2, the capacitor C_1, and the rectifier tube have been redrawn for simplicity. Note that the polarity of the voltage across the secondary and the polarity of the charge appearing across the capacitor are aiding and not opposing each other. In consequence, the secondary of the transformer can be considered as one generator in series with the capacitor, which represents another generator. Thus, the voltage impressed across the rectifier tube is the sum of these two voltages. Hence, the peak inverse voltage which appears across the rectifier tube during nonconduction is 846 volts as the following calculation indicates

$$\text{Peak inverse voltage} = 300 + 300 = 600 \text{ volts (rms)}$$
$$600 \times 1.41 = 846 \text{ peak inverse volts}$$

From the foregoing, it is evident that with a capacitor input filter, the rectifier tube must be able to withstand 846 volts in the reverse direction to normal current flow and for safety should have a peak inverse voltage rating of 1,000 volts or more. In gas-filled rectifier tubes the danger of arcing is much greater and the specifications for the gas-tube rectifier regarding its peak inverse voltage rating must be referred to before using such a tube. In most instances the gas-filled rectifiers should be used with choke input filters, since the input choke reduces the amplitude of the voltage which is applied to the capacitor following the filter choke.

Figure 14-19(C) shows a full-wave power supply. Here, the peak inverse voltage is of a value twice that produced by one-half of the secondary winding. Thus, if each half of the secondary winding delivers 300 volts as shown, the peak inverse voltage is 846 volts. This is the amount of voltage which appears across the rectifier which is in a nonconducting state. For instance, at the instant the voltage polarities are as shown in Fig. 14-19(C), the rectifier V_1 is conducting because its anode is positive, while rectifier V_2 is not conducting, because its anode is negative. It is across V_2 that the peak inverse voltage appears at this instant. During the next alternation of the a-c which appears across the secondary, V_2 conducts, and the peak inverse voltage appears across the cathode-anode of V_1.

During the time one tube is conducting, its internal resistance is low. A gas-rectifier has a particularly low internal resistance during conduction because of the ionization which occurs. For the full-wave rectifier shown in Fig. 14-19, when V_1 is conducting, the cathode will be at a potential which is almost that of the top of the secondary winding because the low internal drop between cathode and anode would create only a small potential difference in the voltage across cathode and plate. Hence, the point marked X in the drawing would have a high peak inverse voltage value regardless of the filter type in the full-wave power supply. With the point marked X common with the cathode of the rectifier having the same potential as the top of the secondary winding, there will be a 600 volt rms difference between the cathode and the anode of the nonconducting tube. This condition would prevail even if only a load resistor were present without the filter network.

POWER SUPPLY BLEEDERS

As mentioned earlier, a resistor (or several resistors in series) may be placed across the output of a power supply, as shown in Fig. 14-16. Such a resistor (or resistors) is known as a *bleeder,* because the latter maintains a constant current drain on the power supply and, by thus "bleeding" off some of the current, a slight though constant load is imposed on the power supply to help stabilize it and to improve regulation.

The bleeder should be designed to consume between 5% and 10% of the current drawn by the load (the load in this instance referring to the radio circuits, amplifier circuits, or other systems which are furnished power from the supply). Regulation is improved somewhat when 10% current is drawn by the bleeder instead of a lower value, but the higher bleeder current requires a larger wattage bleeder resistor, and the additional current drawn by the bleeder must not impose an undue load on the power supply transformer secondary windings. A bleeder should not be used if the power supply is already loaded to its full current capabilities.

If the load in Fig. 14-20(A) draws 200 milliamperes, and the bleeder is to consume 5% of such current (10 milliamperes), the value of the bleeder resistor would be

$$R = \frac{E}{I} = \frac{400}{0.01} = 40,000 \text{ ohms}$$

The wattage in power consumed by the bleeder would be

$$P = EI = 400 \times 0.01 = 4 \text{ watts}$$

Since the bleeder consumes 4 watts of power, it is necessary to employ

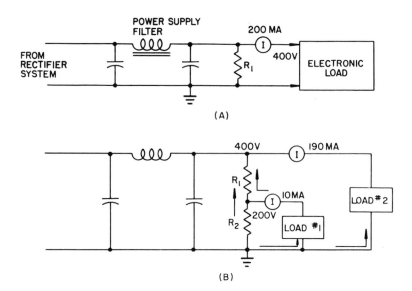

Fig. 14-20. Load distribution in power supplies.

a resistor having a sufficiently high wattage rating to withstand the heat generated. Hence, to minimize overheating and to provide a margin of safety, a resistor having a wattage rating of about 10 watts is preferable over lower wattage values.

When two or more series resistors are used in the bleeder section to supply intermediate voltages (in addition to the maximum voltage), the bleeder section is also referred to as a *voltage divider*. Such a voltage divider bleeder is shown in Fig. 14-20(B), and consists of R_1 and R_2. For this power supply, load No. 2 draws 190 milliamperes at 400 volts, while load No. 1 draws 10 milliamperes at 200 volts.

Assume that resistor R_2 has 100 milliamperes of current flowing through it. As shown in Fig. 14-20(B), resistor R_2 is shunted by load No. 1, which also draws 10 milliamperes. Hence, resistor R_2 is in parallel with load No. 1, and the combination will draw a total of 20 milliamperes through resistor R_1, since the current for both R_2 and load No. 1 flows through this resistor, as shown by the arrows in the schematic.

Since there is a 200-volt drop across R_1 and 20 milliamperes of current flow through it, by Ohm's law the resistance value of R_1 must be 10,000 ohms. Resistor R_2 also has 200 volts across it, and with 10 milliamperes of current flowing through it the resistance value must be 20,000 ohms. Load No. 1 must also be 20,000 ohms, since it also has 200 volts across it and draws 10 milliamperes. The total resistance of R_2 and load No. 1 must, therefore, be 10,000 ohms. It is obvious that both R_1 and the combination of R_2 and load No. 1 must have equal resistance values, in order to divide the 400 volts in half.

Voltage dividers can employ several resistors in series to obtain intermediate values of voltage division, as required. Each load which shunts a section of the voltage divider draws additional current, and such additional current will flow through the resistors above it in similar fashion to the two loads illustrated in Fig. 14-20(B).

THYRATRON RECTIFIER

The thyratron gas tube described earlier in Chapter 12 is also a rectifier, but unlike the diode rectifiers, it contains a grid for initiating current flow. Once current flows through the tube, however, the grid loses control and can't stop conduction unlss the anode voltage is removed. The basic circuit shown in Fig. 14-21 will help demonstrate the thyratron characteristics. Here, when the switch (SW) is closed the battery potential is applied between cathode and anode (in series with the load resistance R_L). Since the grid is negative, however, no current flows through the thyratron. If the grid voltage is now reduced by moving the variable arm of R_1 toward the cathode, current will flow through the tube and ionization occurs. If the negative bias is now applied again to the grid it will be ineffectual and current flow continues because of the ionic space charge which is set up around the grid as described in Chapter 12. In order to stop conduction it is necessary to open the switch in the anode circuit. When current flow and ionization stop, the switch may again be closed and the negative potential at the grid will again hold the tube in the nonconduction state.

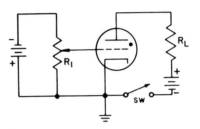

Fig. 14-21. Circuit illustrating thyratron characteristics.

The firing time of thyratrons is related to the amplitude of the anode voltage, the gas pressure within the tube, and the type of gas it contains. The internal structure also affects firing time because it determines the grid sensitivity. In some thyratrons, the grid can be slightly negative for firing, while in others (with more shielding between anode and cathode) it is necessary to reduce the bias to zero or to a small positive value.

The rapidity with which ionization occurs is known as *ionization time* and in many thyratrons it is less than 5 microseconds. The *deionization time* (the minimum interval of time for neutralization of the ionic space charge surrounding the grid after current flow has been interrupted) in many thyratrons averages 500 microseconds, though some have a deionization time of less than 100 microseconds. When deionization time is long, usage of the device is limited to power sources having a 60-cps frequency.

The presence of the grid in the thyratron takes it out of the class of an ordinary rectifier and permits it to be used for the control of the amount of power applied to a load. Hence, thyratron devices (including the solid-state type discussed later) find wide application in industrial control, automation, and in other areas where the amount of power to a load must be varied. With the thyratron, a small grid potential of negligible power can control thousands of watts of power.

Since the thyratron is a rectifier it lends itself to operation with a-c at both the grid and anode circuits. With a-c, the control of the power applied to the load is determined by the relative *phase* of the grid signal versus the anode signal. Because the grid control is lost once the tube is conducting, the use of an a-c signal at the anode permits the grid to regain control. This is so because successive alternations of a-c to the anode causes conduction to be interrupted, regardless of the polarity of the grid signal.

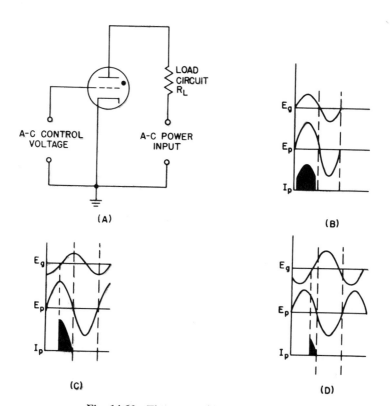

Fig. 14-22. Thyratron control characteristics.

Operation with a-c signals is shown in Fig. 14-22. At (A) is shown the basic circuit, with the power source for the load applied to the anode circuit below the load resistance R_L. If the grid signal is in phase with the a-c power input signal as shown at (B), the thyratron will conduct for successive positive alternations at the anode, as shown. When the grid signal E_g is positive-going at the same time as the plate voltage E_p, plate current I_p starts to flow as soon as the anode potential reaches a value which will cause ionization. When the grid signal is negative-going, the phase coincides with E_p and conduction ceases. Thus, the tube acts as a half-wave rectifier in a fashion similar to the others described earlier.

If there is a 90-degree phase difference between E_g and E_p as shown at (C), the tube will not start conducting until the grid bias is reduced sufficiently to permit conduction, even though the anode is positive initially. When the anode potential drops to the point where ionization ceases, conduction stops even though the grid waveform is still positive. With a greater shift of E_g as shown at (D), the interval of conduction is still shorter, and in consequence less power is applied to the load circuit. Thus, by shifting the phase of the grid potential a considerable variation of output power is possible. The pulsating d-c produced can be filtered, if necessary, for ripple reduction.

SILICON-CONTROLLED RECTIFIER

A solid-state counterpart of the vacuum-tube thyratron is the *silicon-controlled rectifier* shown at Fig. 14-23(A). This device combines some of the characteristics of both the solid-state diode and the transistor, as shown at (B). (Symbols which have been used for this device are shown at (C).) The threaded terminal is the anode, and this is bolted to the chassis, with the flange acting as a heat sink as with the silicon diodes

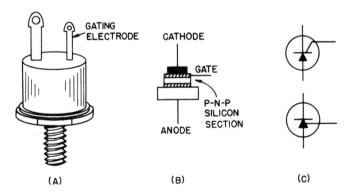

Fig. 14-23. Silicon-controlled rectifier.

previously described. The controlled rectifiers come in various sizes as required, and units that are approximately a half inch wide and 1.5 inches high handle currents up to 15 amperes at 400 volts.

While the solid-state thyratrons have similar characteristics to the gas-tube types, they offer a number of advantages. The tube types of the larger sizes require forced-air or water circulation for cooling purposes, require power for heater (filament) operation, and need to have the filaments brought up in temperature before anode voltages are applied. The silicon-controlled types need no warmup, their life span is much longer than the tube types, there is no filament deterioration, and they have lower internal resistance during conduction. Switching is also more rapid than with the gas-tube types (often less than 12 microseconds).

The silicon-controlled rectifier can be used as a straightforward rectifier without employing a gating electrode voltage, as shown at Fig. 14-24(A).

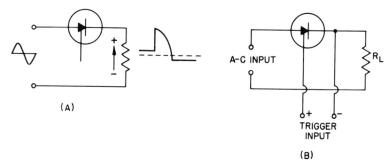

Fig. 14-24. Controlled rectifier circuitry.

If the reverse breakdown-voltage is not reached by the peak swings of the negative a-c alternations, the output will be in the form of pulses occurring at the line a-c rate as shown. When the pulsating d-c (or filtered d-c) is to be controlled by switching it to the load circuit at specific intervals as with the tube thyratrons, a trigger voltage is applied between the gate electrode and the cathode, as shown at Fig. 14–24(B). The trigger voltage must be applied to coincide with a positive alternation of the a-c input signal, just as with the tube thyratron. By applying timed (or phased) signals to the gate, conduction can be set for the precise intervals required.

IGNITRON RECTIFIER

Another widely-used gas-filled rectifier for industrial power requirements is the *ignitron,* which has the basic construction shown at Fig. 14-25(A). The tube contains a pool of mercury, an anode, and an *ignitor* element. The latter is a pointed tip of silicon carbide or boron carbide which dips into the mercury as shown. The ignitor tip is rough-surfaced so that when a voltage is applied across the ignitor and mercury cathode, small flash points will occur to initiate current flow and ionization. Without any voltage applied to the ignitor, conduction would not result because of the cold-cathode type of rectifier. Thus, with a positive voltage at the anode *and* ignitor, the arcing at the ignitor starts the emission process.

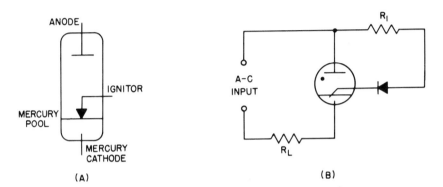

Fig. 14-25. Ignitron and basic circuit.

The basic circuit is shown in Fig. 14-25. The diode connected in series with the ignitor lead prevents the application of a reverse polarity across ignitor and cathode. A reverse voltage (even though of low amplitude) can damage the ignitor by causing electron flow from ignitor to cathode. Resistor R_1 drops the voltage to that required for creating the initial arc at the ignitor. The a-c supply power is in series with the load circuit, as shown, and with the mercury pool.

During the time when the a-c voltage is negative at the upper terminal and positive at the lower terminal, no conduction occurs because both the ignitron anode and the diode anode have negative potentials applied to them and hence are inoperative. When the upper terminal is positive with respect to the lower terminal, the diode conducts and initiates the emission and ionization process, permitting full conduction. Thus, the load receives rectified a-c (pulsating d-c) which again can be filtered to reduce the ripple component if required.

The ignitron has a number of advantages over the gas-tube thyratron. No filament excitation must be maintained; the ignitron mercury pool has unlimited life and will withstand high overloads without damage, and the anode can be placed in closer proximity to the mercury pool for lower internal resistance and increased efficiency. As with the other thyratrons, the ignitron can be fired at any point on the cycle, thus having the same advantages of applied-load power control. The disadvantages are bulk, cost, and the necessity for vertical operation because of the mercury-pool structure.

As with other rectifiers, the ignitron can be operated for full-wave rectification as shown in Fig. 14-26. The a-c supply power is applied to

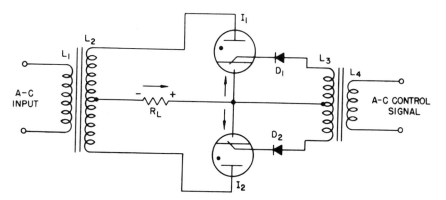

Fig. 14-26. Operating the ignitron for full-wave rectification.

the two ignitrons from across the input transformer composed of L_1 *and* L_2. During the time the upper portion of L_2 is positive, ignitron I_1 conducts in the direction shown by the arrow at the load resistance R_L. At this time the bottom of L_2 is negative and ignitron I_2 is in a nonconducting state. When the polarity reverses across L_2 the lower ignitron conducts in the same direction through the load circuit as was the case with the upper ignitron. The ignitors obtain their control signal from across the transformer composed of L_3 and L_4, as shown. By phasing this control signal, the full-wave alternations can be triggered at any part of the cycle desired.

REVIEW QUESTIONS

1. Briefly explain the advantage of a power supply over a battery power source.

2. Briefly explain the basic function of a half-wave power supply.

3. (a) What is the advantage of a full-wave power supply over a half-wave type?

(b) Is it necessary to employ more filtering with the half-wave power supply than with the full-wave type?

4. What is meant by a filter network? Explain its function.

5. Why does an input capacitor filter provide a higher voltage output than a choke input filter?

6. Briefly explain one system for doubling the voltage without the use of a power transformer.

7. What is the difference between a synchronous and a nonsynchronous power supply? How do these differ from an industrial chopper?

8. (a) What is the purpose of a buffer capacitor in a vibrator power supply? (b) In what manner does the synchronous vibrator power supply eliminate the necessity for employing a rectifier?

9. Briefly illustrate and explain one method for achieving voltage tripling.

10. Explain what is meant by "regulation" and by "percentage of voltage regulation."

11. Briefly explain the advantages and function of a swinging choke.

12. Briefly explain how the regulation of a power supply can be improved by employing a gas-filled tube or a zener diode.

13. (a) What factors must be considered when replacing the filter choke in a power supply? (b) What factors must be considered when replacing the filter capacitors of a power supply?

14. (a) What is meant by the peak inverse voltage encountered in a power supply? (b) What is meant by the bleeder network of a power supply? Explain its purpose and function.

15. Briefly explain how a thyratron can be used to control the amount of power applied to a load circuit.

16. What are the advantages of the solid-state thyratrons over the gas-tube types?

17. What are the advantages of the ignitron over the gas-tube thyratron?

18. What are the disadvantages of an ignitron as compared to a thyratron?

19. Why is a diode used in series with the ignitor of an ignitron?

20. Redraw Fig. 14-26 and include a choke-input filter circuit.

PRACTICAL PROBLEMS

1. In a power supply such as shown in Fig. 14-5, the first filter capacitor (following the rectifier) is to have a value of 8 microfarads. The transformer supplies 300 volts rms on each side of the center tap to the rectifier. Assuming no loss in the rectifier diodes, how can the following capacitors (in series or parallel combinations) be used to obtain the proper capacity value and safety with respect to the working voltage? Explain the reasoning behind your conclusion.

Power Supplies

Number available	Capacity	Working voltage
2	16 microfarads	150
2	8 microfarads	300
2	16 microfarads	450

2. In a capacity-input 400-volt power supply, the bleeder draws 20 milliamperes and the electronic load 180 milliamperes. Which of the following filter chokes should be used? Explain the reasons behind the choice made.

No. 1   5 henrys   200 milliamperes
No. 2   10 henrys   150 milliamperes
No. 3   15 henrys   250 milliamperes
No. 4   20 henrys   100 milliamperes
No. 5   20 henrys   180 milliamperes

3. In Fig. 14-20, assume that load No. 2 draws 160 milliamperes at 400 volts, and load No. 1 draws 40 milliamperes at 200 volts. Resistor R_2 has 10 milliamperes flowing through it. What must be the value in ohms of R_1 and R_2? What is the value in ohms of load No. 1?

4. A 16-microfarad, 600-working-volt capacity is required for a power supply. A number of 16-microfarad capacitors are available, but each one is only rated at 300 working volts. How can a number of these available capacitors be combined to get a total value of 16 microfarads at 600 working volts? Sketch how these capacitors would be connected together.

5. What is the peak inverse voltage of a capacity input half-wave power supply, if the secondary delivers 375 volts rms?

6. What is the approximate inductive reactance of a choke coil of 20 henrys rated at 200 milliamperes and used in a full-wave power supply connected to a line voltage source of 110 volts, at 60 cycles?

7. What would be the approximate inductive reactance of the same choke of Problem 6 if it were used in a half-wave power supply from the same a-c line?

8. In an industrial power supply it was noticed that the output voltage dropped from 1,000 volts to 800 volts after the load was applied. What is the percentage of voltage regulation?

9. In a laboratory power supply it was found that the rated regulation was 33%, with a load current of 100 milliamperes. After installing a new voltage-regulator diode, it was found that the no-load voltage of 2,000 dropped to 1,600 volts with a 100-milliampere load. What was the percentage of regulation with the new regulator diode? Was this an improvement in regulation?

10. In designing a 400-volt power supply for a 5,000-ohm load circuit, it was decided to include a bleeder resistor which would have a current flow through it equal to 10% of the load current to improve regulation. What must be the value of the bleeder resistor?

15

BASIC

AMPLIFIERS

INTRODUCTION

Virtually all circuits found in various branches of electronics are concerned with the handling, generation, modification, or utilization of some sort of electric signal voltage or power. When such signals are first generated, or obtained from circuits which handle them initially, the signal amplitude is usually insufficient to perform the functions intended, hence it must be brought up to the level required. Circuits which thus increase the voltage or power of signals are known as *amplifiers*. The design of a particular amplifier is dictated by the nature of the signal to be handled in terms of whether it has d-c or a-c characteristics, is of low frequency or high frequency, and whether its voltage amplitude or power must be increased. A photocell used for automatic lighting control, for instance, need only indicate d-c changes, hence if amplification is required, the type amplifier would differ from that used to amplify the type of signals received by an antenna system.

In transmitting systems, generators are used to produce high-frequency signals, so the latter can be used to "carry" lower-frequency signal information such as audio, picture information, or the pulse and square-wave signals described later. The high-frequency signals are necessary because low-frequency signals cannot be sent any appreciable distance, as also described more fully later. The high-frequency signals in transmitters must also be amplified so that they are brought up to the proper power level for sending out over the air. At the receiver, the high-frequency signals reaching the antennas are too weak for immediate usage and, again, amplifiers must be employed. Similarly, specific amplifier types are required to handle the signals employed in the electronic circuits used in industrial control systems, radar networks, computers, and other commercial gear. Also the type amplifier used to increase the signal level from a microphone (which produces a signal having a-c characteristics) differs from those used to handle other signal types. This chapter covers the type amplifiers used to increase voltage levels of d-c and a-c signals. Power amplification and other signal types are covered in subsequent chapters.

TYPES OF AMPLIFIERS

Amplifiers fall into a number of categories, and the two fundamental types are voltage amplifiers and power amplifiers. The voltage amplifiers are designed to increase the voltage amplitude of a signal which may have negligible power. The power amplifiers either convert the voltage-type signal to one with a high-level energy component, or amplify a power signal an additional amount. Besides the designations of voltage and power amplification, reference must also be made to whether an R-F type signal is handled, or whether a low-frequency (such as an audio) signal is involved. Thus, a voltage amplifier could also be a radio-frequency amplifier or an audio amplifier. Similarly, a power amplifier could be a radio-frequency type or an audio (or other low-frequency signal) type.

The term "radio-frequency" does not imply that the signals must be ordinary radio-type signals commonly received by home radios. Radar, television, frequency-modulation, and other such devices, handle high-frequency signals other than only radio-frequency signals, but the term radio-frequency signal (abbreviated *R-F* signal) from long usage, is still applied to such signals.

The characteristics of an amplifier in relation to its bias and design also place it in another specific category. Thus, if an amplifier is biased on the linear portion of its curve, and if the input signal is kept within certain amplitude bounds, the amplifier is designated as a *Class A amplifier*. (The specific characteristics and linear operation are discussed in detail later in this chapter.) The Class A amplifier could be designed specifically to handle R-F signals, or built primarily for amplifying audio- or other low-frequency waveforms. Also, it may be intended to function as a voltage amplifier, or the circuit may be so made up to perform as a power amplifier. Other amplifier types include the Class AB_1, AB_2, B and C. These are described in the next chapter. The characteristics and circuitry of the Class A amplifiers are covered in detail in this Chapter.

LOW-FREQUENCY AMPLIFICATION

Low-frequency signals such as procured from photocells, microphones, tape playback heads, phonograph pick-up devices, and other units described later are usually applied to a low-frequency amplifier of the Class A type initially. If the signal-amplitude level is still insufficient, additional amplifier stages are employed to increase the signal amplitude to that required for application to relays, control units, loudspeakers, recording devices, or modulators. Often, the amplification system consists of one or more stages of signal-voltage amplification, so that the signal voltages can be increased to a sufficient level for application to *power* amplifiers, since signal power rather than signal voltage is required to operate the output devices mentioned. If, for instance, audio amplification is involved, the sequence may be as shown in block-diagram form in Fig. 15-1. Here, two stages of audio

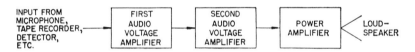

Fig. 15-1. Block diagram of audio amplifier.

amplification increase the weak electric signals obtained from the input device, and in turn apply a relatively high signal voltage to the final audio-amplifier tubes or transistors, for conversion of these signals into power signals.

LEVEL CONTROL

The amplitude of the signals applied to the input of an amplifier is usually regulated by a variable resistor known as a *gain control* which, if audio signals are involved, is also called a *volume control*. The gain control is usually located in the grid circuit (or base circuit of a transistor) of the first amplifier stage following the low-frequency signal source. If, for instance, the system is designed for audio amplification, a typical volume control circuit would be as shown in Fig. 15-2.

In some cases, the volume control potentiometer (R_1 in Fig. 15-2) has

an additional terminal, as described earlier in Chapter 3, and as shown in
Fig. 3-3. This extra terminal is utilized for *bass compensation,* by using a
capacitor (C_5 in Fig. 15-2) from the additional terminal to ground. Bass

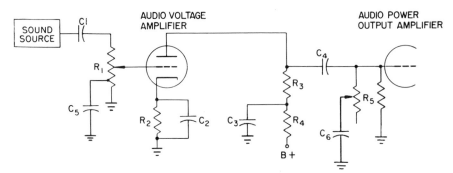

Fig. 15-2. Volume control with bass compensation.

compensation is employed so that, at low volume levels, some of the high-
frequency signals are diminished in amplitude. When high-frequency
audio signals are diminished, the low-frequency signals are comparatively
greater in amplitude than the high-frequency signals, and hence sound
louder. The reason for accenting low frequencies at low volume levels is
because the ear is less sensitive to bass notes when the latter are heard at
low volume levels. Thus, when the volume control is reduced, so that
music is reproduced softly, the bass tones will still be audible, because of
the bass compensation circuit.

Capacitor C_5 has a shunting effect for higher frequencies, since it
provides a lower shunt reactance for them. When the volume control
movable arm is turned down so that it is opposite the extra terminal or
below it, the shunting effect of capacitor C_5 is greatest.

Potentiometer R_5 and capacitor C_6 form a *tone-control* network. When
the potentiometer is regulated to have minimum resistance, there will be
a miximum shunting effect for higher frequencies, because of the low
capacitive reactance of C_6 for high frequencies. Thus, the diminished higher
frequencies are not heard as much, but the undiminished lower frequencies
will appear more prominent. When R_5 is adjusted for maximum resistance,
the impedance of the network is high, and the frequency response is not
altered to any appreciable degree. The tone control operates at any volume
levels, while bass compensation operates only at low volume levels.

The tone-control circuit composed of R_5 and C_6 makes the lower tones
sound louder than the higher tones. If an inductance is employed to form
a tone-control circuit, high notes will be boosted by virtue of diminishing
low-frequency tones.

BIAS METHODS

The bias for the tube is the negative potential which is placed on the grid, as mentioned in Chapter 11. Such bias is necessary in order to provide a minimum of distortion in the reproduced signal. If no bias were provided, full plate current would flow within the tube, and thus the current could only decrease, but could not alternately increase and decrease, as required during amplification. With a fixed bias, however, the plate current is reduced below its maximum value, and thus can vary both above and below a given level, during amplification. Referring again to Fig. 11-8, when a positive-going *signal* is applied to the grid, the positive polarity of the *signal* has the effect of momentarily reducing the bias, because the positive-going signal opposes the existing negative bias. The temporary reduction in bias will also temporarily increase plate-current flow. Similarly, a negative-going signal will decrease plate-current flow below that set by the bias. These variations in plate current will alternately increase and decrease the current through the plate resistor, above and below the idling current set by the bias. The current variations in the plate resistor cause voltage variations, and such voltage variations constitute the amplified signal. The latter has a frequency and wave shape which conforms to the grid signal, as mentioned in Chapter 11.

One method for applying bias to the grid of a vacuum tube is shown in Fig. 15-3(A). Here, a battery is applied to the bottom of the grid leak

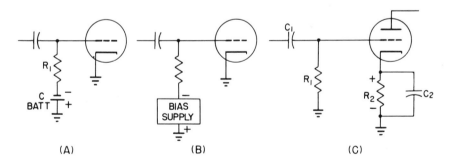

Fig. 15-3. Various bias methods.

R_1, so that the negative terminal of the battery is toward the grid, while the positive terminal is toward the chassis (ground). Since the cathode is also at ground potential, it can be considered as connected to the positive terminal of the bias battery. (As mentioned in Chapter 11, when a battery is used for bias purposes, it is known as a C battery, to distinguish it from the A battery for filament, and the B battery utilized for the anodes of tubes.)

Since no current flows in the grid circuit, there is no voltage drop across the grid leak R_1. In consequence, full battery potential exists between grid and cathode and, if a 4-volt battery is utilized, the grid will be negative with respect to the cathode by 4 volts. A similar bias method would be the substitution of a power supply for the battery. The use of a power supply for bias is advantageous in high power transmitters and, in such cases, the power supply replaces the C battery, as shown in Fig. 15-3(B).

Another method for obtaining bias is the use of a resistor in the cathode circuit as shown in Fig. 15-3(C). Since current flow from the anode supply of the tube must be through the cathode circuit to the plate, such current flow through the cathode resistor (R_2) will cause a voltage drop across it, with a polarity as shown. If, for instance, the voltage across the resistor is 3 volts, the cathode will be positive with respect to the grid by 3 volts, since the grid leak R_1 is connected to ground, like the cathode resistor R_2. Again (in Class A amplification), no grid current flows, so that no voltage drop occurs across R_1. For the latter reason, a 3-volt drop across R_2 makes the grid negative with respect to the cathode by 3 volts. Such a voltage can be measured by placing a voltmeter across R_2, or by placing the voltmeter between the grid and cathode terminals of the tube. The bias voltage cannot be read by placing the voltmeter across R_1, because no current flows in this resistor, and hence no voltage difference exists across it.

Capacitor C_2 is placed across the cathode resistor R_2 to minimize signal voltage variations across the latter. This capacitor is necessary in order to realize the full benefits of the bias voltage developed across R_2, and to prevent such a bias from varying at a rapid rate. Without capacitor C_2, the voltage across R_2 would vary, since the plate current amplitude varies at a rate determined by the input signal to the grid of the tube. The capacitor filters this voltage variation from across R_2, and thus prevents a bias variation.

If capacitor C_2 were omitted, the circuit would be degenerative, and would have reduced gain. This gain reduction comes about because the changing bias which occurs across R_2 (due to the changing plate current amplitude) would act inversely to the signal at the grid. If, for instance, the grid signal is positive-going, it would cause the plate current to increase. This increase in plate current through R_2 would cause an increase in the voltage drop across the latter resistor. This larger voltage drop would make the cathode more positive than the grid, and thus the grid would become more negative (a bias increase). The increase in negative grid bias reduces some of the current flow through the tube, and the current reduction counteracts some of the increase in current flow established by the positive-going grid signal. Degeneration, of course, also occurs for a negative-going grid signal. The negative grid signal causes an increase in the negative bias, which reduces the current flow in the tube, and consequently reduces the current through R_2. The reduced current through R_2 decreases the voltage drop across it, and thus reduces the negative bias at the grid of the tube. This reduction in bias causes the plate current to increase somewhat which counteracts some of the plate-current decrease caused by the negative-going grid signal. Thus, this inverse function causes a decline in the amplification of the signal.

The amount of filtering which cathode capacitor C_2 accomplishes depends on its capacity. A fairly large capacity must be used in order to have an equivalent low-shunting reactance across the cathode resistor R_2. Because the capacitive reactance shunts the cathode resistor, a lower value of capacitive reactance will cause a decrease in the impedance represented by the resistor-capacitor combination. The lower the impedance, the smaller the signal voltage drop which occurs across it and hence the less such voltage variations will affect the bias. The cathode resistor must have a value necessary for the amount of bias required, and hence cannot be reduced in its ohmic value. Also, if the circuit is analyzed on the basis of the capacitive reactance bypassing signal voltage variations because of its low reactance, it is obvious that C_2 will not provide the same degree of filtering for lower frequencies than it does for higher frequencies. If the circuit shown at (B) is an audio amplifier, for instance, and the capacitor has a value of 0.1 microfarads, the capacitive reactance would be slightly over 1,500 ohms at 1,000 cycles. If the cathode resistor R_2 is also 1,000 ohms, the capacitor is only partially effective. At 2,000 cycles, however, the capacitive reactance would be less than 800 ohms and now acts as a more pronounced shunt across the 1,000 ohm resistor. Since the capacitive reactance decreases with increased frequency, the higher audio frequencies are filtered to a much greater degree than the lower. The greater the filtering of the signal voltage variations in the cathode, the less is the resultant degeneration. Hence, the size of the capacitor C_2 should be of such a value that the reactance at the lowest signal frequency to be employed is appreciably less than the ohmic value of the resistance of R_2.

In some applications, the cathode capacitor is deliberately omitted, in order to improve frequency response. This is often done in the video amplifiers of television receivers, as well as in the output audio stage of an amplifier system. As previously mentioned, this procedure sacrifices signal gain in favor of a good low-frequency response.

Still another method for furnishing bias is to use resistors across the

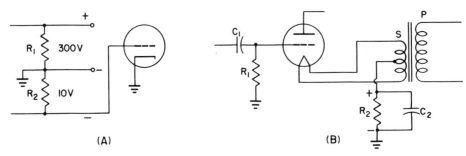

Fig. 15-4. Additional bias methods.

B battery or power supply, as shown in Fig. 15–4(A). Assume the power supply voltage is 310. Instead of grounding the bottom of R_2, as was done in the bleeder networks shown earlier, that section of the resistive network is not grounded, but the ground terminal is placed at the junction of the two resistors, as shown. Thus, the positive terminal of the power supply will furnish 300 volts with respect to the grounded center section, which is of a negative polarity with respect to the positive terminal. The negative bias for the tube is obtained from the bottom section of the lower bleeder resistor R_2, because this point is more negative than the ground terminal. (Actually, the bottom of R_2 is negative with respect to the top of R_2, and thus the grounded negative terminal is positive with respect to the lower end of R_2.) If the voltage drop across R_2 is 10 volts, the grid is negative by 10 volts with respect to the cathode, since the cathode is also grounded and, therefore, common with the grounded terminal of the power supply.

When vacuum tubes employ the directly-heated principle, as in Fig. 15-4(B), the bias can be established by utilizing the center tap of the

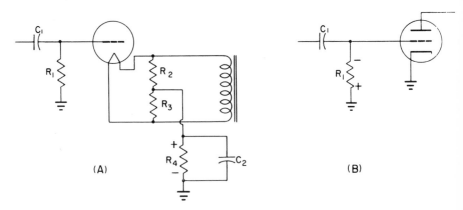

Fig. 15-5. Bias in filament and self bias.

transformer secondary, as shown. Here, a resistor (R_2) is placed in series with the transformer center tap and ground and shunted by C_2, in similar fashion to the bias method shown in Fig. 15-3(C). In the circuit shown in Fig. 15-4(B), the power supply would be connected in conventional fashion with positive to the anode and negative to ground. Hence the plate current flow from the power supply must, of necessity, be through resistor R_2, to reach the filaments and plate. This path establishes a voltage drop across R_2, with a polarity as indicated, and thus it will make the grid more negative with respect to the cathode (filament) of the tube.

In instances where the directly-heated tube is fed by a transformer which does not have a center tap, the method shown in Fig. 15-5(A) is employed. Here, two resistors (R_2 and R_3) are placed across the filament winding of the transformer. These resistors have a low ohmic value (approximately 30 ohms *each* for a 6-volt filament section). The two resistors establish an electric center at their junction. At this junction, the bias resistor R_4 is added, as shown, with the usual bypass capacitor C_2. Thus, the voltage drop across R_4 will give the cathode (filament) a positive potential with respect to the grid, and hence the grid will be negative with respect to the cathode. Since R_2 and R_3 have low ohmic values, they will not have an appreciable effect on the bias, because the cathode resistor would be much larger in value. Resistors R_2 and R_3 also act as a hum-reducing circuit, by placing the ground connection (via C_2) at the electric center of the transformer. A single potentiometer can replace resistors R_2 and R_3, with the variable arm of the potentiometer attached to the top of R_4. The potentiometer circuit provides a means for balancing the system to minimize any hum which may be present in the amplifier.

Yet another form of bias is the contact potential bias which is obtained from electrons striking the grid wires in a vacuum tube. A circuit of this type is shown in Fig. 15-5(B). At first glance, it would seem that this tube is unable to develop a bias. However, the grid leak R_1 has a high value and, if the bias requirements are low, as is the case with high-mu tubes, enough bias will be developed by virtue of the electron bombardment of the grid structure. The random electrons which strike the grid wires will establish a voltage across R_1 which has a low-potential value. The fractional volt, however, is often sufficient for bias purposes, for certain tubes having low bias requirements.

Another method for obtaining bias is that found in certain circuits such as the oscillators, limiters, and Class C amplifiers discussed later. In such devices, the grid signal has a high value and drives the grid of the tube positive during positive signal peaks. When the grid is positive, current flows from cathode to grid, and this current consists of the signal energy component. Thus, for a brief interval of time, the grid and cathode of the amplifier tube may be considered as the anode and cathode of a diode rectifier. The resultant current flow is in the direction shown by the solid arrows in Fig. 15-6(A), and the current path continues through the cathode-grid section of the tube, and on to capacitor C_1. The electron flow toward capacitor C_1 will cause an accumulation of electrons on that side, giving it a negative potential.

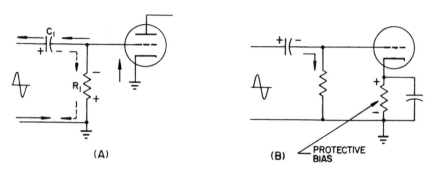

Fig. 15-6. Generation of self bias.

The piling up of electrons on one side of the grid capacitor will cause a repulsion of the electrons on the other side of the capacitor and, in consequence, the electrons will flow away from the left side of capacitor C_1, giving that side a positive potential. If the positive peak of the signal voltage is 10 volts, for instance, the capacitor will charge to this approximate value. When the signal declines below its 10-volt peak, the tube will no longer conduct, because capacitor C_1 holds a 10-volt negative charge at the grid and, since this is a higher negative potential than the declining positive-going grid signal, the grid is predominately negative, so that no current will flow between cathode and grid. Hence, no additional charge of energy is placed across the coupling capacitor C_1. During this time (and while the signal is going through its negative alternation), the capacitor C_1 will discharge through the grid leak R_1, in the direction shown by the dashed arrows. This discharge establishes a negative bias potential across the grid leak R_1, with a polarity which is negative at the grid and positive at ground (cathode), as shown in Fig. 15-6(A).

Since the grid leak is of a high value, and since the tube does not conduct until the next positive signal alternation, the capacitor does not discharge fully, but rather maintains a fairly constant bias potential between grid and cathode. Before the capacitor charge can decline to an appreciable extent, another positive signal alternation arrives at the grid, and will again cause grid conduction. In consequence, the positive grid voltage will again recharge capacitor C_1 to its full value, to repeat the initial process.

During the time when the grid of the tube conducts, the grid circuit may be considered as having a short time constant (short RC). This short time constant permits a virtually full charge to appear across C_1. During the time the grid of the tube is not conducting, however, there is a long time constant established and, therefore, the rate of discharge for C_1 is much lower than its charging rate. At the time the tube conducts, the signal energy flows through the tube (cathode to grid) rather than through R_1, because during the time the tube conducts it has a very low impedance and hence, is in virtual shunt across the grid leak R_1. Thus, current flow takes the easiest path, which is through the vacuum tube, since the latter has the lowest resistance. Resistor R_1 and the cathode-grid sections of the vacuum tube during conduction may be considered as two parallel resistors, one of which has a high ohmic value, and the other a very low ohmic value. During the signal peaks, current flows through the low ohmic value resistor (the tube) in greater proportion than through the higher resistor, composed of R_1. When the input grid signal value is less than the positive peaks, the resistance represented by the vacuum tube can be considered as having been removed from the circuit, because during no-current flow conditions the tube resistance is infinitely high. The latter condition leaves only resistor R_1 as a discharge path.

The method shown in Fig. 15-6(A) has the advantage of being able to develop a bias which is beyond cutoff, as required for certain types of circuits, which will be described later. Cutoff bias cannot be secured by a cathode resistor alone, because, if the point is reached where the bias is at cutoff, no current flows through the cathode resistor. In the absence of such current flow, no bias would be developed, and hence the current flow would again be at a maximum. Thus, the cathode resistor cannot be used to bias the tube beyond the cutoff point, no matter how high a value of cathode resistor is employed.

The disadvantage with the type of bias obtained by driving the grid positive is that, when there is no signal input present to the grid of the tube, an excessive amount of current flows through the tube. For this reason, circuits employing this bias method often utilize an additional source of bias, by use of a cathode resistor and bypass capacitor. Such an additional bias is for protection against excessive current flow. The protective bias circuit in the cathode is shown in Fig. 15-6(B). The protective bias need not have a high value, but only a value sufficient to limit the current flow which would result during the absence of the input signal when no cutoff bias is developed.

The bias factors relating to transistors were covered in Chapters 12 and 13. Generally, the bias for either tubes or transistors has the same objective of establishing the operating point for the type of amplifier desired. In transistor circuitry both the potentials applied to the input and output sections are referred to as bias, while in vacuum-tube circuitry the anode

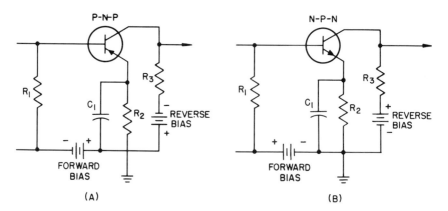

Fig. 15-7. Transistor bias.

potential is often referred to as the "B" supply. For transistor amplifiers of the Class A variety, the bias applied between base and emitter conforms to the polarity designations of the *P* and *N* zones and is known as *forward bias,* as detailed in Chapter 12. Hence, for the *P-N-P* transistor shown at Fig. 15-7(A), the bias polarity is negative to the base and positive to the emitter. For the *N-P-N* transistor circuit shown at (B), the forward-bias polarity is positive to the base and negative to the emitter. Both, however, are in the forward-bias direction as required for class A operation. Similarly, the reverse-bias polarities for the two circuits differ as shown, so as to apply the necessary polarity to the collector opposite to the zone designation of either *N* or *P*.

Note that a resistor and capacitor (C_1 and R_2) are in series with the emitter lead in a fashion similar to the bias resistor arrangement in the cathode circuit of the vacuum tube. This resistor-capacitor combination does not serve the same purpose of producing grid bias as does the vacuum tube. Instead, the two emitter components are used for stabilizing the transistor circuit as more fully explained for the transistor R-F amplifier covered later in this chapter. As with tube amplifiers, the foward-bias potentials can be eliminated or reversed in polarity to form other classes of amplifiers, as detailed in Chapter 16.

COUPLING METHODS

There are several circuit arrangements for a *Class A amplifier.* One of these is the *resistance-coupled,* or *resistance-capacitance coupled* method, as it is sometimes called. Such a system is shown in Fig. 15-8(A). Here,

C_1 is the coupling capacitor which links the signal energy from the previous stage (or from a device such as a microphone, etc.) to the grid of the first amplifier tube. Resistor R_1 is the conventional grid leak, while R_2 and C_2 form the bias arrangement previously discussed. The signal energy develops across the plate resistor, known as a *load resistor* (R_L) and, from the latter, the signal is transferred to the next amplifier stage with another coupling capacitor (C_3). The advantage of this coupling method is economy, since no costly transformers or other inductances are employed. The disadvantage is that the coupling capacitors and cathode capacitors limit low-frequency response as more fully described later.

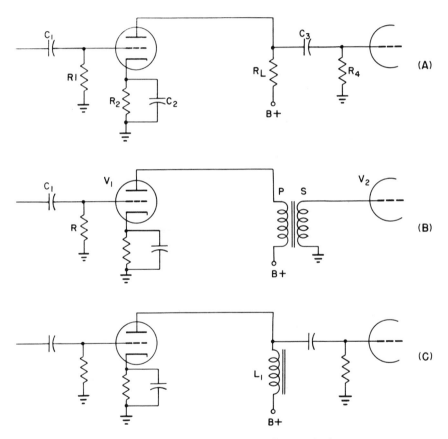

Fig. 15-8. Interstage coupling method.

Another coupling method employed for Class A audio-voltage amplification is shown in Fig. 15-8(B). This system utilizes a transformer to couple the energy between the first tube (V_1) and the second tube (V_2).

Such transformer coupling is more costly than the resistance-coupled method previously described. The advantage of transformer coupling, however, is that an increase in signal voltage can be realized across the transformer, because there is a step-up turns ratio which increases the signal voltage applied to the grid of V_2 over that which is present at the anode of V_1. Transformer coupling can be employed in each stage, or a combination of resistance and transformer coupling can be used, as shown in (B) where the input coupling to V_1 is of the resistance-capacitance type. Transformer coupling is used in R-F circuitry though rarely used in inter-stage audio circuits, since the slight gain in signal strength is overweighed by the cost and bulk of the transformer. With modern design, the resistance-coupled types can give good frequency response and, by employing high-mu tubes, the slight advantage of increased gain in transformers is no longer important.

Another method for interstage coupling is shown in Fig. 15-8(C). Here, an iron-core inductance is utilized in place of the resistor or trans-former, and it is across this inductance that the signal voltages are de-veloped. This energy is then coupled to the next tube, using a conventional grid coupling capacitor and grid leak. The additional bulk and cost of the coil do not warrant its inclusion in modern circuits and, for this reason, it is rarely encountered in audio amplification systems, though it is employed in some R-F circuits.

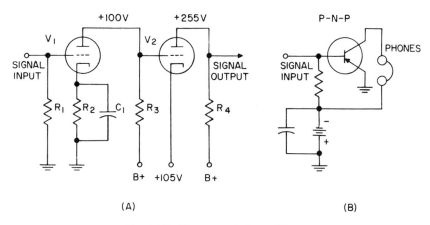

Fig. 15-9. Direct-coupled amplifiers.

One stage can be coupled to another stage without the use of a coupling capacitor or transformer, by direct coupling, as shown in Fig. 15-9(A). This method is sometimes used in pulse and square-wave amplifiers, as well as in high-fidelity audio systems and in picture signal amplifiers of television receivers, because it does not suffer the disadvantages of either capacity or transformer coupling. In capacity coupling, the reactance may be fairly high for lower frequencies, unless a large-sized capacitor is employed. A large capacitor, however, may have excessive leakage, and might shunt signals to ground, if placed too near the chassis, because of capacity effects between the capacitor and the chassis. A transformer also has a changing reactance for different frequencies, in addition to distributed capacities, all of which affect the frequency response. With direct coupling, all frequencies are transferred from one tube to another without some being diminished with respect to others.

When direct coupling is employed, as shown in Fig. 15-9(A), voltages must be carefully apportioned. If 100 volts are present at the plate of the first tube, as shown in (A), such a voltage will also be present at the grid of V_2. In order to make the grid negative, a higher positive potential must be applied to the cathode. If the bias on V_2 should be minus 5 volts, the cathode voltage must be plus 105, which would make the grid negative by 5 volts with respect to the cathode. If the plate potential for V_2 should be 150 volts, it will be necessary to apply 255 volts to the plate of V_2, so that it will be positive with respect to the cathode by 150 volts. Thus, 255 volts must be present at the plate of V_2, as shown in Fig. 15-9(A). Successive stages of amplification will require progressively higher anode voltages and, hence, are difficult to design. Direct-coupled amplifiers must have steady d-c voltage sources for proper operation. When power supplies are used instead of batteries, voltage regulating principles must be employed, as discussed earlier.

Transistor amplifiers also utilize the direct-coupling principle in a fashion similar to that used for vacuum-tube circuits, and the same considerations apply with respect to voltage relationships. In both transistors and vacuum tubes, however, no problem arises if the direct coupling involves only one stage. An example of this is shown in Fig. 15-9(B), which shows a *P-N-P* transistor amplifier coupled directly to a set of head-phones. Here, no special consideration need be given to voltage distributions, beyond what is required in a normal circuit. This is a grounded-emitter transistor circuit, and compares to the conventional grounded-cathode vacuum-tube circuit. If an *N-P-N* transistor is substituted for the *P-N-P*, the only circuit change required would be a reversal of the battery or power supply potential.

If dissimilar transistors are used for successive amplifier stages, the *complementing* factor of their combination permits the design of a transistor d-c amplifier without the disadvantage of having to increase supply potentials for each stage. A typical circuit of this type is shown in Fig. 15-10. Here, the first transistor (input) is an *N-P-N* type, with its collector coupled directly to the base of the second transistor, a *P-N-P* type. Note that the forward- and reverse-bias requirements are met for both transistors with a single power source. For the input *N-P-N* transistor, the emitter has applied to it the necessary negative potential from the minus terminal of the battery, through the common ground leads. The positive terminal of the battery is applied to the top of the two series resistors R_1 and R_2, which act as voltage dividers. Since both resistors have equal values, a positive potential of 3 volts is present at the base of the input transistor with respect to its emitter. The collector of this transistor is positive with respect to the emitter, because the collector is coupled to the positive terminal of the battery through resistor R_3.

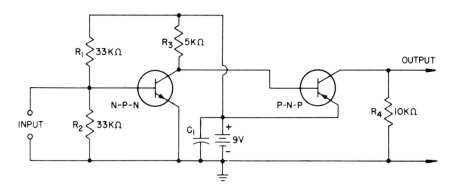

Fig. 15-10. D-C coupling with complementing transistors.

For the output *P-N-P* transistor the emitter is connected to the positive terminal of the battery as shown, for the necessary forward bias. It would seem that the base of this transistor is also positive because of its connection to the positive terminal of the battery through R_3. However, R_3 in conjunction with the impedance of the input transistor also shunts the battery and thus forms a voltage divider. Hence, the junction of R_3 and the collector of the input transistor is *negative with respect to the positive terminal* of the battery. Thus, the base of the output transistor is made negative to a definite degree with respect to the positive emitter. For the collector of the output transistor, a negative potential is applied through R_4, satisfying the reverse-bias requirements of this *P-N-P* type.

With this complementing feature, additional stages can be used without increasing battery potentials to the proportions needed for vacuum-tube d-c amplification. The only increase in potentials would be that necessary to satisfy the additional power-handling factors for the succeeding stages.

For the third stage of Fig. 15-10, an *N-P-N* transistor would be used, with a *P-N-P* for the fifth stage, etc.

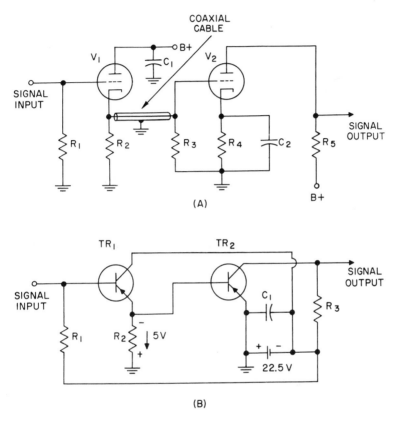

Fig. 15-11. Cathode follower type circuits.

Instead of coupling from the plate of one tube to the grid of the other, coupling can also be accomplished from the cathode of one tube to the grid of the next tube, as shown in Fig. 15-11(A). When the signal is derived from across the cathode of a tube, the circuit is known as a *cathode follower*. As shown, a capacitor (C_1) at the anode of V_1 bypasses the signal energy, so that none appears in the plate circuit. Resistor R_2, the cathode resistor, is actually the load resistance for V_1. Resistor R_2, in conjunction with interelectrode capacities, forms a low impedance output circuit, as compared to the high impedance of the grid circuit of V_1. Hence, a cathode follower circuit acts in a fashion similar to a step-down transformer, since the cathode follower circuit has a high-impedance input and a low-impedance output. Because of the impedance step-down characteristics of a cathode follower, the latter is often used when an amplifier output signal must be transferred to another circuit through a low-ohm coaxial cable. For this reason, the cathode-follower circuit is frequently employed as a wide-band step-down impedance transformer in transmitters and receivers, without the necessity for using an actual transformer.

The polarity of the cathode output signal *follows* the polarity of the input signal; hence, the term *cathode follower*. As the cathode resistor R_2 is not bypassed with a capacitor, signal variations occur across the resistor. Degeneration takes place because of the unbypassed resistor and, hence, the signal voltage gain which would normally result across a vacuum tube is not realized, as mentioned earlier.

In Fig. 15-11(B), a transistor counterpart of the circuit in (A) is shown. Here, the first transistor circuit is a *grounded-collector* type and, hence, acts like the vacuum-tube cathode follower. In the vacuum tube cathode follower circuit, the plate is at *signal* ground as mentioned earlier. With the transistor circuit, the collector is at signal ground, by virtue of the bypass capacitor C_1. The emitter of the first transistor (TR_1) is above ground by an amount determined by the ohmic value of R_2. The base of TR_1 is at a negative potential, as established by the battery, while both emitters of the transistors are at positive potential. Resistor R_2, however, has a voltage drop across it, with a polarity as shown on the drawing, because current flow is from the emitter to the positive-polarity ground terminal. Hence, if the battery is 22.5 volts and the voltage drop across R_2 is 5 volts, the emitter of TR_1 is positive with respect to ground by 22.5 volts minus 5 volts, or 17.5 volts. The negative 5 volts at the emitter, however, appears at the base of TR_2, and hence the base of TR_2 is negative with respect to its emitter, thus satisfying the forward-bias principles discussed earlier, in Chapter 13. The signal energy developed across resistor R_2 is directly coupled from the emitter of the previous stage to the base input of the following stage.

Besides the circuit components shown in Fig. 15-9 to Fig. 15-11, several other resistors and capacitors may be found in audio amplifier circuits. Typical of such additional components are those shown in Fig. 15-12, where the complete circuit for a pentode audio-amplifier stage is given. Here, C_1 is the usual coupling capacitor which transfers the signal energy from the previous stage to the grid of the tube. Resistor R_1 is the grid leak, and resistor R_2, in combination with capacitor C_2 is for bias purposes. Because a screen grid is present in this tube, an additional resistor, R_3, is employed for dropping the power-supply voltage to the value required for the screen grid. In order to minimize signal voltage variations across the screen voltage dropping resistor, a capacitor (C_3) is

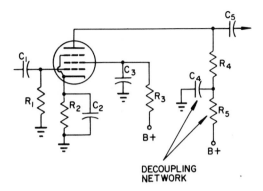

Fig. 15-12. Pentode with decoupling network.

placed across the resistor to filter out signal voltage variations. The principle involved here, in terms of signal loss, was discussed in Chapter 11. The load resistor consists of R_4 across which signal energy develops, and it is from this resistor that the energy is coupled to the next stage via capacitor C_5.

Below the load resistor, R_4, are shown another resistor, R_5, and a bypass capacitor, C_4. Capacitor C_4 and resistor R_5 form a network which is known as a *decoupler*. The decoupling network principle is extensively employed to isolate one stage from another, in both audio and R-F amplifiers. Isolation refers to *signal isolation,* and is based on the fact that all the circuits of an amplifier system utilize the same power supply, so that the power supply forms a common coupling device for the various stages. For this reason, amplified signal energy of a last stage can be coupled to an early stage, and can thus cause either regeneration or degeneration, depending on the phase of the signal energy which is coupled between the stages. To isolate one stage from another with respect to power supply coupling, the decoupling network is employed below each load resistor. A voltage drop develops across resistor R_5 for the energy which is fed back, and C_4 provides an effective bypass for such signal energy, and prevents the signal energy from being coupled to R_4 and the anode circuit. Resistor R_5 is usually much lower in value than R_4, and R_5 consists of approximately 5,000 to 10,000 ohms. Capacitor C_4 is made sufficiently large so as to have a low reactance for the lowest frequencies handled by the amplifier.

The decoupling network can also be employed to increase low-frequency response in an amplifier, by proper choice of capacitor C_4. As this capacitor has a fairly high reactance for low frequencies, it will develop a signal voltage drop across the impedance formed by C_4 and R_5 for lower frequencies. Thus, for low audio frequencies, the total load resistance value is increased, since it is composed of R_4 in combination with the decoupling network. The effectively increased R_L represents two signal voltage drop components in series. Because the total ohmic value is increased, the signal energy developed across the combination of resistor R_L and the decoupling network will be increased for the lower frequencies. At the higher audio frequencies, C_4 has a low reactance and acts as an effective shunt preventing any signal voltages from developing across R_5. Thus, the low-frequency signal components are boosted and their potential is raised in proportion to the higher audio-frequency signal components.

The same requirements apply when the amplifier is used for pulse signals, square waves, and other types of waveforms discussed later. Not only do such special signals have low-frequency components which must be retained in their progress through an amplifier, but high-frequency signal components as well which must not be diminished. In audio amplification the circuit must also be capable of handling the *dynamic* range of sound, that is, the soft and loud passages, without overloading on the latter and distorting them. Obviously, then, an amplifier does not have the sole function of increasing signal level alone, but must amplify without undue loss of any part of the frequency range of the signals applied to the circuits, and without distorting or otherwise degrading the quality of the original signals, whether such are audio signals, pulses, or other type waveforms. A better understanding of the necessity for good amplifier design will be gained by considering the characteristics of sound, composite signal waveforms, and distortion factors relating to amplifying systems.

AMPLIFIER CHARACTERISTICS

When the air pressure is increased and decreased at a certain rate, the air pressure variations strike the ear drum and produce a sensation of sound for the listener. Among individuals, the sensitivity of the ear for the various sound frequencies differs to some extent. Younger people can hear sound frequencies as high as 20,000 cycles per second, while older people will experience a decline in their hearing at the upper audible frequency range and, in consequence, may hear frequencies only up to 15,000 cycles per second or, in later life, only up to 10,000 cycles per second.

Speech frequencies, as well as all the fundamental tones of musical instruments, are below 5,000 cycles per second; hence, one might wonder about the usefulness of frequencies extending to 10,000 or 20,000 cycles per second. The primary use for such frequencies, however, is in lending

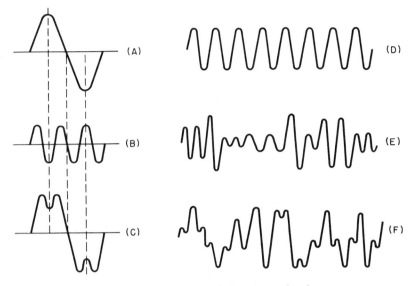

Fig. 15-13. Various audio-frequency signals.

certain characteristics to fundamental frequencies, so that the fundamental frequencies have distinguishing features which will permit recognition of them, as compared to other similar fundamental frequencies.

When a clarinet and a violin play the note A in the middle musical register, a fundamental frequency of 440 cycles per second is generated by each instrument. Despite the fact that each is generating a fundamental frequency of 440 cycles, however, the ear immediately recognizes one note as being the tones derived from a violin, and the other from a clarinet. This difference, which also characterizes the individuality of various other instruments, is due to the *harmonic content* of the fundamental tone generated by each instrument. Thus, a musical instrument will produce not only a fundamental tone, but also related harmonic frequencies, which may range considerably higher than the fundamental.

The harmonic frequencies are usually lower in amplitude than the fundamental, and have decreasing amplitudes for higher harmonic frequencies. The amplitude of the various harmonic frequencies, however, plus the particular harmonic frequencies generated by the musical instrument, combine to produce the identifying tonal characteristic of that instrument.

How a fundamental frequency signal can combine with others to form a composite frequency signal is illustrated in Fig. 15-13. In (A), a single alternation of a fundamental frequency signal is shown, and, for purposes of this discussion, we will assume that it represents a 500-cps signal Part (B) shows another signal, having a frequency three times that of the signal in (A), and thus the signal in (B) represents a third harmonic having a frequency of 1,500 cycles per second. When these two signals appear at the input of an amplifier, the tube grid or transistor base receives a signal which is the additive sum of the two; that is, at points where both signals in (A) and (B) are in phase, the resultant signal (in (C)) which appears at the amplifier input will have an increased amplitude. Where there is a phase difference between the signals in (A) and (B), the resultant signal in (C) will have a correspondingly lower amplitude. Thus, when a fundamental frequency signal of 500 cps is combined with another signal having a higher frequency, a resultant signal occurs, as shown in Part (C). This waveform is now complex, rather than simple, since it contains frequencies other than the fundamental frequency. A musical tone would contain many other higher order frequencies, making the resultant waveform which appears at the input of the amplifier even more complex.

To illustrate the foregoing discussion by showing successive cycles of the a-c signal waveform, a pure fundamental frequency is shown in (D). Here, each cycle is identical to the others, both in amplitude and in frequency. In (E), various fundamental frequencies are shown, and the over-all waveform begins to have a more complex appearance. Not only are cycles of various frequencies present, but amplitude changes occur as well. Thus, the waveform in (E) could represent the injection into the amplifier of various fundamental frequencies, some having higher volume levels than others. In (F), the type of waveform produced by music or speech reproduction is shown. Here, there are not only various frequencies and amplitudes present, but harmonic frequencies as well. During speech or music, the waveform would be undergoing a continuous change, as different tones and volume levels are introduced into the input of the amplifier.

Because of the harmonics just mentioned (or *overtones,* as they are sometimes called), it is necessary for audio-amplifying systems employed in electronics to be able to handle the wide span of frequencies required for true reproduction of the original sound. The rendering of the harmonic frequencies, as well as the fundamental, during music reproduction, adds reality to the reproduced music and gives the illusion that the musical instrument is actually *present* in the room. This characteristic of a good amplifier is known as *presence* to define reproduction which closely resembles the original.

The typical frequency span of various sounds, as well as the approximate levels of sound by decibel comparisons (see the discussion on decibels in Chapter 5), is given in the following tables:

TYPICAL FREQUENCY SPAN OF VARIOUS SOUNDS	
Type of Sound	Approximate Frequency Span (in cps)
Desirable range for good speech intelligibility	300 to 4,000
Audibility range (normal hearing, young person)	16 to 20,000
Piano	26 to 4,000
Baritone	100 to 375
Tenor	125 to 475
Soprano	225 to 675
Cello	64 to 650
Violin	192 to 3,000
Piccolo	512 to 4,600
Harmonics of sound	32 to 20,000

APPROXIMATE LEVELS OF SOUND BY DECIBEL COMPARISON	
Type of Sound	Relative Intensity in Decibels
Reference level	0
Threshold of average hearing	10
Soft whisper; faint rustle of leaves	20
Normal whisper; average sound in home	30
Faint speech; softly playing radio	40
Muted string instrument; softly spoken words (at a distance of 3 ft.)	50
Normal conversation level; radio at average loudness	60
Group conversation; orchestra slightly below average volume	70
Average orchestral volume; very loud radio	80
Loud orchestra volume; brass band	90
Noise of low-flying airplane; noisy machine shop	100
Roar of overhead jet-propelled plane; loud brass band close by	110
Near-by airplane roar; beginning of hearing discomfort	120
Threshold of pain from abnormally loud sounds	130

HARMONIC DISTORTION

An amplifier should reproduce at its output a signal which is an exact duplicate of the input signal, in all respects except amplitude. Thus, the amplifier should build up the signal which is applied to its input without adding other signal frequencies to it, or otherwise distorting the original signal. Vacuum tubes and transistors, however, are not perfectly linear devices. That is to say, their characteristic curves exhibit curvatures, and hence do not consist of straight lines. If the characteristic curves of tubes and transistors were perfectly straight lines, no distortion would be intro-

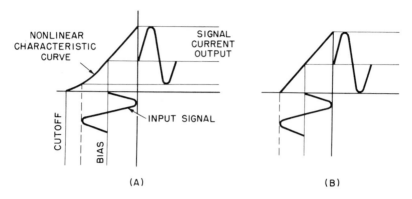

Fig. 15-14. Distortion of output signal.

duced, because the output waveshape of the amplified signal would be the same as the input signal waveshape. How curvature in the tube or transistor characteristics introduces distortion can be more easily understood by referring to Fig. 15–14, where a nonlinear characteristic curve is shown in (A), and a straight-line (linear) characteristic curve is shown in (B). For purposes of emphasis, the curvature for the nonlinear characteristic shown in (A) has been confined to the lower portion of the curve.

As shown in Fig. 15-14(A), the input signal applied to the grid circuit of the tube is a pure sinewave. As the signal goes in a positive direction, it has the effect of decreasing the bias and increasing the plate-current flow through the tube. When the input signal swings in the negative direction, it has the effect of increasing the bias (making the grid more negative) and, hence, there will be a decrease in plate current. These alternate increases and decreases in the plate current represent the signal energy flowing through the load resistance. As will be noted in (A), the output signal current has a waveshape which is not representative of the input signal. The plate-current signal change is greater for the first alternation than for the second alternation, and hence some harmonic distortion is present. This is known as *amplitude distortion*. If the tube characteristic is perfectly linear, as shown in (B), then a variation of the grid voltage, by virtue of the application of a signal, will cause a plate-current change which is in proportion and which faithfully follows the input-signal change of voltage. Hence, no distortion is introduced.

To minimize distortion, the vacuum tube can be operated on its most linear portion, as shown in Fig. 15-15. Here, the bias is set at the approximate center of the linear portion of the characteristic curve, and the input signal is held at a low value, so that its amplitude excursions do not go into the curvature region of the tube's characteristic curve. Under these conditions, the output current signal change will be fairly uniform with respect to the grid voltage change representing the input signal. When the tube is operated in this fashion, it is known as Class A. A current flow through the tube exists, whether or not an input signal is applied to the grid. Class A operation can also be applied to a pentode characteristic curve, such as shown in Fig. 15-16. In (A), a triode characteristic curve is shown for comparison with the pentode curve shown in (B). Because of the steeper slope of the pen-

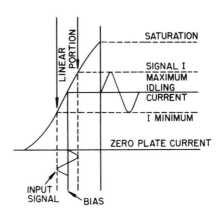

Fig. 15-15. Class A operation.

tode characteristic curve, a larger plate-current change is obtained for a relatively smaller input grid signal. In consequence, pentodes or beam-power tubes are capable of much greater signal amplification than triodes.

Triode tubes develop harmonic distortion which has primarily an even harmonic content. Thus, triode tubes generate a second harmonic distortion, as well as additional harmonics. The second harmonic will be the most dominant, while the higher order of even harmonics will be progressively lower in amplitude than the second harmonic. Pentode tubes produce a harmonic distortion primarily composed of odd harmonics. In pentodes, the third harmonic is the most dominant, with successively higher odd harmonics having a progressively lower amplitude.

A good amplifier is designed so that such a distortion will be at a minimum. An acceptable level for distortion is 5%. Distortion below 5% is usually not noticeable to the average ear, though in high-fidelity applications the distortion is often reduced to less than 1%. In

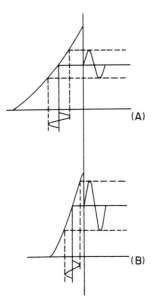

Fig. 15-16. Linear operation —triode versus pentode characteristics.

some applications, distortion as high as 8% or 10% can be tolerated, where the primary purpose is speech reproduction or where the *quality* of music which is reproduced is not too important a factor. In audio or R-F *voltage* amplifiers, Class A operation is usually employed, in contrast to some of the other amplifier types, such as Class AB₂ or B, as more fully described for power amplifiers in the next chapter.

The harmonic distortion which occurs when an amplifier is operated in the nonlinear portion of the characteristic curve of a tube or transistor means that harmonic-frequency signals are *generated within* the tube or transistor. Because such signals were not present in the original signal applied to the amplifier, these harmonic signals are referred to as *distortion* and are considered undesirable. We must, however, distinguish between *harmonic distortion* and the *harmonic signals* normally present in complex waveforms such as musical tones and square waves. The harmonic signals present in musical tones and other complex waveforms usually encountered, are applied (with the fundamental tone) to the input of the amplifier and, hence, both the fundamental tone and its inherent harmonic content should be amplified to the same degree. If other harmonic signals are generated within the tube, they represent an undesired addition to the signals being amplified, because neither even nor odd harmonic generation is desired in amplifiers.

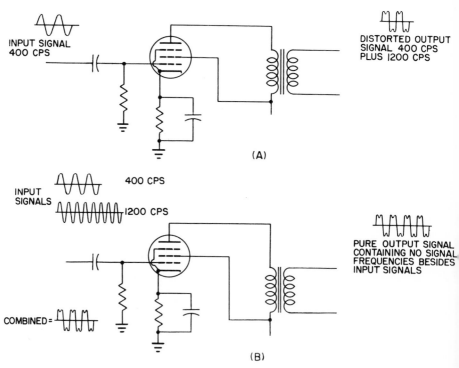

Fig. 15-17. Harmonic distortion in an audio amplifier.

To emphasize the difference between harmonic distortion and the natural harmonic content of musical or other audible tones, see Fig. 15-17. In (A), a pure 400-cycle sinewave is applied to the grid input circuit of the amplifier. If the output signal contains not only the original fundamental 400-cycle signal, but also a 1,200-cycle signal, the output signal is considered to contain harmonic distortion. (The additional 1,200-cycle signal represents a third harmonic component of the original signal. The 1,200-cycle signal, however, was not present in the original signal, but was generated within the tube and added to the 400-cycle signal.)

If, on the other hand, the output had consisted of only a 400-cycle audio amplified tone, the output signal would have been undistorted. The output signal shown in (A) is considered to be distorted only because it contains signals which were not present at the input of the amplifier. The 400-cycle output, plus the 1,200-cycle output, could be an undistorted output under other input conditions, as shown in Fig. 15-17(B). Here, two input signals to the grid of the amplifier are indicated. One is a 400-cycle per second tone, and the other is a 1,200-cycle per second tone. These two frequencies could represent *the two fundamental tones generated by two musical instruments.* Since the grid voltage must either increase or decrease, the two signals will combine in additive fashion at the grid, as mentioned earlier. Hence, the output will be an amplified version of this combined input signal, and the output would contain both the 400-cycle per second audio tone and the 1,200-cycle per second audio tone. In this instance, the output signal *is not distorted,* since no frequencies are present except the frequencies originally introduced into the grid circuit.

FREQUENCY DISTORTION

There are various factors which may prevent an amplifier from having a flat frequency response over the desired range of frequencies which are to be handled. In a transformer-coupled amplifier, both the primary and secondary windings exhibit various reactances to signals of different frequencies. At the higher audio frequencies, the reactances of the transformer are high and, in consequence, larger signal voltage drops occur across the transformer. At low audio frequencies, however, the transformer reactances are also low and, hence, the low-frequency signals are not amplified to the same degree as the higher signal frequencies. In addition, the transformer windings have considerable *distributed capacitances,* which occur between individual turns of wire, as well as between layers of the wire turns making up the primary and secondary. Hence, higher signal frequencies cause the distributed capacities to have low capacitive reactances, which tend to shunt signals having high frequencies. The result of the foregoing is a loss of low frequencies, because of inductive reactances in the transformer, and a loss of high frequencies, because of the distributed capacitances. This is known as *frequency distortion*. To minimize such losses, it becomes necessary to employ transformers having larger cores with characteristics such that permeability is increased considerably. The increase in permeability causes an increase in inductance, permitting fewer wire turns to produce the required inductance, and thus lessening the total distributed capacity.

If a coupling capacitor is employed instead of a transformer, a variable factor is again introduced with respect to amplification. The higher signal frequencies find a low reactance, and thus encounter little opposition in reaching the next amplifier stage. The lower frequency signals, however, find a higher reactance, and hence are diminished (attenuated) in transferring across the coupling capacitor. If the coupling capacitor is increased in size (larger capacity), the reactances for lower frequencies will be decreased, but the larger physical size of the capacitor may set up shunt capacities to the chassis (or nearby components), and may thus tend to shunt some of the higher frequency signals. Even though the stray capacity existing from the body of a capacitor to the chassis may be small, the higher frequency signals may find a sufficiently low reactance so that an appreciable portion of the high-frequency signal energy is lost. Even undue lengths of wire which connect a coupling capacitor from the plate circuit of one stage of the grid circuit of the following stage, may introduce losses. Long leads tend to increase inductive effects, because even a short length of wire has some inductive characteristics. The inductance of the wire length may be small, but high-frequency signals find a greater inductive reactance in the wire length than do low-frequency signals, and hence the high-frequency signals suffer some attenuation. Also, any wire connecting circuits may present some shunt capacity to the chassis or other nearby components. If such wires carry signals, the stray capacity will provide a shunt reactance which will cause signal losses.

Vacuum tubes and transistors also contribute to signal losses because of their *interelectrode capacitances.* Such capacitances exist between the plate and grid of a tube, as well as between the grids of multielement tubes. In addition, capacity also exists between the control grid and the cathode. For a minimum signal loss at high frequencies, tubes and transistors must be chosen which have the least interelectrode capacitances consistent with the type of tube needed for the particular circuit. Fig. 15-18 illustrates the various factors which can contribute to signal losses in an amplifier, and this drawing summarizes the principles outlined in the foregoing discussions. In a well-designed audio amplifier, where all necessary signal loss precautions have been observed, it is possible to obtain a substantially flat response for signals ranging in frequencies from approximately 30 cycles per second, to well over the hearing limit of 20,000 cycles per second. The frequency response of an amplifier can be ascertained by applying to the input various signals, starting from the lowest and progressively increasing the frequency, in steps. Each signal applied to the amplifier input is held at a constant amplitude. The output signals from the amplifier are then measured for amplitude by a calibrated test instrument, as shown in Fig. 15-19(A). The results, in the form of a graph of the frequency response, then appear as shown in Fig. 15-19(B).

The over-all gain which can be realized from a triode amplifier is dependent on the amplification factor of the tube (or the gain factor of the transistor), as well as on the value of the load resistor used and the plate resistance.

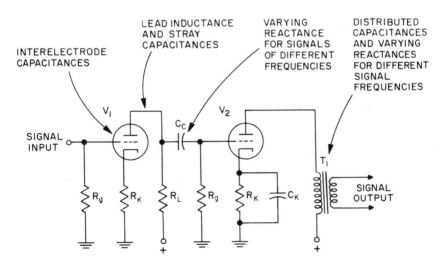

Fig. 15-18. Loss factors in an amplifier.

In triodes the input capacitance existing between grid and cathode will shunt high-frequency components of a complex wave, but in addition, the grid-plate capacitance also has a pronounced effect on input capacitance. This comes about because the amplified signal appearing in the anode circuit will be coupled back to the input circuit via the grid-plate interelectrode capacitance. Since the amplified signal is 180 degrees out of phase with the input, it cancels some of the input signal in proportion to the amplitude of the signal fed back. The end effect is similar to what it would be if the grid-to-cathode capacitance *were increased,* and this characteristic is known as the *Miller effect.* The tube itself could have only a few micro-microfarads of input capacity, but the Miller effect could increase this to an equivalent of 100 micromicrofarads or more, and would be the primary factor in the shunting effect of higher-frequency signal components. With greater amplifier gain, the Miller effect is correspondingly increased and input capacitance lowered.

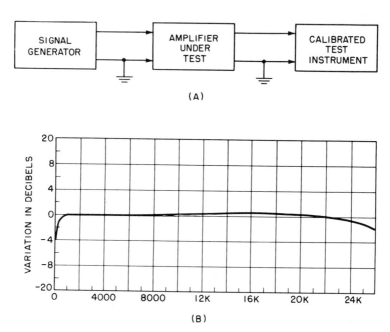

Fig. 15-19. Measuring audio-frequency response of an amplifier.

Since input capacitance shunts higher-frequency signals, it can also affect the higher-frequency components of a complex waveform applied to the input. This is shown in Fig. 15-20. Here, the grid-plate capacitance C_1 provides the Miller effect and has the end result of increasing the input capacitance represented by C_2. If a waveform (as shown) were applied (containing a fundamental and a third-harmonic component), the higher-frequency portion would find a greater shunting effect due to the input capacitance, resulting in a decrease in the high-frequency portion of the amplified signal. Thus, the output-signal waveform no longer duplicates the input, and frequency distortion is the result.

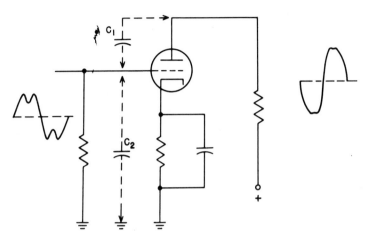

Fig. 15-20. Miller effect and frequency distortion.

PHASE DISTORTION

A coupling capacitor in conjunction with the grid leak forms a voltage divider for the signals applied to an amplifier. Actually, the grid input is not resistive alone, because the grid leak is shunted by the cathode-grid capacitance, and hence forms an impedance. Because the capacitor has a low reactance for higher frequencies, it will not have as much signal voltage drop across it for the higher-frequency signals (or components of the signal) as it would for the lower frequencies, again causing some frequency distortion. At lower frequencies the reactance may be appreciable and the signal voltage developing across the capacitor causes a signal decrease across the resistor. Since the signal applied to the grid is obtained from across the resistor only, as shown in Fig. 15-21, there is an obvious decrease in the input signal over that which would prevail if the reactance of C_1 were only a fractional value of the impedance formed by R_1 with the input interelectrode capacitance.

The varying reactances of C_1 and the shunting interelectrode capacitances will cause a phase shift between high- and low-frequency signals as well as the frequency attenuation mentioned. When higher-frequency signals (or the high-frequency components of a complex wave) undergo a phase shift with respect to the lower-frequency signals, the result is *phase distortion* of the amplified signal, as shown in the output waveform for Fig. 15-21. This can be understood more readily by referring again to

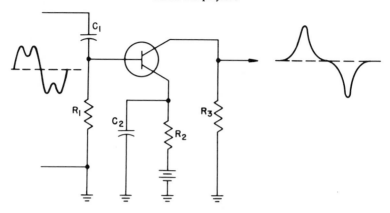

Fig. 15-21. Phase distortion.

Fig. 15-13. If the third-harmonic component shown at (B) were shifted (either to the left or right) in comparison to the fundamental signal at (A), the output waveform would no longer resemble that at (C), but may have the phase-distorted waveshape as shown at the output of Fig. 15-21. This is particularly objectionable in amplifiers handling visual-type signals such as in radar, television, and oscilloscopes. Phase shifting will cause a shift of picture information and a blurring of images.

SIGNAL-VOLTAGE GAIN

The plate resistance of triode vacuum tubes may range between a few thousand ohms and 15,000 ohms, depending on design. (See Chapter 11 for the formula used to calculate R_p.) The input resistance (grid input) of a vacuum tube is much higher than the plate resistance, and may be well over a megohm. A triode transistor, on the other hand, will have an input resistance (to the base) of only a few hundred ohms, while the collector output resistance in a grounded emitter circuit may be as high as 50,000 ohms. Thus, in a vacuum tube, there is an impedance or resistance decrease across the tube, while in a transistor there is a resistance increase.

The output resistance of the amplifier tube or transistor has a bearing on amplification, because it acts as though it were in series with the load resistance, as shown in Fig. 15-22. Here, the plate cathode of the tube is considered as a generator, because it creates the amplified version of the input signal. (In a grounded-emitter transistor circuit, the emitter and collector can be considered as an equivalent signal generator.) The plate resistance (R_p) is shown external to the generator, to illustrate its series relationship with respect to the load resistor (R_L). While it is true that the grid resistance (R_g) of the following tube effectively shunts the load resistor (particularly at higher frequencies, where the coupling-capacitor reactance is low), the grid resistance is so much higher than the load

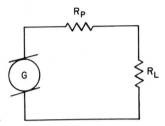

Fig. 15-22. Equivalent circuit of an amplifier.

resistance that only a small difference is contributed by R_g. Hence, the value of R_L need only be considered in setting up a formula for calculating the gain of an amplifier. Therefore, the *signal voltage gain* of an audio-amplifier circuit may be found by taking the ratio of the signal output voltage to the signal input voltage, as affected by the amplification factor and the series resistances of R_p and R_L:

$$\text{Voltage gain} = \frac{\mu R_L}{R_p + R_L} \qquad (15\text{-}1)$$

Often, the load resistor is chosen to have a value some two or three times that of the plate resistance, for an increased signal voltage drop across the load resistor. (A value of load resistor substantially higher than three times the plate resistance may result in signal distortion, and hence is usually avoided.) Since the chosen load resistance is usually of a value no higher than three times the plate resistance, the maximum gain which can be realized is only ¾ of the rated amplification of the tube. Thus, when the load resistor is three times the plate resistance, ¼ of the signal develops across the internal plate resistance of the tube, and the other ¾ across the load resistance. (Impedance matching, for maximum *power* transfer, is discussed in the next chapter.)

Pentode tubes have a much higher amplification factor than triodes, as well as a much higher plate resistance. The latter, for pentodes, may range from several hundred thousand ohms to over a megohm. In consequence, the load resistor is not made larger than the plate resistance, because of the current limitation which would result. Instead, the load resistor is made substantially lower than the plate resistance, and hence it is convenient to base the calculation for voltage amplification on the transconductance (g_m) of the tube, as follows:

$$\text{Voltage gain} = g_m R_L \qquad (15\text{-}2)$$

This is derived from the previous formula for voltage gain, but since R_L is much smaller than R_p, the addition of R_L to the plate resistance value in the denominator of the equation will alter the value of the denominator very little, hence the equation may be written as:

$$\frac{\mu R_L}{R_p} \qquad (15\text{-}3)$$

Since μ/R_p represents the transconductance (g_m) of a tube, the formula finally can be expressed as $g_m R_L$, as shown in (15-2).

R-F AMPLIFICATION

As mentioned in the Introduction to this chapter, R-F signals encountered in both transmitters and receivers must be amplified, to bring them to the levels necessary for proper transmission and reception of radio and television. As with audio amplification, R-F amplifiers must be designed to handle not just a single frequency signal, but a group of signals having various frequencies. In transmitters, the basic R-F signal (known as the *carrier*) must be modified by a process known as *modulation,* in order for the carrier to convey the audio or video signals, as more fully detailed in a subsequent chapter. This modulation process generates additional signal frequencies immediately above and below the carrier frequency, such additional frequencies being termed *sidebands.* Thus, the R-F amplifier must be capable of amplifying to the same degree both the carrier and the sidebands involved.

How much space a station may occupy in the frequency spectrum is determined by the Federal Communications Commission, which also allocates the particular carrier frequency which a station must employ, as well as the power which may be used in transmission. In standard AM radio, for instance, the allocated spectrum is from 550 kilocycles to approximately 1,600 kilocycles. (See Fig. 15-23.) Each station occupies approximately 10 kilocycles. (The reason for the approximation is that the total space occupied by a station may vary, because the number of sidebands will vary during broadcasting, as more fully explained later.) Because a number of stations occupy the broadcast spectrum, the R-F amplifiers which are employed must have selective characteristics. Selectivity means that the amplifier must be capable of selecting and amplifying a band of frequencies for a particular station, while rejecting nearby signals of adjacent stations.

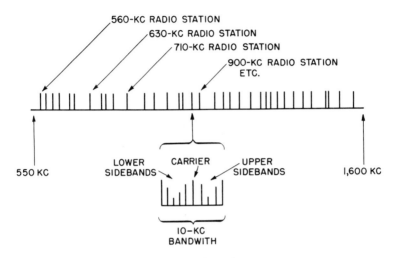

Fig. 15-23. AM radio station spectrum.

The selectivity of an amplifier must be chosen to accommodate the type of transmission to be handled. In AM broadcasting, the selectivity of an R-F amplifier must be such that it ranges over approximately 10 kilocycles, as previously mentioned. In FM (frequency modulation), however, an R-F selectivity (known as *bandpass*) of 150 kilocycles is necessary. As compared to AM, FM is actually a wide-band type of selectivity. Wide-band selectivity is also necessary in television transmission and reception, where the tuner amplifiers must have a selectivity ranging to 6 megacycles (6,000 kilocycles). To obtain selectivity in an amplifier, so that it will select the desired station, while rejecting unwanted stations on either side of the desired one, tuned resonant circuits must be employed. The Q of such circuits is regulated by introducing a certain amount of resistance, so that the bandpass will be sufficient to accommodate the carrier and the sideband signals. Selectivity factors were described at greater length in Chapter 10, and the resonant theory section of that chapter should be reviewed, to refresh the reader's memory of the fundamentals which apply to this topic.

In Fig. 15-24(A), one type of input circuit of an R-F amplifier is shown. Inductances L_1 and L_2 form a transformer arrangement, in which L_1 couples the signal energy from the previous stage to L_2. Both L_1 and L_2 have shunting capacitors (C_1 and C_2) which are variable, so that both the L_1 and L_2 sections can be tuned to resonance. Components C_3 and R_1 form the grid-leak capacitor combination, while R_2 and C_4 in the cathode circuit form the bias network. Signal energy is inductively coupled from L_1 to L_2, and the high-impedance parallel circuit of L_2 in conjunction with C_2 develops a high signal potential component which is applied to the grid and cathode circuit of the R-F amplifier. Accumulations of electrons on the grid are shunted to ground via the grid leak R_1. The circuit can also be rearranged as shown in Fig. 15-24(B), where the grid leak and capacitor are placed at the lower end of the L_2 input inductance.

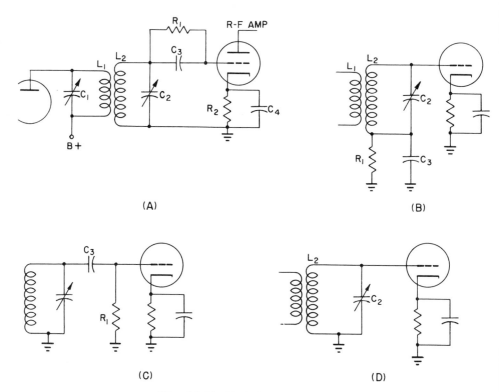

Fig. 15-24. Variations in grid circuits.

Functionally, this is similar to the input shown in (A), except that (B) is preferred in many instances, since it lends itself more readily to the application of automatic-volume-control voltages or automatic-gain-control voltages, which will be discussed later. Capacitor C_3 places the bottom of L_2 and C_2 at ground potential, with R_1 acting as a grid leak by bleeding off an accumulation of electrons at the grid through the low resistance winding of L_2.

Another possible arrangement is that shown in (C), where grid leak R_1 is placed from grid to ground, with capacitor C_3 acting as a conventional coupling capacitor. The method shown in (D) can also be employed, and dispenses with both grid leak and the coupling capacitor. Here, the signal energy is coupled directly into the grid input circuit, and the parallel resonant circuit composed of L_2 and C_2 forms a high-impedance network for the signal energy, but a low d-c shunt path is present through L_2 for the accumulated electrons resulting from grid bombardment. Circuits such as shown in (A), (B), and (C) are also employed in limiters and oscillator circuits, as more fully described subsequently.

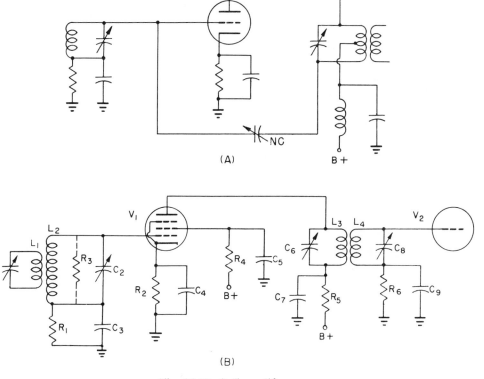

Fig. 15-25. R-F amplifiers.

When a triode is used as an R-F amplifier, as in Fig. 15-25(A), where a tuned circuit is present in both the grid and plate sections of the tube, the circuit would oscillate, that is, it would generate a signal of its own instead of simply amplifying an income signal. While oscillators as such are important in electronics, they consist of special circuits, as described in Chapter 19. An amplifier, on the other hand, should not exhibit oscillatory characteristics.

The reason why oscillations occur in a triode R-F amplifier is that the interelectrode capacities of the tube act to couple the amplified signal energy at the anode side of the amplifier back to the grid side. This *feedback* converts the amplifier into an oscillator, and the signals generated by the oscillations are undesired, because the amplifier output should only contain the signals fed to the input from the previous stage (or from a microphone, etc.). To prevent undesired oscillations in an R-F triode amplifier, it is necessary to neutralize the circuit, as shown in Fig. 15-25(A). This process is accomplished by applying the d-c supply voltage to the center tap of the plate transformer winding, so that a signal can be obtained from the *bottom* of this inductance, such a signal being 180 degrees out of phase with the plate signal at the top of the inductance. A portion of this signal at the bottom of the plate resonance circuit is coupled to the grid via a capacitor (marked *NC* in the drawing). This capacitor not only couples a portion of the signal from the plate to the grid, but also blocks the d-c at the plate, and prevents such voltage from appearing at the grid. The coupling capacitor is referred to as the *neutralizing capacitor* and is usually marked *NC*. The amount of signal fed to the grid can be regulated by adjustment of the neutralizing capacitor, since the latter is variable. Thus, the reactance of the neutralizing capacitor is adjusted so that it will feed back a signal to the grid, which signal is of the same amplitude as the undesired signal coupled by the interelectrode capacity of the tube. Because of the 180-degree phase difference between the two signals, cancellation occurs and oscillations are prevented.

Since neutralization in receivers would involve the use of an additional component, as well as the necessity for adjustments at the factory and in the home, modern R-F amplifiers in receivers employ pentodes which normally require no neutralization.

A typical pentode R-F amplifier is shown in Fig. 15-25(B). Here, the energy is again coupled from L_1 to L_2, and then developed across the resonant circuit composed of L_2 and C_2. The capacitor C_3 places the bottom of this resonant circuit at ground potential for the signal, while R_1 performs the function of the grid leak resistor. A conventional cathode resistor R_2 and capacitor C_4 furnish the necessary bias for the tube. If this amplifier is utilized in broadband work such as television, an additional resistance may shunt the resonant circuit, as shown by resistor R_3. Use of such a shunting resistor will broaden the characteristics of the parallel resonant circuit, and will lower the Q sufficiently so that the circuit is enabled to cover the requisite band of frequencies. (When the Q is lowered, the selectivity is also decreased, but when several R-F stages are employed in succession (*cascade*), the desired selectivity for good rejection of unwanted signals can be re-established.)

The screen voltage for tube V_1 is applied via the voltage drop in resistor R_4, with C_5 having a bypass effect on signal voltage variations at the screen. In the plate circuit, another resonant circuit is formed, using capacitor C_6 and inductance L_3. This circuit is fed from the B voltage supply through the decoupling network composed of R_5 and C_7. Capacitor C_7 also establishes the bottom of the plate resonant circuit at ground potential for the signal. If capacitor C_7 has its ground side connected near cathode capacitor C_4, a direct return path for a completely closed anode signal circuit is provided, with a short span of circuitry. The decoupler also minimizes interaction between successive R-F amplifier stages, in similar fashion to that employed for the audio-frequency amplifier. The energy developed across the resonant circuit composed of C_6 and L_3 is coupled to the grid resonant circuit of the next stage through inductive coupling, by L_3 and L_4. In the grid circuit of the next stage, a similar arrangement is found, which is virtually identical to the input grid circuit of the previous stage.

If the pentode R-F amplifier is used at very high frequencies, the interelectrode capacities, even though small in a pentode, may still have sufficiently low reactance at such high frequencies to provide some coupling between input and output circuits. For this reason, a pentode tube may exhibit the tendency to oscillate, when utilized at high R-F frequencies, and some form of neutralization may be necessary. One method, often utilized, is to use a screen grid bypass capacitor which is smaller in value than normally employed, so that it will not be fully effective as a bypass capacitor. The inadequate bypass capacitor introduces some screen-grid degeneration, which will then minimize the tendency toward oscillation in the amplifier circuit.

A typical transistor R-F amplifier is shown in Fig. 15-26. Here, an interstage transformer is utilized, consisting of L_1 and L_2. The amplified signal energy develops across the high-impedance parallel resonance circuit composed of L_1 and C_3, and this energy is inductively coupled to the secondary resonance circuit composed of L_2 and C_5.

In many instances, at high frequencies, the resonant circuits are tuned by a variable iron core, as mentioned in Chapter 8 and illustrated in Fig. 8-15. For the transistor R-F amplifier shown in Fig. 15-26, a common variable core is used, as symbolized by the solid arrow between L_1 and L_2. The single variable core tunes both the primary and secondary resonant circuits, hence capacitors C_3 and C_5 are not made variable.

A grounded emitter circuit is employed, with the reverse bias negative potential applied to the collector via resistor R_2. The latter is a combined

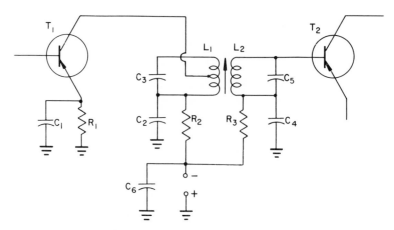

Fig. 15-26. Transistor R-F amplifier.

voltage-dropping resistor and decoupling network. Capacitor C_2 is the decoupling capacitor, and capacitor C_6 is a bypass for the battery or power supply, thus shunting any signal energy around the power source. The positive potential of the power source is applied to the emitter circuit of transistor T_1 (forward bias) via resistor R_1. Resistor R_1 and capacitor C_1 resemble the bias arrangement used in the cathode circuits of vacuum tubes. In transistor circuits, however, such a resistor-capacitor combination in the emitter circuit is for purposes of circuit stability. Current flowing through R_1, from emitter toward the positive ground, sets up a voltage drop across R_1 which opposes the positive potential present at the emitter. Assume, for instance, that the battery potenial is 22.5 volts, and the voltage drop across R_1 is 3 volts. If the drop across R_2 is 2 volts, the total emitter voltage would be a positive 17.5 volts. The R-C network compensates for variations in transistor conduction caused by temperature changes, as well as variations in transistor characteristics. An increase in battery current through R_1 raises the voltage drop across the resistor, and hence decreases the positive potential at the emitter, causing a decrease in conduction. A decrease in battery current through R_1 lowers the voltage drop and raises the positive potential at the emitter. The increased positive potential at the emitter increases current flow and compensates for the reduced current flow which may have been caused by temperature changes, or transistor replacement by one having different characteristics. Capacitor C_1 prevents *signal voltage* variations across R_1.

The collector lead of T_1 connects to a tap on the primary winding of the transformer, so that the impedance of the collector is more nearly matched to the impedance of the coil.

As with the triode vacuum-tube R-F amplifier, the transistor R-F amplifier shown in Fig. 15-26 would tend to oscillate, unless special precautions were taken regarding neutralization feedback circuit additions. Both triode vacuum-tube and triode transistor amplifiers can be designed, however, where special neutralization procedures are unnecessary. For the vacuum tube, a *grounded-grid* circuit such as shown in Fig. 15-27 is employed. Since the grid is grounded, the signal is applied across an input circuit in the cathode of the tube. For the circuit shown, the input signal is developed across the high-impedance resonant circuit composed of L_2 and C_2 between cathode and ground. (Resistor R_1 is for bias purposes, and capacitor C_3 places the bottom of the cathode resonant circuit at signal ground.)

While it appears as though the signal is applied to the cathode circuit only, it is actually present between cathode and grid. Assume, for instance, that a positive alternation appears across the cathode circuit. The positive alternation will increase the cathode voltage drop, and an increase in cathode potential means an increase in the negative *grid* potential. Hence, current flow through the tube decreases and plate voltage rises. A negative-going alternation at the cathode circuit decreases the cathode potential, and hence lowers grid bias. Plate current now increases, and plate voltage drops, developing a negative-going signal at the output. From this analysis, it can be seen that the phase of the output signal is the same as that of the input signal, a characteristic of the grounded-grid amplifier.

The fact that the grid is grounded minimizes oscillations in the triode amplifier, because the grounded grid acts as an electrostatic shield between the grid-cathode and the grid-plate circuits, just as the screen grid (at signal ground by virtue of a bypass capacitor) isolates the input and output circuits of pentode amplifiers.

The output circuit of the grounded-grid amplifier is conventional, as shown in Fig. 15-27. Resonant circuits are employed, and may be tuned by variable capacitors C_4 and C_6, as shown, or by movable-core tuning slugs within the coils.

The transistor counterpart of the grounded-grid amplifier is the grounded-base circuit shown in Fig. 15-28. Here, the signal is applied between the emitter and base, as shown. (Capacitor C_5 places the positive side of the battery, as well as the bottom of the input resonant circuit, at signal ground.) A positive alternation of the signal at the input aids the forward-bias conditions of the transistor input circuit, increasing current flow (and current carriers) in the base-emitter circuit. The increase in current carriers influences the collector-base side, with the resultant increase in current flow in the output circuit. The current increase in the output circuit increases the voltage drop across the output resonant circuit, and amplification occurs. As with the grounded-grid circuit, the grounded-base

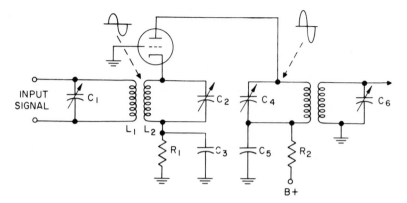

Fig. 15-27. Grounded-grid amplifier.

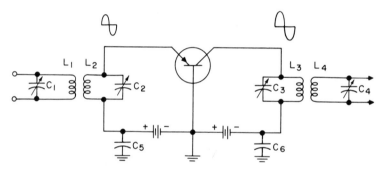

Fig. 15-28. Grounded-base transistor amplifier.

circuit has no phase reversal of the signal between input and output of the amplifier. The grounded-grid circuit has a high input impedance and a lower output impedance, as mentioned for the conventional vacuum-tube amplifier discussed earlier. The grounded-base circuit, on the other hand, has a low input impedance (below 1,000 ohms) and a high output impedance, ranging up to 500,000 ohms. (Reference should be made to Chapter 13 for a review of basic transistor theory.)

LOAD LINES

The static characteristics of a vacuum tube can be established as detailed in Chapter 11. For plate voltage-plate current curves, a fixed bias is used on the tube and the plate current is measured for various plate voltages. The bias value is then changed and another set of readings is taken, until the static set of plate characteristics can be drawn graphically, as shown in Chapter 11.

While such plate characteristic curves indicate the amount of plate current which flows for a given bias and plate voltage, they do not indicate the dynamic characteristics of the tube; that is, the tube characteristics which are established when a signal is applied to the grid. During signal input to a tube, the plate current varies by an amount established by the input signal amplitude and the tube gain.

In order to illustrate the condition which occurs when the tube is operating with a signal input and is amplifying, a *load line* must be drawn, as shown in Fig. 15-29. The load line is represented by the heavy diagonal

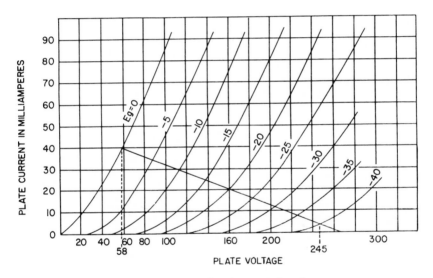

Fig. 15-29. Load line for a triode tube.

line drawn through the grid-voltage curves. With such a load line, the dynamic operating conditions of the tube can be calculated, and such information can be gathered as power output, plate efficiency, percentage of harmonic distortion, as well as the value of the load resistor itself.

For a load line illustrated in Fig. 15-29, a load resistance of approximately 5,342 ohms is indicated. This value can be calculated by assuming a maximum signal swing, and then ascertaining the maximum and minimum values of plate current and plate voltage. For the tube illustrated, assume a normal bias of minus 20 volts. The maximum signal swing would presumably start at this bias value of minus 20 volts and swing to zero, then back to 20 volts and on up to minus 40 volts of bias. Assuming such a signal swing, the ohmic value of the load resistance can be found from the following formula:

$$R_L = \frac{(E_{max} - E_{min})}{(I_{max} - I_{min})}$$ (15-4)

Thus, the maximum voltage swing would be approximately 245 volts, based on the intersection of the minus 40-volt bias line with the load line. Minimum voltage swing would be approximately 58 volts, established by the load-line termination at zero bias. When the signal swings to minus 40, the current would be approximately 5 milliamperes (0.005 ampere) and, at zero bias, the current would be approximately 40 milliamperes (0.04 ampere). When the difference in voltage (187 volts) and the difference in current (0.035 ampere) are used according to Formula (15-4), the ohmic value of the load resistance will be found. (The accuracy of the results are determined by how carefully the current and voltage values are established from the graph.)

When no load line is given on a set of tube characteristics, one can be drawn in arbitrarily, and calculations can be made from it. A horizontal load line will give the least distortion, and also the least output. If the load line is sloped toward the vertical position, the output and distortion will increase. As the load line is slanted toward a vertical position, the line enters the nonlinear portion of the static characteristic curves which corresponds to the region of high distortion. (The subject of linearity versus distortion is discussed more fully in the next chapter.) Thus, a higher value of load resistance will, within certain limits, decrease distortion below that which would prevail for a lower value of load resistance. With a lower value of load resistance, however, the frequency response limits of the amplifier are extended, since there is less shunting effect of the interelectrode capacity of the tube. As the load resistance approaches the interelectrode capacity values, the latter will have a greater shunting effect. Since the higher frequency components of the signals lower interelectrode capacitive *reactance,* the upper frequency response is decreased with a large value of load resistance. For this reason, a low value of load resistance is used in video amplifiers, where it is necessary to pass frequencies up to 4 megacycles. For audio work, however, where frequencies above 15,000 cycles are rarely encountered, the larger value of load resistance will give good frequency response with greater output.

The larger the load resistance, the more horizontal the load line becomes. Thus, several load lines can be drawn in a static set of curves, and calculations will then indicate which one is preferable from the standpoint of signal amplitude output with a minimum of distortion. In most instances, a compromise will have to be made between the distortion and signal output levels.

If a representative load line is desired without drawing several arbitrarily, two points can be established on the static set of characteristic curves which will permit the load line to be drawn. One such place is the *operating point,* which can be calculated by use of the following formula:

$$\text{Zero signal bias} = \frac{-(0.68 \times E_b)}{\mu} \qquad (15\text{-}5)$$

In this formula, E_b is the chosen value of d-c plate voltage at which the tube is to be operated. This is derived from the fact that cutoff is normally equal to E_b/μ and bias is proportional to Formula (15-5), which establishes the bias so that operation is on the linear part of the characteristic curve. The constant 0.68 was established by R.C.A. engineers in a number of tests conducted on many tubes. The formula is an approximation, and gives an average bias for the general tubes encountered. Average plate current, however, should always be chosen so that it does not exceed the plate dissipation of the tube.

One point for drawing the load line has now been established, the zero signal bias. If the desired value of load resistance is known beforehand, the following formula can be used to establish the place where the load line intersects the zero plate-current axis:

$$E_b + I_b R_L \qquad (15\text{-}6)$$

In this formula, the operating plate voltage is given as E_b, and I_b is the operating plate current.

As the limit of the signal swing is at zero, the load line ends at zero bias, establishing the third point. This gives us E_{min} and E_{max} automatically, for if the bias changes from zero to 40 volts, then the extent of signal swing would also indicate the minimum and maximum voltage and current points.

The amplifier circuits described in this chapter are of the signal-voltage type. In a signal-voltage amplifier, the primary purpose is to raise the signal voltage (not power), and hence the load resistor is made fairly large in audio applications, or parallel resonant circuits with a high impedance are used in R-F amplifiers. While power output is low, it can be solved for if necessary, once the load line has been drawn. The formula used is given here for reference, though it is more applicable to the power amplifier circuits discussed in the next chapter.

$$\text{Power output} = \frac{(E_{max} - E_{min})(I_{max} - I_{min})}{8} \qquad (15\text{-}7)$$

The power-output formula is based on the fact that the alternating components of voltage and current have peak amplitudes that are one-half of the total swings of plate potential. The power delivered to the load resistor is equal to one-half the product of the peak a-c signal voltage and the peak signal current as in Equation (15–7). In d-c circuits, the power in watts is equal to the product of voltage times current, and in resistive a-c signal circuits, such as amplifiers, the same calculations apply. Therefore, if the extent of the signal swings are multiplied, and the result again multiplied by a factor which takes into consideration the effective values (as required in a-c calculations), the result will be the average power delivered to the load resistor, as derived from the formula for power output in (15-7).

The plate efficiency of the tube can also be calculated on the basis of the load line, using the following formula:

$$\text{Plate efficiency} = \frac{(E_{max} - E_{min})(I_{max} - I_{min})}{8E_pI_b} \times 100 \text{ (per cent)} \quad (15\text{-}8)$$

The second harmonic distortion can be solved by either of the following formulas:

$$\frac{\frac{I_{max} + I_{min}}{2} - I_b}{I_{max} - I_{min}} \times 100 \quad (15\text{-}9)$$

$$\frac{(I_{max} + I_{min}) - 2I_b}{2(I_{max} - I_{min})} \times 100 \quad (15\text{-}10)$$

In drawing load lines, the operating bias may be furnished, in which case one point is already established for the load line. If the value of the load resistance is also known, the second point can be established by the formula previously given: $E_b + I_bR_L$.

REVIEW QUESTIONS

1. (a) Where is a *voltage* amplifier employed? (b) Where is a *power* amplifier employed?

2. Reproduce the gain-control circuit shown in Fig. 15-2 and explain its function.

3. Briefly explain what is meant by bias, and illustrate two methods for supplying bias.

4. Why is it important to have a large-value capacitor across the cathode resistor of an amplifier circuit?

5. How is cutoff bias secured in limiters, oscillators, and Class C amplifiers?

6. Describe two methods for interstage coupling.

7. Briefly describe the purpose and function of a decoupler circuit.

8. Briefly explain the differences between frequency, phase, and amplitude distortion.

9. Explain what is meant by the *Miller Effect*.

10. What are the basic characteristics of a Class A amplifier? How does it minimize distortion?

11. How may frequency distortion be minimized?

12. Briefly explain why a certain degree of selectivity must be employed in R-F amplifiers.

13. How may the Q of a resonant circuit in an R-F amplifier be altered?

14. Give several reasons why modern R-F amplifiers employ pentode tubes in preference to triode tubes.

15. Why is regeneration deliberately introduced in certain R-F amplifier circuits employing pentode tubes?

16. Briefly explain what is meant by a *load line*.

17. How can the ohmic value of the load resistor and the power output of an amplifier be determined by the load line?

18. What is the effect of a large value of load resistance on frequency response?

19. Why is a low value of load resistance used in some amplifiers?

20. If a load line inclines toward the horizontal, would the load resistance be higher or lower than with a load line which inclines toward the vertical?

21. Briefly explain how two points can be plotted on a static set of tube curves for drawing a load line.

22. What effect on selectivity occurs when the circuit Q is lowered?

23. Why is an inadequate screen grid bypass capacitor employed in pentode R-F amplifiers used at very high frequencies?

24. Briefly explain what effect the interelectrode capacities of a tube have on the frequency response of an amplifier.

PRACTICAL PROBLEMS

1. A triode, used as a signal-voltage amplifier has a μ of 100 and an R_p of 80,000 ohms. If the load resistance is chosen as 160,000 ohms, what would be the signal voltage gain?

2. If a load resistance double that given in Problem 1 were chosen, what would be the signal voltage gain for the same amplifier circuit?

3. In a laboratory test of a pentode amplifier, it was found the tube has a g_m of 9,800 micromhos. If the load resistor has a rating of 100,000 ohms, what is the signal voltage gain?

4. The E_p-I_p curves for a triode tube indicate the following values for a given signal swing:

$$E_{min} = 200 \text{ volts};\qquad E_{min} = 25 \text{ volts};$$
$$I_{max} = 40 \text{ milliamperes};\qquad I_{min} = 5 \text{ milliamperes}.$$

What is the value of the load resistance?

5. What is the approximate zero-signal bias for a triode operated at 200 volts and having a mu of 50?

6. Where does the load line for a triode amplifier intersect the zero plate-current axis if the operating current is 20 milliamperes, the operating voltage is 160, and the load resistance value is 5,340 ohms?

7. The characteristic curves for an amplifier indicated the following values for a given signal swing:

$$E_{max} = 240 \text{ volts};\qquad E_{min} = 40 \text{ volts};$$
$$I_{max} = 40 \text{ milliamperes};\qquad I_{min} = 6 \text{ milliamperes};$$

What is the power output for this amplifier?

16

POWER

AMPLIFIERS

INTRODUCTION

Power amplifiers are designed to furnish *signal energy* to a load, rather than *signal voltage* as with the amplifiers discussed in the preceding chapter. The load resistance (R_L) fed by a power amplifier may convert the signal energy to a physical movement as is the case with a loudspeaker or a recording stylus which plots curves electronically. Such devices are known as *transducers* because they convert one form of energy (electrical) to another form (mechanical). On the other hand, the load may utilize the signal energy without reconverting it, as is the case when a power amplifier feeds another stage which requires power input to the grid circuit. The power output may also be applied to an antenna system for transmission, or to tape recording heads, industrial control devices, and other similar units. Thus, power amplifiers are called on to handle signal energy from a few milliwatts to many hundred kilowatts. The signal energy may be of the R-F type or the audio type.

Voltage amplifiers, as discussed in the previous chapter, are usually Class A, although power amplifiers are employed in Class A, AB_1, AB_2, B, and C applications. Of the foregoing, Class C amplifiers can only be used for R-F power amplification, though for audio amplification all the other types from A to B can be employed.

371

In comparison with voltage amplifiers, where signal currents are low, power amplifiers have relatively higher signal currents. In voltage amplifiers, the load resistor is usually of a high value to obtain a large signal voltage drop, while in power amplifiers the load impedance and the circuit arrangement are such as to permit a high signal current.

A power amplifier will transfer a maximum amount of signal energy to the load (a loudspeaker or another amplifier stage) when the output impedance of the power amplifier (plate resistance) matches the load impedance. If the load resistance or impedance is lower than the circuit impedance which generates the signal, less power output will be developed. Less power is also developed for a mismatch where the load impedance is higher than the source impedance.

In voltage amplifiers, an impedance match is usually not important and, in many instances, the load resistance is two or three times higher than the plate resistance. The reason for this lies in the fact that a maximum transfer of power is not desired or needed, because *voltage* amplification is the primary goal, as mentioned earlier.

In power amplification, *impedance matching* is more closely adhered to, in order to provide for a maximum signal power transfer. It is only when distortion is to be minimized that a slight mismatch is tolerated. Because impedance matching is often misunderstood, and because it is an important aspect of the general subject of power amplifiers, a more thorough discussion of impedance matching follows.

IMPEDANCE MATCHING

As mentioned in the preceding chapter, a vacuum tube (or transistor) can be considered as a generator, since its output circuit generates an amplified version of the signal applied to the grid. Thus, if an analysis is made of how a load resistor is to be applied to the output of a vacuum tube, we must consider the vacuum tube as a generator having an internal resistance, as discussed earlier.

To simplify the discussion, low values of resistance will be employed to illustrate the application of Ohm's law. Figure 16-1 thus shows a generator (G) with an internal resistance of 8 ohms, which is represented as a series resistor (R_G), as shown in Fig. 16-1(A). The generator has an output of 48 volts, and since the load resistor (R_L) of 8 ohms is in series with R_G, total resistance is 16 ohms. Thus, 3 amperes of current flows through the network. The power consumed by the load resistance is 72 watts. This is clearly evident from simple Ohm's law calculations, as follows:

$$\text{Current } (I) \text{ through network} = \frac{E}{R} = \frac{E}{R_G + R_L} = \frac{48}{16} = 3 \text{ amperes}$$

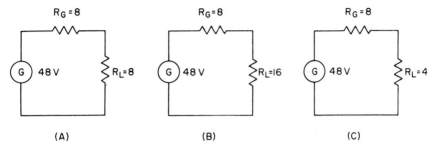

Fig. 16-1. Impedance matching.

Voltage (E) across $R_L = I \times R_L = 3 \times 8 = 24$ volts

Power dissipated in $R_L = E_{R_L} \times I = 24 \times 3 = 72$ watts

As long as the generator voltage remains at 48 volts, and its internal resistance is 8 ohms, no other value of load resistance will be furnished as much power as one having an 8-ohm value. When the load resistance has a value either higher or lower, less power will be developed in it. In Fig. 16-1(B), the load resistance has been changed to 16 ohms to illustrate how the power in the load decreases when its resistance is other than 8 ohms. With the 16-ohm load resistance, the power in the load drops to 64 watts, as indicated by the following calculation:

$$I = \frac{E}{R} = \frac{E}{R_G + R_L} = \frac{48}{24} = 2 \text{ amperes}$$

E across $R_L = I \times R_L = 2 \times 16 = 32$ volts

Power in $R_L = E_{R_L} \times I = 32 \times 2 = 64$ watts

It will be noticed that, in this instance, the voltage across the load resistor has increased, and, if an output *voltage* were desired instead of an output power, the increase in the value of the load resistance would be preferable. Since, however, we are concerned with the power available across the load resistor, the power delivered from the generator to the load is of primary importance.

The opposite instance from Fig. 16-1(B) is shown in (C), where the load resistance has now been reduced to 4 ohms. By Ohm's law calculation, the power dissipation in the load resistor is again below the 72 watts obtained when the internal resistance of the generator matches the load resistance. This is indicated by the following calculation:

$$I = \frac{E}{R} = \frac{E}{R_G + R_L} = \frac{48}{12} = 4 \text{ amperes}$$

E across $R_L = I \times R_L = 4 \times 4 = 16$ volts

Power in $R_L = E_{R_L} \times I = 16 \times 4 = 64$ watts

It will be noted that the current through the load resistor, Fig. 16-1(C), is larger than when the load resistor matches the internal resistor of the generator, as shown in (A). The lower value of load resistor in (C), however, results in a lower voltage drop and a corresponding decrease in power output. As the value of the load resistor is decreased (or increased) below or above that which constitutes a match with the internal resistance of the generator, the resultant power in the load resistor will always be less than the maximum obtained when the impedances are matched. (For simplicity, these examples assume that the generator voltage remains constant with varying current drains. This is rarely the case, however, unless voltage regulators are employed. In any event, impedance matching procures a maximum power transfer.)

Previously, it was mentioned that the load line indicates the dynamic operating characteristics of the tube. The load line itself does not necessarily have the same ohmic value as the plate resistance of the tube, because the slope of the load line is chosen to get the best results, in terms of minimum distortion and a good range of frequency response. Thus, the load resistor value is chosen by performance requirements, and may be somewhat higher or lower than the plate resistance. When the load resistance is not the same as the plate resistance, the maximum power output of the tube is not realized, though the output may be *near* the maximum. The slight decrease in power output is sacrificed in the interests of better performance.

In power-output amplifiers, an actual resistor is not used for the load, because a high resistive value would decrease current flow too much and result in considerable power reduction. Instead, the actual load is the input impedance to another stage, or the *voice coil* of a loudspeaker. To minimize excessive inductive reactance variations in the voice coil for different frequencies, voice-coil impedances are kept quite low, ranging from a few ohms to about 50 ohms. Because the voice coil must transform audio signal power into audible sounds, the voice coil is the actual load resistance and, hence, must be matched to the calculated load resistance to prevent power loss, as more fully explained in the following discussion.

AUDIO-POWER AMPLIFIERS

Figure 16-2 shows a typical audio output-power amplifier, such as employed in low-power phonograph amplifiers, or in the audio output systems of some radio or television receivers. Capacitor C_1 couples the signal voltage from the previous audio voltage amplifier to the grid of the pentode output-power amplifier tube. A triode or beam-power tube can, of course, also be employed instead of the pentode shown.

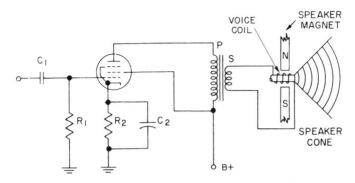

Fig. 16-2. Audio-power output stage.

Resistor R_1 is the conventional grid-leak resistor, and resistor R_2 furnishes bias, by virtue of the current flow through this resistor and the voltage drop across it. Since the cathode becomes more positive with respect to the grid, a negative-bias voltage is applied to the latter. Capacitor C_2 is for signal bypass purposes, to stabilize the d-c voltage drop across R_2.

Since a maximum transfer of power is desired, a transformer is utilized, as shown, to match the calculated load resistance to the voice coil. The primary of the transformer, even though it occupies the same position as that of the load resistor in voltage amplifiers, does not constitute the load resistance for the audio output power amplifier. Actually, the load resistance is the loudspeaker *voice coil,* and the primary and secondary of the transformer only serve as an impedance adjusting device, so that the relatively low ohmic value of the voice-coil impedance can be made to appear equal to the higher value of the load resistance chosen for the particular power-amplifier tube used.

Because a transformer can be employed for stepping up or stepping down voltages, as explained in Chapter 8, an impedance transfer can also be obtained. If the number of turns in the secondary is less than the number of primary turns, a high impedance in the primary can be stepped down to appear as a low impedance to the secondary. Conversely, a low impedance in the secondary will appear as a high impedance in the primary circuit, by virtue of the step-up function obtained with the transformer.

The step-up or step-down ratio is not directly proportional to the number of turns in primary and secondary. That is to say, if there are 400 turns in the primary and 100 turns in the secondary, the impedance ratio will not be four to one. Since the primary and secondary windings are wound one on top of the other, there is a cross-transfer of impedance consisting of capacity, resistance and inductance. In consequence, the turns ratio of the transformer (for matching two dissimilar impedances) must be calculated on the basis of the following formula, which was also given in Chapter 8:

$$\text{Turns ratio} = \sqrt{\frac{Z_1}{Z_2}} \qquad (16\text{-}1)$$

Thus, if the larger impedance is designated as Z_1, and if this quantity is divided by the smaller impedance Z_2, the square root of the ratio would indicate the number of turns necessary to obtain an impedance match in the transformer.

Suppose, for instance, that a vacuum tube is employed which requires a load resistance of 10,000 ohms for best performance. The amplifier is to drive a loudspeaker having a voice-coil impedance of 5 ohms. The calculation for finding the turns ratio would then be

$$\sqrt{\frac{10,000}{5}} = \sqrt{2,000} = 45$$

The foregoing calculation indicates that the transformer must have a turns ratio of 45 to 1, in order to match the relatively high load resistance, as determined by the load line, to the low voice-coil impedance.

The actual number of turns in the primary and secondary is not indicated by the formula, but only the turns ratio. Thus, if there are 225 turns in the primary, there would have to be 5 turns of wire in the secondary. The relative impedances will be maintained as a match, so long as the proper turns ratio prevails.

The transformer is assumed to have virtually no internal resistance. If the resistance of the primary winding is appreciable, some power will be consumed in the primary. This is undesirable, since such power consumption in the transformer is wasted. As much as possible of the power generated within the tube should develop across the voice-coil impedance, so that the loudspeaker cone will be actuated at a higher efficiency. To obtain a minimum of d-c resistance, the primary winding can be made of fairly large wire. Actually, the wire must have a diameter sufficiently large to carry the plate current without undue overheating. An overheating of the transformer indicates that the internal resistance is consuming considerable power, and such power, whether audio signal energy or B power from the power supply, is a waste of energy. When the primary has such a low resistance that it is a negligible factor, the *signal power* circulating in the primary is transferred into the secondary with the greatest efficiency. A well-designed transformer has an efficiency of well over 95%.

The primary of the output transformer *is not* the actual load resistance; neither is the secondary. This point needs emphasizing, since many students often mistakenly assume that the primary of the transformer is the load resistance because current from the power supply flows through it to the vacuum-tube circuit, in similar fashion to the load resistor in a voltage amplifier. It must be understood, however, that neither a pure inductance nor a pure capacitor consumes electric energy, and hence neither the primary nor the secondary, with its negligible resistance values, will consume any appreciable audio power. Rather, the audio signal power is applied to the voice coil, and the resultant signal current sets up varying magnetic fields. The latter aid or oppose the fields of the dynamic speaker magnet, causing the loudspeaker diaphragm cone to vibrate and produce audible sounds. Thus, the electric energy of the power amplifier is converted into acoustical energy.

If the transformer has an appreciable distributed capacity, some of the high-frequency audio signal components will encounter a shunting effect, and hence will be attenuated. For this reason, the transformer design should be such that a minimum of distributive capacities are present. For the same reason, the wire size should be held at a minimum, because a larger wire size contributes to capacity effects between adjacent turns, as well as between adjacent layers of the transformer.

Another factor in transformer efficiency is the quality and quantity of the laminated core. A larger core increases permeability, and hence the number of turns in the primary and secondary can be reduced, while still holding the required amount of inductance constant. The reduced number of turns means less distributive capacity, as well as a decrease in the internal resistance of the transformer. Consequently, less signal energy is shunted by distributive capacities, and less signal energy is wasted because of the series d-c resistance of the primary winding. The d-c resistance will consume audio signal-energy power (which is a-c), as well as d-c power from the power supply.

Another factor to be considered is the variation of inductive reactance with changes of signal frequency as mentioned earlier. A low audio signal frequency will decrease the reactance of the primary and hence less signal voltage develops across it than is the case for higher signal frequencies. This factor tends to attenuate the lower-frequency audio signal components, and upsets uniform response. Good transformer design, however, helps keep such variations to a minimum, as well as reducing the higher audio signal losses by virtue of their being shunted due to distributed capacitances within the transformer. While transformers are not ideal except from the over-all efficiency standpoint, they serve useful purposes in electronic applications and hence are widely used.

A typical output-power amplifier employing a single transistor is shown in Fig. 16-3. A grounded-emitter circuit is utilized in conventional form. The output transformer must match the load (such as the voice coil) to the load-line resistance of the transistor, as with the vacuum-tube amplifier.

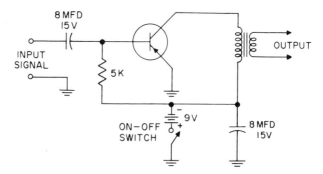

Fig. 16-3. Transistor output-power amplifier.

The negative battery terminal, as well as the bottom of the output transformer primary, are placed at signal ground, by virtue of the 8-microfarad bypass capacitor shown. In transistor circuits, both bypass capacitors and coupling capacitors are chosen to have much larger values than such capacitors have in vacuum-tube circuits. With the relatively low input impedances of transistors, and the low battery resistances, the capacitive reactances of bypass and coupling capacitors must be much lower than comparable units in vacuum-tube circuits. Hence, it is common to find bypass and coupling capacitor values from several microfarads to well over 10 microfarads, in some instances. With the low voltages encountered in transistor radios or other low-power equipment, the size of the capacitors is kept down by using low-voltage units. As a comparison, coupling capacitors in vacuum-tube amplifier circuits may range from 0.01 to 0.25 microfarad.

PUSH-PULL

Two audio-power amplifiers tubes or transistors may be utilized in a symmetrical circuit arrangement as *push-pull,* to produce greater power output. One method for doing this is to utilize an interstage transformer between the voltage amplifier and the two push-pull tubes, as is shown in Fig. 16-4. Push-pull operation requires that the grid of one amplifier tube receive a signal which is out of phase with the signal at the other grid. There are several methods for obtaining such out-of-phase signals, and one of them consists in employing a transformer T_1, as shown. This transformer has in its secondary a center tap which effectively divides the signal energy developed across the secondary into two signals, each of which is out of phase with the other. (For a detailed analysis of polarities across the secondary of a transformer, refer to the section on synchronous vibrator

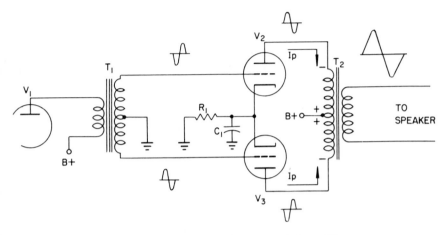

Fig. 16-4. Push-pull transformer-coupled amplifier.

power supplies, in Chapter 14.) The out-of-phase signals can also be obtained by a method known as phase inversion, as discussed later.

Resistor R_1, in conjunction with capacitor C_1, provides the necessary bias for both the push-pull power amplifier tubes. Both cathodes are tied together, and the voltage drop across the resistor will, therefore, be proportional to the current flowing through it for both tubes. Thus, each grid will be negative with respect to the positive potential at the common cathode. For instance, if the voltage drop across the cathode resistor R_1 has a potential of 6 volts, the grids of V_2 and V_3 each will be negative by 6 volts with respect to the positive cathode, because the grids are connected to ground through the T_1 secondary winding of the transformer. (This circuit is designed for Class A operation. No d-c grid current flows, and hence no voltage drop occurs for the bias potential across the secondary winding at T_1. Factors regarding other classes of operation will be discussed later.)

The plate circuits of push-pull tubes usually employ an output transformer also having a center tap as shown. The positive terminal of the B supply is applied to the primary center tap, and the current flow through each tube and through the transformer is in the direction shown by the arrows.

When a push-pull system is Class A, idling current flows through each tube, with or without signal input, as is the case with the single-ended power amplifier tube previously discussed. The idling currents through the output-transformer primary set up polarities as marked in Fig. 16-4. The actual voltage drops across each half of the primary would be low, particularly in a well-designed transformer, where the internal resistance of the windings is kept low. In the absence of a signal, the d-c idling current is, of course, a steady-state condition and, because there is no current *change* through the transformer primary, no voltage is induced into the secondary of the output transformer.

When the voltage amplifier tube, V_1, develops a signal across the primary of T_1, the signal which appears across the secondary will be divided, and a portion applied to the grid of V_2 and another portion to the grid of V_3. These signals will be out of phase with each other. Thus, the grid of V_2 may have a negative signal applied for one alternation, while V_3 would have a positive signal applied, each grid signal being 180 degrees out of phase with the other. When a negative-going alternation appears at the grid of V_2, the plate current through this tube decreases, and this decreasing current through the upper half of the output transformer primary establishes a *changing* field. With decreasing current through the upper half of the transformer primary, the polarity at the plate side of V_2 becomes less negative.

The increasing current through V_3 will flow through the lower section of the transformer primary, also establishing a changing field. As current is increased, the polarity at the plate side of V_3 becomes more negative. Thus, the *total* changing field in the transformer primary is the result of both currents of V_2 and V_3, V_2 current establishing the positive polarity at the top of the transformer primary, and V_3 the negative polarity. Hence, the combined current change induces a voltage across the secondary of the output transformer, and the resultant current flow represents signal power from both tubes. Thus, one signal alternation appears at the transformer secondary. With the arrival of the second signal alternation at the push-pull tube grids, a field (opposite in phase to the one just described here) is generated in the primary, with the result that the second alternation of the output signal is developed. The respective polarity of the output signal is not necessarily as shown in Fig. 16-4. It can be reversed 180 degrees by simply transposing the output leads.

The opposing current changes in the push-pull transformer tend to reduce transformer core saturation and, at the same time, the changing fields established by the current changes induce in the secondary the sum of the audio power developed by each tube. When triodes are used in push-pull, there is a marked reduction in even harmonic distortion. Thus, the audio-power output from a triode push-pull amplifier will be *more than twice* the power developed by a single tube, because of the reduction of harmonic distortion.

If, for instance, a single tube were capable of delivering 10 watts of power, but 1 watt of such power is in the form of second harmonic distortion, the undistorted output power would only be 9 watts. With push-pull, however, the reduction in harmonic distortion would result in an undistorted power output which would be more than double that of a single tube of the same type.

Pentode tubes produce a high degree of odd harmonic distortion and, in consequence, are not employed as advantageously in push-pull circuits as are triodes, insofar as reduction of distortion goes. Pentode and beam-power tubes are used in push-pull amplifiers, however, when the added increase in power output is desired, as in public-address systems, or in other instances where the higher distortion can be tolerated.

The reduction of harmonic distortion in push-pull comes about because of the balanced circuit arrangement which is employed. If, for instance, one of the audio-power amplifier tubes produced a greater potential for the positive polarities of the signal, second harmonic distortion would be present. With tubes in push-pull, however, the deficiencies in the tubes will be diminished, if the circuit has good balance. Assume, for instance, that the vacuum tubes employed for the circuit shown in Fig. 16-4 have characteristics as illustrated in Fig. 16-5(A) and (B), where 20 milli-

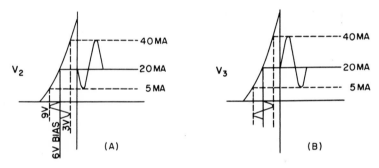

Fig. 16-5. Distortion in push-pull.

amperes of idling current flows under no-signal conditions. Note that the tubes have the same nonlinear characteristics, since, for a given signal, the current will rise more in the positive direction than it will decrease in the negative direction. Thus, V_2 shown in (A) may have a plate-current decrease of only 15 milliamperes (from 20 milliamperes to 5 milliamperes), when a negative signal voltage appears at the grid. For a positive-going signal alternation of the same amplitude on the grid, however, the plate current rises by 20 milliamperes (from 20 milliamperes to 40 milliamperes). These unequal plate-current changes would introduce severe second harmonic distortion, because of the uneven amplitude of the output sinewave alternations produced by this tube.

When the *input* signal has a constant amplitude for each alternation, the output alternations of the amplified signal energy should also have identical alternation amplitudes. In push-pull, however, the current for the two tubes would combine to form the total current. Thus, if the characteristics of the second tube, V_3, shown in Fig. 16-5(B), are similar to those of V_2, shown in (A), the *over-all* effect would be diminished by the push-pull circuit arrangement. Therefore, when current flow in one tube *decreases* by 15 milliamperes, it *increases* by 20 milliamperes in the other tube, giving a total current *change* of 35 milliamperes. At the second alternation of the input signal, the first tube would increase in current by 20 milliamperes, while the second tube would decrease by 15 milliamperes since the decrease in each tube is less than the current increase. Thus, the result would again be a total change of 35 milliamperes, and both alternations of the output signal waveform would be equal. Under this condition, the second and even harmonic components would have been eliminated or diminished. Push-pull does not, however, eliminate all harmonic distortion. Odd harmonic distortion is relatively unaffected, though all even harmonic components are diminished in amplitude. Such reduction of distortion, however, is proportional to the balance in circuit and tube design. If the transformer is not perfectly center-tapped, or if one tube draws more current than the other (or has different emission characteristics than the other), the unbalance which occurs would affect the harmonic reduction characteristics of push-pull design.

Since the changes of signal current through each push-pull tube will be equal but opposite in polarity, in a balanced circuit arrangement, signal voltage variations across the common cathode resistor (R_1 of Fig. 16-4) would be at a minimum, whether or not bypass capacitor C_1 is employed. Thus, C_1 is often dispensed with in actual circuits. In Class A operation, the idling current to each tube depends on the type of tubes employed. Assume, however, that 20 milliamperes flows through each tube. Thus, 40 milliamperes of current would flow through resistor R_1 to establish a voltage drop which applies the required bias to each tube. For any given input signal polarity, the current through one tube would *decrease* and the current through the other tube would *increase*. With a symmetrical circuit, the current decrease in one tube will be proportional to the current increase through the other, and hence the current through R_1 would remain unchanged. Capacitor C_1 is only necessary when an unbalanced circuit causes voltage variations across R_1. Voltage variations in the cathode circuit cause degeneration and a decrease in the amplified signal output.

TRANSISTOR PUSH-PULL AMPLIFIER

As with vacuum tubes, several transistors can also be used in a push-pull circuit arrangement for increasing the power output over that obtainable from a single transistor. Also, as with the triode push-pull circuit

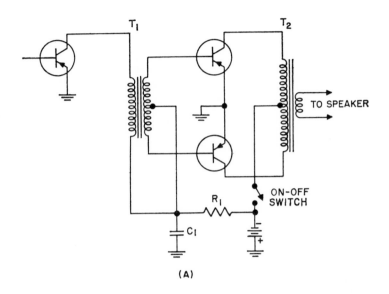

(A)

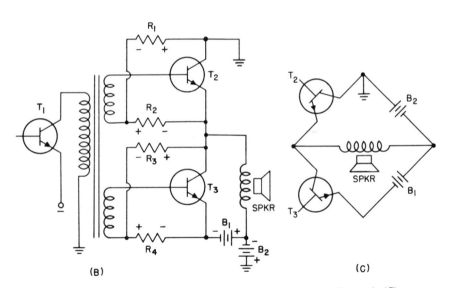

(B)   (C)

Fig. 16-6. (A) Transistor push-pull power amplifier. (B) and (C) Transistorized output and equivalent circuit.

previously described, even harmonic distortion is reduced in a balanced circuit. The transistorized push-pull amplifier can employ either *P-N-P* or *N-P-N* transistors, and a typical circuit using *P-N-P* transistors is shown in Fig. 16-6(A). For *N-P-N* operation, the battery is merely reversed to change circuit polarity, and the circuit is identical in every other respect. The conventional grounded-emitter circuit is used.

Transformer T_1 is for phase-inversion purposes, and applies a signal to the base input of the upper push-pull transistor, as well as to the base input of the lower transistor. The signals applied to the base inputs are out of phase with each other. A d-c voltage of negative polarity is applied to both base circuits, via the tap on the secondary of T_1. Resistor R_1 provides the necessary voltage drop for the base-emitter circuits, and capacitor C_1 acts as a signal voltage bypass for R_1. Each emitter of the push-pull stage transistors is placed at ground potential (positive), in accordance with forward-bias requirements. The collectors of the push-pull transistors are at negative potential (reverse bias), which is applied via the center tap of the primary of T_2. As with vacuum tubes, the total power output depends on the type of transistors used, their relative efficiency, and the amplitude of the input signals applied.

Another version of a transistorized push-pull output-power amplifier is shown in Fig. 16-6(B). Here, no output transformer is required as with the version shown in Fig. 16-6(A). Transistors T_1, T_2, and T_3 could be *P-N-P* types, instead of the *N-P-N* shown, with appropriate battery polarity reversals. For the upper push-pull transistor T_2, the necessary bias for the emitter (negative for the *N-P-N* type) is obtained from battery (or other power source) B_2, and applied through the speaker voice coil. The positive potential for the T_2 collector is applied by the ground connection from the bottom of battery B_2, thus completing the reverse-bias polarities for the output side. The forward bias for the emitter of T_2 is obtained from the voltage-divider resistors R_1 and R_2. A careful study of the circuit will indicate that resistors R_1 and R_2 are in shunt with the negative and positive battery potentials of B_2, via the ground path of T_2. Hence, the polarity of the voltage drops across these two resistors is as shown in Fig. 16-6(B), establishing the base of T_2 as positive with respect to the emitter in accordance with the forward-bias requirements of the *N-P-N* transistor.

The forward bias for transistor T_3 is also obtained by voltage division, using resistors R_3 and R_4, which shunt battery B_1. Hence, the voltage drop across R_4 applies a positive potential to the base of T_3 and a minus potential to the emitter (with respect to the base). The negative-bias potential for the emitter of T_3 is procured from battery B_1 and the necessary positive potential for the reverse bias of the collector of T_3 is applied through the speaker inductor.

The interstage coupling transformer has a split secondary winding, as shown, to provide out-of-phase signal voltages. Thus, the base of each transistor is fed with a signal which is out of phase with the signal at the other transistor base, in conventional push-pull design, just as was the case with the tapped secondary winding previously discussed.

Note that the collector-emitter sections of T_2 and T_3 are actually in series across the split battery potential source. The circuit design, however, is such that the two transistors are in parallel with the load (the speaker coil). This becomes more apparent by an inspection of Fig. 16-6(C), where the equivalent bridge circuit is shown. If the two push-pull transistors are well matched, each will have a voltage drop across it equal to that of the other. Also, if both power sources (or batteries) have the same voltage and internal R, the network bridge will be balanced and *no d-c current* will flow through the speaker inductor. When, however, an audio signal appears across the interstage transformer, one transistor base receives a positive signal alternation and the other transistor base receives a negative signal alternation. Hence, one transistor will conduct more than the other, causing an unequal current flow and an unbalance of the bridge network. This unbalance will cause audio-signal voltages to appear across the speaker inductance (voice coil) and audio-signal currents to flow through it, producing the sound output.

With this transistorized push-pull system the speaker load impedance required to match the transistor push-pull circuit is only a fractional value of what is normally required in conventional vacuum-tube push-pull stages. Since the transistor circuitry has a low impedance, a good match can be obtained with low-ohm voice coils. If such a circuit were attempted with conventional push-pull design, a center-tapped voice coil would be required. Because only one-half of such a voice coil would receive signal energy at any time interval, the efficiency would be lowered and design and production problems would be increased.

PHASE INVERSION

While a transformer will function satisfactorily as a device for obtaining the necessary phase difference between the grid signals of the push-pull tubes or transistors, transformers are costly, when properly designed to minimize signal losses. Transformers also contribute bulk to the amplifier system, besides producing stray magnetic fields. The latter condition requires that shielding precautions be taken for minimizing spurious signal pick-up by nearby circuit components. Because of the foregoing, circuit arrangements are usually employed which dispense with the interstage push-pull transformer, in favor of some other means for obtaining the necessary phase reversal of the signal for application to each of the push-pull tubes.

One method is to use the circuit shown in Fig. 16-7. This system is a plate-cathode type of phase inverter which utilizes a single tube for obtaining the two out-of-phase signals. A single tube can be used, because the signal voltage across a cathode resistor is out of phase with the signal

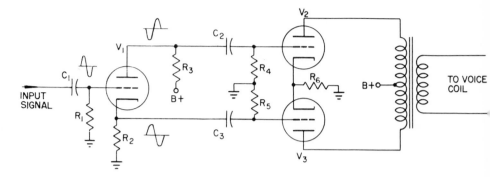

Fig. 16-7. Single-tube phase inverter.

voltage across the plate load resistor. Thus, if the input signal to the grid is of the polarity shown in Fig. 16-7, the first alternation (positive) will cause an increase in the current flow through the cathode resistor, since a positive alternation applied at the grid has the effect of decreasing bias. A bias *decrease* causes an *increase* in plate current and, hence, there will be a proportionate voltage *increase* across the cathode resistor. Such a voltage change across the cathode resistor represents an *in-phase* signal condition with respect to the input signal, as opposed to the *out-of-phase* signal developed across the load resistor, R_3. For the circuit of Fig. 16-7, cathode resistor R_2 and load resistor R_3 are made equal in value, so that each push-pull tube will have grid signals of equal, though opposite polarity, values. Coupling capacitors C_2 and C_3, which transfer the signal voltages to the respective grids of the push-pull amplifier tubes, are also chosen to have equal values. Also, grid resistors R_4 and R_5 have equal values.

The unbypassed cathode resistor R_2 causes considerable degeneration and, consequently, the gain of the stage associated with the phase inverter vacuum tube V_1 is adversely affected. In most instances, the gain for the phase-inverter tube V_1 is less than unity, which means that the tube has the prime function of phase inversion, and not of amplification. A bypass capacitor cannot be employed across cathode resistor R_2, because it would nullify the signal voltage changes which occur across the cathode resistor and, hence, no signal would be obtained from this resistor for application to the grid of V_3.

Another form of phase inversion which is more symmetrical and has more gain than the method just described is shown in Fig. 16-8. Here, an additional tube is used for phase inversion, and the grid-input signal for this tube is procured from a tap in the grid resistor section of push-pull tube V_3. As shown in Fig. 16-8, V_1 is a conventional interstage voltage amplifier which precedes a power amplifier. When a signal voltage, with a

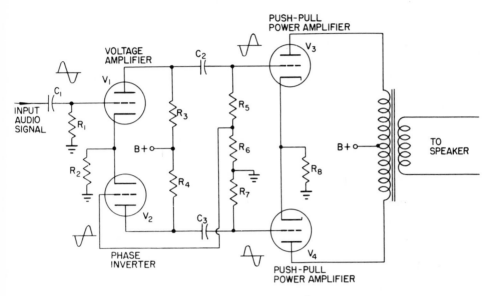

Fig. 16-8. Dual-tube phase inversion.

polarity as shown, is applied to the grid of V_1, the output signal will have the usual 180-degree phase reversal. This amplified output signal will appear across the grid resistor network consisting of R_5 and R_6. The signal at the grid of the push-pull amplifier tube V_4 must be out of phase with that applied to the grid of V_3. This requirement necessitates that the signal which is applied to the V_2 phase-inverter grid be 180 degrees out of phase with the signal at the grid of the voltage-amplifier tube V_1. To obtain such an out-of-phase signal for the grid of V_2, the junction of R_5 and R_6 is tapped and the signal thus obtained is applied to the grid of V_2. Thus, tube V_2 furnishes to V_4 the necessary inverted signal with respect to the signal applied to the grid of V_3.

The amplitude of signal voltage which is tapped off the grid resistor network of V_3 must be the same as the amplitude of the signal applied to the grid of V_1. Hence, the gain realized from V_1 must be considered in ascertaining the correct value of resistor R_6. For instance, if the voltage amplifier tube V_1 has an actual gain of 50, any signal voltage applied to the grid of V_1 will be amplified 50 times. Thus, the value of R_6 should be made one-fiftieth of the total grid resistance at V_3, so that the required voltage percentage will be tapped off for application to the grid of V_2. This procedure not only applies identical signal voltages to the grids of V_1 and V_2, but also establishes identical potentials of amplified signals at the grids of V_3 and V_4. The quality of vacuum tubes V_1 and V_2 should match because, if one tube has a greater gain than the other, the phase-inversion circuit will be unbalanced.

Tube V_2 does not contribute any circuit gain in addition to that furnished by V_1. Thus, the signal input applied to the grid of V_1 is amplified only in proportion to the gain of V_1, since V_1 and V_2 are not used in cascade; that is, the plate of V_1 does not feed the grid of V_2 in sequential amplifier arrangement. For this reason, the combined tubes (V_1 and V_2) furnish no more *interstage amplification* than would be realized from V_1 alone. Instead of using separate tubes for V_1 and V_2, a dual triode tube such as the 6BL7 or the 12AX7 can be utilized.

The phase-inversion system just described is substantially self-adjusting for various amplitudes of input signal levels. Thus, if 1 volt appears across the input circuit to V_1, 50 volts would appear across the resistive network R_5 and R_6, if the actual gain of V_1 and V_2 is 50. Since 1/50 of this voltage is tapped off from across R_6, the voltage applied to V_2 will be 1 volt, the same value as the potential applied to V_1. If the signal amplified from the audio source rises to 2 volts at the input of V_1, the gain of 50 would result in 100 volts developing across the resistive network R_5 and R_6. Again 1/50 of this voltage would be applied to V_2, and hence the grid of the latter tube again has the same voltage appearing on it as appears at the grid of V_1.

Since resistor R_5 is usually over 50 times larger in value than resistor R_6, the inclusion of R_6 in the grid circuit of V_3 does not upset the grid resistance to any appreciable degree. If a closer balance is desired, however, an additional resistor equal in value to R_6 can be inserted between R_7 and ground. Thus, the grid-leak resistance for V_3 and V_4 would be identical.

Another type of phase-inversion circuit is shown in Fig. 16-9. In this circuit, V_1 is the conventional interstage voltage amplifier which follows the detector (or the volume control, or other input voltage source), while V_2 is the phase-inverter tube. Resistors R_5 and R_6 are the respective load resistances for the voltage amplifier tube and the phase inverter. Two additional resistors (R_3 and R_4) are employed in the anode circuits of V_1 and V_2. These resistors are placed from the plate of V_1 to the plate of V_2, and the signal for the grid of the phase-inverter tube is obtained from the junction of these two additional resistors, and coupled via capacitor C_4 to the grid of V_2.

The signal which develops across resistor R_4 must be 180 degrees out of phase with the signal which develops at the grid of V_2. Similarly, the signal occurring across R_3 is out of phase with the signal appearing at the grid of V_1. At the junction of these two resistors, a signal of proper polarity for application to the grid of the phase-inverter tube *is automatically present*. This must be so, because the circuit must reach a balance

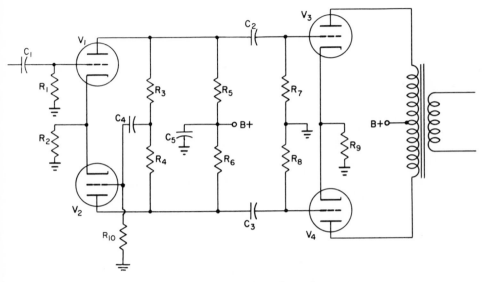

Fig. 16-9. Balanced phase inversion.

in order to function at all. If no signal appears at the grid of V_2, there will be no signal developed across R_4. In consequence, the signal which is derived from R_3 and fed to the grid of V_2 would have a proper phase to start the system into symmetrical operation. Thus, an output would be developed across R_4 which would tend to oppose the signal developed across R_3. Complete cancellation, however, cannot occur. Therefore, a circuit is established which is virtually self-adjusting, and the signal which appears at the grid of V_2 will always be approximately of the same amplitude as the input signal applied to the grid of V_1. The system is self-balancing, and is sometimes preferred to the phase-inversion circuit previously discussed, since the grid circuits to the push-pull tubes are not disturbed by loading effects and, thus, the input impedance is not affected, as may be the case when deriving an input lead for the phase-inverter tube from the grid circuits of V_3 and V_4.

Since resistors R_3 and R_4 shunt the load resistors R_5 and R_6, voltages will develop across them but, since the center tap is to the grid and not placed at signal-ground potential, resistors R_3 and R_4 do not function as the actual load resistors. Resistors R_5 and R_6 are at signal ground at the B plus tap, by virtue of the bypass capacitor C_5. In the absence of such a bypass capacitor at this point, the bypass effect would still be established, because of the filter capacitors in the power supply. Thus, the placement of the junction of R_5 and R_6 at signal-ground potential applies the signal from across the load resistor R_5 to the grid and cathode circuits of V_3, while the signal developed across the load resistor R_6 is applied to the grid and cathode circuits of V_4.

INVERSE FEEDBACK

NEGATIVE-VOLTAGE TYPE

Inverse feedback in an amplifier is a method for feeding a portion of the amplified signal back to the input of the amplifier, or to some other previous stage, in such a manner that the signal which is fed back is opposite in phase to the signal at the circuit to which the feedback is applied. Two basic types of feedback are utilized, one being the *negative-voltage type,* and the other the *negative-current type.*

When a signal voltage is fed back to a previous stage out of phase, degeneration occurs, because the out-of-phase signal will cancel a portion of the input signal, in proportion to the amount of signal fed back. Hence, the process is often referred to as *negative feedback*. Voltage feedback reduces plate impedance, and also decreases the gain of the amplifying system. On the other hand, however, it reduces harmonic distortion, as well as tube noises, and therefore is used extensively.

As shown in Fig. 16-10, the feedback may be procured from the transformer of the output audio-amplifier stage and applied to the cathode circuit of a previous stage. Feedback, in such an instance, could also be from the plate of V_2 to *any* previous stage. Since a negative, or out-of-phase, signal voltage is desired, the places marked X at the output trans-

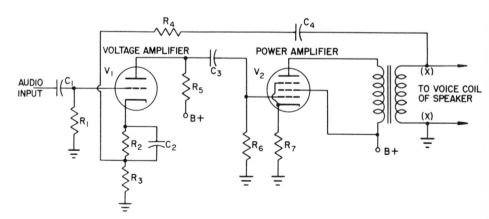

Fig. 16-10. Inverse feedback (voltage).

former secondary must be reversed, if positive feedback should occur. The signal voltage which is fed back from the secondary of the output transformer is applied across resistor R_3 which applies the signal to the cathode circuit of V_1. The amount of signal voltage which is fed back is determined by the values of resistors R_3 and R_4. Capacitor C_4 is a coupling capacitor which prevents any d-c components in the cathode circuit from being shunted by the low d-c resistance of the output transformer secondary.

Inverse feedback reduces harmonic distortion generated within vacuum tubes, in proportion to the amount of signal voltage which is fed back. For instance, if a pure sinewave is applied to the grid of V_1 and duly amplified in the anode circuit, signal distortion may occur because of nonlinear vacuum-tube characteristics. The distortion would become part of the amplified signal at the output of V_1, and thus would be applied to the next amplifier stage, where the original distortion would add to any new distortion which is generated. The accumulated distortion finally gets to the loudspeaker and becomes audible.

The manner in which inverse feedback reduces harmonic distortion will be evident by tracing the process involved. Initially, assume a 5-volt, 2,000-cps signal is applied to the input of the amplifier. If the feedback circuit is such that 0.5 volt of the amplified signal is fed back, the latter will cancel 0.5 volt of the input signal. Such cancellation will reduce the output of this stage, since less signal is now present at the input. Normally, the reduced gain is not a detriment because, if the amplifier has reserve power, the volume control can be turned up to bring the gain to the level desired.

The 0.5-volt signal which is fed back not only contains the 2,000-cycle original signal, but also any harmonic distortion signal present at the output of the amplifier. The distortion signal, however, being higher in frequency than the 2,000-cycle signal, will not be cancelled at the feedback point across R_3, because of the frequency difference between the feedback distortion signal and the input signal. Thus, if the distortion signal which is fed back is 0.1 volt, there would be 4.6 volts of the input signal left after the feedback component had been applied to the input system across R_3, plus 0.1 volt of distortion signal. Now, the 4.6-volt original signal plus the 0.1-volt distortion signal are amplified by V_1, and the distortion component introduced by the feedback will be inverted in phase when it appears in the output across load resistor R_5. The amplified distortion, now out of phase with the particular distortion developed by V_1, cancels out a portion of the *distortion developed by the tube*. The amount of cancellation which occurs depends on how nearly the negative feedback signal amplitude matches the amplitude of the distortion developed in the tube. If the amplitude of the signal which is fed back is made high, the reduction in harmonic distortion is increased. As mentioned, however, the greater the feedback, the higher the degeneration and gain loss which occurs. Any tube noises or other spurious signals which are developed within the tube and are not a part of the applied signal, will also be reduced in proportion to the amount of negative-voltage feedback which is utilized.

The reduction of plate resistance which occurs at the output tube, when using inverse feedback, has some advantages. The lower plate resistance tends to dampen, and thus diminish, the resonance effects of loudspeaker systems, because any spurious signal developed at the loudspeaker voice coil and fed back to the anode circuit would find a shunting effect, due to the lowered impedance.

Inverse feedback also broadens the frequency response of an amplifier. If, for instance, a particular amplifier does not amplify the lower-frequency signals as much as other frequency signals, there would be reduced output for such signals, and hence the amplitude of the feedback voltage of such signals would also be lower than other signals. Consequently, less inverse feedback degeneration occurs for the lower-frequency signals, and thus the over-all gain of the amplifier would tend to flatten out.

The resistive values of R_3 and R_4 determine the amount of inverse feedback. Experimentally, R_3 and R_4 can be varied until harmonic distortion has been reduced to the degree where the output power has not dropped to a value too low for usefulness. Coupling capacitor C_4 should have a value sufficiently large so that it will have a low reactance for the low-frequency signals handled by the amplifier.

NEGATIVE-CURRENT TYPE

Negative-*current* feedback is also shown in Fig. 16-10, and is represented by the unbypassed cathode resistor R_7 of the power-amplifier tube V_2. Negative-current inverse feedback obtains the feedback signal voltage from an unbypassed cathode resistor. The amplitude of the feedback signal is thus proportional to the signal-current flow through the cathode resistor. Negative-current feedback increases the plate impedance of the amplifier tube, as opposed to the decrease in plate impedance for voltage feedback. As with the latter system, however, gain is decreased because of degeneration.

The function of negative-current feedback depends on the inverse signal voltage with respect to grid bias which occurs across the cathode resistor. Without a signal input to the amplifier stage, normal bias develops across R_7, by virtue of the current flow through the resistor. The cathode becomes more positive with respect to ground, and since the grid is connected to ground through the grid resistor, the grid is negative with respect to the cathode, as previously mentioned.

Resistor R_7, not being bypassed, will develop signal voltages across it, whenever signals are applied to the grid of the tube. If, for instance, a positive alternation of signal is applied to the grid, plate current will increase. The increase in plate current through R_7 will also increase the voltage drop across this cathode resistor. The higher voltage at the cathode will *increase* the negative grid bias and cause plate current to decrease. Thus, the grid signal and the signal current change in the cathode resistor act inversely to each other. Where the positive grid signal causes a plate current increase, the changing voltage across the cathode resistor causes a plate-current decrease. With the negative-alternation input signal, degeneration also occurs, because the negative grid signal decreases plate-current flow. A decrease in current through R_7 lowers the cathode voltage with respect to the grid potential, hence plate current increases because bias is decreased.

As with negative-voltage feedback, the frequency response of the amplifier with negative-current feedback increases, thus permitting the amplifier to handle a wider range of frequencies. Omission of the cathode bypass capacitor increases low-frequency response, because of the absence of the increased reactance at lower frequencies. If the bypass capacitor has too high a reactance, some negative-current feedback occurs for lower frequencies. Without the capacitor, the cathode circuit is not instrumental in lowering the gain for signals having lower than normal frequencies. The value of resistor R_7 determines the degree of negative-current feedback. If the ohmic value of R_7 is increased to a sufficient degree, the amplifier stage will have a gain less than unity because of the excessive degeneration which results.

INVERSE FEEDBACK IN TRANSISTOR CIRCUITS

The application to transistor circuitry of the two inverse feedback systems just described is shown in Fig. 16-11. Voltage feedback is coupled from the output of the second transistor stage to the emitter circuit of the first stage by resistor R_8 and capacitor C_4. Current flow in the emitter circuit is in the direction shown by the arrow at R_2. The voltage drop across R_2 opposes to a certain degree the normal positive charge of the emitter versus the base of transistor T_1. Thus, instead of the emitter having 4.5 volts, it would have only 4 volts if 0.5 volt develops across R_2. If a signal, as shown, is applied to the input of the amplifier, the first positive alternation will also oppose the normal forward bias, because the positive alternation of the signal will lower the negative base potential. Thus, current flow in the base-emitter circuit is reduced. The inverse-feedback signal, however, places a positive alternation across R_2, and thus decreases the opposing voltage developed across the latter resistor. In consequence, base-emitter current increases. Thus, where the input signal alternation tends to decrease base-emitter current, the feedback voltage tends to increase base-emitter current, providing an inverse function. Reduction of harmonic distortion, increase of frequency response, and all other factors discussed for the vacuum-tube counterpart of voltage feedback, also apply to the transistor circuits shown in Fig. 16-11.

The absence of the bypass capacitor across resistor R_6 also causes degeneration, and this is a current feedback similar to the condition set up for the vacuum tube in Fig. 16-10, where R_7 was not bypassed. Again, there is a reduction of gain, a change of circuit impedance, as well as a reduction of harmonic distortion, just as with the vacuum-tube negative-current feedback.

Use of *N-P-N* transistors, instead of the *P-N-P* transistors shown in Fig. 16-11, does not alter the feedback circuitry. With *N-P-N* transistors, the only change would be that of battery supply potentials. There would still be the same phase reversal of the signal across each grounded-emitter circuit, and the same feedback principles would apply.

CLASSES OF AMPLIFIERS

The amplifiers previously discussed have all been of the Class A type. A Class A amplifier is, however, also applicable for R-F amplification, as more fully discussed later.

The purpose for using Class A circuitry is to obtain a faithful amplified

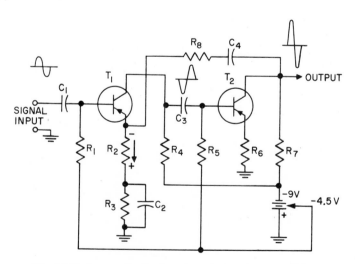

Fig. 16-11. Inverse feedback systems in transistor amplifiers.

version of the input signal. Thus, a Class A amplifier is biased on the linear portion of the characteristic curve of a tube, as mentioned earlier. The signal applied to the input has an amplitude which does not reach either the zero bias level or the cutoff portion of the tube's characteristic curve. A Class A amplifier has a minimum of harmonic distortion as compared to other amplifier types, but the efficiency is relatively low. Efficiency (conversion of d-c power to signal power) depends on the bias and signal amplitude, and may range between 10% and 15%.

Class A amplifiers can be resistance-, impedance-, or transformer-coupled. Class A amplifiers are often employed as power-output amplifiers, as previously illustrated, though they also find application as voltage amplifiers in the R-F stages of television, radio, and other receivers. Class A amplifiers may be employed in a single-ended arrangement or in push-pull, as previously described.

Another type of amplifier is that known as Class AB_1. The Class AB_1 amplifier is employed when more output power is desired than can be obtained from a Class A arrangement. In Class AB_1, the negative bias of the amplifier is a little higher than in Class A, and such bias permits use of a greater plate voltage than can be employed with Class A. Screen potentials can also be increased over Class A operation in pentode applications.

Class AB_1 finds use in audio power-output amplifiers, where the slightly higher distortion level can be tolerated. In push-pull Class AB_1, the even harmonic distortion is reduced, as with Class A. The input signal applied to the grid is held at such an amplitude that the negative peak does not extend into the tube's cutoff region. The subscript "1" is used to denote the condition where the grid does not run positive for any portion of the input signal. Efficiency for the Class AB_1 amplifier ranges between 20% and 35%, depending on exact bias setting and other design factors.

Another type of amplifier which is often utilized is the Class AB_2 amplifier, with which, as with the Class AB_1, the negative grid bias is raised above that used in Class A amplifiers. Plate and screen potentials are usually also increased over the values utilized for Class A. Thus, more output power is obtained, though the distortion level as compared with Class A is considerably higher. The subscript "2" indicates that some grid-current flow occurs, because the positive peaks of the input signal have sufficient amplitude to overcome bias and drive the grid positive. Class AB_2 amplification is employed in audio power-output stages, where more power output is desired than can normally be obtained from Class A or Class AB_1 amplifiers using equivalent d-c supply systems. Push-pull operation is preferable with Class AB_2 applications, to increase power output and reduce distortion. The efficiency of the Class AB_2 amplifier

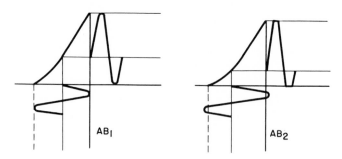

Fig. 16-12. Class AB_2 and AB_1 characteristics.

ranges between 35% and 50%, depending on bias and signal input factors.

The characteristics of Class AB_1 and Class AB_2 are illustrated in Fig. 16-12. Note that, for Class AB_1, the full swing of the input signal from zero bias to the cutoff bias point involves operation over the non-linear portion of the characteristic curve and, hence, harmonic distortion is increased considerably over Class A operation. For Class AB_2, the signal swings beyond cutoff and at the opposite swing drives the grid positive. When the signal at the grid has sufficient positive amplitude to overcome the negative bias and make the grid positive, energy is absorbed from the input signal. With the grid positive, grid current will flow, such current being furnished by the input signal. Hence, in any amplifier where the signal causes grid-current flow, the input signal must be capable of furnishing *power* and not just voltage, as in a voltage amplifier. The waveform which results, because the grid becomes positively charged, has flattened peaks which contribute additional distortion to that already generated through operation on the nonlinear portion of the curve. For reduction of the high distortion present with a single tube, push-pull is utilized for both these classes of operation.

Schematically, the circuits for Class AB_1 and Class AB_2 resemble those for Class A. The differences present are in terms of higher-power d-c supplies, bias differences, and the amplitudes of input signals. Thus, an inspection of the amplifier schematic may not necessarily indicate whether the amplifier is Class A, AB_1, or AB_2, unless the design features are analyzed with respect to the amount of bias being used, and whether or not higher output power is available than would be obtained in Class A operation.

Another type of amplifier is that known as Class B. The Class B amplifier can be designed to handle either audio- or radio-frequency signals, and a typical Class B *audio amplifier* in an equivalent push-pull arrangement is shown in Fig. 16-13(A). The Class B amplifier is biased approximately at cutoff, as shown in Fig. 16-13(B). Because one tube only reproduces about one-half of the signal, two tubes are necessary in order to reproduce the full signal information in audio work. In a push-pull arrangement, one tube produces the amplified positive half of the output cycle, while the other tube produces the output negative half of the output cycle. The grid is driven positive by alternate peaks of the input signal, as shown in (B).

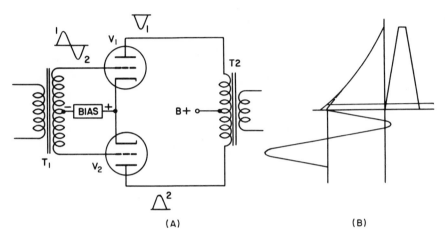

Fig. 16-13. Class B push-pull audio amplifier.

As shown in (A), if the first alternation of the input signal is positive, it will reduce the bias at the grid of V_1. Hence current flow through this tube increases, and the single signal alternation shown above V_1 is reproduced. During this time, vacuum tube V_2 would be in a nonconducting state, since the positive signal alternation across the secondary of T_1 establishes a plus potential at the grid of V_1 and a negative potential at the grid of V_2. When the second alternation of the input signal appears across the secondary of T_1, the grid of V_1 is driven into the cutoff region, while the grid of V_2 is driven into the positive region. Thus, V_2 conducts to produce the alternation shown directly below it. Consequently, every other alternation is reproduced by V_1, and the "in-between" alternations which are missing are furnished by V_2. Hence, the full waveform of the signal is reproduced. The Class B amplifier is characterized by high efficiency, which ranges between 60% and 70%, but with a correspondingly higher distortion, as compared to other types of audio amplifiers.

The bias for Class B is often set at what is referred to as the *projected cutoff,* as shown in Fig. 16-13(B). The projected cutoff is the bias point which is found when the linear portion of the curve is projected downward to meet the horizontal line of the graph. The dotted line section of the curve in Fig. 16-13(B) illustrates the projection of the linear portion of the curve to get projected cutoff. Because the projected cutoff is slightly below the actual tube cutoff point, a low value of idling current flows through the tube, when no signal is applied to the grid. With an input signal, however, the plate current varies as shown in Fig. 16-13. The input signal will develop half alternations in the plate circuit which are produced by operation on the linear portion of the characteristic curve. Despite projected cutoff operation, however, signal distortion is still much higher than for Class A, although, in a carefully balanced circuit, distortion can be held at a level comparable to that obtained from Class AB_2 operation. To obtain good balance, the tubes in the Class B push-pull arrangement must, therefore, be closely matched to hold harmonic distortion at a minimum. It is also essential that the center taps of the transformers be at the actual electrical center of the inductance for a balanced system.

Because plate-current flow in a Class B amplifier varies from a low idling value (with no signal input) to a high average value (for signal input), it is not desirable to obtain bias by use of a cathode resistor, as is the case with Class A operation. To prevent bias variations with d-c current changes, an external fixed bias must be utilized, as shown in Fig. 16-13(A). Such a fixed bias can be a battery or a power supply. In either case, the unit is connected with its negative terminal at the center tap of the secondary of T_1, and the positive terminal at the cathode (ground) of the push-pull circuit.

CLASS B TRANSISTOR AMPLIFIER

Transistors can be used in Class B circuits in a fashion similar to the methods employed for vacuum tubes. A typical transistor Class B circuit in a push-pull arrangement is shown in Fig. 16-14. Note that the base-emitter leads of each transistor are at the same potential. Thus, instead of the usual forward-bias arrangement at the input of the transistor, zero potential is used. With the base and emitter at the same potential (zero), there is no forward bias to overcome the potential barriers with the transistor, and collector current drops to a value almost at cutoff, the latter being equivalent to the projected cutoff bias used for vacuum-tube Class B operation. (As with vacuum tubes in Class B, if the collector were operated at zero current flow, the distortion would increase, because of operation on the nonlinear portion of the transistor's curve.)

If the first alternation of the input signal is positive, as shown, the top of the transformer secondary is at positive potential, while the bottom is at negative potential. The positive potential at the base of the upper transistor establishes the equivalent of a forward bias (positive to the base and negative to the emitter, in an *N-P-N* transistor). Hence, amplification occurs for the first alternation in the top transistor. For the lower transistor, however, the negative potential at the base, and the relatively

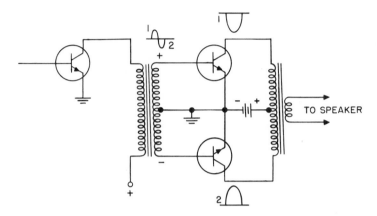

Fig. 16-14. Class B transistor amplifier.

positive potential to the emitter, create a reverse-bias condition which will cut off collector current completely (similar to the signal extending into the cutoff region of a vacuum tube). When the second alternation (negative) of the input signal arrives, the lower transistor has an amplified output alternation, while the upper transistor is now at cutoff. Thus, as with vacuum-tube Class B systems, each transistor contributes one-half of the amplified signal output cycle. For *P-N-P* transistors, circuit operation is identical, and the supply battery polarities are merely reversed.

R-F POWER AMPLIFIERS

Power amplifiers for handling R-F signals usually consist of Class B and Class C types, and are used primarily in radio, television, FM, or other broadcast transmitters. The Class C type (discussed later) is generally used for amplification of an R-F pure carrier signal. The Class B, on the other hand, is usually employed when it is desired to amplify a modulated R-F type signal in transmitting systems. The Class B R-F amplifier can be employed either in push-pull or as a single-ended stage. It will function as a single-ended stage because of the energy interchange effect between the capacitor and inductance of the resonance circuit. This energy exchange (flywheel effect) supplies the missing alternation for the individual pulses of plate current which flow in Class B. The pulses of plate current occur at a repetition rate corresponding to the frequency of the input signal, and such plate-current pulses supply continuous R-F energy to the resonant circuit composed of an inductance and capacitor. The interchange of energy between the capacitor and inductance of the parallel resonant circuit forms a complete sinewave type of R-F signal, even though only supplied with timed pulses of power.

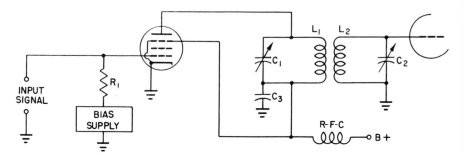

Fig. 16-15. Class B R-F amplifier.

Figure 16-15 illustrates a typical single-stage Class B R-F amplifier. The input signal develops across the grid and cathode sections, as shown. A bias supply, consisting of a battery or power supply, furnishes the necessary negative bias near the cutoff point. The amplified signal energy develops across the parallel resonance circuit composed of capacitor C_1 and inductance L_1. Capacitor C_3 is a return signal path from the resonant plate circuit to the cathode circuit. Thus, capacitor C_3 prevents signal energy from developing across the power supply. In series with the B voltage is an R-F choke (RFC) which, because of its high reactance for the R-F signals, acts as an opposition for signal energy, and reduces leakage of the latter to the power supply. By transformer coupling of L_1 and L_2, the energy in the plate resonant circuit is transferred to the grid resonant circuit of the next stage. The plate resonant circuit could also be coupled to an antenna system, if the Class B stage is the final R-F amplifier of a transmitter. Since a pentode is used, neutralization should not be necessary.

The Class C amplifier, in contrast to the other types previously discussed, is only on R-F power amplifier and cannot be employed for audio-power amplification. Hence, the Class C circuit is used only in R-F power amplifiers in transmitters. Bias for Class C operation is set *beyond* the grid voltage cutoff point of the tube (usually from two to three times cutoff). Signal input must be capable of furnishing power, as with Class AB_2 and Class B amplifiers. The signal input, therefore, must have sufficient amplitude to drive the grid positive at alternate positive peaks. In a Class C amplifier, the grid-current flow during the positive alternation peak of the input signal will charge the grid capacitor, which in turn will discharge across the grid leak, as previously discussed in Chapter 15 and illustrated in Fig. 15-9. Thus, the Class C amplifier is capable of furnishing its own bias.

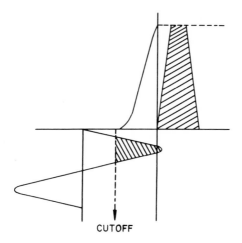

CUTOFF

Fig. 16-16. Graph showing the portion of input signal current flowing in a Class C amplifier.

Since bias is set beyond the tube's cutoff point, plate current flows for only a portion of the applied input signal (less than the duration of one alternation). This factor is illustrated in Fig. 16-16. The shaded portion of the positive alternation of the input signal is the only section causing current flow, because the remainder of the input signal is beyond the cut-off bias point of the tube. Hence, plate current flows for only a portion of each positive alternation of the input signal, as shown. The remainder of the input signal (beyond the cutoff point) is not reproduced by amplification, and thus the Class C amplifier is not useful for audio amplification, even if a push-pull circuit is employed. If a Class C circuit were utilized for audio, severe distortion would result, because some of the audio components would be missing from the amplified signal developing across the load impedance or resistance. Thus, Class C is useful only for R-F amplification, where only the *frequency* and *amplitude* of the signal are involved, and not the *wave shape*.

A typical Class C R-F single-ended amplifier is shown in Fig. 16-17. The energy from the previous stage is coupled to the input of the Class C amplifier via capacitor C_1. The input signal energy is known as *excitation*.

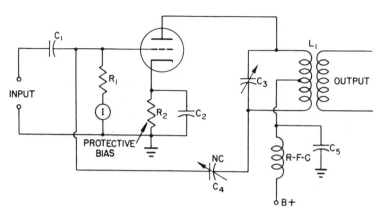

Fig. 16-17. Triode class C amplifier with neutralization.

Resistor R_1 is the conventional grid leak. The self-bias which develops by virtue of the grid being driven positive will cause a current flow through R_1, which can be read by a milliammeter placed in series as shown. Since there would be no bias developed in the absence of an input signal, a cathode resistor and capacitor are also employed for protective bias, as shown. As with the Class B amplifier previously discussed, the amplified signal energy develops across the anode resonant circuit composed of C_3 and L_1. Because a triode tube is employed here, neutralization is necessary, as discussed previously. Adjustments are made to the neutralizing capacitor (NC), consisting of C_4.

The high efficiency of the Class C amplifier is due to the short duration of the plate-current pulse. The current-surges in the plate circuit pulse the resonant circuit (sometimes referred to as the "tank") into a flywheel type of oscillation. Thus, when the pulse appears across the tank circuit shown in Fig. 16-17, it charges capacitor C_3 to its full value and this, in turn, discharges across L_1. The collapsing field of L_1, after C_3 has been exhausted, produces a back-emf which recharges capacitor C_3. This flywheel motion reproduces a sinewave in the tank circuit, despite the momentary pulses of energy which are present in the anode circuit.

Since current flow is from cathode to plate, and thus down through the tank circuit to the power supply, the pulse of energy developed across the tank circuit is in a negative-going direction. During the time of maximum current flow, the impedance of the tube is low, while the impedance of the tank circuit is high for the resonant frequency. This means that most of the energy from the power supply is developed across the tank circuit during a time when tube impedance is low and consuming little energy. In consequence, a high order of efficiency is obtained in the Class C amplifier, and a well-designed unit may have an efficiency rating in excess of 90%.

Tuned resonant circuits are highly selective, as mentioned earlier. Selectivity, however, can be regulated by the degree of resistance introduced into the resonant circuit. Resistance will lower Q and decrease selectivity. Thus, a Class C amplifier can be designed to handle a signal of only one particular frequency. Signals of other frequencies will be diminished, because of the flywheel effect selectivity of the tuned resonant circuit. With resistance added to the circuit, the amplifier can be designed so that its selectivity is somewhat broadened; that is, the amplifier will handle a narrow band of signals having frequencies grouped around the center resonant frequency.

In the input circuit of Fig. 16-17, the value of capacitor C_1 and resistor R_1 must be chosen so that the R-C constant is proper for the frequency of the applied input signal. Capacitor C_1 must be capable of charging to the peaks of the rectified energy when the grid runs positive, while resistor R_1 must be capable of dissipating the energy contained within C_1 in sufficient time to prevent grid saturation. At the same time, resistance R_1 should not be so low in value that it dissipates an excessive amount of the input signal energy. If too much energy is drawn from the previous circuit, excessive loading effects on the previous circuit may upset the normal function of the latter.

The tuned resonant circuit in the plate side is adjusted for the frequency of the input signal by adjustment of capacitor C_3. When resonance is achieved, a maximum grid signal will flow, and the largest value of bias is developed across resistor R_1. For this reason, resonance indication while tuning can be obtained by observing the grid-current flow with a d-c ammeter, or by measuring the bias voltage drop which appears across resistor R_1. The protective bias furnished by C_2 and R_2 may have a value anywhere below cutoff. The larger the resistor, the greater the voltage drop, and the more negative the grid will be with respect to the cathode. A value of protective bias is chosen which will provide sufficient bias for protection against excessive plate current during the absence of the input signal, without wasting an excessive amount of power from the supply.

When a pentode tube is employed, no neutralization is necessary, provided that the tube is of such a design that interelectrode capacities have a high reactance for the frequencies handled by the amplifier. When a triode tube is utilized, however, neutralization is necessary to prevent feedback (regeneration) and consequent oscillation. If the Class C amplifier oscillates because of feedback, it will generate a frequency of its own which is independent of the applied frequency of the input signal. Hence, during oscillation, the usefulness of the Class C stage as an amplifier is lost.

When the tank circuit is not tuned to resonance, maximum plate cur-

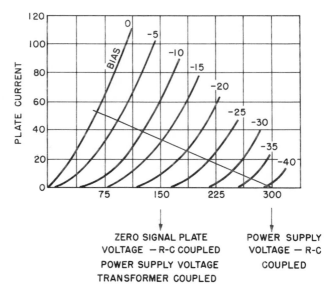

Fig. 16-18. Dynamic load-line factors. (RC versus transformer coupled).

rent will flow, because of the low impedance presented by the tank circuit on each side of the resonant frequency. With high-power Class C amplifiers, excessive currents can flow, unless some protective measures are taken to limit the plate-current flow during the tuning process. Without a load, the Q of the tank circuit is very high, and excessive voltages are present, because of the high impedance. Under normal load conditions, the Q drops to a value as low as 10 or 15.

LOAD-LINE FACTORS FOR POWER AMPLIFIERS

With a *resistance-coupled* amplifier stage, the supply voltage indication on a load line drawing is the *right-hand termination* of the load line at the zero current line, as shown in Fig. 16-18. Thus, the supply voltage for a resistance-coupled circuit for this tube is 300 volts. The voltage swing across the load resistor for a signal input can then reach the maximum value of 300 volts, since this is the maximum available from the power supply. The operating voltage would be 150 volts, since this is the drop across the load resistance without signal input.

With an output transformer-coupled amplifier such as is employed in power-amplifier circuits, the actual supply voltage would only be 150 volts for this tube, the same as the operating voltage shown for the dynamic load line in Fig. 16-18. The function, insofar as the dynamic characteristic is concerned with signal input, however, is essentially the same as with an actual load resistor in series with the power supply. In a transformer-coupled system, the actual load is that which is applied to the secondary of the transformer, such as a loudspeaker voice-coil, as mentioned earlier. The function, in terms of plate-current swing, comes about because of the action of the inductance through which the plate current of the power amplifier must flow. Thus, if the grid signal potential swings in a negative direction sufficiently to reduce the plate current to a small value, the sudden change in current through the inductance induces a voltage across this inductance, which adds to the plate supply potential. The effect is to increase the *instantaneous* plate potential to a value considerably above the operating potential, and hence above the plate supply voltage. A positive grid signal swing also creates a sudden current change condition in the primary inductance, and induces a voltage across the primary inductance opposite to the previous instance. Thus, the plate-voltage signal swing reaches values above and below the normal operating potential, when an output transformer is employed.

As long as the average d-c plate current does not change when the signal is applied to the grid circuit, the same dynamic characteristics hold for the resistance loads as for the transformer-coupled loads, and reference should be made to Chapter 15 for representative formulas and processes for calculations.

Pentode and beam power tubes have characteristic curves which exhibit a more horizontal slope after the plate voltage reaches a certain value, as shown in Fig. 16-19. Load line calculations are more complex than for triodes. The most complex calculation is the one for finding the third harmonic distortion, since such a calculation must take into consideration the equivalent effective (rms) values of the peaks of signal alternations.

A typical circuit for the tube shown in Fig. 16-19 is illustrated schematically in Fig. 16-20. Here, a beam-power tube is shown in the output power amplifier stage of an audio system. The cathode resistor is listed as having a value of 190 ohms, and the power supply voltage is 125 volts. Since the screen grid is also connected to the same voltage source, 125 volts also appears at the screen. Assume that, for this tube, 3.3 milliamperes of screen current are flowing, and that the recommended load resistance is 2,700 ohms. The operating current is 44 milliamperes for the anode.

If the load line shown in Fig. 16-19 were not drawn in, two points on the characteristic curves could be ascertained from the information given above. Initially, the bias value can be calculated and this will determine the operating point on the 125-volt vertical line. Since 44 milliamperes of

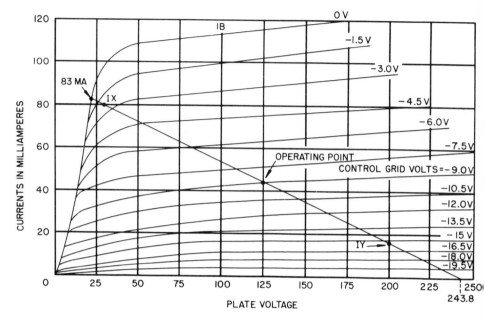

Fig. 16-19. Pentode-load line.

current are flowing through the cathode resistor for the anode, and 3.3 milliamperes are also flowing through the cathode resistor for the screen grid, the total current flow through the cathode resistor is 0.0473 amperes. When this current value is multiplied by the value of the cathode resistor (190 ohms), the bias value is found to be 9 volts. This establishes the

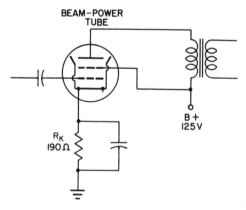

Fig. 16-20. Beam-power output audio amplifier for tube of Fig. 16-19.

operating point shown in Fig. 16-19. The place where the load line meets the zero current line at the right can be solved for as follows by using Equation (15–6):

$$E_p + I_p R_L = 125 + 44 \times 2{,}700 = 243.8 \text{ volts}$$

This establishes the second point, and the load line can now be drawn in as shown in Fig. 16-19.

The second harmonic distortion can now be calculated as follows from Equation (15-10):

$$\frac{I_{\max} + I_{\min} - 2I_p}{2(I_{\max} - I_{\min})} \times 100 = 2\%$$

To solve for third harmonic distortion, the following formula must be employed:

$$\frac{I_{\max} - I_{\min} - 1.41(I_X - I_Y)}{I_{\max} - I_{\min} + 1.41(I_X - I_Y)} \times 100 \qquad (16\text{-}2)$$

In the foregoing, the minimum values of current swing must be subtracted from the maximum values, and the values of I_X and I_Y ascertained. The latter two values are based on the full signal swing. Since the bias is minus 9 volts, the full signal swing would be from this value to zero bias, and from minus 9 volts to twice this value, or 18 volts. Calculations of third harmonic distortion, however, must be based on the rms values of each peak alternation of the full signal swing. The value for I_Y gives the rms value of the negative signal swing at the grid, and is found as follows:

$$0.707 \times 9 \text{ volts} = 6.3$$
$$6.3 + 9 = 15.3 \text{ volts}$$

The foregoing 15.3-volt bias value indicates the rms value of one alternation of the signal swing. When this bias value is marked on the load line, as shown in Fig. 16-19, it indicates that approximately 16 milliamperes flows at this instantaneous value of signal. The other required point of I_X is found by subtracting the rms value of 6.3 from the 9-volt bias value, as follows:

$$9 - 6.3 = 2.7 \text{ volts}$$

This 2.7 volts establishes the I_X point on the load line, as shown. This point is approximately 79 milliamperes. Now that the two plate-current values for I_X and I_Y have been found, they can be set into the formula for calculating the third harmonic distortion, as follows:

$$\frac{83 - 8 - 1.41(79 - 16)}{83 - 8 + 1.41(79 - 16)} = \frac{75 - 88.8}{75 + 88.8} = \frac{13.8}{163.8} \times 100 = 8.4\%$$

In the foregoing calculation, the smaller value of 75 is subtracted from the larger value of 88.8, leaving 13.8. Hence, the third harmonic distortion is indicated as being slightly over 8%. To solve for power output, Equation (15-7) previously given is used, where minimum and maximum values of current are involved, as follows:

$$\frac{(E_{max} - E_{min})(I_{max} - I_{min})}{8} = 2 \text{ watts (approximately)}$$

LOAD LINES FOR PUSH-PULL

In push-pull circuitry, one tube is connected across only one-half of the primary of the output transformer, as can be seen from inspection of the push-pull schematics given earlier for tubes and transistors. Because the tube is only across one-half of the primary, the load impedance which is reflected to the tube from across the transformer will only be one-quarter of the total impedance reflected into the total primary winding. The reason for this is that the reflected impedance varies as the square of the turns ratio. Thus, in push-pull, the load resistance must be one-half of the value which would be employed when only one tube is used, in order to obtain at least double the power output which would be obtained from a single tube of the same type. When standard formulas are used for calculating the load resistance for push-pull circuits, the results usually indicate a load resistor value somewhat higher than one-half of that for a single tube. The higher value of load resistor increases power output (to more than double the power output obtained with a single tube), though the harmonic distortion is somewhat higher. Since push-pull reduces the second harmonic (and even harmonic) distortion of triodes, this increase in the value of the load impedance when triodes are used is permissible.

To find the push-pull *plate-to-plate* load resistance, we must first use a formula to find the push-pull load resistance as follows:

$$R_L = \frac{(E_p - 0.6E_p)}{I_{max}} \tag{16-3}$$

The plate voltage, as indicated in Fig. 16-21, is 250 volts. The formula indicates that 6/10 of the plate voltage value is to be subtracted from the full plate-voltage value. Six-tenths of 250 = 150, and the latter subtracted from 250 leaves 100 volts:

$$R_L = \frac{100}{I_{max}}$$

The next step consists in ascertaining the value of the maximum current at the 150-volt value ($0.6E_p$). The current maximum is found by finding the point where the 150-volt value intercepts the zero bias line. As shown in Fig. 16-21, this point is at the 220-milliampere level. Hence, the formula now becomes

$$R_L = \frac{100}{220 \text{ milliamperes}} = \frac{100}{0.220 \text{ ampere}} = 454.5 \text{ ohms}$$

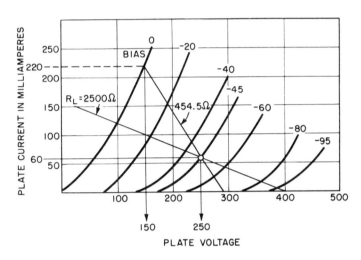

Fig. 16-21. Push-pull load-line graph.

The load line representing the above value can be drawn on the graph by starting at the zero bias line, from the 150-volt point, and running the new load line through the same operating point used for the single tube (at the −45-volt bias point). To solve for the plate-to-plate load resistance, however, it is necessary to multiply the results obtained for R_L by four, as follows:

$$\text{Plate-to-plate } R_L = \frac{(E_p - 0.6E_p)}{I_{\max}} \times 4 = 1,818 \text{ ohms}$$

The power output for the push-pull stage can be found by multiplying the current maximum at the zero bias line by the plate voltage, and dividing by five:

$$\text{Power output} = \frac{(I_{\max} \times E_p)}{5} \qquad (16\text{-}4)$$

Relating this equation to the values obtained from the graph shown in Fig. 16-21 solves for the output power for this particular push-pull circuit:

$$\frac{(0.220 \times 250)}{5} = 11 \text{ watts}$$

TRANSISTOR LOAD LINES

Transistors are essentially power amplifiers and, as with vacuum-tube amplifiers, load lines are useful for determining dynamic operation conditions. The characteristic curves for the grounded-emitter transistor circuit were given in Fig. 13-8, plus a discussion of the current gain calculation (beta). For comparison, the characteristic curves of a typical *grounded-base* circuit are shown in Fig. 16-22. The load-line factors discussed herein are applicable to either type graph.

Current gain for the grounded base can be ascertained without a load line drawn in on the graph. As with the grounded-emitter circuit, current gain is equal to output signal current divided by input signal current. For the grounded emitter, the equation given in Chapter 13 was:

$$\text{Current gain } \beta \text{ (beta)} = \frac{dI_c}{dI_b}$$

where d represents a *change* of current. For the grounded base, the equation is

$$\text{Current gain } a \text{ (alpha)} = \frac{dI_c}{dI_e} \qquad (16\text{-}5)$$

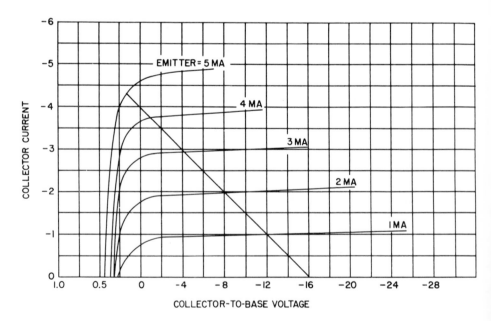

Fig. 16-22. Grounded-base transistor curves.

Because the base is grounded, the emitter-base current is denoted as emitter current I_e. Current gain for the grounded base circuit is less than unity, but power amplification occurs because of the higher impedance in the output circuit. Since power equals I^2R, the higher output resistance versus the very low input resistance of the grounded base circuit produces signal power amplification.

The characteristic curves shown in Fig. 16-22 are for a *P-N-P* transistor circuit, such as shown in Fig. 16-23 (or Fig. 15-28 of Chapter 15). Be-

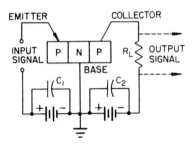

Fig. 16-23. Basic circuit of a transistor amplifier.

cause of the reverse bias, the negative battery potential is applied to the collector, hence the *collector-to-base voltage* values indicated on the horizontal axis of the graph in Fig. 16-22 are shown as negative quantities. For the same reason, the *collector current* values along the vertical axis are also negative. For an *N-P-N* transistor, the positive values would be shown.

The load resistor R_L in Fig. 16-23 is represented as an actual resistor because, even if the stage were transformer-coupled to a loudspeaker, the actual load reflected back to the transistor from the speaker represents pure resistance (the component which consumes power).

The operating point (zero signal conditions) is chosen on the basis of the total swing of the input signal, as well as the limits of the power which can be dissipated by the particular transistor. (Manufacturer's specifications usually indicate the operating point.) For the load line shown in Fig. 16-22, the collector-to-base voltage line (−8 volts) intercepts the 2-milliampere emitter-current curve, and this establishes the operating point. (As mentioned earlier with respect to vacuum-tube amplifiers using an output transformer, the operating-point plate voltage also equals the power-supply voltage.)

With the load line shown, a signal swing at the emitter-base input of the circuit produces the emitter currents indicated along the load line. For instance, if the input signal at Fig. 16-23 consists of a positive alternation, it aids the forward-bias conditions, and emitter current increases. If the input signal has sufficient amplitude to increase emitter current to about 4.5 milliamperes, collector-to-base voltage becomes zero at the instantaneous peak value of the input signal. (The voltage drop across the load resistance opposes battery voltage.) With the input signal swing in the negative direction, forward bias is reduced and emitter current drops to zero. Because of the transformer action, the instantaneous collector-base voltage swings to -16 volts. As is the case with vacuum tubes, if an actual resistor were present for the R_L, the battery voltage would have to be -16 initially. At zero signal conditions, the operating-point voltage would be -8 volts, with 8 volts dropping across the R_L.

The load resistance represented by the load line is calculated by using the same formula as was the case with vacuum tubes:

$$R_L = \frac{(E_{max} - E_{min})}{(I_{max} - I_{min})}$$

For the load line shown in Fig. 16-22, consider the load line from zero collector-base voltage to -16 volts, with a collector-current change of zero current to 4 milliamperes (along the vertical axis of the graph). Applying these figures to the formula gives a load line of 4,000 ohms:

$$\frac{16}{0.004} = 4,000$$

Power output (signal power) can be calculated by again using the formula previously given for vacuum tubes:

$$P_{out} = \frac{(E_{max} - E_{min})(I_{max} - I_{min})}{8}$$

where voltage changes refer to the collector-base voltage changes on the horizontal axis of the graph, with the load line indicating the limits. The current changes are the collector current values indicated by the vertical axis, also within the limits imposed by the load line shown. Other vacuum-tube formulas (distortion, etc.) can also be applied to the transistor load line.

REVIEW QUESTIONS

1. What is meant by a power amplifier?

2. What do the subscripts "1" and "2" designate, in Class AB_1 and AB_2 amplifiers?

3. Briefly explain what is meant by impedance matching, and where it is important.

4. In a power-output transformer feeding a loudspeaker, which has more turns of wire, the primary or the secondary?

5. Why is it necessary to have a minimum of d-c resistance in the primary winding of an audio-output transformer?

6. What type of harmonic distortion predominates in a triode tube? In a pentode tube?

7. What type of harmonic distortion is minimized in a push-pull amplifier system?

8. Briefly explain the necessity for a phase inversion circuit, and reproduce a sketch of a typical phase inverter.

9. Briefly explain what advantages are derived from using voltage-type inverse feedback.

10. Explain how current-type inverse feedback can be obtained, and what effects it has on gain and plate resistance.

11. (a) Can a Class B audio amplifier be used in a single-ended stage?
(b) Can a push-pull Class C amplifier be employed for audio amplification?
(c) Can a Class B amplifier be used in a single-ended stage for R-F amplification?
(d) Can a single-ended Class C amplifier be employed for R-F amplification?

12. Explain the approximate efficiency of the following amplifiers: Class A, Class B, Class C.

13. Briefly explain how the plate voltage can swing above the power supply voltage, in a transformer-coupled output audio-power amplifier.

14. Briefly explain how the characteristic curves of pentode or beam-power tubes differ from those of triode tubes.

15. Give the formula for finding the third harmonic distortion in pentode tubes.

PRACTICAL PROBLEMS

1. In a phase-inverting system like that shown in Fig. 16-8, the actual gain of V_1 is 60 and the value of R_5 is 500,000 ohms. For proper voltages during phase inversion, what should the value of R_6 be?

2. From a set of characteristic curves, the idling plate current in a Class A amplifier is indicated as 50 milliamperes. The operating point shows a negative bias of 14 volts, while the schematic diagram has a value of 200 ohms marked for the cathode resistor. What screen current flows in this pentode amplifier?

3. In a power amplifier, a signal amplitude change of from 50 volts to 250 volts causes a plate-current change from 250 milliamperes to 50 milliamperes. What is the power output?

4. In the design of an output transformer for a power amplifier, the actual load resistance to be used was 16 ohms, and the recommended load resistance was 10,816 ohms. What must be the turns ratio of the transformer?

5. In a push-pull amplifier, I_{max} at $0.6E_p = 200$ milliamperes. If E_p is 300 volts, what is the plate-to-plate load resistance?

6. What is the power output for the amplifier described in Problem 5?

7. In a grounded-base transistor amplifier, a change of emitter current from 1 milliampere to 3 milliamperes causes a change of collector current from 1.2 milliamperes to 2.8 milliamperes. What is the value of alpha?

8. A set of characeristic curves for a transistor in a grounded-base circuit indicates that when the collector-to-base voltage changes from zero to 20, a change in collector current occurs from zero milliamperes to 5 milliamperes. What is the value of the indicated load resistor?

9. If the transistor in the foregoing example is to be matched to an 8-ohm speaker, what must be the turns ratio of the transformer which is used to couple the transistor output circuit to the loudspeaker?

10. In a push-pull Class A amplifier, each tube draws 50 milliamperes. Bias for each tube should be a negative 10 volts. What must be the value of the single common cathode resistor and what wattage is dissipated therein?

17

OSCILLATOR CIRCUITS

INTRODUCTION TO RESONANT-CIRCUIT TYPES (PART 1)

Oscillators are generators of signals, and hence are used extensively to originate the various low-frequency, intermediate-frequency, and high-frequency signals required in the operation of electronic equipment. In radio and television receivers, for example, oscillators are used in the tuning stages, as more fully detailed in Chapter 19. In transmitters, oscillators are used to generate the fundamental signal which is to be sent for many miles to various receivers. Tape recorders also use oscillators for erasure of recorded tape, and electronic organs employ oscillators for generating the fundamental musical tones. Oscillators are also widely used in radar, electronic computers, and other electronic devices.

Some oscillators are employed for the generation of audio-frequency *sinewave* signals, while others are used to generate signals having square or rectangular shapes. Oscillators are also designed to produce R-F sinewave signals ranging from a few hundred kilocycles to well above several thousand megacycles. Some oscillators employ resonant circuits, while others use resistance and capacitance combinations for the generation of signals having specific frequencies. Certain oscillators have provisions for varying the frequency of the output signal by manual adjustment (variable-frequency oscillators), and others have a fixed frequency which cannot be changed readily without circuit modifications (fixed-frequency oscillators). Generally, all oscillators have low signal output, and must be followed by amplifiers to raise the signal level to that desired for practical applications. For better classification and discussion of the various oscillators, Chapter 17 has been broken into two parts, this section discussing the resonant-circuit types, and the next section discussing the resistance-capacitance types.

FLYWHEEL SINEWAVE GENERATOR

The sinewave type of signals usually employ resonant circuits as frequency-*determining* devices, and include such types as the Hartley, Colpitts, and others described in this section. To understand how such oscillators function, it is necessary to investigate more fully the characteristics of a resonant circuit with respect to the *flywheel effect,* mentioned with reference to the R-F amplifiers in the last chapter.

When a capacitor is connected across an inductance, as shown in Fig. 17-1(A), the combination becomes a basic generator of a-c waveforms.

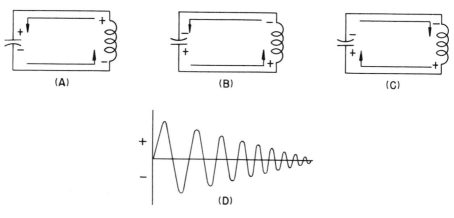

Fig. 17-1. Flywheel effect.

If the capacitor is charged with a polarity as shown, and the *charging source is removed,* the capacitor will immediately start to discharge through the inductance, and the electron flow will be in the direction indicated by the arrows. During such discharge, current flows through the inductance, setting up a magnetic field. The potential across the capacitor gradually declines, and when the capacitor has completely discharged its energy across the coil, the fields of the coil will collapse and produce a back-electromotive force (voltage). According to Lenz's law, the current flow from the coil will be in the same direction as the charging current, and the back-electromotive force will cause a polarity change across the inductance, as indicated in (B), since the source of electrons will now be at the top of the coil and will charge the capacitor with the polarity opposite to the initial charge.

After the collapsing field has recharged the capacitor, the capacitor then discharges across the coil again, as shown in (C). Thus, the reversal in the direction of the electron flow in the circuit will create a voltage which is of sinewave form. The circulating energy which constantly reverses direction is known as the *flywheel effect*.

If there were no resistance in the circuit to consume the energy, the interchange of energy between coil and capacitor would continue indefinitely. This is similar to the momentum of a pendulum. After energy has been imparted to the pendulum to start it swinging, it would keep up such motion for an indefinite period if the energy were not consumed by the resistance of the air or the friction in the bearing or pivot by which the pendulum is suspended. Since some friction is always present, however, the pendulum eventually slows down, and so does the energy circulating in the resonant circuit shown in Fig. 17-1. Some resistance is always present in the coil and, in consequence, the amplitude of the generated waveform gradually declines as the energy is consumed by the resistive component of the circuit. Thus, a parallel resonant circuit will have a gradual decline of its waveform, as shown in (D). This is known as a *damped wave*.

The frequency generated by the parallel resonant circuit depends on the inductive value of the coil and on the capacitive value of the shunt capacitor. If a larger value of capacity is used, it will take longer for the capacitor to charge fully, and also longer to discharge. Hence, the *frequency* of the sinewave would be reduced. The frequency can also be lowered by increasing the inductance. With a larger value of inductance, it would take longer for the capacitor to discharge through the coil because of the greater number of opposing fields which are produced. If either the capacitor or the coil is made smaller, or if both are reduced in size simultaneously, the charge and discharge time is reduced and consequently a signal of a higher frequency is generated. The frequency which is generated depends on the resonant-circuit conditions previously detailed, and the frequency would be the one at which the inductive reactance of the coil equals the capacitive reactance of the capacitor. The formula for the resonant frequency of such a circuit is

$$f_r = \frac{1}{2\pi \sqrt{LC}} \qquad (17\text{-}1)$$

This formula gives the resonant frequency when the inductance in henrys and the capacity in farads are known. The farad, however, is too large a value, and in electronic work the microfarad is employed. Hence, a more workable formula is one which utilizes the microfarad value such as shown below. By also changing henrys to microhenrys, the answer will be the frequency in kilocycles:

$$f_r = \frac{159}{\sqrt{LC}} \tag{17-2}$$

A simple capacitor and inductance combination, as described, will generate the basic waveform with the desired frequency, but the small amount of energy contained in such a circuit cannot be utilized practically. As soon as the energy is taken from the circuit, the fields collapse and the circuit stops oscillating. Thus, it is necessary to furnish power to the circuit, so that it can deliver a continuous amount of energy. The most practical way to do this is to furnish the circuit with d-c power, and permit it to convert this power to the necessary a-c energy. This can be done by employing vacuum-tube or transistor circuits. These circuits are so designed that they supply energy at the proper time intervals to replenish the losses incurred as the a-c energy is removed from the circuit by the load. This function can be understood by inspection of the previously discussed Fig. 17-1. In (A), any energy which would be applied to the circuit must have a polarity conforming to· the existing polarity *at the instant of application.* If the replenishing device applied energy in opposite polarity, it would oppose the energy in the circuit and would cause a collapse of the field and of the circulating flywheel energy. The device which furnishes energy over a period of time to the circuit shown at (A) must apply that polarity in the proper time interval. A vacuum-tube or transistor oscillator will perform this timing function, and will pulse or supply the resonant circuit energy of proper polarity and in sufficient amounts to maintain a constant amplitude output from the oscillator.

FEEDBACK OSCILLATOR

The *feedback oscillator* illustrated in Fig. 17-2 was one of the first types of oscillator developed. It is not so extensively used at the present time as some other types, but may be encountered occasionally in special circuits.

A feedback inductance, sometimes referred to as a tickler coil, is utilized to couple some of the signal energy developed in the plate circuit back to the grid circuit. The windings of the tickler coil must be such that the signal which is inductively coupled to the grid inductance is of proper

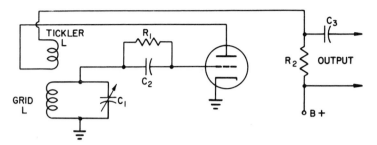

Fig. 17-2. Feedback oscillator.

polarity to sustain oscillations. The degree of coupling between the two coils is adjusted for maximum oscillation amplitude. The variable capacitor across the grid inductance is used to tune the oscillator to the desired frequency, since it will change the ratio of L to C.

Bias for the oscillator is developed in similar fashion to the self-bias developed in Class C amplifiers discussed earlier. With the cathode grounded, any positive alternation on the grid will cause the latter to become positive with respect to the cathode and, in consequence, the grid will draw current. The signal current which flows from the cathode to the grid will charge the grid capacitor, as described earlier.

When the oscillator is first turned on, the lack of bias will permit full tube conduction. Thus, the rising plate voltage in the anode circuit creates a magnetic field to the feedback inductance, which in turn places a rising positive potential on the grid. The increasing positive signal on the grid will cause greater conduction within the tube, and the plate-current flow rises to a still higher value. This, in turn, induces a greater amplitude positive potential on the grid. This continues until tube saturation has been reached, when plate current can rise no higher.

It is at this point that the grid capacitor will have acquired a charge equal to the peak of the signal voltage. At saturation, plate current no longer increases and, when no current *change* exists in the plate inductance, induction ceases and no voltage is transferred to the grid inductance by mutual coupling. The flywheel effect in the resonant circuit of the grid will now cause a voltage swing in the opposite direction. When the grid signal swings in the negative direction, the peak charge at the capacitor will hold the grid to a negative value beyond cutoff. As soon as the signal swing is beyond the cutoff region, plate current ceases. When the signal swings toward the positive direction again, it will overcome the negative bias of the grid capacitor and again cause tube conduction. As the grid signal voltage swings toward the zero and reduces bias, the rising plate current will again induce a voltage in the grid inductance, because the rise is a change of current. The current rise continues until current saturation is reached. Thus, the oscillator continuously generates a signal, and feeds a portion of the amplified energy in the plate circuit to the grid circuit, to sustain oscillations. Even though plate current only flows intermittently, the flywheel effect of the circuit provides a sinewave signal. The output from the oscillator is taken from across R_2 and coupled to a subsequent stage by coupling capacitor C_3.

The tuned-grid oscillator is not as stable as the electron-coupled or crystal oscillators subsequently described. Stability depends on the regulation of the B voltage, as well as on the characteristics of the components involved.

TRANSISTOR FEEDBACK OSCILLATOR

The transistor lends itself readily to the application of oscillator circuits, and a typical circuit of this type is shown in Fig. 17-3. This is an R-F feedback type of oscillator utilizing a grounded-base circuit. A comparison between the transistor feedback oscillator circuit shown in Fig. 17-3 and

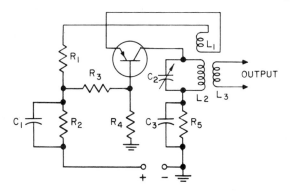

Fig. 17-3. Transistor R-F feedback oscillator.

the vacuum-tube tuned grid oscillator of Fig. 17-2 will indicate that the feedback principle is identical. The resonant circuit which determines the frequency of the oscillator consists of the variable capacitor C_2 and the inductance L_2. A portion of the energy in the resonant circuit is coupled back to the emitter circuit by use of a "tickler" coil, in a fashion similar to that employed for the vacuum-tube type. As with the latter, the inductance L_1 must be coupled so that the energy which is fed back is in phase, which will permit regeneration (and oscillations).

Resistor R_2, in conjunction with capacitor C_1, is a decoupling network for isolation of the signal energy from the power source. The decoupling network prevents R-F energy from being transferred (coupled) to other circuits which may be supplied d-c energy from the same power source. Resistors R_1 and R_3 are for the purpose of establishing the proper voltage potentials at the emitter and base of the transistor. Since current flow through resistor R_4 is from the negative terminal of the power source, this resistor helps maintain stability as explained for the transistor R-F amplifier in Fig. 15-26. When not bypassed, some degeneration results and output power decreases. The degenerative circuit, however, improves general performance as explained in the current feedback topic discussed earlier. Capacitor C_3 places the bottom of the resonant circuit at ground potential for the signal, while R_5 provides the required voltage drop for the collector and also forms a decoupling network in conjunction with capacitor C_3.

THE HARTLEY OSCILLATOR

The Hartley oscillator shown in Fig. 17-4 has been extensively used as the local oscillator in broadcast receiver applications as well as in certain FM transmitter applications. The resonant circuit of the Hartley oscil-

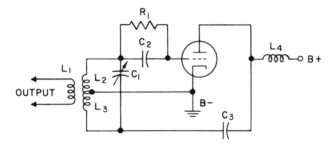

Fig. 17-4. Hartley Oscillator.

lator is composed of the usual parallel circuit of inductance and capacitor, though in the Hartley oscillator the inductance is tapped by the cathode circuit. Because of the tap, the resonant-circuit inductance is divided into two sections, composed of L_2 forming the grid circuit, and L_3 forming the plate circuit.

The power-supply voltage is shunt-fed to the plate of the tube by use of an isolating R-F choke coil, L_4. Thus, the B supply potential shunts, rather than flows through, the resonant-circuit inductance. Use of the isolating capacitor C_3 prevents the B voltage at the plate from being shorted to ground through L_3.

The amplified signal energy, which is developed in the plate section of a coil (L_3), is inductively coupled to the grid section by virtue of the auto-transformer characteristics of the tapped coil. The inductive coupling thus sustains oscillations by virtue of the proper in-phase feedback network. Capacitor C_1 can be varied to change the frequency of the signal which is generated. The final frequency developed, however, is also influenced by the lumped inductances of the circuit, as well as by interelectrode capacities and stray capacities.

A pentode tube instead of a triode can also be employed. The cutoff bias is produced by the grid leak-capacitor combination of R_1 and C_2, in a fashion similar to that described for the feedback oscillator.

TRANSISTOR HARTLEY OSCILLATOR

The Hartley oscillator circuit using a *P-N-P* transistor is shown in Fig. 17-5. The circuit is similar to the vacuum-tube Hartley oscillator. The grounded-emitter circuit is employed, with the inductance tap also grounded

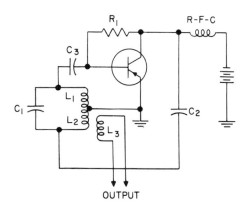

Fig. 17-5. Grounded-emitter Hartley Oscillator.

and, hence, at emitter potential (equivalent to the cathode of a vacuum tube). Capacitor C_2 isolates the negative voltage of the battery from ground (positive potential), while C_3 prevents the inductance from applying the positive ground potential to the base. Forward bias to the base-emitter circuit requires that the base have a negative potential. Resistor R_1, between the collector (negative potential) and the base, establishes the base at the required negative potential with respect to the emitter. The output signal is obtained by inductive coupling (in transformer arrangement) to the base-collector coil, as was also done for the vacuum-tube version.

THE COLPITTS OSCILLATOR

The Colpitts oscillator shown in Fig. 17-6 resembles the Hartley oscillator discussed previously. Instead of using a tapped inductance, however, two capacitors are placed across a common inductance, and the center of the two capacitors is tapped. A transistor, as in Fig. 17-5, could also be used, with a tapped capacitor arrangement employed, as in Fig. 17-6.

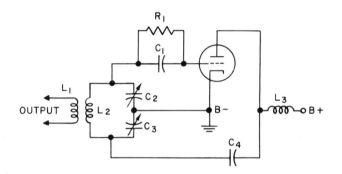

Fig. 17-6. Colpitts oscillator.

The two capacitors, C_2 and C_3, in conjunction with inductance L_2, form the resonant circuit. As with a Hartley, the inductance L_2 forms part of the grid circuit as well as the plate circuit. The B voltage is again shunt-fed, using an R-F choke coil L_3. Capacitor C_4 couples the R-F energy developed in the plate circuit to the bottom of the parallel resonant circuit. Capacitor C_4 also isolates the d-c potential of the power supply, and prevents it from being applied to the grid circuit through inductance L_2 and resistor R_1.

The curved-arrow sections of C_2 and C_3 are the movable portions of the variable capacitors, and these sections are grounded. Hence, the grounded rotors have the same potential as the cathode and are at the B minus level. By grounding each rotor of the two variable capacitors, the oscillator's resonant circuit is effectively divided into two sections, with capacitor C_2 forming the grid resonant section and capacitor C_3 the plate resonant section. Inasmuch as the two sections are connected together, common coupling between the output and input circuits of the oscillator exists. Thus, oscillations are sustained.

Cutoff bias is developed in the grid circuit in a fashion similar to the process described for the Hartley oscillator.

THE TUNED-PLATE TUNED-GRID OSCILLATOR

A typical tuned-plate tuned-grid oscillator is shown in Fig. 17-7. This differs from the Hartley or other oscillators previously described because the grid and plate circuits are separated, so that no mutual inductance exists. Coupling between the output and input circuits is established, by virtue of the interelectrode capacity, to produce oscillations.

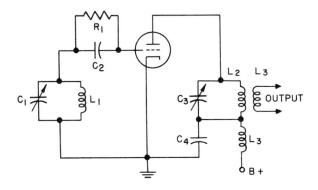

Fig. 17-7. Tuned-plate tuned-grid oscillator.

Capacitor C_4 establishes the bottom of a plate resonant circuit at signal ground, and thus maintains the R-F path from plate to cathode. This is necessary to complete the connection from the resonant circuit to the oscillator tube. An R-F choke is placed in series with the resonant circuit and the power supply, for isolation purposes. As with R-F chokes previously mentioned, a high reactance is present for the R-F energy, and this minimizes leakage to the power supply.

Common coupling between the anode resonant circuit and the grid resonant circuit exists by virtue of the interelectrode capacities of the tube, as well as capacitor C_4, which places the bottom of the anode resonant circuit at the same ground potential as the grid resonant circuit.

The frequency of this oscillator is influenced to a considerable degree by the interelectrode capacities and circuit capacities. Also, one of the resonant circuits must be tuned off frequency for oscillations to occur. This can be understood by assuming that the grid resonant circuit composed of C_1 and L_1 is tuned to resonance. At resonance, the inductive reactance of the L_1 would have a value equal to the capacitive reactance of C_1 and, since the two reactances have opposite characteristics, the respective reactances would, in effect, cancel out and the circuit would be a resistive one. Thus, the grid circuit is primarily resistive, with some capacitive reactances contributed by interelectrode capacities and the external capacitor C_2. The latter, however, has a very low reactance for the frequency of the oscillator.

If the plate resonant circuit is also tuned to resonance, it too becomes primarily resistive, since the effective reactance is again cancelled. In lumping together the various components which now exist in the oscillator circuit, it would be found that only resistance and capacities are present, the capacities being contributed by the interelectrode and stray capacities. Since the inductances have been effectively cancelled out, oscillations cannot occur, because no flywheel effect can be created when there is no interchange of energy between the inductance and the capacity.

In order to create oscillations, the resonant circuit in the plate side of the oscillator can be tuned slightly above the frequency which the oscillator is to produce. When this is done, the inductive reactance of L_2 decreases and the capacitive reactance of C_3 increases. This comes about because a resonant circuit, when tuned above the generated frequency, creates a condition equivalent to having a resonant circuit of a certain frequency and applying a lower frequency across it. When a frequency lower than the resonant frequency is impressed on a circuit, the capacitive reactance increases and the inductive reactance decreases.

The reduced inductive reactance now decreases the high impedance which formerly existed in the parallel resonant circuit. The decreased impedance is created because the inductive reactance of the coil is now lower. Hence, the signal energy finds less opposition in the coil and flows through it. The circuit becomes primarily inductive, since it is the inductive reactance which has been decreased, and creates a lower opposition to signal energy flow. Inasmuch as the anode circuit is now primarily inductive, interchange of energy between circuit capacity and the inductive anode circuit is possible. Consequently, the oscillator can generate a signal, because the lumped constants consist of inductance, as well as resistance and capacity.

The function of the tuned-plate tuned-grid oscillator is closely duplicated by the crystal-controlled oscillator described next. In the crystal oscillator, only a single frequency can be obtained, because of the fixed-frequency characteristics of the crystal. In the tuned-plate tuned-grid oscillator, however, the resonant circuit in the grid can be varied, as well as the resonant circuit in the plate; hence, the signal output can be changed for frequency by readjustments of the grid and plate capacitors. The desired frequency, however, is only obtained under the conditions previously detailed, with respect to tuning one of the circuits to resonance, and the other above resonance.

If a pentode tube is used instead of a triode, difficulty in establishing oscillation may be encountered, because of the smaller value interelectrode capacities in a pentode. For low-frequency operation, an additional capacitor must be placed between the grid and plate terminals of the tube. For higher-frequency operation, however, the decrease in the interelectrode capacities' reactances eliminates the need for the external capacitor.

CRYSTAL OSCILLATOR

When the grid resonant circuit of the tuned-plate tuned-grid oscillator previously discussed is replaced by a crystal, an oscillator is formed which has a high order of frequency stability. For this reason, crystal oscillators are used extensively to control the carrier frequency of a radio, FM, or television transmitter. They are also used in other electronic applications where a high order of frequency stability is needed in a signal generator.

The type of crystal utilized is the piezoelectric quartz crystal, which has the property of vibrating at a frequency which depends on the thickness of the unit and the type of cut employed. Fig. 17-8 illustrates how some typical crystal slabs are derived from the raw crystal.

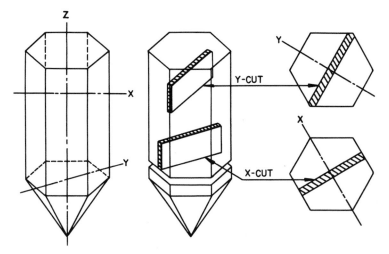

Fig. 17-8. Piezo-quartz crystal structure.

In transmitting, or in other applications where accurate frequency is required, the crystal is placed in a small enclosure and is subjected to a controlled temperature. The enclosure is referred to as a *crystal oven,* and a resistance-strip heating element is utilized to maintain a constant crystal temperature for stability purposes. With most crystal types, a perceptible frequency difference results when the crystal temperature varies.

The crystal is held by two plates to form the contacting elements for each crystal surface. The two plates are then mounted in a crystal holder of low-loss plastic material. This holder usually has two terminal prongs, so that the crystal can be plugged into the oscillator socket provided for it. (See Fig. 17-9.)

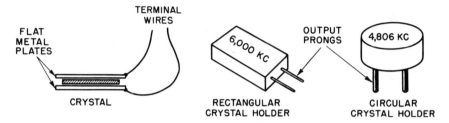

Fig. 17-9. Crystal holders.

The two plates which hold the crystal form a capacitor, since the plates are metal, and the crystal acts as the dielectric of the capacity. Because of the capacity characteristics thus formed, the crystal also assumes the function of the grid capacitor in conjunction with a grid leak. This is shown in Fig. 17-10, which illustrates the basic crystal oscillator circuit.

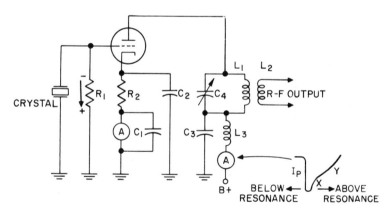

Fig. 17-10. Crystal oscillator.

In similar fashion to the tuned-plate tuned-grid oscillator, the signal in the plate tank circuit of the crystal oscillator is coupled to the grid circuit through interelectrode capacities, to maintain oscillation. When triodes are used in crystal oscillators, the interelectrode capacity is sufficient for coupling purposes. When a higher amplitude of output power is desired, however, pentodes are used and, frequently, these have insufficient interelectrode capacities to produce oscillation as mentioned earlier for the tuned plate-tuned grid oscillator. For this reason, an additional capacitor is usually connected between plate and grid to establish the necessary degree of coupling.

As with R-F oscillators previously described, the peaks of grid signal drive the grid positive, and the latter draws current. This, in turn, places a charge across the capacity represented by the crystal and, during signal intervals other than positive peaks, the charged grid capacitor will discharge across the grid leak resistor, and thus establish a bias as indicated by the arrow at R_1 in Fig. 17-10. In most instances, however, a small amount of additional bias is provided by a cathode resistor (R_2), to act as a protection, should the crystal fail to operate. In the absence of oscillations, no bias would be developed at the grid leak, and currents would become abnormal within the tube. The cathode resistor provides sufficient *protective bias* to limit currents below excessive values.

The capacitor C_2 acts as a bypass across R_2 to prevent signal variations across the latter, which would result in degeneration and lowered output. A milliammeter can be placed in the cathode circuit to read plate-current flow. This is useful when tuning the plate circuit to resonance. Capacitor C_1 shunts signal energy across the meter and prevents damage to the d-c instrument.

Capacitor C_3 places the bottom of the plate resonant circuit at ground potential, while L_3 is an R-F choke which provides a high reactance to signal energy, and prevents it from getting to the power supply.

Tuning C_4 establishes the optimum oscillation point. As shown by the plate-current waveform besides the plate current meter, plate current is high when the circuit is off resonance. As the circuit is tuned toward the resonant frequency, there is a sharp drop in plate current, and then a gradual rise as C_4 tunes to a higher frequency. The most stable operation occurs within the limits X and Y of the slope of the plate-current curve. An attempt to operate the oscillator right at the dip of the plate-current curve usually results in instability and loss of oscillation.

Since the piezoelectric quartz crystal which is used operates at a frequency dependent on the type of cut and the thickness, it forms a resonance circuit which could be replaced by physical components of inductance, capacity, and resistance, in similar fashion to the tuned-plate tuned-grid oscillator previously discussed. The inductance of the crystal can be considered as an electronic equivalent of the mass which determines vibration, while the capacity is contributed by the holding plates plus the mechanical compliance of the quartz. The mechanical friction set up during crystal vibration is equivalent to the resistive component of a resonant circuit.

Because of the foregoing, the frequency of a crystal oscillator can be changed to a limited degree by introducing components of either inductance, capacity, or both, across the crystal. In some commercial applications, a small variable capacitor is placed across the crystal for limited tuning purposes, so that the frequency of the crystal can be adjusted closer to that desired, without the necessity for having to grind the crystal thickness to close tolerances.

When used in transmitting, the crystal oscillator is followed by successive stages of Class C R-F power amplifiers. These build up the power produced by the crystal oscillator, until the desired carrier power is secured at which the station is to operate.

As with all oscillators, plate-current flow in the plate resonant circuit (the "tank") is in the form of pulses. Because of the flywheel effect in the resonant circuit of the plate, however, the signal energy which is produced is a sinewave. Since a resonant circuit is highly selective, it will develop the greatest signal energy for the resonant frequency, while rejecting frequencies below and above the resonant frequency. Since an oscillator often generates a high order of harmonic frequencies, the resonant circuit will reject such undesired frequencies while favoring the desired frequency. Subsequent stages, which also contain resonant circuits, add to the degree of selectivity desired, and further suppress spurious harmonics generated by the oscillator.

TRANSISTOR CRYSTAL OSCILLATOR

A crystal oscillator using a *P-N-P* transistor is shown in Fig. 17-11. A grounded-base circuit is used and, as mentioned earlier, there is no phase reversal between the signal at the emitter and that at the collector. Thus, the signal currents in the emitter are in phase with the signal currents in the collector, and all that is necessary to produce oscillations is to couple some of the signal energy from the collector directly back to the emitter side. For the circuit shown in Fig. 17-11, the piezo-quartz crystal is employed as the resonant feedback loop from collector to emitter. Not only does the crystal form the feedback loop, but, because of its resonant characteristics, it also establishes the oscillator frequency and maintains it with good stability. Capacitors C_1 and C_2 are for battery bypass purposes.

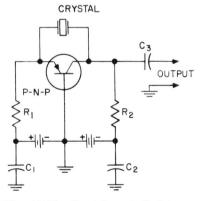

Fig. 17-11. Crystal-controlled transistor oscillator.

ELECTRON-COUPLED OSCILLATOR

Another type of oscillator which is much more stable than the variable-frequency types discussed earlier, is the electron-coupled oscillator. A well-designed oscillator of the latter type has a stability which almost equals that of the crystal oscillator previously discussed.

Basically, the electron-coupled oscillator employs a variable-frequency oscillator, such as the Hartley previously described or any other similar type. A special circuit arrangement is employed, however, wherein the output circuit (the load) is isolated from the primary oscillator circuit. Hence, variations in the amount of signal energy which might be drawn from the oscillator (load variations) and might normally have an undue influence on frequency stability, have a negligible effect on the electron-coupled oscillator.

A typical electron-coupled oscillator is shown in Fig. 17-12, using the basic Hartley oscillator previously described. The essential difference between this oscillator and the conventional Hartley is that the *screen grid* of the pentode tube is used as the *anode for the Hartley oscillator*. Grids of vacuum tubes can be employed as anodes if a plus potential is applied to them. Since, however, the grid wires do not have the larger surface area of plates, they are unable to handle as much power as a plate element can. But the lower power generated can be increased to the amount desired by subsequent Class C amplifiers.

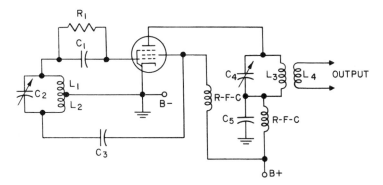

Fig. 17-12. Electron-coupled oscillator.

For the electron-coupled oscillator shown in Fig. 17-12, the Hartley circuit is that portion of the tube consisting of the cathode, the control grid, and the screen grid. Thus, the inductance split into two sections, L_1 and L_2, in conjunction with capacitor C_2, forms the parallel resonant circuit for the Hartley oscillator. The plate of the pentode is coupled to another resonant circuit which is independent of the resonant circuit of the Hartley oscillator. Hence, the plate resonant circuit does not contribute toward establishing the resonant frequency of the oscillator.

The Hartley oscillator section of the electron-coupled oscillator generates a signal having a frequency established by the resonant circuit, as mentioned. Thus, the signal voltages are present at the grid, and signal current flows in the screen grid, the actual anode of the Hartley oscillator section. Consequently, the current which flows from cathode to the screen grid varies in accordance with the signal amplitude changes. *Plate* current for the pentode, however, also flows from cathode to anode, hence the signal current variations between cathode and screen grid influence the plate-current flow. When the grid signal swing cuts off current flow to the screen grid (the anode of the Hartley section), plate current also ceases. Thus, the plate resonant circuit composed of C_4 and L_3 is pulsed in a timing that coincides with the frequency established by the Hartley oscillator section. For the foregoing reasons, the output resonant circuit is *electron-coupled* to the oscillator section, and loading effects are held at a minimum.

A load resistor could also be substituted for the resonant circuit of the plate. The resonant circuit in the plate, however, improves the output selectivity, and thus insures better harmonic frequency rejection. Since all oscillators generate signals rich in harmonics, additional resonant circuits help select the desired frequency and reject the undesired harmonic components. In some applications where a higher frequency is needed than generated by the oscillator, advantage can be taken of the harmonic frequencies to produce frequency multiplication as described in Chapter 24.

REVIEW QUESTIONS

1. Briefly explain what is meant by flywheel effect and how Lenz's law applies.

2. Explain how the values of inductance and capacitance are related to resonant frequency.

3. What two factors relating to a tickler coil must be observed with respect to the feedback oscillator?

4. What is the purpose for a decoupling network in the transistor feedback oscillator?

5. Explain why the Hartley oscillator shown in Fig. 17-4 can also be called a shunt-fed oscillator.

6. What are the essential circuit differences between a Hartley oscillator and a Colpitts oscillator?

7. Why is it sometimes necessary to place a capacitor between the plate and grid terminals of the tube in a tuned-plate tuned-grid oscillator?

8. Why is protective bias sometimes employed in crystal oscillators?

9. To what ordinary circuit components can the piezoelectric crystal be compared?

10. What is the primary advantage of the electron-coupled oscillator, as compared to the basic Hartley oscillator?

PRACTICAL PROBLEMS

1. In the design of an oscillator, the parallel resonant circuit had a total inductance of 0.00005 henry and capacity of 0.00025 microfarads. What is the resonant frequency?

2. The engineering specifications for an R-F oscillator gave the product of LC as 0.0253. If the inductance was in microhenrys and the capacity in microfarads, what is the resonant frequency in kilocycles?

3. An R-F oscillator designed to operate above the broadcast band has a total LC product of 0.00045, with L rated in microhenrys and C in microfarads. What is the resonant frequency in kilocycles?

4. In testing a crystal oscillator such as shown in Fig. 17-10, it was found that 150 milliamperes of plate current flowed when operating with a normal load and resonant circuit conditions. If the voltage drop across the cathode resistor is 6 volts, what is the value of the resistor? Would a 2-watt resistor be adequate?

5. In an experimental electron-coupled oscillator designed to operate at approximately 652 kilocycles, a capacitor of 85 micromicrofarads was used with a 704-microhenry inductance. Interelectrode and stray capacitances, however, contributed 15 micromicrofarads of capacity to the resonant circuit. What is the actual resonant frequency?

6. In the oscillator in Problem 5, and R-F choke coil of 20 millihenrys was used. What is its reactance?

INTRODUCTION TO RESISTANCE-CAPACITANCE TYPES   (PART 2)

In addition to the resonant-circuit R-F oscillators previously described in Part 1 of Chapter 17, a variety of nonresonant oscillators are found in industry. The nonresonant oscillators are primarily employed to generate low-frequency signals from 500 kilocycles down to frequencies in the audio ranges (below 20,000 cycles per second). Such low-frequency oscillators find applications in radar, electronic computers, transmitting and television receiving systems, in test equipment, and in other electronic circuits.

The low-frequency, nonresonant oscillators are known as *relaxation* oscillators, and depend on the values of resistance and capacitance employed in the circuits to determine the desired frequency of the signals generated. Such oscillators can also be synchronized so that the frequency of their signals can be precisely controlled by other signals. Such frequency-control of an oscillator is often necessary in certain electronic applications, as more fully discussed later.

PLATE-COUPLED MULTIVIBRATOR

A basic relaxation-type oscillator is the one known as the *multivibrator*. A typical circuit of this type is shown in Fig. 17-13(A). This oscillator is known as the plate-coupled multivibrator, to distinguish it from another popular type, the cathode-coupled, described next. The multivibrator does not, of course, vibrate physically. The term simply designates an electronic

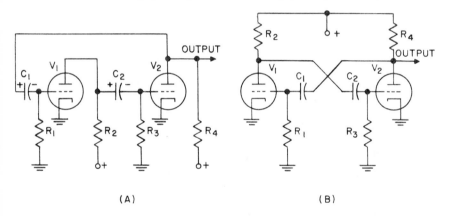

(A)   (B)

Fig. 17-13. Plate-coupled multivibrator.

vibration, or oscillation. The multivibrator is a free-running generator similar to the R-F types previously discussed. Thus, the multivibrator generates a signal continuously, so long as power is applied to the circuits. One of the primary advantages of this circuit (as well as the blocking-oscillator type of generator described later) is its ability to be locked in by another signal, and thus synchronized and kept in step with another frequency.

The multivibrator generator employs two tubes, either separate or combined in one tube envelope. Superficially, the two tubes have circuits which resemble resistance-coupled amplifiers, where the output from the second amplifier is coupled back to the input of the first. Obviously, any signal which is applied to the input of V_1 will be amplified by the latter and applied to the grid of V_2. In turn, the signal is reamplified by V_2 and fed back to the grid of V_1, by virtue of the feedback capacitor C_1. With continuous amplification and reamplification, however, the signals reach such amplitude that tube saturation occurs. Hence, the operation deviates from that of normal amplifiers, and a more critical analysis is necessary in order to understand how signals are generated and what *type* of signals are produced.

The multivibrator is a symmetrical circuit; that is, each tube is of the same type, and grid resistors have equal values, as do the plate resistors and coupling capacitors. The symmetry of the circuit is more aptly illustrated in a drawing such as shown in Fig. 17-13(B). This is a common schematic for the multivibrator, and is more often found in the literature than the drawing shown in (A).

Despite the symmetrical design, it is virtually impossible to achieve perfect balance between the two circuits; hence, when power is first applied to the multivibrator, one tube will have a current rise slightly before the other, creating some unbalance. The smallest degree of unbalance is sufficient to cause the multivibrator to go into its oscillating state. Assume, for instance, that power is applied to the multivibrator shown in Part A. Voltages at the plates also appear at the coupling capacitors C_1 and C_2, charging them with a polarity as shown (positive to the plate side, negative to the grid side). If the plate current in V_1 starts to rise first, the voltage drop across R_2, the plate resistor of V_1, increases, with the result that the plate-to-cathode voltage declines. The plate voltage of V_1, having dropped below the charge on C_2, causes the latter to discharge toward the lower plate voltage value. The discharge of C_2 is through R_3, and the voltage drop across the grid resistor places a negative bias on the grid, in a fashion similar to the self-bias created in Class C amplifiers, as discussed earlier.

The negative voltage appearing at the grid of V_2 decreases current through this tube and through anode resistor R_4. In consequence, plate voltage for V_2 rises. The increased plate voltage at V_2 charges capacitor C_1 to a higher value, the charging current flowing up through R_1. Current flow, through R_1 toward the capacitor, establishes the bottom of R_1 at negative potential and the top of R_1 at positive potential, hence the grid is made positive. When the grid becomes positive, current through V_1 increases to a very high value, and plate voltage drops by an additional amount. The entire process continues around the circuit, until eventually the current through V_1 reaches saturation and can increase no more. At this time, V_2 is at cutoff. With no current flowing through V_2, no voltage drop occurs across R_4, hence the plate voltage of V_2 reaches a maximum value and is equal to the power supply voltage applied to the bottom of R_4. The voltage relationships for the grids and plates of the two tubes are shown in Fig. 17-14.

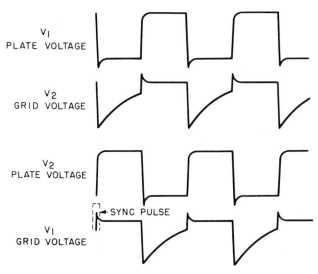

Fig. 17-14. Multivibrator plate and grid waveforms.

The low voltage at the plate of V_1 and the high voltage at the plate of V_2 remain at a standstill for a short period of time. In the meantime, capacitor C_2 slowly discharges to the low plate voltage of V_1. While C_2 discharges, it holds V_2 at cutoff. As the charge across C_2 decreases, however, the grid of V_2 becomes less and less negative, as shown in Fig. 17-14 for V_2 grid voltage. When the charge of C_2 has declined sufficiently so that it no longer holds V_2 at cutoff, current starts to flow through V_2, and a new cycle of changes begins, as shown in Fig. 17-14.

Current through V_2 lowers plate voltage, and C_1 starts to discharge to the lower plate voltage value, making the grid of V_1 negative and reducing current flow through this tube. The current reduction through V_1 raises plate voltage, as shown in Fig. 17-14, which in turn charges C_2 to the new value. The positive voltage appearing at the grid of V_2 increases current flow by an additional amount, and the plate voltage of V_2 declines proportionately. Capacitor C_1 then discharges to the new value, until finally V_1 is at cutoff and V_2 at saturation. Capacitor C_1 then slowly discharges, to start the cycle all over again.

Note that, in either tube, the plate-voltage changes are rather sharp, with periods of inactivity between them. The result is a waveshape in which each alternation resembles a square, rather than the gradual incline and decline found in sinewaves. Because of the square-shaped alternations, this type of waveform is known as a *square wave*. (A more detailed analysis of the square wave, as well as the *pulse* and *sawtooth* waveforms is given at the end of this chapter.)

The free-running frequency of the multivibrator depends on the values of the various resistors and capacitors (the *R-C* constants) of the circuit. A longer time constant will delay the discharge of the coupling capacitors, and will decrease the frequency of the multivibrator. Hence, the resistor and capacitor combinations in the grid circuits are an important factor in determining the free-running frequency of the oscillator. Changes of voltage, however, also have some influence on the frequency, because they affect the electron beam velocity and the rate of charge of capacitors. The changes in plate resistance or in the *R-C* ratios will also alter the shape of the output waveform. Hence, the circuit can be designed to produce a square wave by choosing certain values of plate resistors R_2 and R_4. The amplitude of the voltage which causes tube conduction also has an influence on the waveshape produced from the multivibrator. The output signal can be obtained from either anode of the multivibrator, and not only from the anode of V_2, as shown in Fig. 17-13.

Where precise control of frequency stability is desired, signals in the form of short-duration pulses can be applied to either grid of the multivibrator for synchronization (sync) purposes.

If positive pulses are applied to the grid of V_1, they will cause the grid of V_1 to go positive at certain predetermined intervals, and hence will lock the multivibrator to the frequency of the incoming synchronization pulses. The synchronization pulses could be inserted at the grid of V_2, instead of the grid of V_1, and the system will still be locked in. The synchronization pulses must be of such a frequency that they will occur prior to the normal conduction period of the tube, as shown in the V_1 grid voltage drawing of Fig. 17-14. During the time when the grid capacitor starts its discharging across the grid leak, a normal pulse will not have sufficient amplitude to raise the negative grid voltage of the tube to a conduction voltage, and hence would not influence the frequency of the multivibrator. Thus, sync pulses are applied to the grid at a time when the capacitor has almost fully discharged across the grid leak. At this time, only a low-value positive sync potential is needed.

Since a pulse which occurs halfway between the conduction levels would have an insufficient amplitude to overcome the negative potential at the grid, a synchronizing frequency twice that of the oscillator can also be employed to lock in the latter. Thus, a synchronization frequency of 100 can be used to lock in an oscillator generating 50 cycles per second. In such an instance, *every other* sync pulse triggers the multivibrator, while alternate pulses are insufficient to overcome the higher negative potential which exists between the conduction levels of the grid waveform. The process of using a higher frequency signal to lock in a circuit producing a lower-frequency signal is known as *frequency* division. Hence, such circuits as multivibrators and the blocking oscillators described later, can be used as frequency dividers, instead of just generators of square waves.

CATHODE-COUPLED MULTIVIBRATOR

A modified form of multivibrator is shown in Fig. 17-15. This type is the cathode-coupled multivibrator, so-called because a common cathode resistor, R_3, provides coupling between the two circuits of V_1 and V_2. This multivibrator differs from the one previously discussed by virtue of such common cathode coupling and by the absence of the feedback capacitor from V_2 anode to V_1 grid.

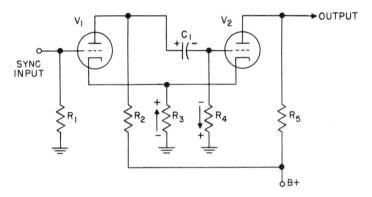

Fig. 17-15. Cathode-coupled multivibrator.

The cathode-coupled multivibrator functions in a manner similar to the plate-coupled type discussed previously. Assume, for instance, that when the power is applied, plate current through V_1 rises. This will cause a corresponding increase in current through the cathode resistor R_3. Since the latter is also common to the cathode of V_2, the increase in voltage across R_3 increases the bias for V_2, causing a negative potential to appear between the grid and cathode of V_2. As the bias on V_2 increases, plate current through V_2 decreases and, in consequence, the voltage drop across R_5 is lowered. Hence, the voltage at the plate of V_2 starts to approach the plate supply potential. As the plate current through V_1 continues to rise, the increasing current through R_3 drives the grid of V_2 farther toward the cutoff region. Also, as the current through V_1 increases, plate voltage drops and, consequently, capacitor C_1 discharges toward the lowered plate voltage value of V_1, also helping to drive V_2 toward the cutoff region, because capacitor C_1 discharges through R_4 making the top of R_4 and the grid of V_2 negative. Finally, when V_1 has maximum current flow (saturation), V_2 is at cutoff because of the bias established by both R_3 and the discharge of C_1. As C_1 discharges, however, the bias on V_2 decreases and, eventually, the point is reached when R_3 alone cannot hold V_2 at cutoff; hence, some current starts to flow through V_2. This raises the voltage drop across R_3 and starts to increase the bias on V_1, lowering current flow through the latter. As current decreases through V_1, plate voltage rises, and C_1 starts to charge to the new voltage level of V_1. The charge, causing current flow *up* through R_4, makes the grid of V_2 positive, increasing current flow through V_2 and R_3, with a consequent increase in bias on V_1 and a decrease in current through V_1. Finally, V_1 is at cutoff and V_2 at saturation. As C_1 stops charging, grid voltage at V_2 drops from its positive value, current through the tube starts to decline, and the cycle begins again.

TRANSISTOR MULTIVIBRATOR

The transistor can be used advantageously in the oscillator circuitry, and a typical transistor multivibrator is shown in Fig. 17-16. Here, a single transistor only is needed, in contrast to the two tubes required for the vacuum-tube multivibrator. Capacitor C_1 is employed for creation of a condition of instability and to establish the oscillations, as well as to control the frequency.

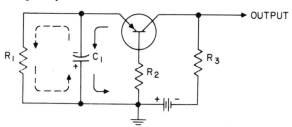

Fig. 17-16. Transistor multivibrator.

Initially, capacitor C_1 is charged by the battery in the collector side, with current flow from the negative battery terminal, to the collector and emitter, piling up electrons at the top plate of C_1 and producing a negative charge. Electrons drawn from the bottom plate of C_1 into the battery create the positive charge, as shown in Fig. 17-16. The charging path is shown by the solid arrows. The negative charge across C_1 places a minus potential at the emitter and a plus potential at the base, creating *reverse* bias. With the emitter base in the reverse-bias state, the transistor is at cutoff, with the potential barriers setting up their highest opposition to current flow.

With the emitter reverse resistance at a high level, capacitor C_1 discharges across resistor R_1, as shown by the dotted arrows. When the capacitor has discharged sufficiently for the transistor to conduct again, and when impedances are low, the low impedance and transistor conduction permits the recharging of the capacitor, and the cycle of operation starts again. Because the transistor is cut off intermittently, the output waveform consists of pulses developed across R_3.

Resistor R_3 establishes the operating point of correct instability for proper operation as a multivibrator. Varying the resistance value of R_2 will affect the width of the output pulses.

BLOCKING OSCILLATOR

Another type of oscillator which is frequently used in test equipment, television receivers, radar equipment, and other electronic devices, is the grid-blocking oscillator. As with the multivibrator previously discussed, one of the advantages of the blocking oscillator is its ability to be locked into synchronization by pulses which occur at a frequency near that of the blocking oscillator.

A typical vacuum-tube blocking oscillator is shown in Fig. 17-17, and contains a single tube instead of the two tubes needed for the multivibrator. In contrast to the multivibrator, however, a transformer is needed for feedback purposes.

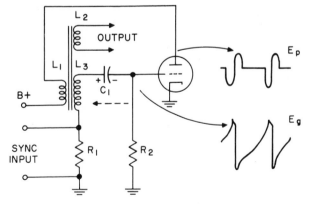

Fig. 17-17. Blocking oscillator.

Note that the B voltage is applied at the anode of the tube through a transformer winding L_1. The grid circuit connects to transformer winding L_3, and hence transformer coupling exists between these two windings. When power is applied, the rising current through inductance L_1 represents a changing emf which sets up magnetic fields and induces a voltage across L_3. The winding L_3 is so connected that the induced voltage establishes a positive polarity at the top of L_3 and a negative polarity at the bottom of the winding. Hence, a positive potential is applied to the grid. When the grid is driven in a positive direction, current flow occurs between the cathode and the grid, and capacitor C_1 is charged so that it has a negative potential at the grid side of the tube. When the grid is driven positive, plate-current flow increases, and the current through L_1 also increases. Grid potential rises by an additional amount, and current through L_3 and the tube increases again. The increase in plate current causes a voltage decrease at the anode, as shown in Fig. 17-17.

When the rise in plate current reaches a maximum value (saturation), there is no longer a plate-current *change* through L_1, and hence the fields of L_1 and L_3 collapse. Capacitor C_1 now discharges across the grid leak R_2, and the negative potential established across R_2 drives the tube to cutoff. At cutoff, the plate voltage rises to a maximum value (the supply voltage value), and the positive alternation of the output waveform is produced, as shown in Fig. 17-17. As the grid capacitor C_1 keeps discharging its energy across R_2, the cutoff bias voltage gradually declines, as shown for the grid voltage (E_g) in Fig. 17-17. Eventually, the bias is reduced to a point where the tube can conduct again and, when this occurs, the rising current through L_1 induces a voltage across L_3, and the entire process is repeated.

The synchronizing pulses are applied across R_1 and, as with the multivibrator discussed previously, the sync pulses are instrumental in locking in the frequency generated by the blocking oscillator. Synchronization will be maintained so long as the sync pulse frequency is near that of the free-running frequency of the blocking oscillator.

TRANSISTOR BLOCKING OSCILLATOR

A transistor blocking oscillator circuit is shown in Fig. 17-18. As with the transistor multivibrator, a capacitor is employed to establish the necessary circuit instability to sustain oscillations. Also, as with the vacuum-tube blocking oscillator, a transformer is used (to couple the changes of output signal at the collector, to the base-emitter circuit). An additional winding (known as the tertiary winding) is used for obtaining the output pulse waveform.

For understanding circuit operation, assume that initially capacitor C_1 has a charge with a polarity as shown in Fig. 17-18, with negative at the emitter and positive at the base. Such a charge opposes the forward-bias voltage furnished by the battery, and hence the transistor is cut off (collector current is zero). The capacitor discharges through R_1 toward

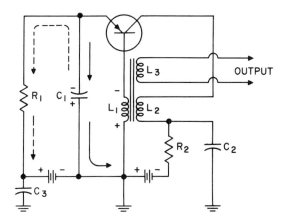

Fig. 17-18. Transistor blocking oscillator.

the positive side of the emitter battery, as shown by the dotted arrows. As the capacitor discharges, the emitter battery potential begins to predominate, establishing the forward bias commonly used at the input of the transistor circuit.

Once the normal forward bias of the input circuit is present, the transistor leaves the cutoff state and starts conducting. As collector current rises, the *change* of current through the base transformer winding L_1 sets up a voltage as shown, with negative at the base and positive toward ground. This potential across L_1 *aids* the forward bias established by the emitter battery, and emitter current also rises. The rising emitter current reduces the potential barriers within the transistor by an additional amount, with an added increase in collector current, until saturation is reached.

The high base-to-emitter current flow charges C_1 as shown by the solid arrows. As the charge builds up across C_1, the opposing polarity of the charge reduces the forward-bias potential of the emitter battery, and emitter current begins to fall off. When the charge across C_1 is sufficient to cut off the transistor, collector current ceases, and the fields of L_1 and L_3 collapse. The absence of the pulse voltage across L_1 reduces emitter-base voltage by an additional amount, and the collector and emitter currents no longer flow. Capacitor C_1 now discharges, and the cycle of operation starts over again.

DISCHARGE CIRCUIT

The multivibrator and blocking oscillators are capable of generating a square-type waveform, as previously explained. In a number of electronic circuit applications, square waves and pulses are used extensively, as more fully illustrated later. On other occasions, however, a waveform of voltage which has a *gradual incline* and a *rapid decline* is necessary. This is the case with television transmitters and receivers, as well as in such test equipment as oscilloscopes, where the gradual incline of voltage can be used to deflect an electron beam either across or down the face of the cathode-ray tube. When a waveform has a gradual incline and sudden decline in periodic intervals, it resembles a sawtooth pattern. Hence, this type of waveform is known as a *sawtooth* waveform. As shown in Fig. 17-19, a sawtooth voltage can be formed by placing a capacitor from plate to ground of a circuit having at its grid a typical relaxation oscillator grid signal which periodically cuts the tube off and then makes it conduct again. Such a capacitor can also be placed directly across an oscillator circuit, or a separate tube and circuit can be employed, as shown in Fig. 17-19.

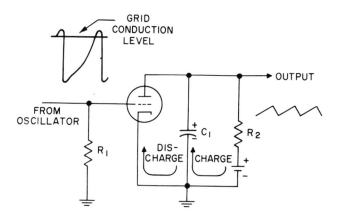

Fig. 17-19. Discharge circuit.

When a separate circuit is used, it is known as a *discharge circuit*. The grid of the tube is attached to the grid of the oscillator, so that the discharge tube grid has a signal applied to it which conforms to that of the blocking oscillator or multivibrator, as shown in Fig. 17-19. Hence, the grid of the discharge tube will periodically have a positive signal which will permit conduction, and for longer periods of time will have a negative voltage applied to it which will keep the tube at cutoff. During the time the tube is at cutoff and no current flows through it, the power supply charges capacitor C_1 in the direction shown by the arrow. Hence, there is a gradual rise of voltage across capacitor C_1, this voltage having a polarity as shown. The gradual rise of voltage across C_1 forms the *initial incline* of the sawtooth waveform. The current also flows through resistor R_2, in its return path to the positive terminal of the power supply or battery. Hence, R_2 limits such current flow and affects the amplitude of the sawtooth which is developed because of the RC constant established.

When the grid voltage waveform goes above the conduction level of the tube, the discharge tube is permitted to conduct and, hence, current from the power supply flows through it. During the time the discharge tube conducts, it has a very low resistance. Inasmuch as the low resistance of the discharge tube shunts capacitor C_1 during conduction, a short RC constant exists and the capacitor will discharge through the tube. Since the tube's resistance is low during the conduction period, C_1 discharges rapidly and the voltage drop across it declines to zero, forming the sharp sawtooth segment. The discharge tube conducts only for a short interval, as indicated by the grid waveform. Abruptly, the tube is again driven to cutoff and, hence, a high resistance path prevails. Again, the power supply charges capacitor C_1 until the tube conducts again. The periodical charge and discharge of C_1 thus forms the sawtooth voltage waveforms, as shown at the output terminals of the circuit in Fig. 17-19.

SQUARE-WAVE AND PULSE FACTORS

The square-wave type of signal generated by the relaxation oscillators previously discussed, differ radically from the simple sinewave signal. Because of the inherent differences between the square-wave signal and other special signals, a more detailed analysis is necessary, in order to understand the factors involved in the handling and applications of such signals in electronic circuitry.

The square-wave type of signal is made up of a fundamental frequency plus a number of odd harmonics. This is in contrast to the simple sine-wave which consists of a fundamental frequency only. A square wave not only has a fundamental frequency, but a third harmonic having ⅓ the amplitude of the fundamental, a fifth harmonic having ⅕ the ampli- tude of the fundamental, a seventh harmonic having ⅐ the amplitude of the fundamental, and successive odd harmonics, up to approximately 15 for a low-frequency fundamental. For higher-frequency square waves, the harmonics may have frequencies extending up to the 200th odd harmonic. In some very-high-frequency square waves (one million square waves per second), harmonics of the fundamental range over a thousand. When a waveform has a fundamental frequency plus a number of har- monic frequencies, all the signals combine to make up the square-wave appearance of the composite signal. The manner in which such signal combinations form the square wave may be understood by reference to

Fig. 17-20. In (A) is shown a sinewave which represents the fundamental frequency of the square wave. A waveform of this type, which has a gradual incline and decline, is composed of one frequency only, provided that the amplitude of each alternation is the same as the others, and also provided that the duration of one alternation is identical to the other alternations. In (B), a signal having three times the frequency of the fundamental is shown. Since the frequency of the signal shown in (B) is three times that in (A), the signal in (B) is known as the third harmonic. If the third harmonic signal is combined with the fundamental, the signal shown in (C) will be produced. The production of the signal shown in (C) is the result of the combination of the in-phase and out-of-phase sections of the signals shown in (A) and (B). At the point of maximum amplitude of the fundamental, an out-of-phase condition exists with respect to the waveform of the third harmonic at that point. Thus, the addition of the two amplitudes at this particular point results in a decrease in the over-all amplitude, because of the out-of-phase conditions. The harmonic signal, however, will not always be out of phase, since it is higher in frequency than the fundamental and, at some points, an in-phase condition exists. Thus, the harmonic signal will result in the addition and subtraction of the amplitude of the fundamental along various points.

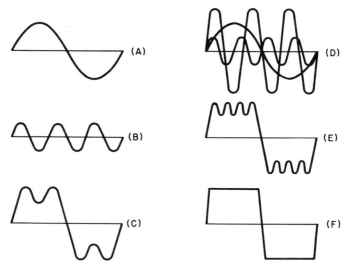

Fig. 17-20. Formation of square wave.

In (D), the fundamental, the third harmonic, and the fifth harmonic signals are shown. Note that, at the beginning of the combination waveforms, in-phase conditions exist which will cause the combination to have a steep rise time. Thus, when a number of odd-harmonic components are added to a fundamental frequency, the composite waveform begins to resemble the square wave. If the fundamental, the third, fifth, and seventh harmonics are combined, the waveform shown in (E) will be formed. Already the composite signal begins to have the sharp rise time characteristics of the square wave. When all of the higher-order odd harmonics are combined with the fundamental frequency, the resultant will be the square wave shown in (F).

The square wave has successive positive and negative alternations and, hence, is a-c in its characteristics. Pulses, on the other hand, consist of either negative or positive polarity signals, and hence have characteristics which differ somewhat from the square wave. The differences between the square wave and the pulse are shown in Fig. 17-21. In (A), a square

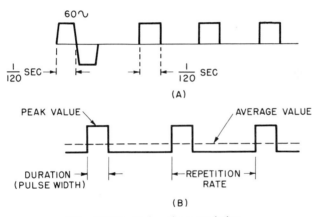

Fig. 17-21. Pulse characteristics.

wave having a frequency of 60 cycles per second is shown. Hence, each alternation of the square wave occurs in $\frac{1}{120}$ of a second. When pulses are formed from this square wave, each pulse will have a duration of $\frac{1}{120}$ of a second, as shown in (A). The pulses, however, need not occur at a rate of 60 per second. In many electronic devices, the pulses may occur at 100, 300, 600, or any other rate per second. The rate at which the pulses occur per second is known as the *repetition rate*. The repetition rate of pulses can be adjusted as desired, regardless of the duration of a pulse. Thus a pulse may have a duration of $\frac{1}{50}$ of a second, or a millionth of a second, but its recurrence may be at a low rate or at a very high rate, as required. This is not the case with an unbroken chain of square waves (or sinewaves), because such waveforms have a repetition rate fixed by the duration of the individual alternations of the signals.

From the foregoing, it is obvious that the assignment of a specific frequency to a series of pulses is meaningless, because it would not impart the necessary information related to the pulses. If we say the repetition rate is 25 per second, it does not tell us whether the pulse has a duration of $\frac{1}{50}$ of a second or $\frac{1}{1,000}$ of a second. Consequently, an evaluation of a pulse waveform must be based on the repetition rate, as well as on the duration of the pulse. When the duration of a pulse is multiplied by the repetition rate, a figure known as the *duty cycle* is obtained. As an example, assume that each pulse in a series has a duration of 4 microseconds. If the pulses are repeated 600 times per second, the duty cycle would be 0.000004 times 600, or 0.0024. Thus, the duty cycle is a designation which relates to the pulse duration, as well as to the repetition rate. Once the duty cycle of a pulse train is known, the average value of the pulse train can also be ascertained. As mentioned earlier, the effective value for sinewaves was obtained by multiplying the peak value by 0.707. A calculation of this type, however, cannot be applied to find the average value in a pulse train, because the repetition rate is a determining factor with respect to the power which is present. The average power for a series of pulses is usually considerably below the 0.707 value obtained when solving for the power in sinewaves. The average value for a series of pulses is shown in Fig. 17-21(B).

The average power for a train of pulses may be calculated by multiplying the peak power value by the duty cycle. Thus, if the duty cycle of a series of pulses is 0.0024 and the peak power of a pulse is 10 watts, the average power would be

$$0.0024 \times 10 = 0.024 \text{ watt}$$

Since the formula for finding the average power is based on the peak power and the duty cycle, the duty cycle can be found by dividing the average power by the peak power. Thus, in the foregoing example, if the average power of 0.024 is divided by the peak power of 10 watts, the duty cycle of 0.0024 will be obtained.

As is the case with the square-wave type of signal, the pulse is made up of a number of harmonics, each higher harmonic having a lower amplitude than the previous harmonic. The more narrow the pulse, the greater the harmonic content. In contrast to square waves, however, the pulse waveforms contain both odd and even harmonics. The maximum number of harmonic frequencies which have a bearing on the shape of the pulse varies inversely with respect to the duration of the pulse. Wide pulses may have significant harmonic components only to the 15th order, while very narrow pulses may have harmonic frequencies ranging to 1,000 or more, as previously mentioned. The rise time of the leading edge of a pulse, as well as the decline time (or decay time) of the trailing edge depend for their sharpness on the harmonic content of the pulse. This is an important factor with respect to the amplifying circuits which must handle pulses (as well as square waves). If the circuits are not well designed and cannot pass some of the higher-frequency harmonics of a square wave or pulse, distortion of the original waveform will result. A pulse which has lost some of its higher frequency signals will no longer have sharp rise time and decline time with respect to the leading or the trailing edges, and hence the pulse will become distorted, because the leading and trailing edges will slope. Hence, amplifier circuits which are used with respect to square waves or pulses must be able to pass all the harmonic components contained within the waveform, for an accurate amplification of the original signal.

The least amount of pulse distortion occurs for loss of the *lower*-frequency components. Often, some of the lower-frequency components of a pulse may be removed without seriously altering the pulse shape. Thus, the requirements with respect to low-frequency response in an amplifier are often based on the repetition rate of the pulses to be handled. For retaining the higher order of harmonics, however, the circuit through which the pulses pass must be able to pass signals having frequencies equivalent to

$$\text{Base frequency} = \frac{1}{\text{duration}}$$

The foregoing formula solves for what is known as *base* frequency, and is indication of the highest frequency which the circuit should pass for good reproduction of the pulse. Thus, if the pulses in a train of pulses each have a duration of 5 microseconds, the base frequency is 20,000 cycles (20 kilocycles). Hence, the circuits handling this pulse train should be capable of passing frequencies from the repetition rate up to the base frequency of 20 kilocycles. If the repetition rate is 1,000 cycles per second, this would establish the limit of the low-frequency response for the circuit.

The formula for finding the base frequency does not utilize the repetition rate of the pulses, because the repetition rate has no effect on the harmonic content of each individual pulse. If the 4-microsecond-pulse mentioned above occurred at a rate of 5,000 per second, the frequencies contained within the pulse would occur more frequently than at a low repetition rate, but the number of harmonics contained within the pulse would not change.

PULSE DISTORTION

As mentioned earlier, square waves and pulses are composed of a fundamental frequency and a number of harmonics. Consequently, any circuit through which such waveforms pass must be so designed that none of the harmonic components are diminished. If some of the harmonic components are lost as the waveform passes through a circuit, signal distortion will result. Two primary types of distortion with respect to square waves and pulses are the loss of high-frequency components and

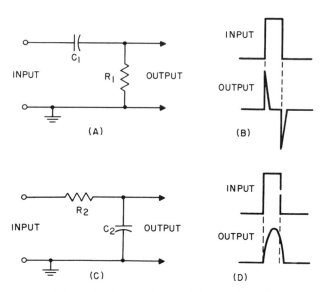

Fig. 17-22. Differentiation and integration of pulses.

the loss of low-frequency components. Figure 17-22 illustrates the types of distortions which result from either high-frequency or low-frequency signal losses. Capacitor C_1 and resistor R_1, in Fig. 17-22(A), represent a typical signal-coupling circuit. A typical application is the RC coupling between two amplifier stages, with R_1 constituting the grid leak and C_1 the conventional coupling capacitor. Usually, C_1 is made sufficiently large in value so that it will have a low reactance and pass all frequencies desired, without undue diminishing of the signal amplitudes. If C_1 has too small a value, its reactance will be high for low-frequency signals and, hence, would diminish the lower-frequency signals to a greater degree than high-frequency signals. If a number of sinewave signals of different frequencies were applied to the input, the lower-frequency signals appearing at the output would have less amplitude than the higher-frequency signals, even though all had the same amplitude when applied to the input.

When a pulse is applied to the input, the circuit behavior follows the time-constant factors given earlier with respect to the universal time-constant chart. The leading edge of the pulse has a sudden rise in voltage and, according to the exponential curve for a capacitor charge, maximum current flows in the circuit during the initial capacitor charge. Hence, the sudden flow of maximum current through R_1 results in a sharp rise of voltage across R_1. With a small-value capacitor, it only takes a brief moment to become fully charged. Thus, during the flat-top portion of the pulse, a steady-state condition prevails and current flow through the capacitor declines, again according to the exponential curve of the time-constant chart. Hence, voltage across the resistor drops, as shown in Fig. 17-22(B). With the capacitor fully charged, current flow ceases, as shown in (B). When the trailing edge of the pulse arrives, the voltage at the input of the circuit drops sharply below the value of the charged capacitor. Consequently, the capacitor suddenly discharges through R_1 and the discharge current flows in the opposite direction from the charge current. Thus, the voltage across R_1 rises in a *negative* direction, as shown in (B). When the capacitor is fully discharged, the voltage across R_1 drops to zero again.

From the foregoing, it is evident that the value of the coupling capacitor (and the time constant of the circuit) can be such that a pulse applied to a circuit can be modified considerably at the output. The output pulse shown in (B) is known as a *differentiated* waveform. The term indicates that the pulse has lost low-frequency components and that the waveform at the output contains mostly high-frequency components. In electronic devices where the pulse must retain its original waveform, it is essential that the capacitor be made adequate in size, so that no differentiation occurs. On occasion, however, the time constants of a coupling circuit may be deliberately changed so that differentiation takes place. A differentiating circuit is employed on those occasions when the important factor of a waveform is a sharp leading edge. A differentiated waveform is ideal for synchronization purposes, and is used in some computer circuitry, as well as in television receivers.

A differentiating circuit can be considered as a high-pass filter, because the high-frequency components of a pulse or square wave pass through the circuit, but low-frequency components are diminished. The differentiating circuit has no effect on sinewave-type signals, other than diminishing their amplitude, depending on the frequency of the signals and the reactance of C_1. The waveshape of sinewaves is not altered when such signals pass through a differentiating circuit.

As mentioned earlier, interelectrode capacities in tubes, circuit capacitors, and the distributed capacities in transformers, having a shunting effect on signals, because of the low-reactance path to ground which prevails due to such capacities. While these capacities will diminish the amplitude of sinewave signals, their effect on a pulse waveform causes distortion to occur, because some of the higher-frequency harmonics of the pulse will be diminished in amplitude. In Fig. 17-22(C), a circuit is shown in which C_2 represents a shunting reactance. If such a capacitance has an appreciable low-value reactance for the higher-frequency components of a pulse, signal distortion as shown in (D) will occur. The leading and trailing edges of a pulse represent high-frequency harmonic components. At the output of the circuit shown in (C), the leading and trailing edges of a pulse will not have the sharp changes contained in the original, but will have slopes as shown at (D). This type of waveform is known as an *integrated* waveform, indicating a decrease in high-frequency signal amplitudes, but containing the low-frequency signal components. An integration circuit is essentially a low-pass filter, which filters out higher-frequency signals, but passes the lower-frequency signals. The various shunt capacities represented by C_2 are usually held at a minimum to prevent pulse distortion. On occasion, however, an integrating circuit is employed deliberately, such as in the vertical sweep systems of television receivers.

CLIPPERS, LIMITERS, AND CLAMPERS

Circuits which perform functions of clipping, limiting, and clamping, are widely used for removing noise or other undesired signals from waveforms, for clipping sinewaves to form square waves, for changing square waves to pulses, for holding waveforms at a constant amplitude, and for establishing a fixed d-c reference level. Such waveform modification is

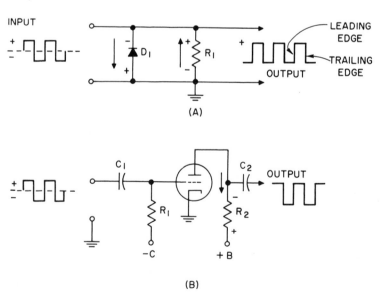

Fig. 17-23. Pulse production by square-wave clipping.

extensively employed in industrial control circuits, automation circuitry, computer systems, communication gear, and other electronic devices. Often the terms clipper, limiter, and clamper are used interchangeably, though strictly speaking, each relates to a different (and specific) circuit function. The three terms may be defined as follows:

Clipper. The amplitude of the output waveform is proportional to those values of the input waveform *exceeding* a certain critical value.

Limiter. The amplitude of the output waveform is proportional to those values of the input waveform *up to* a certain critical value.

Clamper. Relates the amplitude of the waveform (clamps) to some fixed reference level.

The production of pulses from square-wave clipping is illustrated in Fig. 17-23, where every other alternation of a square wave is removed from the signal. A diode-type clipper is shown in Fig. 17-23(A). If the first alternation of the input square wave is positive, as shown, the high reverse resistance of the diode prevents conduction through the latter. Since the diode does not conduct, current flow is through resistor R_1, in the direction shown by the arrow beside the resistor. Thus, a pulse is produced having a positive polarity. For the second alternation (negative), the diode conducts and its forward resistance is so low that the resistance shunts R_1 and no *output* is produced. For the third alternation (positive), the diode does not conduct, and current again flows through R_1 to produce the second positive pulse at the output. If negative pulses are desired, at the output of the diode clipper shown in (A), the diode rectifier is reversed.

Clippers can also be designed using vacuum tubes, as shown in (B) of Fig. 17-23. A bias is supplied to the grid of the tube, which will cause the tube to operate at cutoff. Thus, with no signal input, plate current will not flow and no output results. If a square wave is applied to the input, the tube will conduct, provided the alternation of the square wave is positive. The positive alternation of the square wave will overcome the negative bias and will permit the tube to conduct. Plate-current flow, in the direction shown by the arrow, establishes a negative pulse across the load resistor or tube. When the input consists of the negative alternations of the square wave, no output results. Hence, the output from the vacuum-tube clipper will consist of negative pulses, as shown.

The diode circuit in Fig. 17-23(A) is known as a *shunt clipper* because the diode shunts the load circuit. A shunt clipper with positive bias is shown at Fig. 17-24(A). Here, the bias potential is opposite in polarity to that which would cause the diode to conduct, and can be set at any value desired to provide the degree of clipping needed. For the circuit shown, the diode will conduct only when a positive signal potential

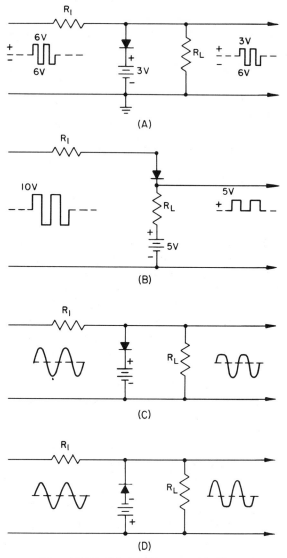

Fig. 17-24. Diode clippers with bias.

at the input exceeds 3 volts. Thus, if the input alternation of a square wave has an amplitude of 6 volts as illustrated, an output signal potential in proportion to the input will develop up to 3 volts. Beyond that, the diode conducts and shunts any signal energy to the input signal above 3 volts. For negative-input alternations, however, the diode is nonconducting and the output is in proportion to the input. Thus, an output is obtained only when the input signal amplitude exceeds (in a negative direction) the critical value established by the bias potential. Similarly, if both the diode and bias potential are reversed, the output waveform would be obtained only when the input amplitude exceeds (in a positive direction) the critical value set by the bias.

In Fig. 17-24(B) is shown a series clipper with positive bias. Here the load resistor is in series with the clipper diode and the bias potential again is opposite in polarity to that which would permit diode conduction. If the bias is 5 volts as shown, the diode will not conduct until a positive input alternation exceeds this bias potential. Consequently no signal current will flow through the load resistor until the input positive alternation rises above the 5-volt bias potential. Thus, the output signal amplitude is proportional to the amplitude of the input signal which exceeds the bias potential value. For negative-input signal amplitudes, the diode does not conduct and hence clips these portions of the signal from the output waveform, producing a pulse train from a square-wave type signal.

The shunt clipper shown at (A) can be used to clip either the negative or positive alternations of sinewaves, as shown at (C) and (D) of Fig. 17-24. For the circuit at (C), the output positive alternations flatten out for values of the input signal above the bias potential. When such input signal values are reached, the diode conducts and shunts amplitudes above that of the bias potential. For the circuit at (D), the bias potential is still such that the diode is held in the nonconducting state, except that the input signal must have a negative amplitude to counteract the bias and permit diode conduction. Thus, if the bias is a negative 5 volts, the output amplitude will be proportional to any input signal amplitude which exceeds this (in a positive direction). For all negative signal amplitudes which are below the bias level the diode will conduct and the output amplitude will be held at a constant level (clipping level).

The circuits shown at (C) and (D) of Fig. 17-24 can be combined to form the parallel clipper shown in Fig. 17-25(A) (sometimes called a *slicer*). This circuit will clip both the positive and the negative alternations of a sinewave and thus produce an output waveform resembling the square-wave type signal as shown. Again, the degree of clipping can be established by the amount of bias potentials used in relation to the input signal amplitudes. The triode clipper discussed earlier can also be used for converting sinewaves to square waves, by setting the bias below the cutoff point and applying an input signal having an amplitude sufficiently high to drive the tube alternately into the cutoff region and to saturation as shown at (B) and (C). This circuit is often referred to as an overdriven amplifier and combines the limiting and clipping functions.

The shunt clipper shown earlier in Fig. 17-24(A) can also be used to

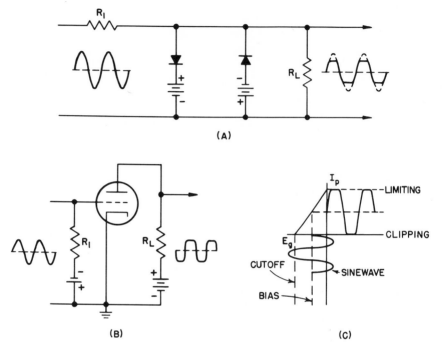

Fig. 17-25. Producing square waves from sinewaves.

limit pulses as illustrated in Fig. 17-26(A). If the bias is a positive 3 volts as shown, the output amplitude will be held at a constant 3-volt amplitude for all input signal values which exceed the 3-volt critical value because of the shunt effect created by the diode when the positive input signal over-comes the bias potential. Thus, if the input pulse train has a varying ampli-tude as shown, the excessive excursions of the pulses will be limited at the output to the preset value determined by the bias. Such a circuit is also useful for removing transients from the pulse peaks as shown at (B). Here, the sharp spikes which reach an 8-volt value are removed by the limiting action. The same results can be obtained by using the triode clipper shown earlier at Fig. 17-23(B). With the tube bias set at the cutoff point and the input signal having sufficient amplitude to drive the tube into the saturation region, the output will be limited and the spike voltages removed from the pulse train.

When pulse waveforms are amplified in conventional tube or transistor circuits with capacity coupling, the d-c component which characterizes the pulse train is lost. This is shown at Fig. 17-27(A), where a number of pulses (with negative polarity) are applied to the base circuit of a transistor

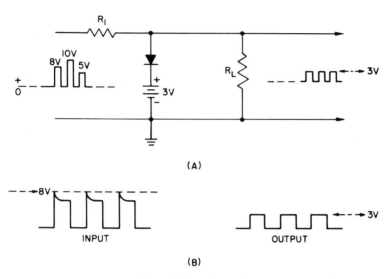

Fig. 17-26. Shunt limiter.

amplifier. At the collector side the pulse train reappears in amplified form and with a positive polarity as shown. Assume, for instance, that there is a 25-volt drop across the collector load resistor in the absence of a signal, and that the voltage change for the signal rises to 75 volts for the peak of the pulse. In such an example the pulse amplitude is 50 volts and the d-c component still prevails, being equal to the *average* voltage of the pulse train.

When these pulses are coupled to the base of the next transistor, the d-c level is lost because of the coupling capacitor's inability to pass d-c. Consequently, the pulse train at the base of T_2 has a zero reference level at the place which was the average value. Now the pulse train has positive and negative values and its identity has been altered. Thus, after the pulse train has been amplified to the degree desired, it is necessary to clamp the waveform to a d-c (or zero) level to restore the original d-c component characteristic. When the waveform is clamped to the zero level, the process is often known as *d-c restoration*.

A typical clamping circuit is shown at Fig. 17-27(B). As with the clippers and limiters, a tube could also be used instead of the solid-state diode shown. For clamping pulses of opposite polarity, the diode is reversed. The capacitor in the circuit at (B) represents the coupling capacitor C_1 shown at (A), and the transistor base resistor R_1 at (A) is also shown at (B), with the diode shunting this resistor. In the absence of a pulse signal (at time t_1) the capacitor C_1 charges through the collector load

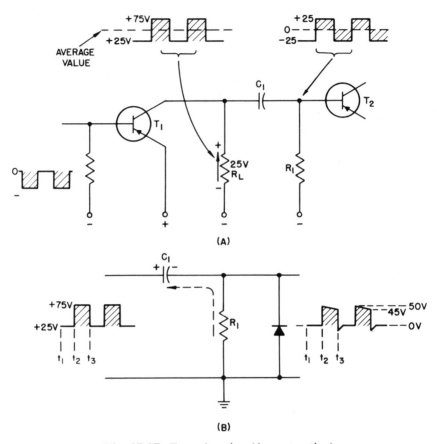

Fig. 17-27. Zero clamping (d-c restoration).

resistor R_L with a polarity as shown and in the direction indicated by the arrow.

At time t_2 the pulse signal arrives and increases the applied potential to 75 volts. The rapid rise time of the leading edge of the pulse does not permit the capacitor to charge (long time constant). The high leading current during this short time interval places the full pulse amplitude across the resistor. Hence, the voltage across the resistor is the difference between the 75-volt peak of the pulse and the idling voltage charge across the capacitor. This comes about because the 75-volt peak amplitude of the pulse places a polarity across the input terminals opposite to the capacitor charge, or 50 volts. Thus, the output waveform rises to this 50-volt peak as shown at (A). The time constant of C_1 and R_1 is long compared to the pulse duration, hence the capacitor charges only slightly more for the duration of the pulse (t_2 to t_3) and resistor current is low. If the capacitor charge increases, for example, to 30 volts at the end of the pulse duration, the output pulse amplitude declines by 5 volts, to a value of 45 volts at t_3 as shown at Fig. 17-27(B).

When the input pulse amplitude drops to the 25-volt level again (at t_3) the capacitor charge of 30 volts predominates and the voltage across the resistor now becomes $-30 + 25$ volts $= -5$ volts. Hence, at this t_3 time, the output voltage becomes -5 volts, producing a short negative spike in the output waveform as shown. This negative potential across the diode causes conduction and the low resistance of the conducting diode shunts R_1, changing the long time constant to a short time constant momentarily. The result is a rapid discharge of the -5-volt potential capacitor charge through the diode, leaving the original 25-volt charge on the capacitor. Since this charge is a static condition for the time interval between pulses, there is no current flow through R_1, and hence no voltage drop across it. Thus, the interval between the output pulses is clamped to zero level as shown.

If it is necessary to clamp the output to some voltage level above (or below) zero, the circuit can be modified by the inclusion of a fixed potential below the resistor and diode. Assume, for instance, that it is desired to clamp the pulse train at 10 volts above the zero line. To do this, a voltage source from a power supply or battery is applied with the positive polarity toward the diode anode as shown in Fig. 17-28. Capacitor C_2 is the normal bypass capacitor used to shunt signals across the power-source resistance or impedance. This capacitor has a high capacity (and hence very low reactance) for the signal. At time t_1 the charge across capacitor C_1 would normally be a fixed 25 volts, but the 10-volt bias (which also places a voltage across C_2) will oppose the charge voltage and C_1 charges only to -15 volts.

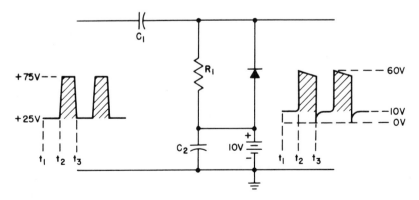

Fig. 17-28. Positive-voltage clamping.

At t_2 the circuit function is similar to that described for the zero-clamp circuit. The sudden rise of the pulse amplitude is too rapid for the long time constant of the two capacitors and resistor to permit any charge to build up across the capacitors during the leading-edge time interval. Hence, full pulse current flows through resistor R_1 causing 50 volts to appear across it. Since current flow is *up* through the resistor, the polarity of the voltage drop across the resistor coincides with the bias polarity, producing a voltage rise at the output to 60 volts $(50 + 10)$. Now assume that the time constant is such that during the flat-top pulse interval an additional 10-volt charge builds up across capacitor C_1. The additional charge raises the charge across C_1 to -25 volts again, since it had a -15-volt charge on it originally. Now, the output pulse amplitude would decline to 50 volts.

At t_3, when the input pulse drops to the 25-volt level again, there is an excessive negative charge of 10 volts across C_1, causing the diode to conduct. The diode conduction discharges the excessive 10 volts and brings the C_1 charge to -15 volts again (25-volt source, minus the 10-volt bias). The discharge produces the negative spike to the zero line as shown in Fig. 17-28. Had the excessive charge on the capacitor only been -5 volts, the spike would not have reached the zero reference line. In either case, however, the output-pulse waveform is clamped to the $+10$-volt level as shown.

REVIEW QUESTIONS

1. Briefly explain what is meant by a *relaxation* oscillator.

2. What are the essential circuit differences between a plate-coupled type of multivibrator and the cathode-coupled multivibrator?

3. Briefly explain the conditions which occur to cause a reverse bias to be applied between the emitter and the base of the transistor multivibrator.

4. Briefly explain the operating principles of a blocking oscillator.

5. How is the conduction in a transistor blocking oscillator intermittently altered from cutoff to current flow?

6. Explain the purpose of a discharge circuit and describe its general function.

7. Explain the type of harmonies which make up a square wave, and explain how the combination of such harmonies produces a sharp leading and trailing edge.

8. Briefly explain the difference between a square wave and a pulse.

9. Briefly explain what is meant by the duty cycle of a pulse, and how the duty cycle is used to find the average power of a train of pulses.

10. Briefly explain the factors which cause distortion of square waves and pulses.

11. Draw a differentiated waveform and an integrated waveform, and also draw the circuits which produce such waveforms.

12. Are the distorted pulses represented by integrated and differentiated waveforms ever employed deliberately? Explain.

13. Explain, in your own words, the differences between limiters, clippers, and clampers.

14. Draw the schematic of a shunt limiter, using negative pulses at the input, with each pulse having a different amplitude than the others. Indicate the limiting function by illustrating the output-pulse waveform.

15. Draw a circuit showing positive-voltage clamping, with the input pulses having an amplitude from 50 to 150 volts, clamped at a $+15$-volt output level.

PRACTICAL PROBLEMS

1. A relaxation oscillator used for industrial control produced pulses having a duration of 2 microseconds each. If the repetition rate is 1,000 per second, what is the duty cycle?

2. If the oscillator mentioned in Problem 1 produced pulses having a peak power of 5 watts, what is the average power of the pulse train?

3. If the oscillator mentioned in Problem 1 were modified to decrease the repetition rate by one-half at the same peak power, what would the average power be?

4. The pulses employed in an automation circuit had a repetition rate of 40 kilocycles, and each pulse had a duration of 5 microseconds. What is the base frequency and the lowest frequency which an amplifier circuit must be capable of passing to handle such pulses?

5. What is the duty cycle of the pulses in Problem 4?

6. In the design of a zero-clamp circuit the capacitor had a value of 0.0001 microfarad and the resistor had an ohmic value of 50,000 ohms. What is the time constant of the capacitor-resistor combination?

7. In a positive-voltage clamp circuit such as shown in Fig. 17-28, capacitors C_1 and C_2 *each* had a value of 0.004 microfarads. If the resistor value is 50,000 ohms, what is the time constant?

18

MODULATION

AND

DEMODULATION

Low-frequency electric signals such as produced from relaxation oscillators, microphones, and other devices are incapable of being transmitted any great distances without employing such enormous power as to make it impractical. High-frequency (R-F) signals, however, can be sent over thousands of miles with power only a fraction of that which would be required to send low-frequency signals over short distances. Thus, the high-frequency signals are utilized to "carry" the low-frequency signals in the manner described in this chapter. When a high-frequency signal is thus utilized it is known as the *carrier* signal, and the manner in which this is done at the sending tranmitter is known as *modulation*. The process is widely used in the various electronic branches. In radar, for instance, the carrier is modulated by a pulse, while in radio the carrier is modulated by audio signals. In television the carrier is modulated by picture-signal information.

AMPLITUDE MODULATION

There are several methods for modulating a carrier with a low-frequency signal. One of the earliest processes was that known as *amplitude modulation*. This system is still used in radio (AM carrier) and in

460

television (picture carrier). Essentially, AM is a system of modulation where other signal components are created in addition to the carrier to produce a resultant (composite) modulated waveform which has amplitude variations conforming to the characteristics of the audio or other signal information to be transmitted.

Figure 18-1 shows a basic transmitting system. When someone speaks, or a musical instrument is played, the varying air pressure on the microphone generates an a-c signal which corresponds in frequency to the original sound. The amplitude of the a-c signal which is generated by a microphone, however, is too low for practical use, and must be increased by several audio-amplifier stages, as shown in Fig. 18-1.

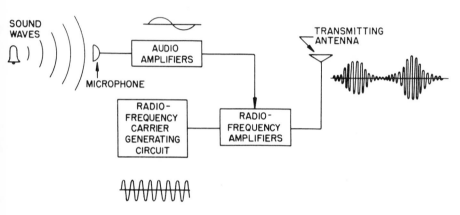

Fig. 18-1. Simple block diagram of radio transmitter.

The transmitter has an R-F carrier generating circuit which produces a high-frequency signal of constant amplitude. This carrier generating circuit usually consists of a crystal oscillator, such as described earlier. The oscillator generates the basic *carrier frequency,* as allotted by the Federal Communications Commission for the particular radio station. For AM broadcasting, a spectrum range from 550 kilocycles to 1,600 kilocycles is allocated. Thus, the carrier frequency for a particular radio station may be 700 kilocycles or 1,000 kilocycles, or any other single frequency in the radio broadcast band. Much higher frequencies are employed in short-wave, television, FM transmission, and radar. Frequency-modulation allocations are between 88 megacycles and 108 megacycles, while television stations have space in both the VHF and UHF regions. (See Appendix.)

The oscillator, like the microphone, does not furnish sufficient signal output for transmission purposes, and hence the a-c carrier signal generated by the oscillator is amplified by several Class C R-F amplifier stages. Most transmitting stations build up the carrier to many *kilowatts* of power.

Such high power is necessary so that the transmitted signal will not only travel over the required distances, but will also place a high-level signal on the receiving antenna.

The amplified audio energy from the microphone is combined with the amplified carrier signal. The two combine in such a manner that the amplitude of the resultant R-F waveform changes in accordance with the audio waveform. This produces *amplitude modulation,* as represented by the waveform drawing besides the antenna of Fig. 18-1.

The manner in which the carrier is modulated by the audio-frequency signal is more clearly illustrated in Fig. 18-2. Here, the unmodulated

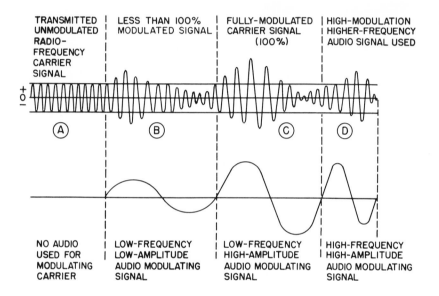

Fig. 18-2. Graph of amplitude modulation.

R-F carrier signal is shown in (A). It is an a-c type of signal which has a constant frequency and constant amplitude. When the audio signal is of a low frequency and amplitude, it will modulate the carrier as shown in (B). Note that the amplitude of the resultant waveform increases slightly for one alternation of the audio signal waveform, and decreases slightly below its normal level for the second alternation of the audio waveform. Thus, the waveform amplitude has been modulated to a slight degree by the low-frequency, low-amplitude audio signal. If this same-frequency audio signal is increased (i.e., if the sound going into the microphone is made louder), it will have a greater amplitude, and thus will have more effect on altering the amplitude of the resultant waveform. This is shown in Fig. 18-2(C), where the amplitude now reaches a level twice that of the normal carrier amplitude for the initial alternation of the high-amplitude audio waveform. For the second alternation of the high-amplitude audio waveform, the resultant amplitude drops to virtually a zero level. This is known as a fully modulated carrier, or a carrier modulated 100 per cent.

If the carrier is modulated more than 100 per cent, the amplitude of the resultant waveform will increase beyond twice that of the normal carrier amplitude and, for the second alternation of the audio waveform, the amplitude would reach zero and remain there for an appreciable interval. Since this cuts off the carrier for a short interval, the carrier would not be transmitted during this time, resulting in high distortion. Such distortion tends to decrease the clarity of the signals at the receiver. This undesired condition is prevented by keeping the modulation below the 100% level.

If a high-amplitude as well as a higher-frequency audio signal is employed, it will cause the waveform amplitude to vary more rapidly, as shown in Fig. 18-2(D). Thus, the resultant waveform increases and decreases in amplitude at a more rapid rate (in a shorter time interval) than for a lower-frequency audio-modulating signal.

The modulated carrier cannot be represented accurately in schematic form, since the high frequencies employed for carriers prohibit indicating the number on a drawing. If, for instance, the carrier is 1,000 kilocycles (1,000,000 cycles) and the audio is 500 cycles, the 500-cycle audio tone would cause the carrier to increase and decrease 500 times per second. Since, in this instance, there are a million cycles of the carrier signal per second, it means that for every audio cycle there will be 2,000 carrier cycles. Thus, one cycle of the 500-cycle audio signal will cause an increase and decrease of a 2,000-cycle sequence of the carrier signal.

It must be noted that, in amplitude modulation, the audio is not really "carried" by the transmitted signal. Actually, the R-F signal waveform has been changed only insofar as its amplitude goes, and the audio component is represented only by such changes in the amplitude of the R-F-waveform *envelope*. At the receiver, a special *detector* circuit must be employed to *demodulate* the carrier and derive from it the audio waveform, as described later in this chapter.

When an R-F carrier is modulated by an audio signal, the original sinewave carrier undergoes a form of waveshape distortion. When a pure sinewave is altered with respect to its wave shape (e.g., duration of one alternation different than the other, or amplitude of the first alternation different with respect to the second), additional frequency components are present. During amplitude modulation, the sinewave of the carrier is distorted with respect to the amplitude of the various alternations. If any cycle is analyzed in the modulated waveform, it will be evident that one alternation has a different amplitude than the other, as shown in Fig. 18-2. This distortion process of the sinusoidal waveform during amplitude modulation results in the creation of two additional frequencies, besides the carrier and audio signals. One of these newly-developed signals will be lower in frequency than the carrier by an amount equal to the audio frequency. The other newly-created signal will be higher than the carrier frequency by an amount also equal to the audio signal. Thus, if the carrier is 1,000 kilocycles, and the modulating audio frequency is 500 cycles, a new frequency (999.5 kilocycles) will be generated below the carrier, and another new frequency (1,000.5 kilocycles) will be generated above the carrier. These two additional signals are known as the *sideband* signals. If the modulating audio voltage is 2,000 cycles, the lower sideband will be 998 kilocycles, and the upper sideband will be 1,002 kilocycles. Thus, for each audio frequency employed in the modulating process, two sidebands are generated. If two audio signals are employed, four sidebands will be present. During the transmission of music, for instance, a number of audio signals would be used to modulate the carrier at any particular time, with the result that many sideband signals would be created.

If the sideband signals were filtered from the composite AM waveform, it would be found that the carrier has a constant amplitude. It is only when the sideband signals are combined with the carrier that the resultant R-F waveform contains amplitude variations.

From the foregoing, it is evident that a carrier, plus its sidebands, will require more spectrum space than an unmodulated carrier, since the latter consists of only a single frequency. In the example cited above, the 2,000-cycle audio tone would generate the two sidebands which, in conjunction with the carrier, would occupy a space of 4 kilocycles. If an audio frequency as high as 5,000 cycles is utilized to modulate the carrier, it would result in two sidebands, one 5,000 cycles below the carrier and the other 5,000 cycles above the carrier. In the latter case, the result is the transmission of a band of frequencies 10 kilocycles wide, as shown in Fig. 18-3.

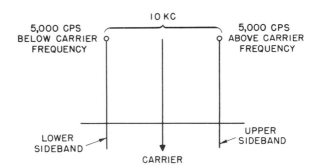

Fig. 18-3. AM bandpass.

Because a *band* of frequencies is generated during modulation, it is necessary that the receiver provide a bandpass in its R-F stages which will accommodate the carrier plus the accompanying sidebands of the transmission. In radio receivers, the bandpass is usually set at 10 kilocycles, since, in normal transmission of AM, the highest-frequency signal components which are transmitted rarely exceed 5,000 cycles per second. There are some higher fidelity AM stations which transmit a band of frequencies extending from 16 cycles to 10 kilocycles. These, in turn, would require a bandpass within the receiver extending to 20 kilocycles for proper reproduction of the higher-frequency audio components above the 5,000-cycle range.

Since AM is also used for the transmission of picture signals in television, an extremely wide bandpass range is required, because video signals have frequencies from 30 cycles to 4 megacycles. For this reason, television receivers must have a bandpass of 4 megacycles in the R-F stages, to accomodate the range of frequencies involved. (Most of the lower-sideband components are suppressed, in television transmission, to eliminate the necessity for employing an 8-megacycle bandpass.)

There are several methods for producing amplitude modulation, and one of these is shown in Fig. 18-4. Here, the plate current for the final

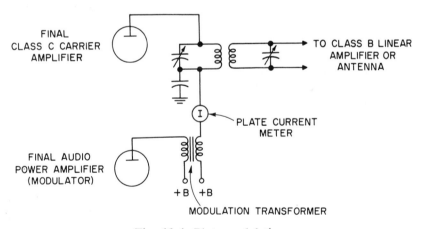

Fig. 18-4. Plate modulation.

carrier amplifier (Class C) is fed through the secondary of a special transformer known as a *modulation* transformer. The primary of the modulation transformer is part of the anode circuit of the final audio-power amplifier. The final audio amplifier, when transformer-coupled to the anode circuit of the Class C carrier amplifier, is known as a *modulator*. (The final audio amplifier is similar to that used in public-address systems, except that higher power is developed for proper modulation of the carrier. The modulation transformer can be likened to the output transformer feeding the conventional loudspeaker. In modulation, however, the anode circuit of the Class C amplifier replaces the loudspeaker. The modulation transformer matches the impedances involved in the two circuits.)

The system shown in Fig. 18-4 is known as a *plate modulator,* because modulation takes place in the plate (anode) of the final Class C carrier amplifier. In this system, the sideband power is furnished by the modulator, since it is the latter which is directly influential in changing the signal-current amplitude and signal voltage in the Class C amplifier. Audio voltages induced across the secondary of the modulation transformer either add to or subtract from the voltage applied to the Class C amplifier, depending on the polarity of the particular alternation developed across the secondary. Thus, the voltages across the secondary have a direct influence on the current amplitude changes, and thus amplitude-modulate the carrier. The sideband power is supplied by the modulator.

In plate modulation, the *output power* of the modulator must be one-half of the Class C modulated amplifier *input* power for 100% modulation. The *input* power to a Class C amplifier refers to the product of the plate voltage multiplied by the plate current. The input power must not be confused with the signal power applied to the input of the Class C amplifier. The signal input power is known as *excitation.* The modulator *output* power refers to the audio signal power developed by the modulator. For the modulator shown in Fig. 18-4, the final audio power amplifier usually consists of push-pull tubes, either Class A or Class B. For high-power transmitters, special large-sized audio power tubes are employed. The anodes of such tubes often dissipate so much heat that forced-air cooling is utilized. In some instances, cooling is accomplished by circulating water through copper tubing around the anode section of the tube. The final Class C carrier amplifier also consists of two tubes in push-pull, in the larger transmitters. For low-power portable-type transmitters, a single tube may be employed, as shown in Fig. 18-4.

Besides employing plate modulation, it is also possible to modulate a Class C carrier amplifier by applying the modulating signals to the grid, as shown in Fig. 18-5. (In some special instances, modulation of the screen grid, or even suppressor grid, may be employed. Circuit factors for such modulation are similar to the grid modulation.) For the Class C amplifier shown in Fig. 18-5, push-pull triodes are shown. Because triode tubes may oscillate, neutralizing capacitors NC_1 and NC_2 are used. In contrast to the neutralization shown earlier for a single tube, push-pull neutralization consists of simply connecting a neutralizing capacitor from the plate of one tube to the grid of the other, and repeating the process for the other push-pull tube. Because each plate has a signal out of phase with the grid of the other tube, neutralization is accomplished without special transformer tapping. Split-stator capacitors C_3 and C_4 are shown, though a single capacitor across L_3 could also be used. Using two capacitors with a common shaft connected to the rotor plates, however, is preferable because the rotor is at ground potential, and thus the hazard of getting a shock when tuning is minimized.

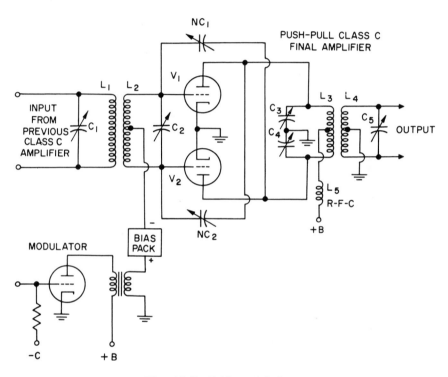

Fig. 18-5. Grid modulation.

The modulator used for grid modulation need furnish only a fraction of the power required for plate modulation. In grid modulation, the modulator signals add to or subtract from the bias voltage furnished to the Class C amplifier tubes and, in this manner, vary the amplitude of the current change in the Class C anode cricuits, in accordance with the audio-modulating signals.

The bias for the Class C tubes is initially set by a battery or power supply (bias pack), as shown in Fig. 18-5. Signal voltage variations across the secondary of the modulation transformer add or subtract from the bias, depending on whether the signal voltage alternations are negative or positive. In grid modulation, the signal applied to the grid of the

Class C amplifier tubes must have an amplitude as shown in Fig. 18-6. With a Class C amplifier tube biased beyond, cutoff, the grid signal (excitation) from the previous stage must be of such amplitude that it extends approximately between cutoff and zero bias, as shown. This setting of the excitation is necessary so that grid modulation can swing the carrier signal both *above* and *below* the unmodulated value. Plate current, in pulses, produces the modulated carrier in the anode resonant circuit, due to the flywheel effect inherent to the resonant characteristics. Because the excitation to the Class C amplifier must be reduced for grid modulation, the efficiency and power output of the Class C amplifier stage is below what it would be for plate modulation. In grid modulation, the Class C amplifier (not the modulator) must furnish the sideband power.

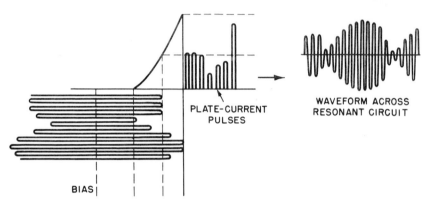

PLATE-CURRENT
PULSES

WAVEFORM ACROSS
RESONANT CIRCUIT

BIAS

Fig. 18-6. Graph of grid modulation.

The AM carrier, whether produced by plate or grid modulation, is represented by the type of drawing shown earlier in Fig. 18-2. In such a representation, the *audio* signal is not present, but is represented by the amplitude changes of the carrier, such amplitude changes being proportional to the amplitude of the audio signal. The recurrence rate of the amplitude changes of the carrier are proportional to the frequency of the modulating audio signal. The over-all waveform, as shown in Fig. 18-7(A), also contains the sideband components in addition to the carrier. If the sideband components were filtered from this waveform, the remaining carrier would be represented as shown in Fig. 18-7(B). The upper sideband would be as shown in (C), while the lower sideband is represented in (D). Note that the carrier has a *constant* amplitude, as does each sideband. It is only when the sideband signals are added to the carrier that the resultant amplitude-changing waveform shown in (A) is obtained, because the point-by-point addition of the waveforms involves out-of-phase signals at certain

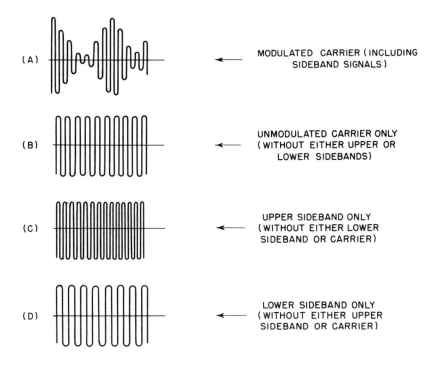

(A) ← MODULATED CARRIER (INCLUDING SIDEBAND SIGNALS)

(B) ← UNMODULATED CARRIER ONLY (WITHOUT EITHER UPPER OR LOWER SIDEBANDS)

(C) ← UPPER SIDEBAND ONLY (WITHOUT EITHER LOWER SIDEBAND OR CARRIER)

(D) ← LOWER SIDEBAND ONLY (WITHOUT EITHER UPPER SIDEBAND OR CARRIER)

Fig. 18-7. Modulated carrier signals.

times and, at other times, in-phase (or partially in-phase) signal conditions. When either sideband is combined with a carrier, the resultant again resembles the composite waveform shown in (A), even though one sideband is absent. Since a signal with amplitude changes is necessary for the detection of a modulated wave, either one or both sidebands, in conjunction with the carrier, must be available for the receiver. Since sideband power contributes to the total signal energy, the reception of a carrier plus two sidebands will result in a louder signal than the reception of a carrier plus only one sideband. The latter procedure, however, can be employed for spectrum-saving reasons. This is done in the transmission of the television AM carrier. In ordinary radio broadcasts, however, both sidebands are transmitted and received.

The two sidebands can be sent out without the carrier, in a transmitting system known as suppressed carrier transmission. This method is employed on such occasions where it is not expedient to transmit the carrier. For proper demodulation purposes at the receiver, however, it is necessary to have available a frequency identical to the carrier, in order to detect the transmitted signal information. This system is employed in color television transmission, where the color subcarrier is utilized for the generation of sidebands, but the carrier is suppressed and only the sideband components are transmitted. At the receiver, however, a separate oscillator must be employed to generate a frequency identical to the carrier frequency employed at the transmitter. This new carrier signal which is generated in the receiver is then mixed with the sideband signals which are received in order to produce the AM signal necessary for detection purposes.

FREQUENCY MODULATION

Another method of modulation other than AM, is that known as *frequency modulation* (FM). This particular modulation principle is utilized in FM transmission, between 88 megacycles and 108 megacycles (standard FM broadcast band). Frequency modulation is also employed with respect to the sound carrier which accompanies the television signal. Besides such standard broadcasting, FM is also utilized in industrial closed-circuit transmission and reception, as well as in special electronic devices employed by the armed forces.

Frequency modulation has several advantages over AM. In FM, the dynamic range is much greater. By dynamic range is meant the difference between loud and soft volume levels of audio. In AM transmission, an excessive amount of modulation can cause severe distortion, because the carrier can be overmodulated. In frequency modulation, however, overmodulation is not possible and, hence, the range of soft and loud sounds is much more realistic, because the ratio between loud and soft is much greater than can be employed for AM. In AM, the frequency range is also limited, since transmission is usually confined to a maximum frequency between 5,000 and 8,000 cycles of audio. In FM, however, an audible range of from 30 to 15,000 cycles per second can be employed. Actually, the AM process itself does not limit the frequency range. The limitation is imposed by the bandwidth employed in AM transmission. At the same time, most of the intermediate-frequency stages of the smaller radios are set at a 10-kilocycle bandwidth to minimize interference from adjacent stations. Hence, the maximum audible range is limited to approximately 5,000 cycles. This is a disadvantage, since many of the overtones of music are not transmitted, and the reality of the reproduced music suffers when compared to the original. In frequency modulation, the extended audio range permits a much more realistic reproduction of music, which produces what is known as "presence" in high-fidelity terminology. The word presence denotes that the reproduced music or sound gives the impression of exact reality, since the orchestra or the performer seems to be *present* in the room.

Another advantage, with FM, is the minimum of interference which results from adjacent stations. Beside interference rejection, one of the primary advantages of FM is the high reduction of static. For normal reception, there is a total absence of static, since static is a form of amplitude modulation and a well-adjusted FM receiver will reject AM signals. Hence, FM reception is not marred by crackling noises, or squeals and whistles, as is often the case with AM radio reception.

The one disadvantage which FM suffers with respect to AM is the fact that a wideband type of transmission must be employed. In AM, most stations utilize only a 10-kilocycle bandwidth, while a few utilize 16 kilocycles if they can use such transmission without interference to adjacent stations. In FM, however, a 200-kilocycle bandwidth allocation is employed for each station in the standard FM broadcast band. In the FM utilized for the sound of television, a narrower FM transmission is employed, approximating 50 kilocycles. In either case, however, a much wider portion of the spectrum is utilized by each FM station than by a standard broadcast AM station. This slight disadvantage, however, is more than outweighed by the many advantages which FM has over AM.

In FM, the carrier is shifted above and below its normal resonant frequency by the modulating audio signal. Thus, if a 400-cycle audio tone is employed for modulation purposes, it will shift the carrier above and below its center frequency 400 times per second. If a 1,000-cycle audio tone is used for modulating purposes, the carrier will shift above and below its resonant frequency 1,000 times per second. (The resonant frequency of the FM carrier is often referred to as the *resting* frequency.)

Thus, the *frequency* of the audio signal determines the *rate* at which the frequency of the carrier shifts above and below its resting frequency. The *degree* of shift (the extent by which the frequency changes) is related to the *amplitude* of the audio signal. Thus, a *low volume* of audio will cause the carrier to shift *only slightly* above and below its resting frequency, while a *loud* (high-amplitude) *audio signal* will cause the carrier to shift to a *greater extent* on each side of its resting frequency. Consequently, the *extent* of carrier frequency shift depends on the *amplitude* of the modulated audio signal.

A better understanding of how the carrier frequency shifts with respect to an audio signal can be gained by analyzing a simple FM oscillator. One such basic circuit is shown in Fig. 18-8, and consists of a variable-frequency Hartley oscillator similar to the type previously discussed. In place of a variable capacitor, however, a *capacitor microphone* is employed, as shown in Fig. 18-8. This capacitor microphone (C_1) will influence the frequency of the Hartley oscillator in a fashion similar to that of a variable capacitor. With a variable capactor, an increase in the capacity will result in the production of a lower frequency from the Hartley, while a decrease in the capacity will cause the frequency of the Hartley oscillator to increase. This same ability to change the frequency of the oscillator holds true with capacitor microphone C_1, shown in Fig. 18-8.

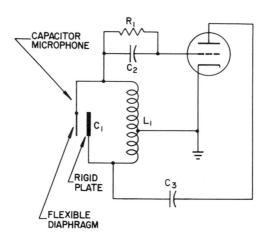

Fig. 18-8. Simple FM.

The influence of the capacitor microphone on the frequency, when sound is impressed on the microphone, can be understood by reference to Fig. 18-9. When sound is generated by a musical instrument or by the spoken word, the air pressure in the surrounding area is alternately increased above normal and decreased below normal. (This increase and decrease in air pressure impinge on the eardrum, and alternately presses the eardrum inward and pulls it outward. This mechanical motion of the eardrum is translated into the sensation of sound by the auditory nerve in the ear.)

What occurs to the diaphragm of the capacitor microphone, when an

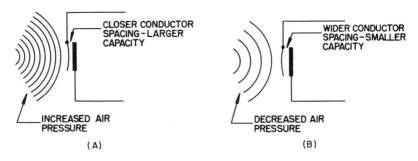

Fig. 18-9. Effects of varying air pressure on capacitor microphones.

increase in air pressure is impressed across it, is shown in Fig. 18-9(A). The flexible microphone diaphragm is pressed inward, and thus is closer to the rigid back plate. This closer spacing of the two conductors (the flexible metal diaphragm and the rigid metal plate) *increases* the capacity of the capacitor microphone. (Bringing the plates of the capacitor close together increases capacity.) Since the capacitor microphone represents the capacity which, in conjunction with the inductance (L_1), forms the resonant circuit of the Hartley oscillator, the frequency output of the latter is changed. Wih a larger capacity, there is a decrease in the frequency output of the Hartley oscillator. Thus, the frequency of the oscillator is lowered by virtue of the increased air pressure. When the air pressure becomes normal, the diaphragm of the capacitor microphone will again assume its regular position, and the oscillator is brought back to its normal resonant resting frequency. When the air pressure decreases, the diaphragm of the capacitor microphone. (Bringing the plates of the capacitor closer Fig. 18-9(B), which results in a smaller capacity. The decrease in capacity will increase the signal frequency of the Hartley oscillator and the result is that there has been a shift to a higher frequency because of the decreased air pressure. When the air pressure again becomes normal, the diaphragm of the microphone reverts to its regular position and the oscillator is brought back to its normal resonant resting frequency.

The increase and decrease in air pressure represents one cycle of the audio tone produced by a musical instrument or by speech. Thus, the frequency of the oscillator decreased, returned to normal, increased, and returned to normal again. This simple form of FM serves to illustrate the actual formation of an FM wave, though more elaborate methods are employed for the FM process, as more fully explained later. The relationships of frequency change, are identical, however, and the simple circuit helps illustrate the process more thoroughly. If the volume of the sound reaching the microphone is increased, it will be obvious that the change in air pressure illustrated in (A) would also increase, and the diaphragm of the capacitor microphone will be forced inward to a greater extent. This closer capacitor plate spacing results in a much larger capacity than was the case with the smaller degree of air pressure increase. Consequently the frequency of the oscillator shifts to a much lower value. The same degree of shift also holds for the illustration in (B). If the air pressure decreases to a greater extent, the capacity is reduced proportionately, and a greater increase in oscillator frequency ensues.

The frequency change is represented also in Fig 18-10, which shows the exact relationships between the audio-modulating signal components and the carrier wave. In (A), the initial portion of the carrier wave is shown in its unmodulated state. When a low-volume audio tone is used for the modulating process, the frequency of the carrier shifts slightly lower. The point of greatest frequency shift will be where the audio

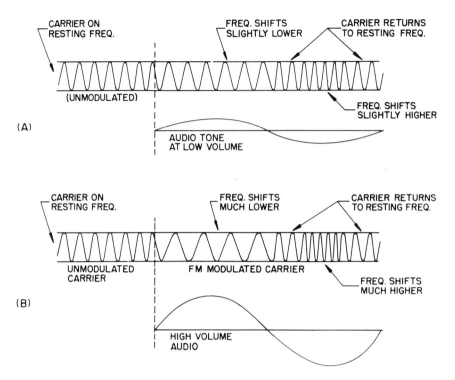

Fig. 18-10. Characteristics of FM.

volume is at its peak level. When the first alternation of the audio tone drops to zero, the carrier returns to its resting frequency. When the second alternation of the audio signal occurs, the oscillator frequency shifts slightly higher, the maximum shift being at the point where the peak negative amplitude of the second alternation occurs. When the second alternation of the audio signal drops to zero, the carrier frequency will come back to its resting frequency.

The increase in carrier shift (deviation) for a louder audio volume is shown in Fig. 18-10(B). The higher value of audio signal causes a much greater shift of the carrier frequency to a lower frequency. Again, however, at the zero level of the first alternation, the carrier returns to its resting frequency. When the negative (second alternation) signal occurs, the carrier frequency shifts to a much higher frequency than was the case with the low-level audio volume shown in (A). At the zero level of audio at the end of the second alternation, the carrier comes back to its resting frequency.

The *frequency* of the audio also has an effect on the carrier shift. If the audio frequency were a 3,000-cycle per second audio tone, the carrier shift would occur 3,000 times per second. If the same audio frequency were employed in Fig. 18-10(B), the carrier would still shift 3,000 times per second, but would now deviate to a greater extent than was the case in (A).

To illustrate the foregoing discussion by using actual figures, assume that a station of 90 megacycles is on the air. The carrier would then be on its resting frequency for the unmodulated condition shown initially in Fig. 18-10(A). When a low-volume audio signal is employed, the carrier may shift from 90 megacycles (90,000 kilocycles) to 89.975 megacycles (89,975 kilocycles), representing a 25-kilocycle shift in frequency, for one alternation of the audio signal. When this audio-signal alternation drops to zero, the carrier shifts back to 90 megacycles. For the second alternation of the audio signal, the carrier shifts to 90.025 megacycles (90,025 kilocycles) and drops back to 90 megacycles when the audio alternation goes to zero. Thus, for one cycle of the audio signal the carrier is made to deviate a total of 50 kilocycles, or 25 kilocycles on each side of resting frequency. In Fig. 18-10(B), where a greater audio volume level is employed, the carrier would shift from 90,000 kilocycles in its unmodulated state to 89,950 kilocycles for the first alternation of the audio modulating signal. At the second alternation, the carrier would shift to 90,050 kilocycles. Thus, the larger audio volume now causes a total carrier deviation of 100 kilocycles, since it deviates 50 kilocycles on either side of its resting frequency. In either case, the carrier would shift above and below its resting frequency 3,000 times per second if a 3,000-cycle per second audio tone is employed.

From the foregoing, it is evident that the loudest signal will cause the greatest carrier deviation. Since the *extent* of carrier deviation for a given audio signal amplitude can be established at the transmitter, it is essential that some regulations be imposed on the transmitting industry, so that a uniform type of transmission is employed by all. For this reason, the Federal Communications Commission has allocated for standard FM stations a maximum deviation of 75 kilocycles on each side of resting frequency. Thus, the *total permissible deviation* for each station is a maximum of 150 kilocycles. Standard FM stations are assigned carrier frequencies between 88 and 108 megacycles. This allocation is just above the lower television stations (Channel 6 has an allocated frequency of 82 to 88 megacycles). The upper FM-band limit of 108 megacycles is followed by other broadcasting services extending to 174 megacycles. Channel 7 begins at 174 megacycles, as shown in the Appendix.

As can be seen from an inspection of the FM carrier in Fig. 18-10, the modulation of a carrier by varying its frequency again distorts any cycle of the modulated wave, by varying the time duration of one alternation with respect to another. Any alternation of the time duration of one alternation with respect to another results in the production of frequencies other than the fundamental frequency. For this reason, sidebands are generated in FM as is the case with the AM. With FM, however, there is virtually an *infinite* number of sidebands generated. As with AM, the first two sidebands (one above and one below the carrier) are spaced from the carrier by a frequency equal to the audio frequency producing the modulation. The additional sidebands in FM are also spaced from *each other* by a frequency equal to the modulating frequency. Thus, if a 1,000-cycle audio signal is employed for modulating purposes, each sideband is spaced from the other by 1,000 cycles, or 1 kilocycle. The sidebands near the carrier frequency have the greatest amplitude, and subsequent sidebands spaced away from the carrier have a decreasing amplitude. Of the many sidebands produced, there are only a few which have sufficient amplitude to prove of value during the reception of the signal. The sidebands which have a value for detection are known as the *significant sidebands.* In standard FM broadcasting, eight significant sidebands are present above the carrier and eight below, during maximum permissible modulation. This is based on the ratio of maximum carrier swing versus the maximum audio frequency employed, and is known as the *deviation ratio.* Thus, in standard FM broadcasting, the maximum deviation is 75 kilocycles, and the highest audio frequency employed for modulation purposes is 15,000 cycles per second. This produces the following modulation index:

$$\frac{75,000}{15,000} = 5$$

For a modulation index of 0.4 or less, only one significant sideband exists above and below the carrier. For a modulation index of 0.5, there are two significant sidebands above and below the carrier. For a modulation index of 1, there are three significant sidebands above and below the carrier. For any modulation index between one and 10, the following significant sidebands exist:

Modulation index	Number of sidebands above and below carrier
1	3
2	4
3	6
4	7
5	8
6	9
7	10
8	12
9	13
10	14

In television, the frequency modulation employed for the sound uses a maximum deviation, on each side of the carrier, of 25 kilocycles. For this reason, the number of significant sidebands is much less than in standard FM since the deviation ratio is lower.

The deviation ratio shown above indicates maximum modulating conditions, and is not representative of normal transmission. Since no musical instruments produce *fundamental* frequencies in excess of 5,000 cycles per second, the frequencies above 5,000 cycles which are generated are only the *overtones* produced when musical instruments are played. Such overtones or harmonics are much lower in amplitude than the fundamental frequency, and for this reason they would not cause as great a deviation of the carrier frequency. At the same time, the sideband components produced by the overtones would be spaced far from the carrier and would have low amplitude. Thus, during normal transmission, the significant sidebands do not extend beyond the 75-kilocycle limit set for deviation on each side of the resting frequency of the carrier. As an added protection, however, 25 kilocycles are added to each FM station channel to guard against spill-over which would interfere with an adjacent station. These 25 kilocycle-sections illustrated in Fig. 18-11 are known as *guard-*

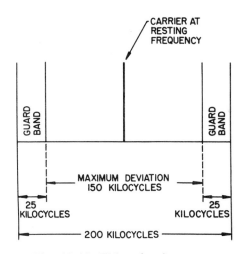

Fig. 18-11. FM station frequency allocation.

bands, and because of them each station has a *total frequency allocation* of 200 kilocycles.

In frequency modulation, the *carrier* must furnish the *sideband power.* Consequently, the carrier amplitude actually varies somewhat during the modulation process, since some of the energy of the carrier is utilized for the generation of the sidebands. Thus, during extensive deviations of the carrier due to a loud AM signal, the total power contained in the sidebands can exceed the carrier power. The typical FM carrier wave shown earlier in Fig. 18-10 is representative not only of the carrier, but also of the sidebands. If the sidebands were filtered from the modulated carrier, the remaining carrier signal would be a single frequency signal having a varying amplitude conforming to the power periodically relinquished to create the sidebands.

REACTANCE CIRCUIT

The capacitor-microphone method for producing FM is unsatisfactory in terms of linearity (equal deviation above and below the carrier) and, in commercial FM systems, other methods are employed for deviating the carrier frequency. The reactance tube process for frequency control is shown in Fig. 18-12(A) and is extensively used in FM transmitting sys-

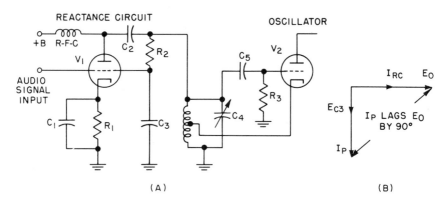

(A)   (B)

Fig. 18-12. Reactance-tube circuit.

tems. Because a reactance tube is capable of controlling oscillator frequency, the reactance circuit is also found in other electronic applications.

The reactance tube circuit is one which has the characteristics of either inductance or capacitance, depending on the particular design. In Fig. 18-12(A), a triode tube is shown, though a pentode can also be employed. The functional components which make the tube reactive are resistor R_2 and capacitor C_3. (Capacitor C_2 is a large-value capacitor, usually between 0.01 and 0.03, for blocking the d-c of the reactance tube anode and preventing its being shorted to ground via the oscillator coil. At the frequency used, its reactance is too low to contribute anything to the reactance function of the circuit.)

Resistor R_2 is chosen so that its resistance is approximately 10 times the reactance of C_3. Thus, R_2 may have a resistance of approximately 100,000 ohms, while C_3 has a reactance value around 10,000 ohms. Note that the reactance tube anode-grid circuit is coupled to the oscillator resonant circuit. Such coupling impresses across the R_2-C_3 network the voltage of the oscillator E_0. For a clearer understanding of the phase relationships which are established, reference should be made to the vector diagram shown in Fig. 18-12(B). The oscillator voltage E_0 is designated by the horizontal line. Inasmuch as R_2 is 10 times as high in resistance as the reactance of C_3, the RC network is primarily resistive, so that the current flow created by E_0 will be virtually in phase with the voltage. Hence, current through the RC network (I_{RC}) is also indicated by a horizontal line in (B). The grid signal voltage of the reactance tube V_1, however, is derived from across C_3 only (E_{C_3}). Also, in a capacitor, voltage lags current. Thus, the grid signal voltage lags the RC network current by 90 degrees, as shown on the vector diagram. In a vacuum tube, plate current is in phase with grid voltage, since a negative grid signal decreases plate current flow, and a positive grid signal increases current. The plate current (I_p) for the vector diagram is thus drawn along the vertical line, to show the in-phase condition with respect to E_{C_3}. Obviously, then, *the reactance tube plate current lags the oscillator voltage* by 90 degrees. A lagging current (or a leading voltage) is indicative of an *inductive reactance,* hence the reactance circuit shown in Fig. 18-12(A) behaves as an inductance. Since this inductance shunts the oscillator resonant circuit, the reactance tube inductance influences the resonance of the oscillator.

Reactance in a vacuum tube depends on current flow, and any change of reactance tube current will affect the reactance value of V_1. Hence, a change of grid potential will alter reactance. The grid potential can be in the form of an audio signal and applied to the grid, as shown in Fig. 18-12(A). (This tube does not have dual grids. The drawing of a grid wire extending out from the tube, both at the left and at the right, is a common expedient used to simplify schematic drawings.)

The value of the inductance originally established by the reactance tube depends on the transconductance (g_m) of V_1, as well as the carrier frequency generated by the oscillator. The inductance can, therefore, be ascertained by use of the formula

$$L = \frac{10}{6.28 f g_m} \qquad (18\text{-}1)$$

Note that the formula takes into consideration the fact that R is 10 times X_c, and also employs the angular velocity figures discussed previously in Chapter 8.

The amount of reactance which the tube is to contribute across the oscillator coil is established initially by use of the formula. The total inductance (reactance tube and oscillator coil) is combined with C_4 to establish the resonant frequency of the oscillator.

In producing FM, an audio signal at the grid of the reactance tube will alternately increase and decrease plate-current flow. The current changes, in turn, alter the zero-signal reactance of the tube by decreasing and increasing the reactive value. This change of inductive reactance at the oscillator resonant circuit shifts the oscillator frequency above and below its carrier frequency, at a rate established by the frequency of the audio-modulating signal. As the amplitude of the AM signal is increased, it creates greater reactive changes in the reactance tube, and hence shifts the oscillator frequency to a greater degree (greater deviation of the carrier frequency).

DEMODULATION (DETECTION)

As mentioned in Chapter 11, the vacuum-tube diode can be employed as a rectifier. A rectifier is a device which has the ability to convert either low-frequency or high-frequency a-c to d-c. Because detection is essentially a rectifying process, the principles of rectification find application in both power supplies and detectors of modulated signals. In the latter application, it follows the R-F amplifiers in receivers, as shown in Fig. 18-13,

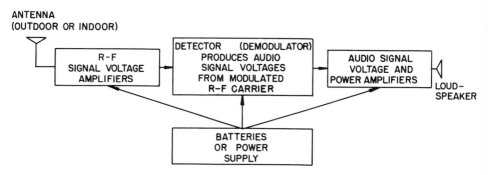

ANTENNA
(OUTDOOR OR INDOOR)

| R-F SIGNAL VOLTAGE AMPLIFIERS | DETECTOR (DEMODULATOR) PRODUCES AUDIO SIGNAL VOLTAGES FROM MODULATED R-F CARRIER | AUDIO SIGNAL VOLTAGE AND POWER AMPLIFIERS | LOUD-SPEAKER |

BATTERIES OR POWER SUPPLY

Fig. 18-13. Basic block diagram of radio receiver.

and produces the audio signal voltages from the modulated R-F carrier.

As discussed in Chapter 11, the diode tube has the ability to rectify, because it permits current flow through the tube in only one direction; that is, current can flow only from the cathode to the plate, and not from the plate to the cathode. For review purposes, the rectifying action is again illustrated in Fig. 18-14(A). Here, an a-c signal is applied to the input terminals of a simple diode circuit, in which a series resistor has been placed. During the positive alternation (alternation No. 1), the top terminal of the circuit is positive and the bottom terminal is negative. Under this condition, the anode of the diode is positive and, hence, will attract the electrons from the negative cathode. Thus, the first alternation will cause a current flow through the diode in the direction shown by the arrows. Since this current flows through the resistor, it will cause a signal voltage to develop across this resistor. Because the current through the resistor is in the form of an alternation of the input a-c waveform, the voltage drop across the resistor also has the waveshape of one a-c alternation. Thus, the series resistor can be considered a load resistor from which the rectified signals can be obtained.

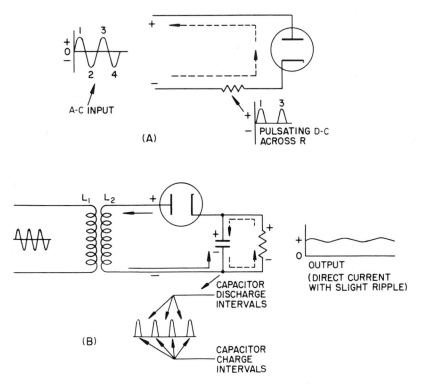

Fig. 18-14. Half-wave rectifier circuit.

During a negative alternation (such as Number 2 or 4), the top terminal of the input circuit would be negative, and hence the *anode* would be negative. The bottom terminal would be positive, hence the cathode of the diode would also be positive. The negative anode would repel electrons, and the positive cathode would attract electrons rather than emit them. Under this condition, therefore, no current flows through the circuit. The signal developed across the resistor thus consists only of the positive alternations developed by rectification of the input a-c signal. If only negative alternations were desired, the diode (whether a tube or crystal rectifier) would be reversed. The polarity of the output signal is chosen to suit circuit requirements, as more fully discussed subsequently.

Often, the input signal is applied to the diode circuit by use of a transformer as shown in Fig. 18-14(B). Here, the input signal is applied across the primary winding L_1, and by mutual inductance transferred to the secondary winding L_2. When a positive alternation appears across L_2, the anode will have a positive polarity and the cathode a negative polarity, and hence tube conduction occurs. During this time, electrons flow in the direction shown by the arrow. In this case, a capacitor has been added across the load resistor, for filtering purposes. During the time of tube conduction, the capacitor will charge to the peak value of the energy in the circuit. In a capacitor, the current leads the voltage and, initially, the capacitor acts as a low-impedance shunt across the resistor. Hence, the electrons will flow on to the capacitor, rather than flow through the higher opposition offered by the load resistor.

When a negative alternation appears across the secondary winding, the anode is made negative and, hence, current flow through the vacuum tube ceases. During this time interval, however, the capacitor will discharge across the resistor, in the direction shown by the dotted arrow. If the capacitor is sufficiently large and has stored a fair amount of the energy during tube conduction, the capacitor will not have discharged completely by the time the next positive alternation appears to cause tube conduction.

When tube conduction occurs again, the capacitor is recharged and, thus, its stored energy is constantly being replenished. This charging of the capacitor during positive alternations, and discharging during negative alternations, provides an action which insures a relatively constant current flow through the resistor. Thus, the capacitor maintains a fairly level charge across the resistor, and acts as a filter for the ripple which would otherwise appear across the resistor. The steady charge now represents d-c instead of pulsating d-c. In this manner, the original a-c signal was converted to pulsating d-c, and then filtered to produce relatively pure d-c. The degree to which the ripple is minimized depends on the filter size and other factors, as more fully discussed earlier in Chapter 14. The circuit shown in Fig. 18-14(B) is a basic rectifier circuit with a simple filter arrangement.

If the input amplitude of the a-c waveform varies as shown in Fig.

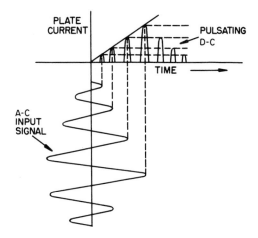

Fig. 18-15. Graph of detection characteristics.

18-15, the output alternations will also increase and decrease in like fashion. This is the underlying principle of detection, wherein the rectifying action of the diode is used for demodulating purposes in receivers. Both the power-supply principle and the detector principle depend on the rectifying action of the diode and, hence, the circuit arrangements are quite similar. Differences exist only because of the nature of the waveform which is handled. When the a-c from the power mains is to be changed into d-c, a constant-amplitude input signal is applied to the rectifier circuit, and a filter arrangement is employed to smooth out the ripple components, as shown in Fig. 18-14(B). In a detector system, however, a much higher frequency signal is handled, but the basic circuit still resembles that in Fig. 18-14(B).

The pulsating d-c produced in Fig. 18-15 has been expanded, in Fig. 18-16(A), to help make clear how detection derives an audio signal from the R-F carrier. By use of an R-F filter capacitor, the pulsating d-c shown in (A) is converted into an average value, as shown in (B). This average value varies above and below a reference level, in the same manner as the carrier amplitude increases and decreases. When this is applied to a subsequent stage by use of a coupling capacitor or transformer, only the a-c component is transferred, and the d-c is kept out of the subsequent stage, since neither a capacitor nor a transformer will pass d-c.

The rectifying process is necessary, since the a-c R-F signal, with its varying amplitudes, cannot be heard if applied to a speaker, *because its frequency is too high above the audible range.* Even though the amplitude variations which extend both both above and below the reference line of

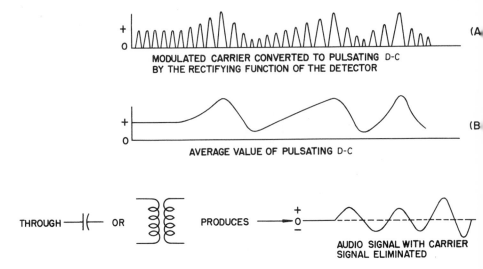

Fig. 18-16. Characteristics of detection process.

zero represent the audio information, the average value of pulsating d-c, not a-c, is necessary to convert the amplitude changes of the R-F carrier into audible signals.

BASIC DIODE DETECTORS

The diode detector can be a vacuum tube, or a small diode crystal mounted in a container having two terminals or leads for wiring into a circuit. The diode detector, in either the crystal or vacuum-tube form, is the most widely used detector in television, radio, and other communications receivers. The diode detector is capable of handling high-amplitude input signals without overloading, and compared to other detector types very little distortion is produced. Unlike some other detector systems, however, the diode detector does not amplify a signal. Its sensitivity is rather low, and it also draws power from the tuning circuit connected to it. Hence, it reduces the tuning circuit's selectivity and sensitivity and lowers the Q. These disadvantages are negligible, however, because modern receivers precede the detector with sufficient R-F amplifiers with their resonant circuits to produce excellent selectivity. The R-F amplifier stages also increase the sensitivity of the receiver and hence compensate for the slight drawbacks of the diode detector.

The diode detector can, of course, be utilized in a simple receiving circuit as shown in Fig. 18-17. This circuit was the forerunner of the modern radio and still gives good results in the areas where signal strength is reasonably high. An outdoor antenna, however, is necessary for good reception of local transmission. The outside antenna, connected to the series circuit composed of the variable capacitor C_1, is adjusted to make it and the series inductance resonant to the frequency of the desired station. Coil L_1 forms a transformer in conjunction with L_2; here again, a variable capacitor, C_2, is employed. The latter is also adjusted to make the circuit resonant for the station desired. For a more simple circuit, the antenna can be attached to the top of L_2 and the series resonant circuit dispensed with. The more simple circuit, however, has decreased selectivity.

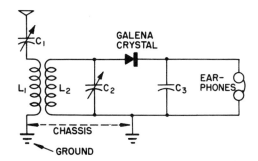

Fig. 18-17. Simple galena-crystal receiver.

The carrier which appears across the secondary winding is rectified by the crystal diode, with the capacitor C_3 (approximately 0.00025 microfarad) acting as a filter component. Thus, across the earphones, the audio (represented by variations in the average pulsating d-c voltage) is heard. The bottom of inductance L_1 is usually connected to an outside pipe driven into the ground, or the connection can also be made to a water pipe; hence this terminal is known as the ground terminal and the symbol for ground is used as shown. While the "ground" designation originated with this simple type of crystal receiver, as the design of radio receivers improved, the ground connection was not necessary, but the symbol for ground is still employed to indicate that a certain wire or terminal is connected to the *chassis* of the receiver. When the chassis is employed for ground purposes, the chassis becomes the interconnecting conductor for the various points shown on the schematic.

A typical vacuum-tube diode detector as used in modern receivers is shown in Fig. 18-18, and its crystal-diode counterpart is shown in Fig. 18-19. In either circuit, the R-F modulated carrier signal input is derived from a previous R-F amplifier stage, and is applied across the primary of the transformer L_1. This signal appears across L_2, and is tuned to reso-

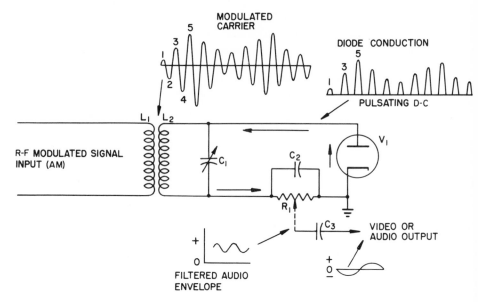

Fig. 18-18. Vacuum-tube diode detector circuit.

nance by variable capacitor C_1. For the first alternation of the waveform, the anode of the detector is positive and, in consequence, current flows in the circuit, as shown by the arrows. For the second alternation, the tube

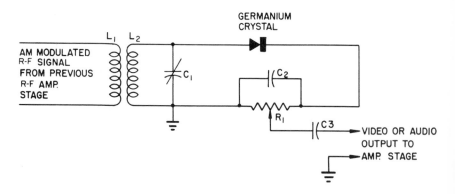

Fig. 18-19. Germanium-crystal detector circuits.

does not conduct and, therefore, there is no current flow through the resistor R_1. For the third alternation, current again flows, but it now has a greater amplitude, because the input signal amplitude is changing. Thus, for repeated positive alternations, the diode will conduct an amount of current in proportion to the amplitude of such alternations.

Capacitor C_2 filters the ripple component by charging to the peak values and discharging only slightly during the valleys between the peak pulses of the d-c, as discussed earlier. The audio signal voltage is developed across the load resistor R_1. Capacitor C_2, because it is a ripple-frequency filter, effectively bypasses the R-F carrier signal from across the load resistor R_1. The latter resistor can be in the form of a *potentiometer,* so that the degree of signal intensity (volume) can be adjusted as desired. Thus, by using a potentiometer for R_1, the latter becomes a *volume control* for regulating the desired output level from the receiver. The signal at R_1, however, is still too weak for operating a loudspeaker, though the audio sounds would be sufficiently audible in earphones. Also, if this is a video (picture signal) detector, the signals would have insufficient amplitude for application to a television-receiver picture tube. In consequence, the signal is coupled via a coupling capacitor C_3 to a subsequent stage or stages for additional amplification.

PLATE DETECTORS

While the diode-type detector is primarily used in modern circuitry, there are a number of other detectors which have been used in the past. Some of these still find specific applications in special AM circuits and, therefore, a discussion of some of the major types is included here for reference purposes.

A detector other than the diode type is one using either a triode or a pentode tube, in a circuit known as a *plate detector.* A typical plate-detector circuit is shown in Fig. 18-20(A), and the input signal is derived from a previous R-F amplifier stage, or from a series resonant circuit in the antenna system, as previously indicated for the crystal galena detector circuit. The signal is impressed across the secondary of the transformer and tuned to resonance by the variable capacitor C_2. A fixed bias near the cutoff point is established by use of a C battery. This bias is as indicated in Fig. 18-21, which shows the input signal and the characteristic function of the tube in graph form. When an input signal of a modulated waveform is placed at the grid, all positive alternations will cause plate current to flow in pulses. This process is, in effect, again a rectification principle, since the plate-current pulses are positive-going, while the grid input signal is both positive and negative, as indicated.

Capacitor C_3 in the plate circuit of drawing (A), Fig. 18-20, will have a bypass effect on the R-F signal energy, and will also charge to the peak values of the plate-current pulses. Thus, C_3 will establish an average value

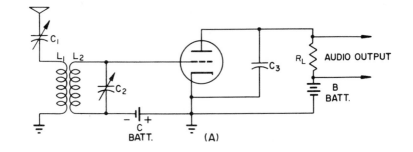

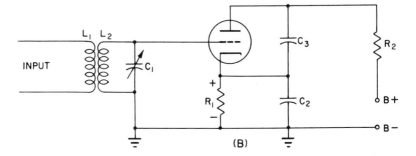

Fig. 18-20. Detector circuits.

of the plate-current pulses, and will obtain the audio component from the signal rectifying process accomplished in the plate circuit. The dashed line in Fig. 18-21 shows the audio waveform developed across the load resistor (R_L).

In the plate-circuit detector, the tube operates on the rectilinear portion of a characteristic curve, as shown in Fig. 18-21. Thus, the ratio between the R-F input signal voltage and the audio-frequency signal output voltage is a linear one. Consequently, this detector is also called a *linear plate-circuit detector*. If the amplitude of the input signal to this circuit is increased in a certain proportion, an increase will also occur at the output. There is some curvature at the bottom of the characteristic curve, however, and the signal input must have sufficient amplitude so that operation will be primarily on the linear portion of the curve. If the signal input has a very low amplitude, some distortion will result, because of operation on the curved or nonlinear portion of the characteristic curve of the tube.

The linear plate detector has good sensitivity, and some amplification of the signal occurs, because of the grid-anode section of the triode. Distortion is low when the signal input has a fairly high amplitude, as previously mentioned, and compares favorably with the diode under good

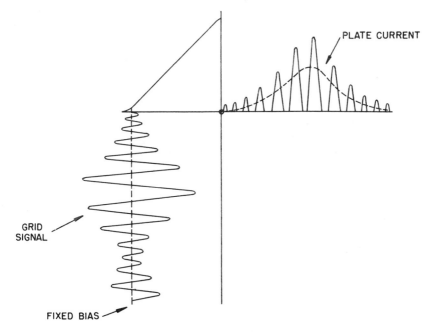

Fig. 18-21. Plate-detector characteristics.

operating conditions. The selectivity is not lowered, as is the case with the diode detector, since the plate-circuit detector has a high input impedance and, therefore, does not lower the Q of the tuned resonant circuit at the input. Because of the simplicity of the diode detector, however, and its ability to handle higher input potentials, the diode detector has been used more extensively in modern receivers. In some special commercial or experimental applications, the plate detector may still be encountered. Grid bias does not have to be applied by a C battery. Instead, a cathode resistor can be employed as shown in Fig. 18-20(B). This circuit is similar to the one previously described, except that resistor R_1 and capacitor C_2 have been added to the cathode circuit and the C battery eliminated. The input signal can be obtained from an antenna resonant circuit or from a previous R-F amplifier stage.

GRID-CIRCUIT DETECTOR

Another form of detector used extensively in the early days of radio is the grid-circuit detector shown in Part (A) of Fig. 18-22. Here, a grid-leak resistor (R_1) and a grid capacitor (C_1) are employed for establishing bias. Since no cathode resistor or C battery is utilized for bias purposes, the initial signal input finds zero bias at the grid. Therefore, at the first positive alternation, the grid is driven positive and grid rectification occurs. The operational characteristics are similar to those of the diode detector, except that the *grid* acts as the *anode,* and that current flows from the cathode to the grid and then toward the resistor-capacitor combination, as shown in Fig. 18-22(B). This current flow will charge the grid capacitor, with a polarity which is negative toward the grid and positive toward the resonant circuit. During the negative alternation, the grid capacitor discharges across the grid leak, as shown in (C). Thus, a steady d-c voltage is established across resistor R_1, by virtue of the discharge of the grid capacitor C_1. For each positive alternation, the capacitor is recharged. The process continues until eventually a fixed bias is established, when the circuit reaches an equilibrium point. This fixed bias can be at the cutoff point or slightly beyond. The resulting self-bias is similar to that obtained with Class C amplifiers as previously discussed.

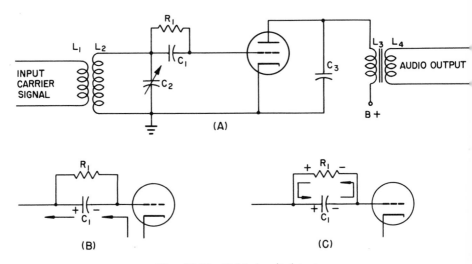

Fig. 18-22. Grid-circuit detector.

For a modulated waveform, the rectification process will occur in the grid circuit, and the audio signal voltage waveform will also develop across the grid-leak resistor R_1, as for the diode detector previously discussed. These audio voltages will also change the grid potential, making it more negative or less negative. Hence, the audio voltage variations which occur across the grid leak will influence the current flow through the tube, and will establish the audio voltage variations across the primary of the transformer in the anode circuit of the detector system. Capacitor C_3 is a small capacitor in the plate circuit which bypasses the R-F current in the latter.

The grid-circuit detector has a high order of sensitivity, but it distorts for a strong signal input. For a weak signal input, the distortion is of a low level and tolerable. Since the grid is driven positive for portions of the input signal waveform, the grid circuit draws current, and thus has a low input impedance. This will lower the Q of the tuned resonant section, and this loading effect has a considerable influence on the selectivity of the circuit. Thus, the grid-circuit detector has a low order of selectivity and, in consequence, is not used much in modern circuitry. On occasion, it may still be found in shortwave receivers or other portable equipment where it is necessary to have a high degree of sensitivity, because of the absence of R-F amplification preceding the grid-circuit detector stage.

The time constant of the grid leak and grid capacitor combination must be suitabe for the range of frequencies for which the detector is employed. For the broadcast band, the grid leak R_1 may range from 1 megohm to 4 or 5 megohms. The higher resistance value will increase the sensitivity to weaker signals. The grid capacitor is usually 0.00025 or 0.0001 microfarads, and the plate capacitor C_3 has the same small value. Such a small value causes the capacitor to have an effective bypass function for the radio frequencies, but it will have a high reactance for the audio frequencies, and hence will not materially reduce their amplitude.

REGENERATIVE DETECTOR

Another type of detector is the regenerative (positive feedback) type shown in Fig. 18-23. Here, a portion of the signal energy in the anode circuit is fed back, via a coil L_3, to the secondary (L_2) of the input trans-

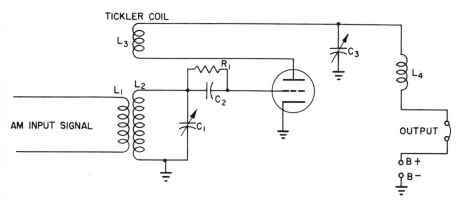

Fig. 18-23. Regenerative detector.

former. By such coupling, L_3 induces some of the amplified signal energy into the secondary inductance L_2, as with the feedback oscillator previously described. If the polarity of the feedback voltage is the same as that of the signal voltage in the L_2 circuit, the fed-back signal voltage will reinforce the signal voltage existing at the grid, so that circuit efficiency will be increased. Since the resistive component of the input circuit is also decreased, selectivity and sensitivity are high. This form of feedback is known as *regeneration*.

The degree of coupling between L_3 (also known as the *tickler coil*) and the secondary coil L_2 can be varied by changing the spacing between the two coils. Another method for controlling the amount of regeneration is to vary the capacitor C_3 in the tickler coil circuit. A third method for controlling the amount of regeneration is to place a variable resistor in series with the B+ lead, and thus change the plate current which flows through the tickler coil.

Inductance L_4, is an R-F choke which offers a high opposition to the signal energy for the radio frequencies. Hence, this series choke coil keeps the R-F frequencies from the output circuit. Capacitor C_3, in addition to being a regeneration control, also bypasses the R-F signal components, while filtering the audio components for reproduction at the output.

The regenerative detector can receive its input from a previous R-F amplifier stage, or from an antenna resonant circuit. The output can be applied to a pair of earphones as shown, or to an audio amplifier stage for additional build-up of the audio signal components.

When the regeneration and positive feedback are increased, there will be a point where so much signal energy is fed back from the output circuit to the input circuit, that the circuit will oscillate. When the circuit oscillates, it has reached an equilibrium with respect to the feedback voltage, and the system becomes self-sustaining; that is, it furnishes its own input signal, and produces or generates a given output frequency. Under such a condition, the circuit would not need a signal input. This type of oscillator was discussed earlier.

The regenerative detector is not used in modern receivers, except in experimental types or in short-wave portable types where a high degree of sensitivity and selectivity is necessary. The regenerative detector shown in Fig. 18-23 produces as much audio signal output as could be obtained from a detector stage with an additional stage of R-F amplification preceding it, for gain-increasing purposes.

The regenerative detector has several disadvantages. Adjustments to produce the maximum regeneration without the circuit going into oscillation are critical. When maximum regeneration is once established, it may not remain fixed for long. For this reason, some instability may result when the regeneration controls are set for too high or too critical a regeneration point. When the circuit is permitted to oscillate, squeals will be heard in the output and, since an oscillator generates a frequency, it will also radiate such energy and cause interference in nearby receivers. The regenerative detector in its oscillating state finds primary applications in short-wave work where it is necessary to receive code signals which have no modulation characteristics, as discussed next.

HETERODYNE DETECTION

There are two types of code signals which are transmitted in short-wave commercial and government applications. One type is obtained by generating a carrier of a fixed frequency and amplitude, and interrupting this carrier to form short and long transmission intervals. This is shown in Fig. 18-24(A), where the short transmission intervals represent dots

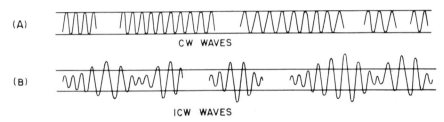

Fig. 18-24. Continuous waves and interrupted continuous waves.

and the longer transmission intervals represent dashes. In this fashion, the Morse code can be transmitted. (The code is named after Samuel F. B. Morse (1791-1872), the American inventor who originated it for use with respect to the early telegraph.)

Another method for sending code is to use a modulated carrier and interrupt it as shown in (B). If the modulated carrier is modulated with a 400-cycle audio tone, for instance, it can be received by any of the detectors previously discussed. The detector will then demodulate the AM waveform, and the detection process will produce a 400-cycle audio tone which will be periodically interrupted to represent the dots and dashes of the Morse code.

When a continuous wave having a constant amplitude and frequency is transmitted, the type of transmission is known as *CW* to indicate *continuous waves*. This designation does not refer to the interruption rate, but rather to the fact that the amplitude is continuous and does not vary. When a modulating tone is utilized and the amplitude varies, the transmission is known as *ICW,* to indicate *interrupted continuous waves*. This term indicates that the continuous amplitude is not maintained but is varied (interrupted), increasing and decreasing at a predetermined rate. The ICW transmission must still be broken up into dots and dashes as with the CW transmission. The CW wave has the advantage that it is a narrowband type of transmission, as opposed to the ICW wave, which occupies more space, since sidebands are generated whenever a carrier is amplitude modulated.

When the CW type of wave is transmitted, the lack of modulation prevents the use of an ordinary detector to demodulate the carrier. To intercept and detect the CW type of code transmission, it is necessary to have an oscillating detector. The regenerative detector shown in Fig. 18-23 can be employed by adjusting the feedback amplitude to the point where sufficient energy is applied to the grid to sustain and generate oscillations. Such detection is known as *heterodyne* detection.

Heterodyne refers to the process by which two signals of different frequencies are combined in special circuitry, to produce additional signals having frequencies other than the original. Earlier, it was pointed out that harmonic distortion is produced when signals are amplified in a circuit having nonlinear characteristics. Such harmonic distortion consists of signals generated within the amplifier and not contained in the original signal. If a circuit is used having severe nonlinear characteristics, and *two* signals are injected into the circuit, the output signals will consist of the initial two signals, plus signals whose frequencies are the *sum* and *difference* frequencies of the original two signals. The additional signals are generated because, in a nonlinear circuit, the two original signals *beat together,* or, to use the more technical term, *heterodyne.* Thus, if one of the original signals has a frequency of 1,000 kilocycles, and the other signal has a frequency of 999.5 kilocycles, the heterodyning process produces a signal having what is known as a *difference* frequency of 500 cycles (0.5 kilocycles). At the output of the circuit, the original two signals are also present, plus the sum frequency of the original two signals (1,999.5 kilocycles).

The heterodyning process is important, not only because it is used in the reception of CW waves, but also because it is used extensively in virtually all modern receivers such as AM radio, FM, television, shortwave, and others which employ the *superheterodyne* principle, as more fully discussed in the next chapter.

For reception of a CW signal, the regenerative detector shown in Fig. 18-23 is adjusted to oscillate, and hence it will generate a frequency of its own. If this frequency is near the incoming CW frequency, an audio tone will be generated. Assume that the CW signal is 25,000 kilocycles. If the regenerative detector is tuned so that it oscillates at 25,001 kilocycles, the difference frequency produced by heterodyning will be an audible signal of 1 kilocycle (1,000 cycles).

When the incoming signal mixes with the signal produced by circuit oscillations, the resultant signal which is produced will have amplitude variations, because the progressive point-by-point addition of the two signals results in decreasing and increasing amplitudes, as the phase between the two signals of different frequencies varies. (This signal with varying amplitude is similar to the modulated type waveform produced by the addition of a constant-amplitude carrier and a constant-amplitude sideband, as discussed earlier in this chapter.) These amplitude variations occur at a rate corresponding to the difference frequency between the two signals. Thus, by the combined heterodyning and demodulation process of the detector, the audio-frequency difference component is detected and made audible at the output. Since the regenerative detector also amplifies, the oscillating detector produces a fairly high volume audio signal at its output.

The oscillating frequency of the detector could also be set at 24,999 kilocycles, and the difference frequency would still be 1,000 cycles and, hence, audible. The oscillating frequency of the detector can be altered to give a variety of audio tones, as desired. If the carrier and oscillating frequencies are close together, a low-frequency audio tone will be developed. As the oscillating frequency and the incoming carrier frequency are separated more and more, an increasingly high audio frequency will be generated. A frequency above 15,000 cycles soon becomes inaudible to the average ear. (Very few individuals can hear frequencies above 20,000 cycles, and many can hear frequencies only up to 15,000 cycles per second.)

The oscillating type of detector is also known as the *autodyne* detector. It has the advantage of excellent sensitivity and selectivity, and does not require a separate oscillator for the reception of CW signals. In instances where diodes or other types of detectors are employed which do not have feedback for producing oscillations, a separate oscillator would have to be used, and the signal from the latter injected into the detector. With the autodyne detector, the oscillator and detector are contained in one circuit and employ a single triode or pentode tube.

If such an oscillator is connected directly to an antenna for the input signal source, the oscillating signals will leak into the antenna system and will be radiated. Hence, such signals can be picked up by receivers tuned to the same frequency, and interference with other stations will result. A regenerative detector should be operated with an isolating R-F amplifier stage between the antenna and the oscillating detector. In addition to this, the detector circuit should be well shielded to minimize radiation from the connecting leads, and from the inductances and other component parts.

The *oscillating* detector previously mentioned is suitable primarily for reception of CW signals which contain no AM. When in an oscillating state, it is not suitable for the reception of AM or FM signals. For CW reception, however, the oscillating detector has several advantages, because, when in the oscillating state, the circuit impedance develops a high order of signal energy, since the resistive component is virtually zero and no losses occur through the power consumed by any circuit resistance. The advantages of the oscillating state can be utilized for the reception of a modulated signal, however, by the special super-regenerative circuit discussed next.

THE SUPER-REGENERATIVE DETECTOR

The super-regenerative detector was devised by the famed American inventor, Major Edwin H. Armstrong (1890–1953), and its basic circuit is shown in Fig. 18-25. The circuit resembles the regenerative or oscil-

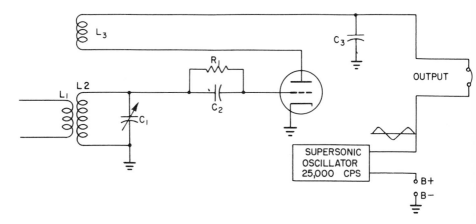

Fig. 18-25. Super-regenerative detector.

lating detector previously described, except that a signal of *supersonic frequency* is injected in series with the B+ lead (to the tickler coil) and tube anode. The B voltage is initially set at the point just below where oscillations would occur. The supersonic oscillator generates a frequency above the audible range, and such a frequency can be 25,000 or 30,000 cycles per second. If the B voltage is set just below the point where oscillation occurs, the supersonic oscillator signal will alternately add positive and negative potentials to the B voltage impressed on the tube. If, for instance, the B voltage is 45 volts, and above this value the circuit would oscillate, a positive alternation of 5 volts from the supersonic oscillator would add to the 45 volts from the B supply and make the total anode voltage 50 volts. With the increased B voltage, the circuit would oscillate. When a negative signal alternation occurs from the supersonic oscillator, it would oppose the B battery voltage. If the negative alternation from the supersonic oscillator is 5 volts, it would decrease the 45-volt B potential to 40 volts and, hence, the circuit would be below the critical regeneration point and would not oscillate. Thus, the super-regenerative receiver is periodically thrown in and out of oscillation at an extremely rapid rate. The rate is above the audible frequency and, thus, the injection of the supersonic signal will not result in the latter being heard at the output. On the other hand, the circuit is in an oscillating state during one-half its operating time, and hence the advantages of high efficiency and sensitivity are realized. Since the oscillating state is not a sustained one, no heterodyning process occurs to produce a beat-frequency signal. Thus, for the reception of voice or ICW, the super-regenerative detector works satisfactorily.

When the receiver is not tuned to a station (no signal input), the electron flow in the tube circuit varies, because of the supersonic oscillator's effect on the B voltage. This rapidly changing B voltage produces a hissing sound in the output which, however, is suppressed during the reception of signals at or above medium strength. The super-regenerative receiver has poor selectivity because of loading effects, though sensitivity and efficiency are high. It finds special applications in the reception of ICW signals or for AM modulated signals which are broadcast in a frequency spectrum not crowded by other transmission.

DISCRIMINATOR FM DETECTOR

Detectors for FM must be so designed that they will interpret the frequency changes of the modulated carrier and produce the equivalent audio signal components. The diode detector described earlier can be employed in a dual-diode arrangement known as a discriminator. Such a detector discriminates with respect to carrier-frequency changes and produces the necessary audio signal components. The amplitude detecting characteristics of the diode, however, are undesirable in an FM detector and, hence, some provisions must be made to eliminate all amplitude changes which reach the discriminator type of detector. One method for doing this is to precede the discriminator circuit with a clipper-type circuit, as shown in Fig. 18-26. The clipper, as mentioned earlier, will have a limiting action if the input signal has sufficient amplification to drive the grid positive. With sufficient grid signal drive, amplitude variations of the signal are limited and, hence, the circuit is known as a limiter, when used in conjunction with a discriminator. The limiter, by eliminating amplitude changes, minimizes static, because the latter arrives at the receiver in the form of carrier amplitude changes.

As shown in Fig. 18-26, the limiter has no fixed-bias circuitry, and the

bias is obtained in a manner similar to that in Class C amplifiers or oscillators. When the grid is driven positive by a positive alternation of the
input signal, capacitor C_1 charges. The discharge of C_1 across the grid
leak R_1 sets the bias slightly beyond cutoff. The positive alternations of the
input signal cause plate current to flow from zero to saturation in the form
of pulsating d-c. The flywheel effect of the resonant circuit, composed of
L_1 and C_2, however, reproduces the sinewave characteristics of the carrier.
Such a carrier now has a constant amplitude.

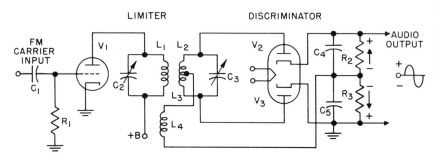

Fig. 18-26. Discriminator-type FM detector.

The discriminator consists of two tubes, as shown, usually contained
in a single duo-diode envelope. The device detects, because of phase differences which occur in the resonant circuits, as the FM carrier deviates
above and below its normal frequency. Because operation is based on
phase changes, it is necessary to employ vector diagrams in explaining
circuit function.

For the discriminator shown in Fig. 18-26, three inductances are employed between the limiter tube V_1 and the discriminator tubes V_2 and V_3.
Inductance L_1 transfers signal energy to the tapped secondary inductance
because of the transformer arrangement. Inductance L_4, however, also
picks up a signal from inductance L_1, such a signal being applied between
the center tap of the secondary and the ouput network of the discriminator.
Instead of the inductance L_4, the necessary additional coupling between L_1
and the center of the secondary can be achieved by use of a coupling
capacitor.

Note that the plates of V_2 and V_3 are connected across the resonant
circuit composed of L_2, L_3 and C_3, and that the cathodes of V_2 and V_3 are
connected to the output circuit. Current flow through V_2 is from cathode
to plate, and hence through R_2 in the direction shown by the arrow. Current flow through V_3 causes a polarity as shown to be established across R_3.

For an understanding of how the discriminator detects FM, an evaluation must first be made of the signal voltage and current relationships which

exist between the limiter and discriminator. Such relationships are shown in Fig. 18-27(A). Here, E_p refers to the signal voltage of the primary. Because L_1 is an inductance, the primary current (I_p) lags the primary voltage, as shown in (A). When the primary current goes through its

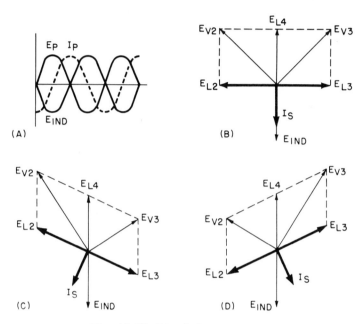

Fig. 18-27. Discriminator vectors.

greatest change (positive peak to negative peak), the lines of force which are produced will induce a voltage across the secondary. As shown in (A), the induced voltage (E_{ind}) lags the primary current by 90 degrees. Hence, there is a phase difference of 180 degrees between the *primary voltage* and the *induced voltage*. Inductance L_4 is also coupled to L_1, and picks up an induced voltage. The leads from L_4, however, are transposed so that the voltage obtained from L_4 is in phase with the voltage across L_1. Thus, the voltage across L_4 is also 180 degrees out of phase with the induced voltage.

In Fig. 18-27(B) a vector diagram is shown for the various voltages of the circuit. Note that the voltage of L_4 (E_{L_4}) is shown with a vertical arrow pointing upward to indicate an out-of-phase condition with respect to the induced voltage (E_{ind}), which is shown with the vertical arrow pointing downward.

The voltage induced across the secondary causes current to flow, such current being in phase with the voltage, because of the resonant circuit formed by L_2, L_3 and C_3. At resonance, the circuit is purely resistive, hence the secondary current (I_s) is in phase with the induced voltage. Thus, the secondary current is also shown by a vertical arrow pointing downward. The secondary current is represented by a heavy arrow, to distinguish it from the induced voltage.

Because the secondary is center tapped, it actually consists of two coils, L_2 and L_3. Thus, the voltage appearing across the secondary actually consists of two voltages, one applied between V_2 and the center tap of the secondary, and the other between V_3 and the center tap. As an individual inductance, the voltage across L_2 will be out of phase with the secondary current by 90 degrees. Also, the voltage across L_3 will be out of phase with the secondary current by 90 degrees. The voltage relationships for L_2 and L_3 are also shown in Fig. 18-27(B), and are represented by the heavy solid horizontal arrows. Signal voltages which appear across the secondary will cause V_2 to conduct at one time, and V_3 at another. Even though the tubes conduct alternately, for simplicity both voltages are represented simultaneously in the vector diagram. The voltage for V_2 is obtained from L_2 and the center tap (the voltage obtained from L_4). Because, however, there is a 90-degree phase difference between the voltage of L_4 and the voltage of L_2, a vector representation of the voltage for V_2 must be drawn with the slanting arrow shown in (B). A similar slanting arrow is shown at the right of the same drawing for the voltage across V_3. This composes the vector shown in (B) and represents the phases of the voltages, when the carrier is at its center frequency. As can be seen from the drawing in (B), the voltage for each diode is identical and, hence, the voltage drops across R_2 and R_3 are also identical. Thus, the output voltage is zero, because the voltage across R_2 is equal and opposite to the voltage across R_3.

When the carrier deviates from its center frequency during FM, the carrier no longer finds a resonant condition in the tuned circuits between the limiter and discriminator, because such tuned circuits are set at the center carrier frequency. If the carrier shift is to a higher frequency, the resonant circuit composed of the secondary inductance and C_3 will become primarily inductive. This comes about because energy is induced from L_1 into the secondary inductance, by virtue of the magnetic lines of force, and not into the capacitor and inductance combination initially. Hence, the voltage is induced as though into a series resonant circuit. At resonance, the series circuit has a low impedance and the inductive and capacitive reactances are equal, though opposite in phase. When the frequency rises above resonance, inductive reactance increases and capacitive reactance decreases. Hence, the rise in inductive reactance offers the greatest opposition and causes the circuit to become primarily inductive. This causes secondary current to lag, as shown in Fig. 18-27(C). The voltages across the secondary inductances L_2 and L_3 are still 90 degrees out of phase with the secondary current, because of the inductive characteristics of L_2 and L_3. Thus, the vector arrows for E_{L_2} and E_{L_3} must also be shown at an angle, to maintain their right-angle relationship with I_s. The parallelograms for the voltage of V_2 and the voltage of V_3 now show a rise of voltage for V_2 and a decline of voltage for V_3. If the voltage across R_3 declines and the voltage across R_2 increases, a positive alternation of the audio signal will be created at the output of the discriminator, as shown in Fig. 18-26. When the carrier shifts back to its normal frequency, the secondary current goes back in phase with the induced voltage, as in (B), and the output alternation drops to zero. When the carrier shifts to a lower frequency, secondary current leads, because the circuit becomes capacitive, and the vector shown in (D) prevails. Now, V_3 voltage increases and V_2 voltage decreases. Hence, R_3 voltage rises and R_2 voltage declines, producing a negative alternation at the output.

RATIO FM DETECTOR

Another type of FM detector is that known as the *ratio detector,* and a typical circuit is shown in Fig. 18-28. The advantage of the ratio detector over the discriminator is that the ratio detector needs no limiter to precede it, because this type of detector will not demodulate AM. The ratio detector uses two diodes in one envelope, as with the discriminator. Note, however, that the secondary transformer composed of L_2 and L_3 is coupled to a cathode and plate, respectively, as shown in Fig. 18-28. Consequently, current flow through the output resistors R_3 and R_4 is in series, as shown, so that the sum of the two voltages appears at the output, when no signal is being produced. This d-c voltage, however, can be blocked

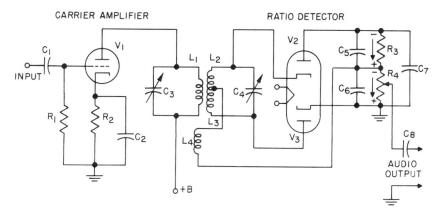

Fig. 18-28. Ratio FM detector.

by the coupling capacitor C_8 and, hence, is not applied to the grid of the following amplifier stage.

The manner in which one tube conducts more than the other to produce audio is similar to the discriminator type of detector, and the vector diagrams of Fig. 18-27 also apply to the ratio detector.

During frequency modulation of the incoming carrier, one tube will conduct more than the other, and vice versa, as with the discriminator. Assume that, initially, 2 volts appears across R_3 and 2 volts across R_4 producing a total d-c voltage of 4. If V_2 conducts more than V_3, the voltage across R_3 may rise to 3 volts and the voltage across R_4 may drop to 1 volt. Now, 4 volts d-c still appears across the combination of resistors, and no voltage *change* has occurred. When the carrier swings in the other direction and V_3 conducts more than V_2, the voltage across R_4 may rise to 3 volts and the voltage across R_3 may drop to 1 volt. Again, no change occurs, because 4 volts still exists across the combination of R_3 and R_4. While the *ratio* of voltages may change, the total voltage does not and, hence, the audio must be derived from one of the two output resistors. Since R_4 is connected to ground, it is more convenient to use the latter as the output resistor. By using a potentiometer for R_4, a volume control is formed. As the carrier deviates, the changing voltage across R_4 will produce the audio signal.

Capacitor C_7 across R_3 and R_4 is a large value, usually several microfarads. This capacitor charges to the value of the d-c voltage across the combination resistors R_3 and R_4. Because a capacitor opposes a change of voltage, C_7 maintains the voltage which appears across R_3 and R_4 at a fairly constant level. In consequence, any sudden changes in the total voltage which might occur because of sharp static bursts are minimized by the action of C_7.

Because C_7 is instrumental in suppressing static and other forms of amplitude modulation, it has an important circuit function. The ratio detector has been extensively used, though often the discriminator type of detector is preferred, because of its greater immunity to high noise interference. As with the discriminator, a balanced circuit arrangement gives best performance. A well balanced circuit means a matched pair of diodes, as well as matched resistors and matched capacitors in the output circuit.

GATED-BEAM FM DETECTOR

Another often used FM detector is that known as the *gated-beam detector*. This system of FM detection was designed by Dr. Robert Adler, of the Zenith Radio Corporation. This is a single-tube detector with a much higher sensitivity and output than the previous types discussed. Consequently, only a single amplifier stage need precede the beam detector, as compared with two amplifier stages usually required for other types. Also, because the audio output is higher, the usual audio-voltage amplifier and audio-power amplifier stages which follow a detector can be reduced to a single audio power-output stage. A typical gated-beam FM detector system is shown in Fig. 18-29, and a special tube is employed. The accelerator

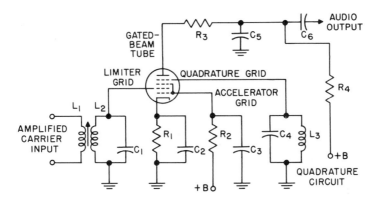

Fig. 18-29. Gated-beam FM detectors.

grid structures of the tube are in reality in the form of plates, which help shape the electrons into a narrow beam. The positive voltage of the accelerator grid structure increases the electron beam velocity and forces the beam through a narrow slot in the accelerator electrode. The electron beam then encounters the limiter grid, which, in conjunction with the quadrature grid, acts to control the electron flow. As with other tubes, the anode is made positive to attract the electrons emitted by the cathode.

The limiter grid has sufficient control over the electron beam to produce cutoff for *any* negative voltage. If the limiter grid has zero voltage or a positive voltage applied to it, however, it will permit current flow within the tube. The quadrature grid, being slightly negative, will also cause plate-current cutoff. Thus, both grids are influential in preventing or permitting current flow within the tube.

With a small value of fixed bias, such as 1 volt, an incoming signal has sufficient amplitude to cause the tube to be operated at saturation for the positive peaks of the grid signal, or at cutoff for the negative peaks of the incoming signal. Because the grid structure releases current flow rather suddenly, and also stops current flow quickly, a square wave of beam current occurs within the tube, in the region beyond the input grid. Thus, the tube acts as a self-limiting device, and will eliminate AM variations in the incoming signal. As shown in Fig. 18-29, a parallel resonant circuit is connected to the quadrature grid. The quadrature resonant circuit is tuned to the center carrier frequency of the incoming FM signal. During signal input, the cloud of electrons (space charge) around the cathode varies, and the quadrature grid is also affected by the electron beam, because of space-charge coupling. Hence, the square-wave type of signal generated within the tube is also present at the quadrature grid, and will pulse the quadrature circuit into a resonant flywheel condition. The signal voltage which appears across the quadrature circuit, however, lags the input signal by approximately 90 degrees. The phase lag occurs because of the nature of the space-charge coupling. With a 90-degree lag between the signal at the quadrature grid and that at the limiter grid, the plate current of the tube is cut off for a greater period of time than would otherwise be the case. This can be seen from an inspection of Fig. 18-30, which shows that

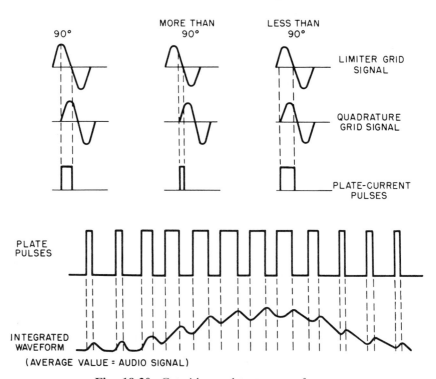

Fig. 18-30. Gated-beam detector waveforms.

the plate current can only flow when neither the limiter grid nor the quadrature grid is negative. Thus, only about one-half of each square-wave alternation reaches the anode during the time the carrier is at center frequency.

When the incoming FM carrier shifts to a higher frequency, the quadrature circuit will be off resonance with respect to the shifted carrier frequency. The quadrature circuit becomes predominantly capacitive, because the higher frequency impressed on it increases inductive reactance and decreases capacitive reactance. Since the capacitive reactance is low, the current through the capacitive reactance is higher than that in the inductive reactance. Because a parallel resonant circuit, with the resonant frequency impressed on it, exhibits a high impedance, the reduction of such impedance through decreased capacitive reactance causes the circuit to be predominantly capacitive. The capacitive characteristics of the quadrature circuit will now cause the signal voltage at the quadrature grid to lag the signal at the limiter grid by more than 90 degrees, which is the lag at center carrier frequency. Because of the increased phase difference between the two current-controlling voltages, *less* than one-half of each square-wave alternation arrives at the anode of the tube. Hence, the *average value* of plate current decreases. When the carrier signal at the limiter grid shifts lower in frequency, the quadrature circuit becomes predominantly inductive, and the voltage tends to lead. As shown in Fig. 18-30, more than one-half of each square-wave alternation reaches the anode and, thus, the average value of plate current increases.

Capacitor C_5 and resistor R_3 in the anode circuit form an integration circuit of the type described previously. An integration circuit has the ability to produce an average value from a series of pulses having various widths.

Resistor R_4 is the conventional load resistor across which the audio signal voltages develop. Capacitor C_5 has a low shunt reactance for the high carrier frequency, and thus eliminates the latter from the output circuit.

AUTOMATIC VOLUME CONTROL (AVC)

Automatic volume control consists in changing the bias on the R-F stages preceding the detector, so as to alter the transconductance of the tubes and, thus, the amplification. The purpose for automatic volume control is to increase the gain of the R-F amplifier stages for weak signals, and to decrease the gain for strong signals. By automatically altering the gain to suit signal reception conditions, the output from the detector will be maintained at a fairly constant level. Thus, if the radio listener sets the volume control to the level desired, the radio receiver will not blast loudly for a local station, when tuning over the broadcast band. Aso, avc will automatically increase the gain for weak stations.

Automatic volume control can be achieved by attaching a lead to the simple diode detector, so as to provide a negative voltage for application to the grid of the previous R-F amplifier stages. Figure 18-31 shows the basic method for obtaining an avc voltage. Since the cathode of the tube conducts electrons through the anode, then through L_2 and to the resistor, the current flow is in the direction indicated by the arrow beside the resistor. Such current flow will develop across R_1 a voltage drop having a polarity as shown (negative toward the L_2 side and positive toward the cathode side). The carrier will establish an average value of voltage across this resistor, though this voltage will vary because of the audio components caused by AM. As previously mentioned, this audio signal component can be taken from the resistor by a movable potentiometer arm in the form of a volume control. The signal is then transferred, via the series coupling capacitor C_4, to the next stage (the voltage amplifier stage).

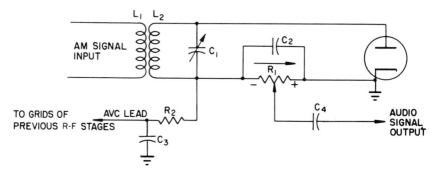

Fig. 18-31. Typical diode detector and AVC.

When a lead is attached to the _negative_ side of the resistor, a voltage is obtained which represents the average value produced by the demodulation process. The _average_ value of the carrier represents a specific negative voltage at this point. In order to eliminate the audio frequency components which cause the average d-c value to fluctuate, a filter resistor, R_2, and a shunt capacitor, C_3, are employed. A voltage drop for the audio signal occurs across resistance R_2, and this audio signal is shunted by the capacitor C_3. Capacitor C_3 has a large value, to provide a low reactance for the audio voltages. The filter capacitor C_3 cannot be connected directly to the negative terminal of R_1 because, in that position, the capacitor would shunt the audio signal components and, thus, would prevent the transfer of these components to the audio amplifier stage following the detector. Therefore, R_2 is needed as an isolating resistor.

The voltage beyond R_2 and C_3 is a relatively steady d-c, which represents the average value of the received carrier. When a strong station is tuned in, the increase in carrier amplitude will develop a larger voltage drop across R_1, and hence a greater negative bias is applied to the grids of the R-F amplifier stages preceding the detector. The increase in bias will reduce the gain in such stages, and hence reduce the loud audio signals which would be developed. For a weak audio signal, less voltage is developed across R_1, and hence a lower negative-bias value is applied to the grids of the R-F stages. The decrease in bias causes an increase in amplification, and hence the signal arriving at the detector will increase. Thus, the avc system regulates, within limits, variations in carrier signal strength which arrive at the receiver. Automatic volume control does not affect the setting of a volume control, however, and the listener can still regulate the volume to suit his taste. Once he establishes the volume desired, the automatic gain control will maintain this volume at a sub-stantially constant level, regardless of whether a strong or a weak station is tuned in. It is only for an extremely strong station within a few miles of the receiver, or an extremely weak station, that the avc characteristics of a circuit become less effective. The automatic volume control can actually be considered as an automatic *gain* control. The term avc is utilized for radio receivers, however, to differentiate between it and a similar system employed in television receivers; in the latter instance, the system is called an *automatic gain control system,* agc, because the gain of the picture signal is regulated.

For avc function, a variable mu (remote cutoff) tube of the type described in Chapter 11 must be used. In such a tube, the gain decreases as the bias is increased. This can be seen from an inspection of the illustration shown in Fig. 11-18(B) shown previously. With a high-bias setting, the average current flow through the tube is low, and a signal variation around the bias line causes only a small change in plate current as compared to the plate-current change which would occur for a lower-bias setting.

DELAYED AVC

The avc system previously discussed will automatically increase the volume level for weak signals, and decrease the volume level for strong signals. There are occasions, however, when it is desirable to omit avc bias during reception of weak stations to increase the volume to acceptable levels. It is true that, for weak stations, very little avc bias is developed, but even a small amount of bias will decrease the gain of the R-F amplifier stages. For extremely weak signals, this is undesirable, since it will reduce the sensitivity of the receiver for such stations. Hence a refinement of the basic avc circuit is sometimes utilized. This consists of a circuit which *delays* the amount of avc bias generated until the signal strength from the station has reached a level where it is necessary to reduce its volume by avc.

A basic delayed avc circuit is shown in Fig. 18-32. This type of circuit does not develop any avc bias for the weak stations, but will develop such a bias for the stronger stations to be received. Basically, the system contains two detector circuits, one for the demodulation of the AM signal, and the other for avc purposes. For this reason, a *dual-diode* is necessary. As shown in Fig. 18-32, the basic detector circuit is still

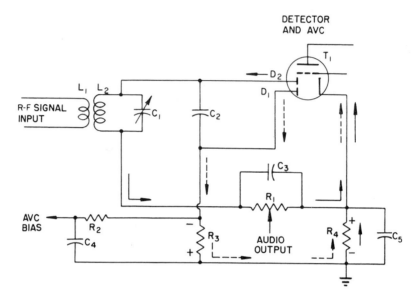

Fig. 18-32. Delayed AVC.

employed. The upper diode is attached to the secondary of the input transformer, L_2, and the path of conduction for this tube is shown by the solid arrows. Resistor R_1 is the conventional volume control, as described for the previous diode detector systems.

For delayed avc purposes, it is necessary to establish a fixed potential on the lower avc diode, so as to prevent this tube from conducting until a predetermined level of input signal is available. The manner in which this is done, in actual practice, is to employ a tube which contains a dual-diode plus a triode in one envelope. The triode tube can then be used to develop the necessary fixed potential previously mentioned, and also acts as the first audio-voltage amplifier circuit. This is shown in Fig. 18-32, where the triode section is marked T_1. For simplicity, the complete circuit is not shown for the triode, but will be discussed after the initial delayed avc action has been described.

The lower diode, D_1, derives the signal energy from the upper diode, D_2, via the coupling capacitor C_2, which bridges both diode anodes. The path for the signal current is as shown by the dotted arrows and, in consequence, the current flows through resistor R_3, resistor R_4, through the cathode, and thence to diode 1. The plate current for the triode section, however, also flows through the cathode circuit. Since the negative potential of the power supply is attached to the ground circuit, the electron flow will be up through resistor R_4, and thence from the cathode to the anode of the triode (T_1). Such plate-current flow for the triode establishes a voltage drop across resistor R_4, with a polarity as indicated. This is similar to the bias arrangement for conventional triode tubes, since the voltage drop across R_4 will make the cathode more positive with respect to the grid. Because the lower avc diode (D_1) is also connected to this resistor, the lower diode anode will be negative with respect to the common cathode. Assume that the voltage drop across the resistor R_4 is 2 volts. This would make the *cathode* of *diode 1* positive by 2 volts with respect to the *anode* of *diode 1*. Hence, the anode of diode 1 will be *negative* with respect to the cathode by 2 volts. Under this condition, diode 1 is unable to conduct, as long as its anode is negative. Thus, any weak signal input which is unable to develop 2 volts will be unable to cause diode 1 to conduct. When a strong signal is tuned in, however, the positive peaks of the carrier signal will overcome the 2 volts of negative potential on the anode of D_1 and will permit the tube to conduct. The tube conduction is in the direction shown by the dotted arrows and, in consequence, a voltage drop appears across R_3, with a polarity as indicated. This voltage drop consists of the avc bias voltage. The latter is filtered by resistor R_2 and capacitor C_4, and is then applied to the previous R-F amplifier stages.

The capacitor C_5 across resistor R_4 is for the purpose of filtering out audio-frequency components from across the cathode resistor. Such filtering is necessary, so that the bias established across R_4 will remain constant and will not vary with signal modulation or audio.

Since the detector diode, D_2, is not connected to the lower section of resistor R_4, no negative potential is applied to the anode of the detector diode. Hence, diode function is not disturbed for the weak signals. If resistor R_1 terminated at the bottom of R_4, instead of at the cathode, it would place a negative bias on the anode of D_2 and, hence, the circuit would not detect weak signals. By placing resistor R_1 at the cathode, however, the negative voltage at the bottom of R_4 is not applied to the anode of D_2. Actually, when no signal input is present, the potential at D_2 is equal to the cathode potential.

The diode characteristics for the delayed avc tube are shown in Fig. 18-33. Here, it is assumed that a bias of 2 volts has been established across the cathode resistor, which makes diode 1 negative by 2 volts with respect to the cathode. As can be seen from this drawing, a weak signal is insufficient to overcome this bias and, hence, the tube cannot conduct. When a strong signal is tuned in, however, it overcomes the 2-

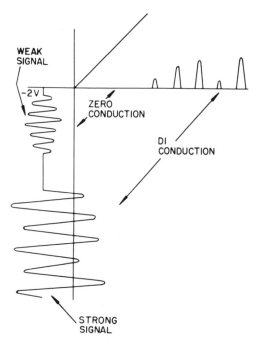

Fig. 18-33. Delayed AVC diode characteristics.

volt negative potential, and hence diode D_1 conducts. The conduction is in the form of variations in amplitude, since the input signal is amplitude modulated. In reality, D_1 will also detect the signal in the same fashion that the demodulator diode D_2 will detect the signal. The audio component which would normally appear across R_3 of Fig. 18-32, however, is filtered by the avc filter network (R_2 and C_4) and, hence, a relatively ripple-free bias is applied to the R-F stages.

A complete commercial AM detector, and an avc and combined first audio amplifier circuits, are shown in Fig. 18-34. This schematic shows the complete detector and delayed avc circuit, as well as the additional filter resistors usually employed in such a circuit. Here, the R-F carrier signal input is transferred across the transformer, consisting of L_1 and L_2, and then appears at the upper diode plate D_2. As described for the basic delayed avc circuit, the signal energy is then transferred to the diode D_1. The latter is held in a nonconducting state by the d-c potential drop across R_4. Since R_4 is also the cathode resistor for the triode circuit, the power-supply current flowing through it sets up a voltage drop across the cathode resistor. The avc diode resistor R_3 is connected to ground, which is the same as attaching it to the bottom of the grounded R_4 resistor. Hence, diode D_1 is negative with respect to the cathode in proportion to the potential drop which develops across R_4. The filtered avc bias is obtained from the output of resistor R_2 and capacitor C_4. The latter capacitor is larger in value than the other capacitors of the circuit, because C_4 must filter the audio components from the signal, while capacitors C_2, C_3, and C_6 handle only R-F signal energy. Hence, the latter three capacitors are usually much smaller in value than the others, and are often around 0.0001 microfarad.

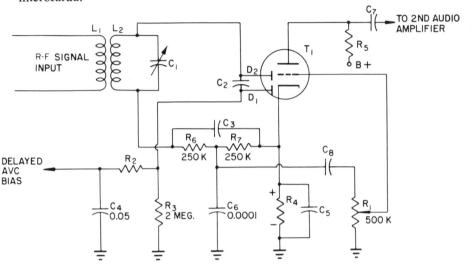

Fig. 18-34. Typical combination of delayed AVC, AM detector, and audio amplifier.

The detector diode (D_2) employs two load resistors, R_6 and R_7. These two resistors have a common capacitor across them, C_3, which bypasses the R-F signal components, and also acts as a filter capacitor for deriving the audio-frequency signal energy. By employing two such resistors, better filtering action is secured, and there is greater isolation between the output audio circuit and the actual avc circuit. The audio signal energy is derived from the junction of resistors R_6 and R_7. Capacitor C_6 is an additional R-F filter capacitor, but does not shunt any appreciable audio signal energy components. A coupling capacitor, C_8, is employed to isolate the volume-control network from the average d-c value which is established by the rectification process of the input signal handled by diode detector D_2. Thus, no additional d-c voltage is applied to the grid of the triode T_1, and the Class A amplifier characteristics of this tube are not disturbed. Resistor R_1 is the volume control for regulating the amount of signal energy applied to the control grid of the triode section T_1. The amplified audio signal energy, which develops in the anode of the triode-tube section, appears across the triode load resistor R_5 and is then coupled by capacitor C_7 to the grid of the second audio-amplifier stage. In small receivers, the second audio-amplifier stage is also usually the output audio-power amplifier circuit which feeds the loudspeaker.

Even when no *delayed* avc circuit is employed, the dual-diode-triode tube is usually utilized in AM receivers, as a combined detector and avc tube. When no delayed avc is incorporated, the diode plates D_1 and D_2 are connected together.

Typical tubes for the circuit shown in Fig. 18-34 are the 6SQ7-GT, which is a standard-size octal base tube, or the 6BS6 miniature type. Several other dual-diode-triode tubes are also available and, for additional information on the characteristics of such tubes, reference should be made to a tube manual. A germanium or silicon crystal diode can also be employed instead of the vacuum tube previously described. Except for replacement of the vacuum tube by the diode crystals, circuit function is the same. With crystal diodes, however, delayed avc is not practical, since a d-c voltage source would have to be obtained from a battery or from a tap on a power supply. Hence, when delayed avc is employed, the combined dual-diode-triode vacuum tube is utilized.

REVIEW QUESTIONS

1. (a) Briefly explain what is meant by a *carrier*.
(b) What is meant by amplitude modulation? Explain briefly.

2. Explain why an AM carrier should not be modulated more than 100%.

3. (a) If a 1,000-kilocycle AM carrier is modulated by a 3,000-cycle audio tone, what sideband frequencies will be produced?
(b) If the volume of the audio in the foregoing example is increased, what changes occur in the AM carrier?

4. For a given percentage of plate modulation, what must the relationships be between the input power to the class C amplifier and the output power of the modulator?

5. (a) In which type of modulation is the sideband power supplied by the modulator?
(b) In which type of modulation is the sideband power furnished by the Class C amplifier?

6. What are the advantages and disadvantages of plate modulation versus grid modulation?

7. Briefly explain how frequency modulation of a carrier differs from amplitude modulation.

8. List several advantages of FM over AM.

9. In FM, an audio signal causes the carrier to deviate 10 kilocycles on each side of its center frequency. Would a change of audio frequency or a change of audio volume cause the carrier to deviate to a greater extent?

10. (a) If a carrier shifts back and forth 1,000 times per second, what type of audio signal would cause the signal to shift back and forth at twice the former rate?
(b) What would cause the carrier in the foregoing example to shift back and forth at half its original rate?

11. Briefly explain what is meant by a reactance circuit, and give a typical example of its application to FM.

12. Reproduce a simple diode detector, and explain its operation with respect to AM.

13. Briefly explain the difference between regenerative detection and heterodyne detection.

14. Briefly explain why a limiter must precede the discriminator type of FM detector.

15. What circuit differences are present in the ratio detector and the discriminator detector which will help identify the detector type?

16. Briefly explain why the ratio detector does not need a limiter preceding it.

17. Briefly explain why a quadrature circuit is necessary in a gated-beam FM detector.

18. Briefly explain the difference between conventional avc and delayed avc.

19. Briefly explain the advantages of avc.

PRACTICAL PROBLEMS

1. In testing a transmitting system, an AM carrier of 1 mc was modulated by a 500-cps signal and a 2,600-cps signal. What sidebands were produced?

2. What is the required bandpass for the modulated carrier in Problem 1?

3. In an experimental FM system, the carrier deviated 30 kilocycles and the highest audio signal had a frequency of 15 kilocyles. What is the modulation index?

4. How many significant sidebands were produced for the system in Problem 3?

5. A reactance circuit for an FM system operated on 90 megacycles, and was similar to that shown in Fig. 18-12. If the tube had a g_m of 5,000 micromhos, what inductance value was developed?

6. In a laboratory experiment a 1,000-kilocycle signal was heterodyned with a 900-kilocycle signal. What additional signal frequencies were developed by the process?

7. For *CW* reception, what signal frequency must be heterodyned with a *CW* signal of 40 megacycle to produce an audio signal of 400 cps?

8. An oscillator producing a signal of 20,230 kilocycle developed an audio tone of 1 kilocycle when heterodyned against a *CW* signal higher in frequency than the oscillator. What is the *CW* signal frequency?

Part 3

Applications
and
Components

19

RECEIVER
PRINCIPLES

INTRODUCTION

In order to acquire a broad background of electronics, a knowledge of the basic principles underlying receivers is essential. This is particularly the case where ultimate activities involve receiver design, modification, or proper utilization of specific types for the services intended. Hence, this chapter is devoted to a discussion of the superheterodyne receiver circuit which is found not only in home radio and television receivers, but in radar receivers, commercial short-wave receivers, and others as well. Block diagrams are included to indicate circuit sequences and one receiver type is discussed in detail as an exercise in circuit analysis and to indicate circuit coupling methods. Some high-fidelity factors are included since they cover some design aspects with which the reader may become involved, and because the fundamental principles also find application in other branches of electronics.

RECEPTION FACTORS

Virtually all types of receivers, when in operation, have a number of signals of various frequencies intercepted by the antenna system and applied to the input circuit. In order to select the desired signal from among all present in the area, it is necessary for the receiver to be tuned to resonance for the modulated carrier signal of the station which is to be received. The carrier signal which is then accepted by the input system of the receiver is amplified, by R-F amplifier stages, to the amount required for application to the detector tube. The latter then demodulates the carrier signals and produces the audio signal, or the video (picture) signal in a television receiver. The demodulated signal is then amplified by an additional amount, before application to the loudspeaker or to a picture tube.

From the foregoing, it is evident that the simplest method for achieving this result is to have several R-F amplifier stages, each of which includes a variable capacitor for tuning the resonant circuits, so that the desired station may be selected. In the early days of radio, such a system was actually employed, and the sequence of circuits in this system is shown in the block diagram of Fig. 19-1. Here, the antenna system picked up the desired signals and applied them to the input of the first R-F amplifier. This vacuum-tube R-F amplifier circuit employed a variable capacitor (designated as C_1 in Fig. 19-1) and an inductance, L_1. Capacitor C_1 was

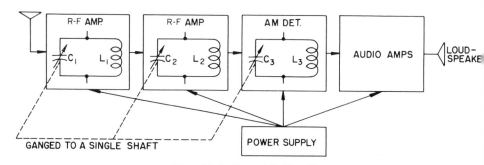

Fig. 19-1. Tuned R-F radio

variable and, when this variable capacitor was closed (meshed), the maximum capacity thus represented tuned the receiver to the lowest station in the AM broadcast band. As the variable capacitor was progressively opened, it tuned to higher stations in the AM broadcast band. When the capacitor was fully opened (representing a minimum of capacity), it tuned to the highest-frequency station in the band.

The second R-F amplifier stage and the detector stage also had a variable capacitor arrangement for tuning. The three variable capacitors of the R-F and detector stages were ganged together, as indicated by the dashed interconnecting lines shown in Fig. 19-1. A single shaft was employed and, when this shaft was turned, it rotated all the capacitors simultaneously.

Such a radio receiver was termed a *tuned* R-F receiver (TRF). This receiver, however, presented some serious drawbacks. Since it was necessary to change the value of the variable capacitors for tuning to the desired stations, there was a considerable variation of Q between the closed and open positions of the variable capacitor. Thus, both the sensitivity and the selectivity of the receiver varied, as it was tuned over the broadcast band range. On occasion, fixed capacitors were employed and the inductance was varied by employing a movable core slug. Each inductance, L_1, L_2, and L_3, had such a variable core, and all three cores were connected to a common shaft, so that they could be moved simultaneously for tuning purposes. Core tuning, however, also suffered the disadvantages of changing circuit Q. For a desired degree of selectivity, the capacitor and inductance of a tuned resonant circuit must be proportioned so that the ratio of coil resistance and reactance produces the desired Q and, hence, the degree of bandpass characteristics desired. In the tuned R-F receiver, it was virtually impossible to maintain a constant Q, since it is necessary to vary either the capacity or the inductance for tuning purposes.

The unfavorable characteristics of the tuned R-F receiver system were overcome by the invention of the superheterodyne receiver by Major Edwin H. Armstrong. In consequence, the superheterodyne receiver principle has superseded the older tuned R-F type of receiver and, now, all modern radio, FM, and television receivers utilize the superheterodyne circuit.

SUPERHETERODYNE PRINCIPLES

A block diagram of a superheterodyne AM receiver is shown in Fig. 19-2. Here, an R-F amplifier precedes a mixer circuit. The R-F amplifier stage uses a parallel resonant circuit with a variable capacitor, in a fashion

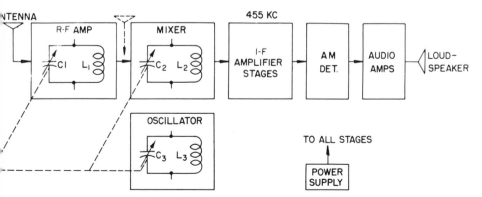

Fig. 19-2. Ganged capacitors in superheterodyne radio.

similar to that employed for the TRF receiver. A similar variable capacitor is included in the mixer stage, and also in the oscillator stage. These capacitors are ganged together, as shown by the dashed interconnecting lines. Rotation of the common shaft permits tuning over the entire broadcast band. The R-F amplifier increases the signal amplitude of the modulated carrier and applies it to a mixer tube. At the same time, an oscillator (termed a *local oscillator*) generates a frequency which is also injected into the mixer tube. The local oscillator differs from the carrier frequency by 455 kilocycles. Thus, if a 1,000-kilocycle station is tuned in, the 1,000-kilocycle carrier will be applied to the mixer tube. The oscillator is tuned to 1,455 kilocycles, and the difference between the carrier and the oscillator signal is 455 kilocycles. The mixer tube is operated so that it has pronounced nonlinear characteristics and, hence, it will heterodyne the carrier and oscillator signals. (A discussion of the basic heterodyning principle is given in the preceding chapter.)

The ouptut from the mixer stage, because of the heterodyning process, consists of the original carrier, the oscillator frequency, the sum frequency, and the difference frequency. All these are still R-F signals, and the R-F amplifier which follows the mixer stage is tuned to resonance for only one of these frequencies, the *difference* frequency. Thus, this R-F amplifier stage is tuned to 455 kilocycles and the selectivity of the tuned resonant circuit rejects the other frequencies. This R-F amplifier stage is designated as the *intermediate-frequency* amplifier stage, to distinguish it from the first R-F amplifier stage, which handles the carrier signals. The intermediate-frequency (i-f) amplifier stage builds up this difference frequency and applies it either to an AM detector, or to one or two additional i-f amplifier stages. The AM detector then demodulates this i-f carrier signal and derives from it the audio signals. The latter are then applied to conventional audio-amplifier stages, and then impressed on the loudspeaker for sound reproduction.

Initially, it may seem that this receiver has no advantages over the tuned R-F receiver, since three variable capacitors are still employed, which affect the selectivity. Actually, however, the required degree of selectivity is established in the i-f amplifier stages, since these i-f stages are not retuned when various stations are selected. The i-f amplifier stages of the receiver shown in Fig. 19-2 are always tuned to 455 kilocycles, and the handling of only this specific frequency permits selecting the proper reactance-resistance ratio for the desired bandpass characteristics.

The reason why the mixer will always produce a 455-kilocycle signal, regardless of the station to which the receiver is tuned, is that the oscillator always maintains a *difference* frequency between it and the R-F amplifier stage. One method for achieving this result is to make the variable capacitor C_3 smaller than capacitors C_1 and C_2. By making C_3

smaller, it will tune to a higher frequency. If the capacity of C_3 is designed to tune the oscillator to a frequency higher than the carrier frequency by 455 kilocycles, it will always maintain this difference frequency because, when C_1 and C_2 are varied, C_3 will vary proportionately. Thus, if a station having a frequency of 700 kilocycles is tuned in by C_1 and C_2, capacitor C_3 will cause the oscillator to generate a frequency of 1,155 kilocycles. This frequency is higher than the 700-kilocycle station by 455 kilocycles, and thus the output from the mixer is again 455 kilocycles. The oscillator could also be designed to be lower in frequency than the R-F amplifier by an amount equal to the difference frequency. Thus, if a 1,000-kilocycle station is tuned in, the oscillator could have a frequency of 545 kilocycles, and the difference would again be 455 kilocycles. It is preferable, however, for the local oscillator to generate a frequency above the incoming R-F carrier. The reason for this preference is that, when the local oscillator is below the incoming station signal frequency, the range over which the oscillator must tune is considerably greater than would be the case if the local oscillator frequency were above the incoming signal frequency. If, for instance, the i-f frequency were 455 kilocycles, the local-oscillator range for the AM broadcast band would be as follows:

550 to 1,600 kilocycles = AM band range
95 to 1,145 kilocycles = local-oscillator range

In such an instance, the local oscillator must have a tuning range from 95 kilocycles to 1,145 kilocycles. Hence, the local oscillator must be capable of tuning from its lowest value to over 10 times the latter. When, however, the local oscillator is above the incoming frequency, its tuning range need only be approximately two times that of its lowest frequency, as shown below:

550 kc to 1,600 kc = AM band range
1,005 kc to 2,055 kc = local-oscillator range

The local oscillator can also be made to tune above the R-F and mixer resonant circuits, by employing a capacitor in series with C_3. This additional capacitor in series with capacitor C_3 will cause the total capacity of the circuit to be less, and hence the oscillator will tune to a higher frequency. This method is sometimes employed when the manufacturer prefers each ganged variable capacitor to be of the same physical size.

Many inexpensive table-model radios dispense with the R-F amplifier stage, and apply the antenna directly to the mixer circuit, as shown by the dotted antenna outline preceding the mixer in Fig. 19-2. Elimination of the R-F amplifier reduces the input selectivity, as well as the sensitivity, so that these receivers do not perform as well as those which have an

R-F stage preceding the mixer. In locations where the signal strength is high and the stations are not too crowded, satisfactory reception is secured.

The i-f frequency does not have to be 455 kilocycles, but can be any frequency between 400 kilocycles and 600 kilocycles. Early radio receivers used an i-f frequency much lower than modern receivers do, but the low i-f frequency caused interference, because of the susceptibility of the receiver to *image-frequency* response. The image-frequency interference is a signal which can enter the receiver and heterodyne with the local oscillator to produce the same i-f frequency which would be produced by the desired signal. As an example, if the frequency of the desired signal is 1,100 kilocycles and the local oscillator is 1,000 kilocycles, the heterodyning of the two would produce a difference frequency of 100 kilocycles. A station having a frequency of 900 kilocycles, however, would also produce a 100-kilocycle difference frequency. If it heterodynes with the local oscillator of 1,000 kilocycles in such an instance, the undesired 900-kilocycle station produces an image-frequency response in the receiver. The relationships in the foregoing example are as follows:

$$
\begin{array}{r}
1,100 \text{ kc (desired station)} \\
-1,000 \text{ kc (local oscillator)} \\
\hline
100 \text{ kc (difference frequency—i-f)}
\end{array}
$$

$$
\begin{array}{r}
1,000 \text{ kc (local oscillator)} \\
-900 \text{ kc (undesired station, image frequency)} \\
\hline
100 \text{ kc (difference frequency—i-f)}
\end{array}
$$

The use of a 455-kilocycle i-f in modern receivers has proved satisfactory from the standpoint of image rejection. Such an i-f frequency also provides a good signal amplitude output from the mixer of a receiver which also has provisions for short-wave reception, as well as broadcast band reception.

Most table model radios employ only one stage of i-f amplification, which is sufficient, since the Q of the resonant circuits is high and, hence, the gain is good. Frequency modulation and television receivers, on the other hand, must tune over a much wider bandpass. A wider bandpass is secured by reducing the circuit Q, and such a reduction of Q also reduces gain. Hence, receivers which employ wideband i-f amplifiers use several stages of such i-f amplification, in order to regain the required amplification which is diminished by virtue of the lower circuit Q.

An FM receiver would resemble the AM receiver shown in Fig. 19-2 in basic block diagram sequence; the only differences would be in the radio frequencies handled. Standard FM receivers operate between 88 megacycles and 108 megacycles and, hence, the R-F amplifier must be capable of tuning within this range, as contrasted to the 550-kilocycle to 1,600-kilocycle range usually found in radio receivers. In FM receivers, the i-f amplifier stages would be tuned to 10.7 megacycles, and one of the FM detectors previously discussed would be employed. In television receivers, the local-oscillator signal heterodynes with two incoming carrier signals (the audio and picture carriers), as more fully discussed later.

The functions of the mixer and oscillator are sometimes combined in a single tube, instead of being separated in distinct mixer and oscillator tubes. Such a combined mixer and oscillator is known as a pentagrid converter tube, as discussed in Chapter 12. This system is often employed in smaller radios. For FM and television receivers, however, a separate local-oscillator circuit is preferred, to minimize interaction and loading effects between the oscillator and mixer sections, and thus increase the efficiency of the circuits involved.

COMMERCIAL AM RECEIVER

A typical superheterodyne table-model receiver is shown in Fig. 19-3. This receiver does not have an R-F amplifier stage. A loop antenna is employed for picking up the signals broadcast by the AM stations. The loop antenna can consist of a flat rectangular coil section, as shown, or of a coil wound on a ferrite core. In either instance, the loop or the coil antenna is mounted inside the radio cabinet. The antenna is actually an inductance which is part of the input parallel resonant circuit. Thus, the loop antenna shown in Fig. 19-3 consists of an inductance L_1, which forms a parallel resonant circuit in conjunction with capacitor C_1. Capacitor C_1 is shunted by a small trimmer capacitor C_2. The variable capacitor C_1 is ganged to the oscillator capacitor C_4. The latter is also shunted by a trimmer capacitor C_5. The trimmer capacitors are for the purpose of correcting for slight *variations* in the *difference* frequency which may occur between the local-oscillator frequency and the station frequency, when tuning over the broadcast band. These trimmer capacitors are used for adjusting the *tracking* so that the oscillator resonant circuit will maintain the proper difference frequency with respect to the converter resonant circuit. The oscillator circuit is in the cathode and first grid sections of the converter tube. The oscillator coil L_6 provides the necessary feedback signal for sustaining oscillations.

The output of the converter is applied to the first intermediate-frequency transformer. The primary and secondary sections of this transformer are tuned to 455 kilocycles and fixed capacitors are employed, in conjunction with the inductances L_2 and L_3. The transformer is tuned to the exact resonant frequency by adjusting the variable-core slug rather than by adjusting the capacitors. The variable-core slug affects the permeability and, hence, the inductance of both the primary and secondary of

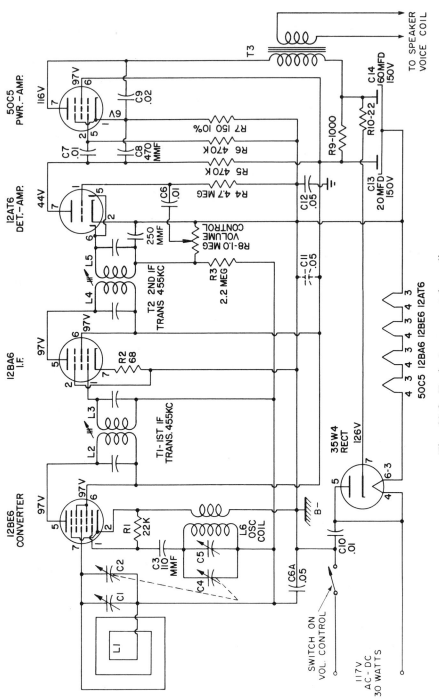

Fig. 19-3. Typical vacuum-tube radio.

the interstage i-f transformer. After the converter, the i-f signal is applied to the i-f amplifier tube. The amplified i-f signal appears in the anode circuit and is impressed across the primary of the second i-f transformer, which is also tuned to 455 kilocycles.

The signal output from the last i-f stage is impressed on the diode section of the 12AT6 combined detector and audio-amplifier tube. The audio signals are developed across the volume control resistor, R_8. The signals are then coupled to the triode grid of the 12AT6 tube via the decoupling capacitor C_6. The amplified audio signals develop across the load resistor R_5, and are coupled to the grid of the power-amplifier tube by capacitor C_7. The output of the power amplifier is applied to a conventional audio output transformer (T_3), and then to the loudspeaker.

Automatic volume control is incorporated in this receiver by picking off the average value of the rectified carrier signal from the volume control R_8, using the series resistor R_3, which resistor couples the avc bias to the grids of both the converter and i-f amplifier tubes. Resistor R_3 and capacitor C_{6A} form the necessary filter network which rids the avc bias voltage of the ripple component produced by the audio signal. Capacitor C_{6A} has a value of 0.05 microfarad, and thus provides a low shunt reactance for audio signals to the B− line. The application of avc voltage to the i-f stage will cause a variation of input capacitance to the tube, each time the avc alters the bias of the tube. It is undesirable to have the input capacity of a tube change, in amplifiers which use tuned resonant circuits, since the input capacity change will affect resonance. If the circuit resonance is altered, the amplifier will be detuned slightly from the station frequency and, hence, maximum amplification will not be secured. Detuning will also increase the noise level, since the signal strength decreases. Some of the signal information may also be lost. To minimize the variations of input capacity during avc bias changes, degeneration is introduced by omitting the usual bypass capacitor across R_2. As explained earlier, this is also a form of inverse feedback of the current type. The unbypassed R_2 will result in a reduction in the gain of the amplifier stage, but the advantage is that there will be a minimum of input capacitance change with a change of bias voltage established by the avc.

A half-wave power-supply circuit is employed, using a 35W4 diode rectifier tube. Since no transformer is used, the voltage is not stepped up, and the receiver will operate on either 117 volts a-c or 117 volts d-c. (Actually it will operate within a range of 110 to 120 volts.)

Since a half-wave power supply requires more filtering than a full-wave type, the first filter capacitor (C_{14}) consists of a 60-microfarad section and the second filter capacitor (C_{13}) consists of a 20-microfarad section. A series resistor, R_{10}, is employed to minimize the voltage surge which occurs when the set is first turned on. An additional resistor, R_9, is employed for filtering purposes, and also for reducing the voltage below that applied to the anode of the power audio amplifier tube.

In the absence of a step-down transformer, filament voltage is supplied to the tubes by placing all tube filaments in series, as shown. The 35W4 rectifier filament is in series with the other tubes. The line voltage can be impressed across the series filament circuit, because the individual voltage drops across the tube filaments add up to a sufficient amount to withstand the line voltage. The rectifier tube has a 35-volt filament, and the audio power-output tube has a 50-volt filment. Hence, the voltage drop across these two tubes is 85 volts. Approximately 36 volts are impressed across the filaments of the other three tubes. Thus, the series filaments of five tubes will have a voltage rating of 121 volts, which provides an adequate safety margin for any line voltage variations which may occur.

Because a half-wave rectifier in a transformerless power supply places the negative d-c return at ground, one side of the a-c line will also be placed at ground potential. If the ground return is then attached to the receiver chassis, the latter may be "hot" for one position of the a-c line plug in the wall receptacle. This comes about because one of the two wires of the line circuit is grounded on the cold waterpipe or grounding rod, and is designated as "cold" with respect to the other a-c line which is ungrounded. Thus, if the input a-c line places the hot side to the chassis, a severe shock can be encountered, if the chassis of the receiver is touched in conjunction with any waterpipe or grounded radiator in the home. This shock hazard can be eliminated by reversing the a-c plug, so that the chassis is placed at the *cold* or *ground side* of the incoming a-c line. To minimize the danger of shock if the plug is in the wrong position, most manufacturers isolate the chassis (B−) from the a-c input line by a capacitor such as C_{12} in Fig. 19-3. This method is sometimes referred to as a *floating ground* or *common return*. As shown in Fig. 19-3, the common a-c return employs a different symbol than the chassis ground. Thus, in the receiver shown, the capacitor C_{10} couples the negative return of the rectifier to a wired section which is not common to the chassis proper. When connections are made to the chassis proper, the chassis symbol is employed, as shown for the ground connection to C_{12}.

The complete radio receiver shown in Fig. 19-3 can also be adapted for short-wave reception by the inclusion of switch-in coils. Short-wave receivers are usually constructed with several coil and capacitor sections, which are switched in to select the desired short-wave bands. The smaller such coil capacitors are, the higher will be the frequency range over which the receiver will tune.

The superheterodyne receiver of Fig. 19-3 can also be one which utilizes transistors. The transistor circuits would be similar to the transistor circuits discussed elsewhere herein. With transistors, of course, the A and B batteries necessary for vacuum-tube operation would be replaced by a single battery. In other respects, the theory of circuit function remains the same.

TELEVISION RECEIVERS

In basic block diagram form, the modern black and white television receiver appears as shown in Fig. 19-4. All present-day television receivers, as with AM and FM receivers, utilize the superheterodyne principle discussed earlier in this chapter. Instead of handling only a single modulated carrier plus its sidebands, as in FM or AM receivers, the television receiver handles both the modulated picture carrier (AM) and the modulated sound carrier (FM). In addition to these two carriers, the receiver also utilizes the synchronization signals which are transmitted to keep the scanning beam of the picture tube in perfect synchronization with the scanning beam at the transmitter.

Just like an AM receiver, the television receiver has a tuner which incorporates an R-F stage, a mixer, and a local oscillator. The local-oscillator signal heterodynes with the two incoming carrier signals (picture and sound) to produce *two* i-f frequencies. These sound and picture i-f frequencies (plus the synchronization signals) are then amplified in several i-f stages, before application to the picture detector circuit.

After they leave the detector, the demodulated picture signals are amplified in the video amplifier and applied to the picture-tube grid circuit. The sound i-f signals are also derived from the video detector and amplified by a special sound i-f amplifier, before detection in the FM demodulator. After the latter stage, the audio is amplified and applied to the loudspeaker.

The picture signals, of varying intensity, affect the picture-tube grid and, hence, control the intensity of the electron beam within the cathode-ray picture tube. The beam, in turn, scans the picture-tube face (internally). The internal picture-tube face or screen is coated with phosphor. The phosphor when struck by the electron beam, will glow (fluoresce) to a degree depending on the beam intensity. The beam sweeps across and down the face of the picture tube, scanning one horizontal line after another to literally "paint" a picture on the screen of the tube.

Synchronization of the beam is accomplished by separating the synchronization signals from the video signal, through use of a sync separator, operated in clipper-circuit fashion similar to the clipper circuits discussed earlier. The signals from the separator circuit are then applied to a

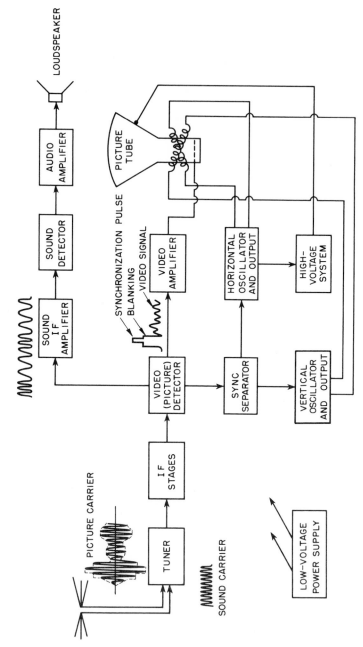

Fig. 19-4. Block diagram of typical television receiver.

LOUDSPEAKER

AUDIO AMPLIFIER

SOUND DETECTOR

SOUND IF AMPLIFIER

PICTURE TUBE

SYNCHRONIZATION PULSE

BLANKING

VIDEO SIGNAL

VIDEO AMPLIFIER

HORIZONTAL OSCILLATOR AND OUTPUT

HIGH-VOLTAGE SYSTEM

VIDEO (PICTURE) DETECTOR

SYNC SEPARATOR

VERTICAL OSCILLATOR AND OUTPUT

IF STAGES

PICTURE CARRIER

TUNER

SOUND CARRIER

LOW-VOLTAGE POWER SUPPLY

528

vertical oscillator and a horizontal oscillator. The vertical oscillator generates a sawtooth-type signal used to pull the beam downward, while the horizontal oscillator generates a sawtooth-type signal for scanning the beam horizontally across the picture-tube face. In combination, the two oscillators cause the beam to scan the entire tube-face area. Inasmuch as the sync pulses are sent out by the television station, they are instrumental in locking in the vertical and horizontal oscillators of the receiver in perfect timing with the frequencies used at the transmitter. Hence, good picture lock-in is possible with a properly adjusted receiver. (Pulse synchronization of *R-C* oscillators was discussed in Chapter 17.)

A standard low-voltage power supply is used, usually of the full-wave type. A high-voltage power supply is also employed, generating approximately 20,000 volts for a 23-inch picture tube. The high voltage is employed to accelerate the scanning beam within the picture tube.

A number of rear and front panel controls must be employed to make proper adjustments of sound, picture, and synchronization. The fine-tuning control is used for precise adjustment of the local-oscillator frequency, so that the proper i-f frequency will be supplied during the heterodyning process between the local-oscillator signal and the incoming signals.

The contrast control regulates the amplitude of the picture (video) signals, just as the volume control regulates the amplitude of the audio signals. The brilliancy control permits manual regulation of the bias on the picture tube and, hence, influences the *background* or *brightness* content of the picture. Hold controls are also present for adjusting the sweep oscillators so their frequency is sufficiently close to the transmitted frequencies of the sync signals for proper lock-in. Other controls include width, height, and linearity, the latter being used for adjustment of vertical and horizontal proportions of the scene, to make them conform to normal.

LOUDSPEAKER FACTORS

Radio and television receivers use either a single-ended power amplifier stage, or push-pull for greater output and better quality sound. Regardless of the type of amplifying system utilized, however, an audio system is no better than the loudspeaker and its accompanying baffle. Some of the factors regarding speaker systems are detailed here, to round out the reader's knowledge of sound amplification, not only with respect to receivers, but also with other amplifying systems, such as public address systems, high-fidelity phonographs, tape recorders, etc.

The PM (permanent-magnet) speaker is the most popular type in use. Basically, its construction is as shown in Fig. 19-5. A metal frame-

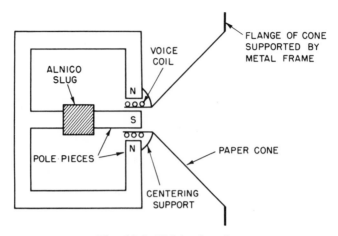

Fig. 19-5. PM loudspeaker.

work, having a cross section which resembles the letter E, is employed. A permanent-magnet core, referred to as a *slug* and usually made of the alloy Alnico, furnishes the necessary magnetic lines of force around the pole pieces at the voice coil. The pole pieces marked N are in the form of a circle, so that the N pole pieces surround the center S pole piece, and thus create a dense magnetic field in the narrow gap between the S and N pole pieces. Into the narrow gap is inserted an extension of the speaker cone. The voice coil is wound around the outside of this circular cone area. When audio signal energy from the output amplifier is applied to the voice coil, the latter produces magnetic lines of force. If the magnetic lines of force of the voice coil create a field opposing the field created at the pole pieces, the voice coil is repelled and the cone moves outward. When the voice-coil field changes, because of the a-c characteristics of the audio signal, the fields of the coil are attracted by the fields of the pole pieces and the cone moves inward. The cone movement varies the air pressure, and sound is produced.

Most speakers have voice-coil diameters of ½ to 1½ inches, with some high-fidelity speakers having a 3-inch voice coil to handle greater power. Conventional speakers have cone diameters ranging from a few inches (in portable receivers) to 15 inches in the larger high-fidelity systems of phonographs, receivers, or tape recorders. Public-address systems may use even larger diameter cones.

HIGH-FIDELITY SPEAKER TYPES

The ordinary PM speaker consists of a single paper cone structure coupled to a small-diameter voice coil. The ordinary PM speaker also has a small-sized magnet. Design is such that the speaker can be manu-factured economically and still produce a sound level output sufficient for average listening. For high-fidelity applications, however, the speaker is modified to handle a greater amount of audio power, while at the same time providing an extended frequency response range. Besides this, special design factors are incorporated for minimizing undesired resonant peaks and for producing greater speaker compliance for low-frequency sound reproduction.

A speaker cone which has good compliance and moves rather freely, will, however, also contribute to overhang effects. The latter, also known as *hangover,* is the condition which prevails in inferior audio systems when sharply defined musical tones are to be reproduced. Such tones, also known as staccato notes, are difficult to reproduce in sharply-defined form from inferior receivers. The audio-frequency *signal* which represents a series of staccato notes is shown in Fig. 19-6(A). The audio-frequency cycles cause the speaker cone to vibrate at a rapid rate. When the interval between such groups arrives, however, the sudden cessation of the audio-frequency signal means that the speaker movement should stop suddenly. Because of inertia, however, and because of the free-moving speaker cone, the cone may vibrate for a few cycles beyond the termination of the staccato note. This will result in a damped wave form being added to the end of the staccato waveform, as shown in Fig. 19-6(B). These trailing tones produce a damped-wave type of signal sometimes known as hang-over, which prevents the reproduced sound from having sharply-defined starts and stops. In consequence, there is a blending effect between the individual tones, as though the sustaining pedal of a piano were depressed.

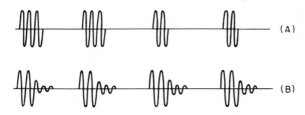

Fig. 19-6. Overhang of brief sounds.

Hangover effects can be minimized by designing the cone to have less compliance, thus inhibiting its free-moving characteristics. This procedure, however, also impedes the free movement of the cone during the greater cone excursions necessary for low-frequency reproduction. Therefore, low-frequency tones will not be reproduced with the desired amplitude. Hangover can also be minimized by using triode output audio amplifiers, which have a lower plate resistance and tend to dampen (consume) the energy created by the cone movement. For ordinary and economical sound reproduction, however, pentodes and beam-power tubes are preferred, because of their higher output. For this reason, stiffer cones are often utilized for minimizing hangover. In high-fidelity amplifiers, tubes are used having a low plate resistance and, consequently, the use of flexible-cone loudspeakers is feasible. For this reason, high-fidelity loudspeakers often have the cones suspended from the speaker housing by a more flexible rim material. If the paper cone is flared out as a support, the flared section may be corrugated to increase compliance, or treated with a creosote compound which remains soft for an indefinite period of time, and thus insures a nonrigid support providing free cone movement. Chamois or felt is also used to mount the rim of a cone to the speaker housing. A soft leather product, such as chamois, assures a maximum of cone flexibility.

The better quality high-fidelity speakers also have a larger voice-coil area, by utilizing a two- or three-inch diameter voice coil mount. This permits the speaker to handle a greater audio-power signal.

A single-cone speaker can be designed to have a fairly uniform response from low audio frequencies to over 8,000 cps. For high-frequency reproduction, a stiffer cone material is desirable, while for low-frequency reproduction a large-area soft cone material is preferred. Some speakers corrugate the outer cone areas for better low-frequency reproduction, and the center cone area is often treated with a lacquer compound to stiffen it for better high-frequency signal reproduction.

High-frequency reproduction can also be extended by adding a small thin stiff paper cone section at the center of the large cone section, as shown on the left in Fig. 19-7. Some speakers also employ an extremely thin cone of aluminum for extending the high-frequency response, as shown on the right in Fig. 19-7. A well-designed speaker of this type can reproduce a frequency range above 10,000 cycles.

A dual speaker system can also be employed, where one speaker is utilized for low-frequency signal reproduction, while the other is employed for the high-frequency signals only. When such a combination is employed, the large-cone speaker used for low-frequency notes is known as the *woofer*. The small high-frequency speaker is known as a *tweeter*.

A tweeter can be incorporated with a woofer in a speaker, as shown in Fig. 19-8. Such a combination is known as a *coaxial* speaker. The tweeter section can be in the form of a small PM speaker, or a small horn-type speaker. In either case, the tweeter speaker should be capable of handling high audio power levels and, for this reason, the ordinary small-cone speaker utilized in table radios is not suitable for tweeter applications. The coaxial speakers have a frequency range extending from approximately 50 cycles to 15,000 cycles, when employed in a suitable enclosure as subsequently described.

Fig. 19-7. High-frequency compensation in speakers. (Courtesy University Loudspeakers, Inc.)

Fig. 19-8. Coaxial speaker. (Courtesy Jensen Mfg. Co.)

A more elaborate type of speaker has also been devised which employs a three-section speaker, known as a *triaxial* speaker. The triaxial speaker has a frequency range extending up to 20,000 cycles per second.

Public-address systems generate a large amount of audio power and, therefore, often use a horn-type speaker to handle the high power. Such a horn type requires a driver mechanism which resembles the PM dynamic speaker, except that a large magnet and small rigid diaphragm are used. The horn section is attached to the driver outlet and helps to reinforce the sounds and bring them to the desired levels. The small output aperture of the horn is referred to as the *throat,* while the flared large opening is known as the *mouth.* The gradual flare of the horn section matches the impedance of the small vibrating diaphragm at the throat to the large-area air medium at the mouth. Most of the larger horns are folded back on themselves to make them more compact.

SPEAKER ENCLOSURES

An unmounted loudspeaker generates acoustical energy from both the front and the back and, for this reason, front and back radiated signals will cancel on those occasions when out-of-phase conditions occur. This is particularly true of low-frequency signals, since the wavelength is long and the path short from front to back of the speaker. Because the high-frequency signal components are of a shorter wavelength, the time factor in the travel of signals from the front of the cone to the back and vice versa will result in only partial cancellation of some of these signals. Therefore, an unmounted loudspeaker will give fairly good high-frequency response, but lacks low-frequency response to an appreciable degree.

Low-frequency response can be improved by increasing the path length of the signals which emanate from the rear and from the front. This can be done by employing a mounting board which acts as an isolation between the front and back of the speaker. Such a simple device can consist of a panel measuring 4 feet by 4 feet. A hole is cut at the center, and the speaker is mounted so that the front of the cone faces through the hole. Under this condition, the path length from front to back is an effective 8 feet. Such a device is known as a *baffle.*

If a larger panel were used, the path length would be effectively increased and, in consequence, low-frequency response would be improved in proportion. A more convenient form of baffle is to utilize a cabinet such as shown in Fig. 19-9(A). The cabinet housing the phonograph or radio device can also be used for speaker baffle. Thus, the baffle is folded back to take up less room, while still providing an effective path length.

While speaker cabinets can be designed to function as adequate baffles, the small size encountered in table radios and phonographs provides insufficient path length for satisfactory low-frequency response. At the same time, the larger cabinets which provide additional path length suffer from cabinet resonance and other undesirable effects which prevent the achievement of maximum efficiency and distortion-free frequency response. Thus, for high-fidelity work, numerous other baffle types have been devised, and these generally outperform the relatively simple baffle arrangement found in conventional radio and television cabinets.

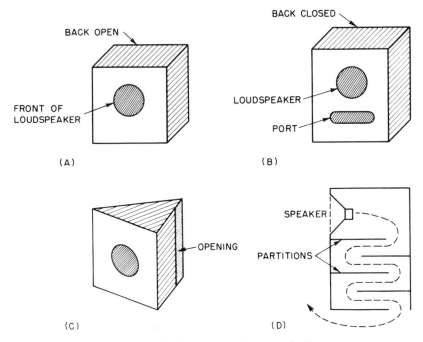

Fig. 19-9. Various types of speaker baffles.

One method for improving the baffle is to employ the bass-reflex principle shown in Fig. 19-9(B). This speaker enclosure is not open at the rear, but a hole (port) is provided below the speaker opening. Sound is emitted from both the port and the speaker opening, with good in-phase conditions for bass tones. The bass-reflex cabinet dimensions are based on the size and resonant frequency of the speaker which is utilized. The port size is also related to the resonant frequency of the speaker.

The bass-reflex cabinet gives a fairly uniform response over the audible frequency range, and minimizes low-frequency attenuation by utilizing a cabinet which extends the resonant effects of the speaker, because of the type of design employed. The cabinet must be padded with a sound-absorbing material.

The bass-reflex cabinet has a relatively high efficiency, as compared to other types which have the rear closed. Cabinets of this type can also be designed for use with dual speakers (separate woofer and tweeter). As with other baffles, the bass-reflex cabinet must be constructed of fairly heavy wood, to minimize cabinet resonance, and joints are usually sealed by employing wood glue and using screws to insure tight connections.

Another speaker enclosure which provides good performance is the folded-horn type illustrated in Fig. 19-9(C). The design of the horn is such that it folds back on itself, and thus occupies a minimum of space for the mouth opening secured. If the folded horn is so designed that it can be placed in the corner of a room, the walls of the room act as an extension of the mouth opening, so that efficiency and impedance matching characteristics of the enclosure are increased. As with the bass-reflex enclosure, the folded horn can also be employed in conjunction with dual type speakers. With the folded horns, the efficiency increases as the size is increased, and an extended frequency range is possible, besides providing a high degree of efficiency in the low-frequency register.

Theoretically, if a baffle had infinite size, there would be no losses suffered by virtue of the undesired effects which result when rear and front sound radiations intermix. Such a device, while theoretically desirable, is not feasible from the practical standpoint. An approach, however, is the so-called infinite baffle type enclosure shown in Fig. 19-9(D). Here, the path length of the sound leaving the speaker rear has been extended by employing partitions within the speaker cabinet, as shown.

A speaker can be mounted in a cabinet which has no openings for the rear-speaker waves to escape. With a completely closed affair such as this, the back waves are damped and more audio driving power is required. Since cancellation effects are minimized, however, the response characteristics of the system are improved considerably over ordinary receiver cabinets. Such an enclosure has gained favor because it can be made small enough for shelf mounting, thus avoiding the more cumbersome cabinet size of the bass reflex and other similar types.

Another system which lends itself readily to shelf mounting because of its smaller size is that shown in Fig. 19-10. Here, the speaker is mounted

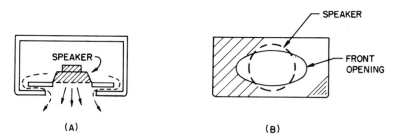

Fig. 19-10. Shelf-type enclosure.

on a separate board and spaced a half inch or so from the front cabinet opening, as shown by the top view at (A). The path of the rear wave (shown by the dotted lines) is now around the speaker mounting board. The front opening is somewhat elliptical in shape as shown at (B). The duct path for the rear waves, through the elliptical front opening, provides a variation in rear-wave path length which broadens the frequency response of the speaker system. One such system, the *Eliptoflex* patented by *Lafayette Radio Electronics Corp.* uses a special diffracting ring around the speaker for minimizing cancellation effects between front- and rear-wave radiation. Cabinet size is approximately 14 inches high, 24 inches wide, and 13½ inches deep.

Other types of speaker enclosures are also found on the market, each having specific characteristics and dimensions designed to extend the frequency response range for a speaker of given size and type. The methods described earlier herein, however, indicate the basic measures generally employed and hence represent fundamental types.

STEREOPHONIC PRINCIPLES

Stereophonic transmission or recording refers to the process whereby directional characteristics are given to the various sounds which are broadcast or recorded. The basic stereophonic audio system utilizes two separate amplifying systems usually contained in one chassis, each separate channel ending in its own speaker system. For stereophonic record reproduction, for instance, two sound tracks are actually recorded in a single record groove, but at different angles. A special phonograph pick-up is employed and the sounds reproduced from each track are then channeled to separate amplifiers and speakers. The latter are placed 6 to 8 feet apart and certain orchestral instruments or singers will appear to be at the left and others at the right, in conformity to the placement of such instruments and singers at the studio. Thus, stereophonic reception not only adds directivity to the recorded music, but also widens the sound source. Instruments or sounds emanating from between the two microphones which pick up the stereophonic sound will be reproduced at equal levels and thus will appear to have a central sound source during reception.

In FM stereo broadcasting, two separate channels are also employed, but the system is so designed that ordinary FM reception is obtainable with a standard FM receiver. For reception of stereophonic sound, however, a special receiver (or adapter for the ordinary receiver) is necessary. When the receiver separates the two transmitted channels, two separate audio-amplifying systems must again be employed (with separate speakers for each). Because reception is possible with an ordinary FM receiver as well as the stereo type, the system is known to be *compatible*. The television color system is also compatible since color transmission can be received on either a color receiver (in color) or in black and white on an ordinary television receiver.

REVIEW QUESTIONS

1. Briefly explain the difference between an R-F type of receiver and a super-heterodyne receiver.

2. Describe why a superheterodyne receiver employs a local oscillator.

3. What is the advantage of having i-f amplifier stages in a superheterodyne receiver?

4. If a superheterodyne receiver is tuned to a station of 1,000 kilocycles, and the intermediate frequency is 455 kilocycles, what is the local-oscillator frequency? (Assume the local-oscillator frequency is above the carrier frequency.)

5. Briefly explain what is meant by an *image frequency*.

6. Briefly explain the difference between a conventional ground connection and that known as floating ground.

7. Show by block diagram what additional circuits are present in a television receiver, as compared to a standard AM radio receiver.

8. Briefly explain why a vertical sweep oscillator and a horizonal sweep oscillator are used in a television receiver.

9. What is meant by *overhang* in audio systems? What causes this condition?

10. Explain what is meant by a *baffle* and why its use is advantageous in sound reproduction.

20

TRANSMISSION LINES AND ANTENNAS

INTRODUCTION

Transmission lines are devices which are employed to transfer signals from a receiver to an antenna, or vice versa, as well as to transfer signal energy between other devices, such as from the output of an audio amplifier to some remote speaker system. The ideal transmission line is one which conveys the necessary signal information without having any adverse effect on the amplitude or characteristics of the signal waveform.

Besides conveying signal information between two points, transmission lines are also used for other purposes. Transmission lines can be employed for introducing a phase shift in sinewave signals, or for producing a delay with respect to pulse signals. Transmission-type delay lines are employed in color-television receivers, computers, radar systems, and other electronic devices. Because transmission lines also exhibit resonant circuit characteristics, they find application as replacements for the usual capacitor-inductor circuits at the very-high and ultra-high frequencies (VHF and UHF). From the foregoing, it is obvious that an understanding of transmission-line characteristics is an important phase of electronic knowledge.

Antenna devices, which are used for either transmitting or receiving the signals, also have special characteristics which must be understood, in order to obtain the highest degree of efficiency both in transmitting and receiving systems. Basic antenna systems are covered later in this chapter, after the necessary foundation has been laid by an analysis of transmission lines.

BASIC TRANSMISSION LINES

There are a variety of transmission lines employed in electronics. The most familiar types of transmission lines are the conductors used in house wiring, as well as the overhead power distribution cables. The two-wire line from a lamp to a base plug can be considered as a form of transmission line, because it transfers the a-c power from the mains to the incandescent bulb. Telephone wires, television lead-in wires, and the shielded cable from a microphone to a public-address amplifier are other examples of transmission lines.

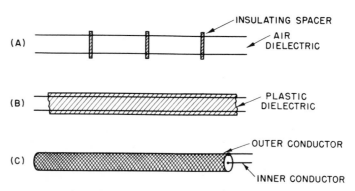

Fig. 20-1. Types of transmission lines.

For higher-frequency work, the most common types of lines are those illustrated in Fig. 20-1. Part (A) shows the so-called *open-wire line*. This line consists of two wires which are held at a certain spacing by plastic or ceramic insulators. When any two wires are brought into close proximity with each other, capacity exists between them. Thus, it is common to refer to the material which exists in the spacing as the *dielectric,* as with capacitors. For the two-wire line shown in (A), the dielectric is air.

Another type of line is shown in Fig. 20-1(B). This is the common *twin lead* used in television reception. Again, two wires are utilized, as with the line in (A), but a soft plastic dielectric material is employed, in this case. The transmission line shown in (C) is known as a *coaxial cable,* or *concentric line*. Here, an outer conductor in the form of a metal tube or metallic braid encloses an inner conductor composed of either solid or stranded wire. A shielded microphone cable is a form of coaxial line, wherein a flexible plastic is used as the dielectric for spacing the inner conductor from the outer metallic flexible braid. For some high-frequency work, the inner conductor is spaced from the outer conductor by insulating washers composed of ceramic or plastic.

CHARACTERISTIC IMPEDANCE

When current flows through the two wires of a transmission line, magnetic lines of force are created around the wire, and electrostatic lines of force are set up between the wires, as shown in Fig. 20-2(A). Thus, all transmission lines have both electrostatic fields and magnetic fields, as shown. These fields have an amplitude determined by the amount of current flowing in the lines, and by the voltage existing between them. When a-c is employed, the fields build up to a maximum for one alternation, and then collapse when the zero level of the a-c is reached. For the next alternation of opposite polarity, the fields build up again, but also have a polarity opposite to what it was originally. Lines of force have an important bearing on transmission-line characteristics, as will be shown later.

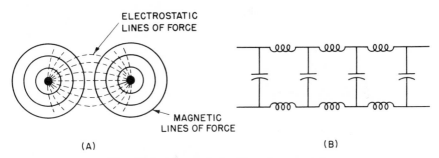

Fig. 20-2. Transmission-line characteristics.

When two wires are brought into proximity, a certain amount of capacity exists per unit length, as shown in Fig. 20-2(B). Because any length of wire has inductive characteristics, a two-wire line also has a certain amount of inductance per unit length, as shown in (B). Each wire of the two-wire line also has some internal resistance, though the latter is usually held at a minimum by making the wire sufficiently large in diameter for the current to be handled. When the dielectric material is other than air, some shunt resistance may also be present across the line, due to the leakage resistance of the dielectric material.

Because a transmission line is composed primarily of the shunt capacitance and series inductance shown in Fig. 20-2(B), it will have a certain *characteristic impedance* (sometimes called surge impedance). If the resistances present in the wire length and in the dielectric material are not appreciable, the characteristic impedance (Z_o) can be ascertained by use of the formula:

$$Z_o = \sqrt{\frac{L}{C}} \qquad (20\text{-}1)$$

When air insulation is used in a parallel-wire type line, the following formula can be used for finding Z_o:

$$Z_o = 276 \log \frac{2b}{a} \qquad (20\text{-}2)$$

where b = distance (center-to-center) of the wires
a = radius of the conductor

The Z_o of a coaxial cable may be found by use of the following formula:

$$Z_o = 138 \log \frac{b}{a} \qquad (20\text{-}3)$$

where b = inside diameter of the outer conductor
a = outside diameter of the inner conductor

When such a line is filled with a dielectric material other than air, the result of the formula should be multiplied by

$$\frac{1}{\sqrt{K}} \qquad (20\text{-}4)$$

where K = dielectric constant of the material.

For convenience in discussing transmission-line characteristics, reference will be made to a *generator* and a *load,* in a fashion similar to that followed for earlier circuit discussions. Thus, a generator attached to a transmission line may be a transmitter, or a receiving antenna, since each sends signals along the line. A load can be a transmitting antenna, or a receiver, since each receives the signal energy sent along the line.

As with other generator-load combinations, maximum signal power is transferred between the generator and the load when impedances are matched. As an illustration, if a television receiver has a 300-ohm input impedance at the tuner, a maximum signal will be transferred to it from the antenna when the latter is also 300 ohms. If a 300-ohm transmission line is also employed, the line will also match the antenna and the receiver. Such a transmission line is referred to as an "untuned" or "nonresonant" line. The designation "flat" line is sometimes employed, because power travels along the line from the generator (antenna) until it reaches the load (receiver), where it is completely utilized. In such a line, the impedance is the same at any point, since the ratio of voltage to current is identical at any chosen section. This flat voltage-to-current ratio is upset when impedances are not matched, as described later.

When an a-c signal flows through a transmission line, current flow in one wire is opposite to that in the other; hence, the fields around the wires oppose each other and tend to cancel. This factor minimizes losses since, if the fields did not cancel, some of the energy would leave the transmission line, because of the lines of force which would extend beyond the influence of the wires. Some losses take place, however, since complete cancellation of the fields would occur only if each wire of the two-wire line occupied the same space, so that the fields would interact perfectly. In the parallel wire lines, losses are kept at a minimum by close spacing of the wires. In coaxial cables, the complete shielding of the inner conductor by the outer conductor prevents losses by radiation of the fields.

STANDING WAVES

Radio, FM, television, and other high-frequency R-F signals travel through space with the speed of light (approximately 186,000 miles per second). Thus, if a generator sends out (propagates) only one cycle of an a-c signal, that part of the signal which first left the generator would have spanned a distance of 186,000 miles at the time the end of the cycle leaves the generator. Consequently, a frequency of one cycle per second has a *wavelength* of 186,000 miles, as shown in Fig. 20-3(A). If the frequency is doubled, each cycle occurs in a shorter interval of time, so that, at the end of one second, two cycles of transmitted energy will span 186,000 miles, as shown in Fig. 20-3(B). Thus, each cycle of the higher frequency has a shorter wavelength. A still higher frequency, as shown in (C), shortens the wavelength again for each cycle. With four cycles spanning 186,000 miles, each cycle has a wavelength ¼ of 186,000 miles, or 46,500 miles. For television and FM frequencies, the wavelengths are so short that they are specified in feet or in inches, rather than in miles. At 200 megacycles, for instance, one cycle has a wavelength of less than 5 feet. (The symbol for wavelength is λ, the Greek letter Lambda.) The wavelength of a particular frequency can be found by use of the following formula:

$$\lambda \text{ (in feet)} = \frac{984}{f} \qquad (20\text{-}5)$$

where f is the frequency in megacycles.

As will be shown later, however, the half-wavelength dimensions are of primary interest; hence, the formula can be restated as follows:

$$\frac{\lambda}{2}\,(\text{in feet}) = \frac{492}{f} \qquad (20\text{-}6)$$

where f again represents the frequency in megacycles.

For ultra-high frequencies, where the wavelength is more conveniently expressed in inches, the following formula applies:

$$\frac{\lambda}{2}\,(\text{in inches}) = \frac{5{,}904}{f} \qquad (20\text{-}7)$$

where f still has the same significance as above.

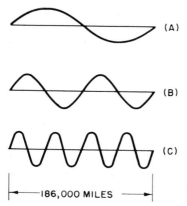

(A)

(B)

(C)

186,000 MILES

Fig. 20-3. Frequency versus wavelength.

In the study of transmission lines, it is often necessary to refer to a line having a specific wavelength. This is because, in many instances, the wavelength of a line determines whether the line has inductive, capacitive, or resonant characteristics. When a transmission line is employed between a matched generator and load, the transfer of the output power from the generator to the load is a function of the transmission line. If a mismatch occurs, however, between the load and the generator, all the energy will not be transferred between the generator and the load. For instance, the transmission line may be matched to the generator and will accept the full amount of signal energy and transfer it to the load. If the load is not matched to the line or generator, however, all the signal energy will not be accepted, and some is reflected back to the generator. The greater the mismatch, the more energy will be reflected back along the wire. Thus, some energy will travel from the generator to the load and, during the same time, energy is reflected back from the load toward the generator. Since the primary signals and the reflected signals are all intermixed along the line, there will be both in-phase and out-of-phase conditions. Hence, at some points along the line, voltages will be in phase and will have a high amplitude, while in other places out-of-phase conditions will occur, resulting in low or zero signal-voltage amplitude. Similar conditions occur for signal current. These high and low amplitudes are the fixed or *standing* positions along the line, and hence are known as *standing waves* of either voltage of current.

A better understanding of standing waves can be gained by inspection of Fig. 20-4; (A) shows one extreme condition of mismatch, since a half-

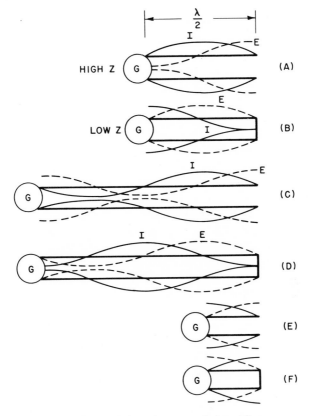

Fig. 20-4. Characteristics of open and closed lines.

wavelength line is open at the end. The open end represents an infinitely high impedance. Note the current and voltage distribution along such a half-wavelength line. When the wave of current reaches the end of the line, it drops to zero. The current decrease creates collapsing fields, and the fields in turn cut the conductor ends and induce a voltage maximum across the ends of the line, as shown. The high voltage and zero current at the end of the line create a high-impedance condition, since Z is equal to E/I. Voltage maximum points are referred to as *voltage loops,* and current maximums as *current loops.* The voltage or current minimums are referred to as *nodes.* At the generator, which is removed from the end of the line by one-half wavelength, a high impedance again exists.

The standing waves on the line will have loops and nodes as shown in (A), though the standing wave itself is of a-c composition, which means that the amplitude alternately changes from maximum to zero, each maximum alternating from a positive to a negative.

In (B), a half-wavelength line is again shown, though now the end of the line is shorted. The closed end of the line again offers a high mismatch, because it represents a zero impedance. Current is now high at the generator and at the end of the line, with voltage reaching a loop at the center of the line, as shown. If the short were replaced by a low value of resistance, the ratio of loops and nodes would decrease as the resistance is increased toward the generator resistance. Above the generator resistance, standing waves again are created. The ratio of either voltage or current loops and nodes is known as the *standing-wave ratio.* The ratio can, therefore, be determined by dividing the maximum voltage along the line by the minimum voltage. The standing-wave ratio indicates the degree of mismatch between the generator and the load. When a complete match prevails, the standing-wave ratio is equal to one, since loops and nodes no longer exist. The standing-wave ratio can, of course, also be determined by current loops and nodes. For instance, if the standing wave of current reaches an amplitude of 20 milliamperes, and the minimum standing wave of current is 2 milliamperes, the ratio is 10, indicating that the load resistance is either 10 times as large as the generator impedance, or one-half the value of the generator impedance.

In (C) and (D), full-wavelength lines are shown. Note that the voltage and current relationships at the end of the line correspond to those shown in (A) and (B). In (E) and (F), quarter-wavelength sections of line are shown and, again, voltage is at a maximum at the open end of the line, (E), but is zero when the line is closed, as in (F). Note, however, that the section of line at the generator has an impedance which is different from that at the end. In (E), for instance, the impedance is high at the open end, but drops to a low value at the generator, because of the voltage decline and the current rise. Because of the impedance difference along such a line, the latter can be used as an impedance matching transformer. It can be utilized as an impedance step-up device, as in (E), or as an impedance step-down device, as in (F). The half-wavelength sections shown in (A) or (B) can be used as a one-to-one transformer, since the impedance at the output is identical to the input impedance. Because this characteristic is repetitive for every half wavelength, a half-wavelength line (or wavelength multiples) behaves as a one-to-one transformer.

The quarter-wavelength section shown in Fig. 20-4(E) behaves as a series resonant circuit for the generator, due to the low impedance of the line at the point where it is connected to the generator. The generator in (F) is attached to a high-impedance point, hence the transmission line behaves as a parallel resonant circuit.

RESONANT SECTIONS

Quarter-wavelength sections of transmission line are actually employed as resonant circuits in VHF and UHF electronic applications, to replace the coil and capacitor combinations. At very high frequencies, the resonant circuits employ smaller values of inductance and capacitance to achieve resonance. As the frequency of the signal is increased, still smaller values of inductance and capacitance are necessary. Consequently, the point is reached where it is more practical to use quarter-wavelength sections of line as the actual resonant circuit. The line sections can be used in either oscillator or amplifier circuits, and typical UHF oscillators using transmission-line sections are shown in Fig. 20-5. In (A), the triode oscillator has its anode connected to one wire of the parallel resonant line, while the second wire of the line is in the grid circuit. This oscillator can be likened to the Hartley oscillator described earlier, though it is sometimes called an ultra-audion type. The resonant-line section which is connected to the anode can be considered as the plate inductance, while the resonant line section at the grid is the grid inductor. The B voltage-feed point is applied to the movable shorting bar, and this point is placed at ground potential for the R-F signals, by virtue of the bypass effect of capacitor C_1. Since the cathode is also placed at ground potential, it is at the same potential as the center of the shorting bar. Thus, the cathode taps the inductance in similar fashion to the Hartley oscillator, where the amplified energy in the plate circuit is coupled to the grid circuit by the interacting lines of force which are common to both inductances.

Capacitor C_2 is the conventional grid capacitor which, in conjunction with grid leak R_1, establishes the proper time constant for the frequency employed and, also, for the generation of the cutoff bias. An R-F choke is employed in the grid circuit, to minimize the shunting effects which the grid-leak resistor may have on the R-F energy at the grid. The output from the oscillator is obtained from a single-loop inductance, shown by the dotted section in Fig. 20-5(A). This single-loop inductance is often referred to as a *hairpin loop*, and is coupled to the parallel section for signal take-off. The degree of coupling will determine the amount of signal trans-

fer, as well as the loading effects on the oscillator, which establish the final
Q and bandpass characteristics. Tuning to proper frequency is accomplished by moving the shorting bar to change the resonant-line length.

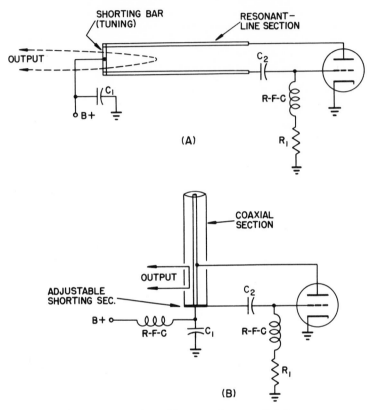

Fig. 20-5. UHF oscillators using parallel lines.

When such an oscillator is used in receivers, the resonant section can
be composed of small-diameter copper tubing or heavy-gauge solid copper
wire (No. 16 to No. 22). The larger-diameter wire is preferred at higher
frequencies, because of the phenomenon known as *skin effect,* which is
present at these frequencies. This factor can be more readily understood
by reference to Fig. 20-6, which shows a magnified cross-section of a wire
carrying electric current. The current flow establishes a series of magnetic
lines of force, which are distributed within the wire, as well as being
present around the outside perimeter. These magnetic lines of force are
representative of the inductive factor of the wire length, and offer a reactance against the R-F current flow. Since inductive reactance increases with

higher frequencies, the changing a-c
signal, if high in frequency, meets with
considerable opposition within the wire
core and, in consequence, has difficulty
flowing through the wire. Since the first
electromagnetic line of force external
to the wire is spaced a short (but definite) distance from the wire surface,
the current flow set up by the pressure
of the voltage finds a path of lower
resistance on the outside of the wire
than it does on the inside. Thus, at

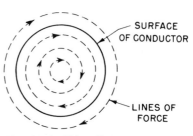

Fig. 20-6. Skin effect.

high frequencies, the current flow can be considered as being along the
surface or "skin" of the wire, and hence the term *skin effect*. As higher
frequency signals are employed, the inside-wire opposition is increased
and, in order to provide a low-resistance path for the R-F energy, it is
expedient to increase the wire size, so as to decrease resistance for skin
effect. Also, a large surface area must be provided for the relatively higher
currents encountered in transmitting work. Since the current flows on the
outside of the wire, it is not economical to use a solid wire of extremely
heavy gauge. For this reason, copper tubing is frequently employed, since
the center-core area is of no current-carrying importance at very high
frequencies.

A coaxial-cable section can also be employed in a high-frequency oscillator instead of the resonant-line section previously described. A coaxial
cable high-frequency oscillator is shown in Fig. 20-5(B). This
oscillator is similar to the one shown in (A) of the same figure, except
for the fact that a coaxial cable instead of a parallel-wire line is used.
The inner conductor of the coaxial cable is used for the anode, while the
outer conductor is attached to the grid at the shorting section. In this
instance, the outer conductor is not at ground potential, except by virtue
of the bypass effect of C_1. The output is derived from a hairpin-loop arrangement which is inserted into the coaxial element via two small holes
in the outer conductor. Because of skin effect, the R-F energy is confined
to the inside of the coaxial-cable section, and will not penetrate and leak
to the outside. Again because of skin effect, the R-F energy within the
coaxial-cable section flows on the outside of the inner conductor, and on
the inside of the outer conductor. A conventional R-F choke is also employed in the grid circuit, and the shorting section for tuning purposes
consists of a metal washer which is often mounted on a threaded rod,
so that exact tuning adjustments can be made.

The parallel resonant line sections lend themselves readily to push-pull
elements, for both oscillators and amplifiers. A typical push-pull R-F

amplifier is shown in Fig. 20-7. A balanced arrangement can be employed, as shown, by using a parallel resonant section for the push-pull plates. The input signals are applied to the grid circuits by use of a hairpin loop, as shown by the dotted line section at the oscillator input. The output is taken off by a similar hairpin-loop arrangement coupled to the anode resonant line section.

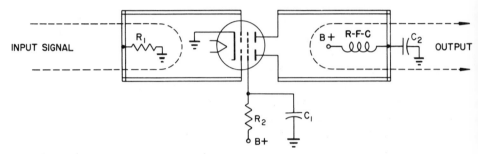

Fig. 20-7. UHF push-pull amplifier.

Resistor R_1 at the center of the shorting bar at the left is the conventional grid leak, while the B voltage is applied to the center of the shorting bar at the anode section. The R-F choke, in series with the B supply, acts to prevent losses of signal energy to the power supply. The resonant anode circuit is placed at ground potential for R-F by capacitor C_2, which returns the R-F signal energy to the cathode circuit. This completes the R-F circuit, without the necessity for making such a completion through the power supply. Radio-frequency energy which leaks to the power supply will, in turn, be induced to the power mains, because of the inductive transfer across the power transformer, with resultant losses of such R-F energy.

The tubes shown in Fig. 20-7 are tetrodes, though pentode and beam-power tubes can also be utilized. If special high-frequency tubes of this type are employed, no neutralization will be necessary, provided the circuit is intended to be used as an R-F signal amplifier. If triodes are used, the circuit will become a push-pull oscillator, in which instance no input signal would be applied, and the output energy would be obtained from the anode circuit, in identical fashion to that shown using the hairpin loop. Basically, the circuit arrangement is similar, whether this stage handles signals in a receiver or in a transmitter, except that, in the latter instance, a larger tube and larger-diameter resonant-line sections are employed.

Two-wire lines are particularly suited for push-pull circuits, because the parallel lines are *balanced* lines; that is, one line is as much above ground potential as the other. The coaxial cable does not lend itself as readily as the parallel-wire line to balanced-line applications. The twin lead utilized for television receivers is also used in a balanced-line arrangement, as shown in Fig. 20-8. The antenna feeds the signals to the transmission line, which in turn applies them across the primary of the tuner input transformer, as shown. With the primary center-tapped to ground, a balanced arrangement is secured.

SECTIONS FORMING L, C, AND R

Sections of transmission lines can also exhibit characteristics of either inductance or capacitance, instead of circuit resonance. For instance, an open section of line which is less than a quarter-wavelength long appears to the generator as a capacity and, hence, has a capacitive reactance. As mentioned earlier, the quarter-wavelength section of line open at the end nearest to the generator appears as a series resonant circuit (see Fig. 20-4(E)). If such

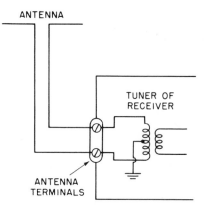

Fig. 20-8. Balanced input.

a section of line is shortened so as to be less than a quarter wavelength, both the series inductance and the shunt capacitance are decreased. According to the inductive reactance formula given in an earlier chapter of this book, when the inductance is decreased the inductive reactance also decreases. According to the capacitive reactance formula, however, a decrease in capacity causes the capacitive reactance to increase. Because the parallel-line section represents a series resonant circuit when the end is open, the larger reactance will predominate if the line is less than a quarter wavelength. Since the capacitive reactance now offers greatest series opposition, the line is primarily capacitive. If the line shown in Fig. 20-4(E) is made longer than a quarter wavelength (but less than a half wavelength), inductance and capacity per unit length increase. Thus, inductive reactance increases, but capacitive reactance decreases. Hence, the series opposition is primarily that of inductive reactance, and the circuit is predominantly inductive. A closed section of transmission line, less than a quarter-wavelength long, has opposite characteristics to the open-type line. Hence, a closed quarter-wavelength line shortened to less than a quarter wavelength acts as an inductance. The shorted line behaves as a parallel resonant circuit and, when made less than a quarter wavelength, both inductance and capacity decrease, as with the open line. Inductive reactance also decreases, but capacitive reactance increases. The low shunt characteristics of the inductive reactance cause most of the current to flow through this section and, hence, the current will be inductive. When the closed-end parallel line is made more than a quarter wavelength, but less than a half, capacitive reactance predominates. The chart shown in Fig. 20-9 shows the characteristics for both the closed and open lines, for various wavelength values.

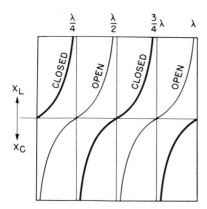

Fig. 20-9. Reactance versus line length.

FILTER SECTIONS

When short lengths of transmission lines are used for adding various values of inductance, capacity, or resonance to a circuit, such lines are referred to as *stubs*. Stubs can be used to form circuits which will hold back some frequencies while passing others. Circuits which have such discriminatory characteristics are known as filter circuits and for audio or R-F frequencies actual capacitors and coils are employed, whereas for UHF and microwave frequencies, stubs are used. Figure 20-10 illustrates the low-frequency filter systems, and their high-frequency counterparts employing stubs. In (A), a series coil and a shunt capacitor are shown in a circuit arrangement known as a *low-pass* filter. Assume that audio signals of various frequencies are applied to the input. For the lower-frequency audio signals, there will be a low inductive reactance established in the coil. For progressively higher audio frequencies, however, an increasing opposition is established in the series inductance because of the rising inductive reactance. Hence, the high-frequency signals do not pass readily through the circuit, and those which do are shunted by the low reactance they create in the capacitor. The signals of low frequencies, however, find little opposition in the inductance and hence pass through.

For the low frequency signals the reactance of the capacitor is high, and little of the signal energy is shunted. A UHF counterpart of the low-pass filter is shown in Fig. 20-10(B). Here, a closed section of line has been inserted in series with a transmission line. The closed section of line (the stub) is less than a quarter-wavelength long and, hence, acts as an inductance. An open section of line less than a quarter wavelength long has been placed across the main transmission line, and this open stub acts as a capacity, in accordance with the chart shown in Fig. 20-9. Thus, the circuit shown in (B) is a high-frequency counterpart of that shown in (A), which handles mostly lower-frequency signals.

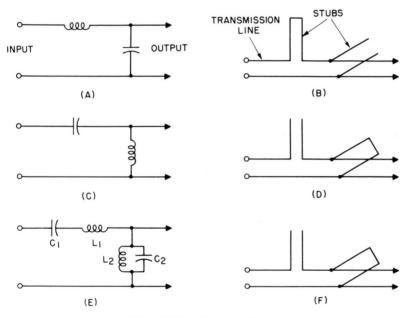

Fig. 20-10. Filter sections.

In Fig. 20-10(C), a high-pass filter is shown. If signals of various frequencies are applied to the input, the higher frequency signals are coupled through the capacitor, because they find a low reactance. The high-frequency signals arriving at the output are not shunted by the inductance because of the high inductive reactance. Low-frequency signals, however, have difficulty passing through the capacitor, since such signals create a high capacitive reactance. The low-frequency signals which appear across the inductance create a low reactance and, hence, are shunted. Thus, this is a high-pass filter, because it passes the high-frequency signals, but filters out the low-frequency signals. In (D) is shown a UHF counterpart of the high-pass filter, using line sections. Again, the open stub acts as a capacitor because it is less than a quarter wavelength long. Hence, the main transmission line is opened up, and a stub is inserted, as shown in (D). For the inductance, a closed stub less than a quarter wavelength is placed across the main transmission line, as shown.

The circuit in (E) is known as a bandpass filter, because it will pass a narrow band of frequencies centered around the resonance of the circuit, but will tend to reject signals of frequencies above and below the resonant frequency. Components C_1 and L_1 form a series resonant circuit which has a low impedance for the frequency (or narrow band of frequencies) to which it is tuned. Hence, the desired signals pass through this circuit. The resonant circuit composed of L_2 and C_2 is also tuned to the desired signals. This circuit is a parallel resonant one and, hence, has a high impedance which prevents any of the desired signals from being shunted. For signals having frequencies above and below resonance, the series resonant circuit will have a high impedance and, hence, will offer opposition. Also, the undesired signals which pass through the series resonant circuit will be shunted by the parallel resonant circuit, because the latter has a low impedance for signals whose frequencies are below or above resonance. Therefore, this circuit passes only a narrow band of frequencies, and filters out all others. A counterpart of the bandpass filter is the circuit shown in (F). For the series resonant circuit, an open stub is employed. The stub is made one-quarter wavelength long, and consequently acts as a series resonant circuit, because the impedance is low where the stub is attached to the main transmission line. For the parallel resonant circuit, a quarter wavelength long closed stub is placed across the main transmission line, as shown in (F).

BASIC ANTENNA TYPES

If the quarter-wavelength open transmission line shown in Fig. 20-4(E) is opened up so that the two wires are horizontal, an antenna is formed as shown at Fig. 20-11(A). For simplicity, the generator, which would be at the center of the two sections, is not shown. The two line sections, after being opened, now form a single line which is a half wavelength long. Each end still has a voltage loop, and current is still high at the center, as was the case for the quarter-wavelength line previously illustrated in Fig. 20-4. The single line represents the shortest length which can be used to form an antenna, and as with the quarter-wavelength open line, it represents a series parallel resonant circuit. Such a half-wavelength antenna is known as a *dipole,* because a popular method of using it is to open it at the center, where the voltage node is located, and to insert the transmission line at that point. When the antenna is opened at the center in such a manner, two quarter-wavelength sections (dipoles) are formed. The center of the antenna is a low-impedance point and, when the transmission line is attached, the antenna impedance is approximately 75 ohms. The dipole section shown in (A) actually has zero impedance at the center, because current is high and voltage zero. When this section is opened, however, capacity is created between the open ends, and the capacitive reactance thus established creates a voltage drop across this section, so that voltage is no longer zero at that point. In some applications, the transmission line can also be attached at one end or the other, if a high-impedance connection is desired.

The half-wave antenna has magnetic lines of force created by the current, and electrostatic lines of force created by the voltage. These are at right angles to each other and, in combination, they form the signal energy which leaves the antenna when the latter is used for transmitting. If the antenna is used for receiving signals, the propagated energy also sets up voltage and current distributions as shown in (A), since basic antennas have a reciprocal function with respect to transmitting and receiving. Hence, the characteristics detailed herein apply, whether a transmitting or a receiving antenna is involved.

The dipole antenna is also known as a *Hertz* antenna named after Heinrich R. Hertz (1857-1894), the German physicist and researcher. The dipole sends or picks up signals at right angles to its length, as shown

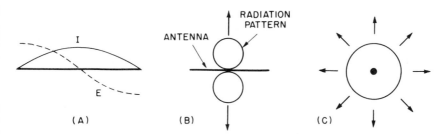

Fig. 20-11. Antenna patterns.

in Fig. 20-11(B). The circles represent the radiation pattern of the antenna, and are also known as *lobes*. The lobes indicate the direction of signal transmission or pick-up of the antenna. The radiation pattern shown in (B) is a cross-sectional illustration. Actually, the same pattern exists whether the antenna is observed from the top, from the bottom, or from the sides. An end view of the antenna is shown in (C) and, here, the radiation pattern is indicated as a circle. This indicates that the antenna can receive or send signals in all directions that are at right angles to its length. In transmitting, the high-frequency signals build up lines of force and, when the polarity of the signals changes, the lines of force would tend to collapse into the antenna and be re-established with opposite polarity for the next signal alternation. However, the rapid change of polarity of the signal at high frequencies does not permit the respective lines of force to collapse back into the antenna, so that they leave the influence of the antenna and are propagated at the speed of light into space. The energy which travels through space consists of a composite signal energy made up of electrostatic and electromagnetic lines of force, representing the respective voltage and current factors of the transmitted power. For FM and television transmission and reception, horizontal antennas are used, and the wave which is propagated is said to be *horizontally polarized.* For AM transmission and for some mobile short-wave applications, vertical polarization is employed; that is, the antennas are vertical rather than horizontal.

The figure-eight radiation pattern shown in Fig. 20-11(B) holds only when the antenna is a half wavelength long for the signal to be received. (The half wavelength in this instance refers to the *electrical length* rather than the *physical length.* Because of capacity effects at the ends, known as *end effect,* the antenna is made physically shorter than a half wavelength by approximately 5%.)

The simple dipole has only 75 ohms of impedance, as previously mentioned, and hence creates a mismatch when used with the standard 300-ohm twin lead utilized in FM and television installations. Consequently, most antennas are modifications of the simple dipole, so that increased impedance is obtained. One such type is the so-called *biconical* antenna shown in Fig. 20-12(A). Two or three quarter-wavelength rods extend from each side of an insulator, as shown, in order to obtain an impedance close to 300 ohms. Because the antenna is to be used for a number of stations, various signal frequencies will be impressed on the antenna. For frequencies higher than the half-wavelength frequency, multiple lobes appear in the radiation pattern. The antenna is tilted forward silghtly so that the multiple lobes combine into a single lobe. The sensitivity of such an antenna is again at right angles to its width and, hence, it will pick up signals in two directions. For increasing signal pick-up from one direction, a *reflector* rod is attached, as shown in (A). The reflector is a true half-wavelength long, and is spaced from the antenna by approximately a quarter wavelength, or less. If the spacing is too close, the reflector will decrease the impedance of the antenna appreciably.

Another antenna having 300 ohms of impedance is the folded dipole shown in Fig. 20-12(B). Again, a reflector can be employed for increasing the pick-up from one direction. Rods can also be placed in front of the antenna, as shown, such rods being referred to as *directors.* The directors

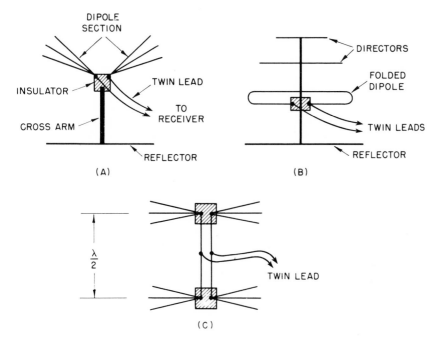

Fig. 20-12. Antenna types.

are made shorter than the antenna, and are spaced approximately a tenth of a wavelength apart. Commercial types use a number of rods and various spacings, in order to achieve broadband characteristics and maintain the required 300 ohms of impedance. Directors, like reflectors, tend to decrease the antenna impedance, and hence are spaced farther from the antenna than required for maximum effectiveness. Reflectors and directors, because they are not connected to the transmission line, may be grounded to the supporting cross-arm, as shown in Fig. 20-12(A) and (B). Since a voltage node exists at the center of the reflectors and directors, no signal losses occur because of the grounding of the reflectors and directors to a metal cross-arm. Reflectors and directors are also known as *parasitic* elements. The type of antenna shown in (B), with one reflector and one or more director, is known as a Yagi antenna, after the Japanese physicist, Dr. H. P. Yagi, its inventor.

When more signal gain is desired than can be obtained from a single antenna, two or more can be stacked, as shown in Fig. 20-12(C). One antenna is spaced above the other by approximately one-half wavelength, and the elements are interconnected by a length of transmission line. The twin-lead line to the receiver is attached to the center, as shown. The two impedances of the antennas are in parallel, and would tend to be halved.

The transmission line section interconnecting the two antennas, however, forms two quarter-wavelength stubs, and tends to raise the impedance at the point where the twin lead is attached, thus helping to maintain the normal impedance of the antennas.

MARCONI ANTENNA

Standard AM transmission is vertically polarized, and hence, for best results, the vertical receiving antenna should be employed. Because of the high degree of sensitivity of modern receivers, however, and the high power used by transmitters, signal reception is usually satisfactory with any antenna type. In most cases, a built-in ferrite-core antenna is sufficient for good reception of all nearby stations.

For transmission, a single quarter-wavelength vertical antenna is used, as shown in Fig. 20-13(A). The bottom of the antenna is grounded, and this procedure eliminates the necessity for using a half wavelength. When a vertical antenna is grounded, as shown in (A), it acts as though it were one-half wavelength long, because of the mirror-image effect. A grounded

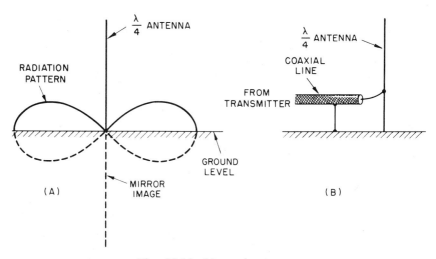

Fig. 20-13. Marconi antenna.

antenna behaves as though it were twice as long, just as a pencil appears twice as long when its end is placed against a mirror. The figure-eight radiation pattern is part of the theoretical mirror image. Hence, the vertical grounded antenna propagates in all directions along a horizontal plane from the antenna proper. This type antenna is known as the Marconi antenna, after G. M. Marconi (1874-1937), the Italian physicist. The vertical grounded antenna is usually fitted with a coaxial-cable arrangement, as shown in Fig. 20-13(B). Because the antenna is grounded, it is an unbalanced type, and the coaxial cable is a suitable transmission line. The outer conductor of the coaxial cable is grounded, as shown, and the center conductor is attached to the antenna a short distance from the ground point. The impedance of the Marconi antenna is zero at ground, and rises with antenna height. Hence, if the inner conductor of the coaxial line is moved along the antenna, a place will be found where an impedance match is obtained. With matched impedances the coaxial line delivers full R-F power to the antenna.

REVIEW QUESTIONS

1. For what other purposes can transmission lines be utilized, other than conveying signal information from an antenna to a receiver?

2. (a) How is the characteristic impedance of a transmission line calculated?
   (b) Is there a difference in the characteristic impedance of a twin-lead type transmission line, if 200 feet is used instead of 100 feet?

3. Briefly explain what is meant by standing waves, and how they are formed on a transmission line.

4. Briefly explain what information is obtained with respect to impedance matching when the standing-wave ratio is known.

5. A quarter-wavelength section of transmission line is attached to a generator, and the other end is short circuited. Briefly explain the type of characteristics such a line presents to the generator.

6. Briefly explain what is meant by skin effect.

7. By a schematic drawing, show a typical example of the use of stubs for constructing a low-pass filter.

8. (a) What is the shortest electrical length which can be employed for a basic antenna?
   (b) What is meant by a dipole type of antenna?

9. Briefly explain what is meant by vertical and horizontal polarization of antennas.

10. (a) What is the impedance of a dipole type of antenna, with respect to a half-wavelength antenna which has not been opened at the center?
    (b) What type of an antenna has more than 75 ohms of impedance?

11. Briefly explain the differences between a Hertz antenna and a Marconi antenna.

12. Briefly explain what is meant by a mirror image, with respect to a vertical antenna grounded at one end.

PRACTICAL PROBLEMS

1. In the design of a flexible transmission line, a section was tested and found to have 2.7 microhenries of inductance and 30 microfarads of capacitance. What is the impedance of the line?

2. In an R-F distribution system an open-wire line was used. Each of the two conductors had a diameter of 0.04 inch and the spacing between them was 2 inches. What is the characteristic impedance of this air-dielectric line?

3. The output from a UHF transmitter was connected to an antenna by a coaxial cable having air as the dielectric. The inner conductor consisted of a quarter-inch diameter copper conductor, and the inside diameter of the outer conductor measured one inch. What is the characteristic impedance of this coaxial line?

4. What would be the impedance of the line in Problem 3 if it has a dielectric material with a *k* of 4?

5. What is the wavelength in feet if the frequency is 123 megacycles?

6. A section of line 6 inches long was to be used as a resonant circuit. Neglecting the reactances contributed by other circuit components, what is the resonant frequency if this section of line is to form a quarter-wavelength circuit?

7. What is the length of a quarter-wavelength section of line at 984 megacycles?

21

TRANSDUCERS

INTRODUCTION

A number of input and output devices are utilized in conjunction with the circuits found in the different branches of electronics. Such units usually convert one form of energy to another and hence are known as *transducers*. Thus, a microphone is a transducer since it converts soundwave energy into electric signals. Similarly, a loudspeaker is a transducer because it converts electric signal energy to soundwaves. The transducer term, however, does not apply solely to the conversion of acoustical energy to electrical. A playback head on a tape recorder, for instance, is also a transducer because it converts the varying magnetic areas on tape to an electric signal. (An electric light bulb can be considered a transducer since it converts electric energy to visible lightwaves.)

While speakers, microphones, and recorder playback heads are common items familiar to most, there are a number of other transducers utilized in automation, industrial control, computer systems, and other allied branches of electronics. This chapter covers the variety of transducers (both input and output) that are encountered in these various branches of electronics, and the circuitry connections are illustrated and discussed.

SOLID-STATE TRANSDUCERS

The piezo effect with respect to crystals was discussed in Chapter 17. This principle is also utilized in the construction of microphones and

phonograph pick-up devices. One type of crystal which has been extensively used is that known as *rochelle salts* which also has a piezo-electric
effect, that is, it will produce an electric signal when sound waves strike
the crystal (or a diaphragm attached to the crystal). When two thin slabs
of the rochelle salt crystal are cemented together a type of cell is formed
which is known as the *bimorph* cell. Such a cell is sensitive to sound waves
and will produce an output signal which has a lower sensitivity than if a
diaphragm were used. For greater sensitivity, the arrangement shown at
Fig. 21-1(A) is used. The larger surface area of the diaphragm picks up
a greater amplitude of the sound waves which strike the diaphragm and
the movement is transferred to the crystal slab with a metal connecting
link as shown. The vibrations transferred to the bimorph cell sets up
mechanical stresses and strains which produce the electric signal output.

Such a crystal is also used in phonograph pick-up devices, as shown
at (B). Here, the phonograph record groove variations are picked up by
the phonograph needle and transferred to the crystal structure. The mechanical distortion which results from the vibrations again produces an
output signal as with the microphone.

Some ceramic materials also exhibit piezo-electric characteristics and
in recent years have been extensively used in microphones and phonograph
pick-ups. Their operating principles are identical to the rochelle-salts crys-

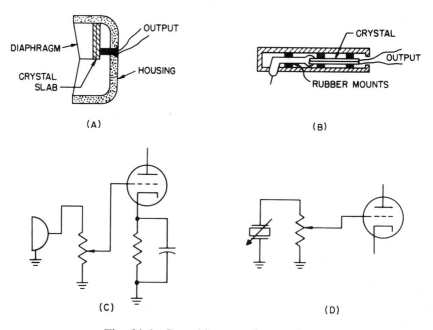

Fig. 21-1. Crystal input audio transducer.

tal except that they are less affected by humidity and temperature. The impedance of both crystal-type transducers is high, and in consequence can be connected directly to the input grid circuit of amplifier tubes without the necessity for using an impedance matching transformer. The input circuits for the microphone and phonograph pick-up are shown at Fig. 21-1(C) and (D). The variable resistor acts as a level (volume) control to regulate the over-all volume and to prevent overloading the grid circuit for high-level recordings or excessive sound amplitudes.

In industrial applications, solid-state transducers are often used to sense pressure or to indicate the relative pressure level. One type is manufactured from rare earths which, when processed, undergo a change in resistance when compressed. The rare earths are processed with zirconium tetrachloride and mounted in small metal housings. They are useful for sensing any variable physical tension, strain, vibration, or displacement.

A typical input system using a solid-state pressure transducer is shown in Fig. 21-2. Here, the 120-volt a-c line potential is stepped down to that required for the particular pressure transducer utilized. The pressure cell resistance will remain unchanged when no pressure is applied, and current flow through resistor R_1 is limited by the value of this resistor, as well as the resistance of the pressure transducer and the transformer secondary. When pressure is applied to the cell, its resistance decreases and more current flows through resistor R_1. The increased current through R_1 will raise the voltage drop across this resistor and hence an increase in output voltage is obtained for increased pressure.

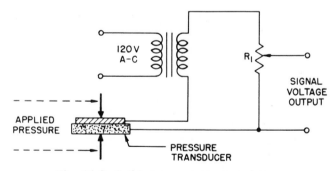

Fig. 21-2. Solid state pressure transducer.

Some pressure transducers have ratings from a few grams up to approximately 10 pounds of pressure, using a 1.5- or a 3-volt supply. Others have ratings to 25 or 50 pounds and still others can withstand a pressure of over 5,000 pounds. In some transducers of this type, a pressure differential of 15 pounds may provide a resistance change from zero to 900,000 ohms. Others, have a resistance of 2 or 3 megohms at 5,000 pounds pressure. The output may also be sensed in microamperes by placing a milliammeter in series with R_1. One application of such a device is in the sensing of pressure in pipe lines. Some types have sufficient sensitivity to indicate oil leakage of 1 pound per 5,000 pounds of oil pressure.

RESISTIVE TRANSDUCERS

As mentioned in Chapter 2, the amount of resistance within a conductor or a resistor depends on its cross section and length, as well as temperature and the composition of the materials making up the resistor. Thus, if a section of thin resistance wire is stretched, the decrease in its diameter and the increase in its length lowers its resistance value. This principle is employed to construct pressure-sensitive transducers for the measurement of force, weight, or strain. Such devices are called *strain gauges* and are widely used in industrial electronics.

One type of strain gauge is shown at Fig. 21-3(A). Here, the resistance wire is cemented to a plastic-treated paper carrier sheet and this is bonded directly to the material which is to be sensed for pressure, strain, or the stress resulting when force is applied. Such a strain gauge is known as a *bonded* type since it is fastened directly to the unit under pressure. When the resistance wire is utilized in this fashion, the wire lengths are usually from a fraction of an inch to approximately 6 inches, with an average diameter of 0.001 inch. The average resistance without stress is approximately 100 ohms.

The resistive change for applied pressure is slight but is detectable in

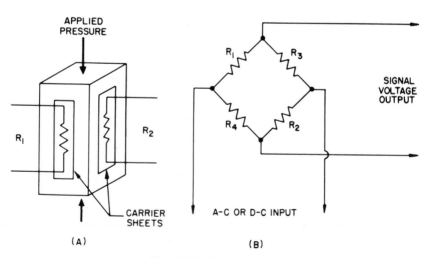

Fig. 21-3. Strain gauge.

a bridge circuit such as shown at (D). The signal output voltage can be amplified additionally as required. When force is applied to the top and bottom of the material which is being tested, the pressure which is created reduces the resistance of the R_1 and R_2 resistor strips. Since these are part of the bridge circuit, as shown at (B), the bridge circuit becomes unbalanced with a change for the resistance values of R_1 and R_2, and an output voltage is procured. (For Wheatstone bridge factors, see Chapter 5.)

Another resistive-type transducer is shown at Fig. 21-4(A). This unit is light-sensitive; that is, it changes its resistance value for changes of light intensity striking its surface. Thus, it is basically a photocell transducer. (Other photoelectric devices are discussed in Chapter 23.)

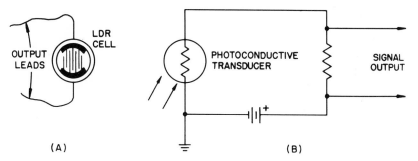

Fig. 21-4. Photocell transducers.

The photocell transducer shown at (A) is known as a *light-dependent resistor* (LDR), most types of which are sensitive throughout the entire visible range of light as well as through a portion of the infrared spectrum. Some of these cells have a resistance ratio in excess of 25,000 to 1 for a light-intensity change from total darkness to 1,400 foot-candles. They do not follow rapid changes in illumination, though the more intense the incident light, the quicker the response.

Their construction consists of a glass envelope containing a plate of photoconductive material approximately 0.028-inch thick. As shown at (A), metal-film electrodes form two interlocking combs which make up one side of the photoconductive coating. These electrodes increase the light sensitivity of the unit and also enlarge the area of sensitivity. The circuit for an LDR is shown at (B), and since these transducers are resistive in their characteristics, a voltage source is required as shown. Such photocells are known as *photoconductive* types in contrast to the photovoltaic types which require no additional voltage source, but produce an output voltage when light strikes the photoconductive surface.

The thermistor can also be employed as a resistive transducer. The thermistor, because resistance changes with the temperature, will produce an output signal voltage as shown in Fig. 21-5 which will vary as the thermistor resistance varies. Generally, however, thermistors are utilized in series with some circuit to provide a higher than normal resistance when current is first applied and then have a decreased resistance after other circuit elements have come up to temperature. One such application is in series-filament strings. When voltage is first applied the resistance of the filaments of the various tubes is low and the filament wires may be overloaded. A series thermistor, however, maintains a fairly high resistance until the filaments have warmed up and increased their resistance. At this time, the thermistor has a decreased resistance. Thus, the thermistor maintains a fairly stable circuit-resistance value during warmup time.

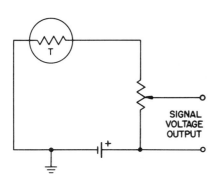

Fig. 21-5. Thermistor as a transducer.

INDUCTIVE INPUT TRANSDUCERS

In addition to the crystal-type microphones discussed earlier, inductive (magnetic) types are also utilized, as for example, the so-called *dynamic* type shown at Fig. 21-6(A). Structurally, this microphone resembles the PM-type speaker discussed in Chapter 19. It has a permanent magnet with E-shaped pole pieces in order to concentrate a strong magnetic field across the small coil between the air gaps. As shown, the coil is attached to a diaphragm in a fashion similiar to a speaker cone. (Actually, a PM speaker (Chapter 19) can be utilized as a microphone, though the quality of sound is not comparable to that obtained from a microphone specifically designed as such. Some intercommunicating systems used at short distances utilize the speaker for a microphone in the "talk" position.)

The dynamic microphone has a low impedance, since there are only a few turns on the coil. Thus, the 5 to 15 ohms of impedance must be stepped up by an input transformer before application to the grid circuit of a vacuum tube.

Another type of magnetic microphone is that shown at (B). This is a *ribbon* microphone (sometimes referred to as a *velocity* microphone.) As shown, a thin corrugated ribbon of aluminum alloy is suspended between two pole pieces. Since there is no diaphragm, a sound wave which impinges on the corrugated ribbon produces a force related to the velocity of the air pressure changes. This comes about because both the front and back of the ribbon are subjected to the sound pressure and the difference between the front- and back-pressure force causes the ribbon to move and cut the lines of force. Thus, a voltage is induced in the circuit composed of the ribbon and the primary of the transformer. As with the dynamic microphone, a step-up transformer is required since the impedance of the velocity microphone is also very low.

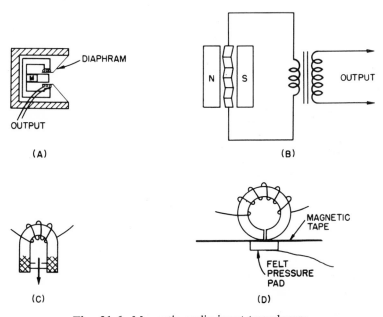

Fig. 21-6. Magnetic audio input transducers.

The magnet-coil principle is also used for phono pick-up units as shown at Fig. 21-6(C). Here, as the needle armature rides in the record grooves and vibrates in accordance with the groove variations, the needle armature cuts across the lines of force produced by the magnet and hence produces an output signal voltage. Here, as with the magnetic microphones, the impedance is low and a step-up transformer is required.

The microphone transducers converted variations in air pressure into electric signals, while the magnetic phonograph pick-up converted mechanical vibrations into electric signals. In tape recording, variations of magnetic density along a plastic tape (coated with magnetic materials) is sensed by a playback head as shown at Fig. 21-6(D). Here, a felt pressure pad presses the magnetic tape against the playback head. The latter has a very small air gap, and as the tape passes over this air gap, the alternating magnetic field, represented by varying degrees of magnetism along the tape, will induce a voltage in the playback head pick-up coil. The output leads from this coil thus furnishes to the amplifier input circuit the signal information which was originally placed on the tape during the recording process.

The plastic magnetic tape is used not only in home tape recorders, but also in industrial electronics, and computer systems, among other fields. In computers, it is used to store pulse information representing numerical or alphabetical values, and as such becomes a storage (memory) section of the computer. In automation, it is used to store a program of sequential steps for milling, fabricating, or other automatic processes. In television, it is used to store picture information for rebroadcasting at a future date.

Reactive transducers are also used in industrial electronics to sense mechanical changes and convert them to electric signals. One such device is the inductive differential transducer shown at Fig. 21-7(A). This operates on the principle that when a plunger-type core is moved in or out

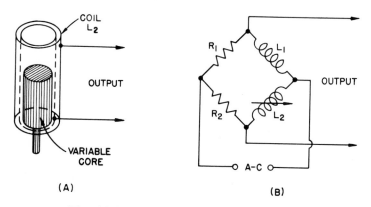

Fig. 21-7. Inductive differential transducer.

of a coil, the inductance changes because the permeability is effected by the metallic core. Usually, the plunger-type core is attached to a rod, and this rod in turn is fastened to a sensing rod, lever, or roller as required. A spring is employed to keep the plunger almost out of the coil, and hence pressure is required to move the plunger into the coil. If a roller is applied to the bottom of the rod, the transducer can be used for measuring and controlling variations in thickness or curvature of any material over which the roller rides. Similarly, a lever arm could be attached to it to sense lateral variations in assembly-line sheet-metal forming or for other control purposes.

Since the inductive differential transducer has a variation in its inductance value for mechanical movements of the core, the inductance changes can be sensed by utilizing a bridge circuit such as shown at (B). When the differential transducer has an inductance equal to L_1, the bridge will be balanced (assuming R_1 and R_2 are also of equal value). Thus, for any mechanical change sensed by the transducer, there will be a change in its inductive value, and hence an unbalance of the bridge. The unbalanced bridge will then produce an output voltage in proportion to the inductance change. The latter, of course, is proportional to the mechanical change sensed by the transducer.

Another type of transducer is that known as the *tachometer*. The tachometer principle is illustrated in Fig. 21-8 and consists of a small d-c generator with a shaft extending from its housing, and a calibrated d-c meter. When the shaft of the generator is rotated, it will produce a voltage having an amplitude proportional to the shaft rotational speed. Thus, the generator is a transducer, since it converts mechanical revolutions to electric voltage. This principle is widely used in industrial electronics for measuring the number of revolutions per minute of a variety of rotating devices such as motors, machine shafts, and spindles. The output from the d-c generator is applied to a d-c meter but the dial of the latter is directly calibrated to read rpm.

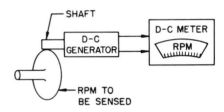

Fig. 21-8. Tachometer transducer.

CAPACITIVE TRANSDUCERS

Shaft rotations can also be sensed by a variable capacitor as shown at Fig. 21-9(A). Here, the shaft which is to be tested for rotation is connected to the rotor of a variable capacitor which can turn completely without stop. The output is then applied to a capacitive bridge and when the shaft rotates from its normal position, the degree of rotation is sensed by the proportionate bridge unbalance. The capacitor can also be utilized to sense pressure changes as shown at Fig. 21-9(B). Here, two metal plates are separated by a flexible dielectric material as shown. With no pressure applied, the capacitor represented as the differential transducer (C_1) has the same value as capacitor C_2 in the bridge circuit shown. When pressure is applied, it compresses the dielectric material and brings the plates of the capacitor closer together. The result is an increase in capacity and an unbalancing of the bridge. The output voltage produced when the bridge is unbalanced will be in proportion to the pressure applied.

The fact that the amount of dielectric in the capacitor affects the capacitance value is also utilized in industrial electronics to sense fluid levels as shown at Fig. 21-10(A). Here, capacitor plates are suspended in a container and when the fluid level is near the top, the fluid between the capacitor plates furnishes a maximum amount of dielectric material and

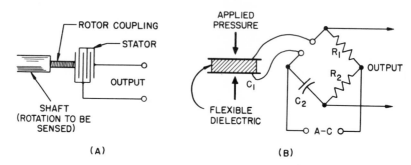

Fig. 21-9. Capacitive differential transducers.

hence the maximum capacity is the result. As the fluid level drops, the dielectric constant also changes and hence the capacitance decreases. Thus, the output capacitance reading can be calibrated in proportion to the fluid level in the container. Again, a bridge network can be utilized to produce a voltage in proportion to the changes in fluid level.

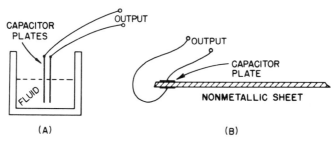

Fig. 21-10. Liquid level and thickness sensing.

Bridge networks need not necessarily be employed to sense reactive changes. The reactance circuit discussed earlier in Chapter 19 can also be used for specific sensing of reactance changes. Meters which read reactance can also be utilized to give a visual indication by having the meter dials calibrated in terms of the mechanical changes which are to be sensed.

The dielectric factor of capacitors can also be utilized for sensing changes in thickness of nonmetallic material as shown at Fig. 21-10(B).

In this case, capacitor plates are placed above and below the material and the thickness which the material should have is the reference point with respect to the capacity value obtained. Thus, as the nonmetallic sheet moves through the capacitor plates, an increase in thickness will result in a decrease in capacitance and a decrease in thickness will produce a higher capacitance. Here again various circuits or measuring devices can be employed and calibrated to indicate actual material thicknesses along the sheet.

In industrial electronics some special type capacitors are also utilized having what is known as *ferroelectric* or *nonlinear* characteristics. Such capacitors have dielectric materials which include titanium dioxide, barium titanate, strontium titanate, etc. When any one of these materials is used as the dielectric of a capacitor, the capacitance value is subject to change over 50% when a voltage change across the capacitor occurs from approximately zero to 200 volts. Such capacitors not only undergo a capacitance change for voltage, but also for temperature.

This is shown in Fig. 21-11, where the dielectric constant of the ferroelectric capacitor is plotted against temperature on the left and voltage on the right. At normal operating temperatures, the dielectric constant is at its highest point, and this peak level is known as the *Curie* point. For either a decrease or increase of temperature around the Curie point, there is a decrease in the dielectric constant and hence a decrease in the capacitance of

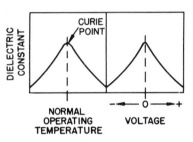

Fig. 21-11. Characteristics of ferroelectric capacitors.

the unit. The temperature at which the Curie point is established depends on the composition of the dielectric material. For the graph at the right of Fig. 21-11, the dielectric constant reaches its highest value when no voltage is applied across the capacitor. For the application of either a negative or a positive potential, however, there is a decrease in the dielectric constant and again a decrease in the capacitance. Thus, such a nonlinear capacitor can be utilized to sense temperature changes as well as voltage changes and hence these devices have transducer characteristics.

INDUCTIVE OUTPUT TRANSDUCERS

There are a variety of output load units utilized in electronics. Speaker systems have already been covered in Chapter 19, and these represent load systems which have transducer characteristics since they convert electric signals into sound energy. In addition to speakers, some of the other devices include those shown in Fig. 21-12. At (A) is shown a magnetic tape-recorder head. This is similar in construction to the magnetic play-back head discussed earlier, except that this device is used to magnetize sections of the tape to conform to the signal current circulating through the recording-head inductance. The output signals from the power amplifier are coupled to the recording head with a step-down transformer, to match the relatively high impedance of the output amplifier to the low impedance of the recording head. The signal energy which then circulates in the coil sets up a magnetic field which varies in intensity to conform to the signal energy. Thus, across the air gap, the changing magnetic lines of force magnetize sections of the tape.

Another type of output transducer is shown at (B) which is extensively used in industrial electronics. Here, a stylus mechanism is used which glides over a moving sheet of paper to graph visually the signal energy applied to the recording head. The stylus or recording pen moves in accordance with the signal energy and hence traces out the signal as shown on the paper. If a mechanism is also employed with the recording head to move it laterally, a plot of both the X and Y axes can be obtained. Crystal-type output transducers could also be used, although the magnetic type are capable of handling more power.

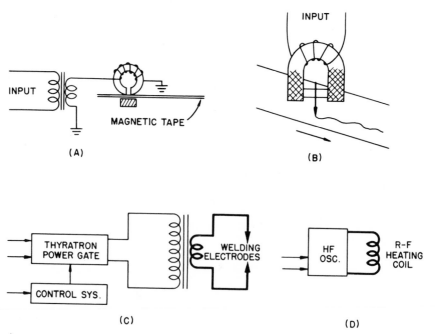

Fig. 21-12. Industrial output transducers.

Another type of output transducer is that found in industrial welding processes. Arc and spot welding, however, are primarily resistive with respect to the load imposed on the amplifier. When an arc is drawn, the current flow through the arc represents power dissipated in a very low resistance with high currents. Similarly, in spot welding, when two metal plates are to be welded they provide sufficient surface-contact resistance to generate heat when passing current from the welding electrodes. The heat causes a fusion of the sheets at the spot to be welded. A typical output circuit for welding is shown at Fig. 21-12(C). The line voltage is applied through gated thyratron circuits and stepped down by the transformer so that a low voltage and high current are available. The voltage may range from approximately 2 to 10 volts but the current which flows may range from a few thousand amperes to well over 50 thousand amperes for the larger welders. The thyratron control circuits assure proper power contol and minimize burn-through or insufficient welding characteristics.

In arc welding, a high-intensity arc is established between the two electrodes and thus applies heat to the metal to be welded. The electrodes are composed of special welding rods which are melted by the arc, so that the melted rod material flows on to the metal being welded.

An inductive type load is established in induction heating, illustrated at (D). Here, a high-frequency oscillator produces an R-F output signal which is applied to the material to be heated by use of the large, high-power-handling coil, as shown. The R-F fields generate heat by induction to the material. In some instances the high-power induction-heating energy is obtained directly from the power mains by using motor-driven generators which have signal frequencies of several thousand cps. These may range from a few kilowatts to over one thousand kilowatts. Industrial applications include the annealing of metals, the heating of metals for specific purposes, hardening, and brazing processes.

TUBE-TYPE OUTPUT TRANSDUCERS

When a vacuum or gas-filled tube is designed to display some sort of visible pattern in proportion to signal voltages applied to it, a transducer is again formed. One such transducer is the tuning-indicator tube used in receivers, some test equipment, and other applications where precise adjustments are necessary. Such tuning-indicator tubes have a florescent material within them which glows when in operation. The area of glow is varied in accordance with the voltage amplitude applied to the grid of the tube.

The basic circuit for the tuning-indicator tube is shown in Fig. 21-13. The control voltage (such as avc) is applied to the control grid of the tube

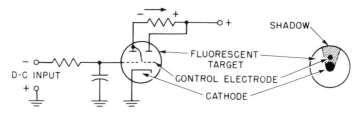

Fig. 21-13. Tuning indicator circuit.

through a filter network made up of a series resistor and a shunt capacitor. The purpose for the filter network is to eliminate any a-c type of signals. The tube itself is composed of a triode section shown at the left, and a fluorescent-target section shown at the right. A control electrode is between the common cathode and the fluorescent target. The latter is in the form of a circular area as shown at the right of Fig. 21-13. The cathode emits electrons which are attracted by the positive potential of the fluorescent target. The latter can be considered as an anode which attracts the electrons from the cathode. The fluorescent coating, however, creates a glow when the electrons strike it. A control electrode is placed between the cathode and the target so that it can repel the electrons which strike one area of the target. The shaded area which is created when the tube is functioning resembles the human eye, and hence the tube has also been called a "magic eye" tube.

When the negative potential which is applied to the control grid is of a low value, plate-current flow from the cathode to the anode of the left section of the tube will be of high value. The high current flow through the plate resistor establishes a polarity as shown. The voltage drop across the plate resistor establishes a potential difference between the anode of the triode section and the fluorescent target. The control electrode, however, has the same potential as the triode plate. Because the control electrode is less positive than the fluorescent target, it tends to repel the electrons from the cathode, and a shadow area is created because few electrons go past the control electrode to strike the fluorescent target. With a negative potential applied to the d-c input, however, current flow from the cathode to the plate of the triode section decreases, and the voltage drop across the plate resistor declines. With a low value of voltage drop across the plate resistor, only a small difference in potential exists between the control electrode and the target. Consequently, the less negative potential of the control electrode does not repel as many electrons and the shadow area becomes more narrow. Thus, the variation in shadow area is an indication of the change of potential applied to the input of the tuning-indicator circuit, and the tube acts as a visual indication of circuit potentials which are to be used as a reference.

There are a variety of other tubes also used as output transducers, which convert electric signal energy to some form of visible light. For instance, a television picture tube is a form of transducer as was discussed in Chapter 19. In Chapter 22, the oscilloscope tube is discussed and this is another form of transducer converting electric energy to visible light information.

Another type of tube transducer is that which displays numerically the numbers from a computer or from some measuring instrument. One such tube is the *Nixie* manufactured by Burroughs Corporation. This tube comes in several sizes, from a 1-inch diameter tube to some almost 2 inches in diameter. The basic tube has 10 cathodes and one common anode and is a cold-cathode gas tube which displays a number by ionization within the tube and a glow around a particular cathode. Each cathode within the tube is an element shaped like a number. When a voltage is applied at one of the pins in relation to the anode, the number corresponding to that pin will become visible by gas ionization glow associated with the pin. If, for instance, the cathode representing the numeral "eight" had a voltage applied to it, this number would appear as shown at Fig. 21-14(A). A number of such indicating tubes can be used side by side to display a number of any desired length. The schematic for the Nixie is shown at (B).

Another indicating tube is the Dekatron shown at Fig. 21-14(C). The design of this tube is such that successive pulses applied to the input

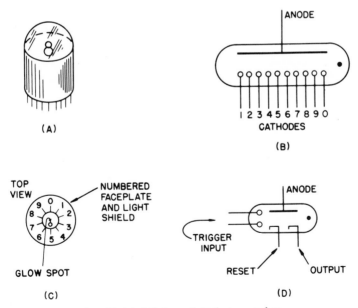

Fig. 21-14. Nixie and Dekatron tubes.

terminals produce a glowing spot which moves progressively around the top of the tube. The glow moves one segment for each pulse applied, and thus can indicate any digit from zero through nine. A faceplate (bezel) is placed over the top of the tube as illustrated at Fig. 21-14(C).

The Dekatron is also a basic transfer device, because an output pulse is produced from an output terminal, shown at (D), for complete progression from zero to nine (decade). Thus, if several such tubes are coupled together, they will form a counter for a pulse train. If pulses are applied to the trigger input, the glow spot will move around the first tube, and when it reaches the count of 10 at the "zero" indication, an output pulse from the first tube triggers the second tube so that its glow spot moves to the "one" position. Thus, an indication of the number to be read out is visible up to the limit of the tubes employed.

SOLID-STATE OUTPUT TRANSDUCERS

As mentioned earlier, crystal output transducers are found occasionally in audio devices. A typical example are the crystal type earphones which are available for either monaural or stereophonic reception. Output crystal recording devices have also been utilized on occasion, though as mentioned earlier, the magnetic types produce greater output. Another type of ouput transducer having crystal characteristics is the ferrite-core assembly utilized in the storage systems of digital computers. These ferrite cores are composed of tiny ferrite rings smaller than a pin head. Ferrite has a crystal spinel composition which is ferromagnetic and brittle; the cores have a very good magnetization factor, and the hysteresis loop is virtually a rectangle. Such a characteristic lends itself to rapid switching from one magnetized state to another, and hence is valuable in the storing of signal pulse data.

Because of the rectangular-loop characteristic, the ferrite core is essentially a bistable device. For computer storage purposes, a magnetic field is applied to cause the ferrite core to become magnetized in one direction. Such a direction is assigned either the representation "zero" or "one" as desired, with the opposite field representing the opposite designation. For instance, if a north and south pole is chosen to represent "one," a south and north pole (magnetized in the opposite direction) represents "zero."

The cores are wired as shown in Fig. 21-15. While only four cores appear in the vertical and horizontal plane, practical ferrite-core storage planes may have as many as 50, 100, or more in a single line.

As shown, individual insulated wires are threaded through each core, with the vertical wires intercepting the horizontal wires at the core centers.

In switching the cores, the amplitude of the signal voltage applied to any single wire is held at a value sufficiently low so that it represents approximately one-half of the amplitude necessary to change the magnetic field. Thus, if such a half-signal voltage were applied to the first horizontal wire, designated as *A*, all the cores in the vertical *A* plane would be subjected to a slight magnetizing field, but not enough to reverse the polarity of the magnetism. The magnetic field which is produced, however, is sufficient to move the flux density along the upper portion of the hysteresis loop to the point marked *P* in Fig. 21-16. Since this is not sufficient to reach the lower-left saturation point of the hysteresis loop, the direction of magnetism is unchanged. If, now, vertical line No. 2 is also energized by such a half-amplitude signal, the combinations of the magnetic fields from the *A* wire and the No. 2 wire become sufficient to switch the magnetic state of the ferrite core intercepted by the *A* and No. 2 wire into the opposite direction. This comes about because the No. 2 wire half-energized the second vertical row of cores, and the *A* wire half-energized the first horizontal row of cores. Only the top second core was energized sufficiently (by virtue of the combined fields) to switch its magnetized state into the opposite direction.

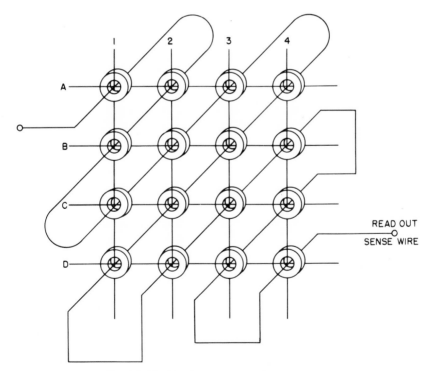

Fig. 21-15. Ferrite-core computer storage.

When the signal energy leaves, the magnetized state will be as shown at Q of Fig. 21-16. Thus, by a proper selection of any two wires, a particular core can be pinpointed for a reversal of its magnetic state from its representative "zero" condition to a representative "one" condition. Thus, any core on the unit can be reversed in magnetic polarity to represent the digit "one." By applying a reverse-polarity signal voltage to the appropriate horizontal and vertical lines, the core can be energized in the opposite direction to represent zero. When a core is switched from the "one" state to the "zero" state, it is known as *clearing*.

The stored information for any particular core is read out by the diagonal wire shown in Fig. 21-15. This wire is sometimes referred to as a *sense* wire. Upon the application of the clearing voltage, the shift of the magnetic field of the core which is being cleared sets up a changing magnetic field which induces a voltage into the sense wire.

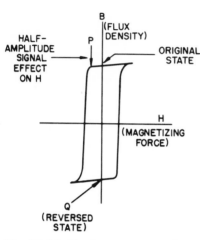

Fig. 21-16. Ferrite-core reversal.

This is utilized at the terminals of the sense wire for read-out purposes and applied to appropriate amplifiers and sensing devices.

The ferrite cores are strung on frames, and a number of frames may be stacked one above the other to increase the number of pulse signals which can be retained.

REVIEW QUESTIONS

1. Why are transformers unnecessary when coupling crystal input transducers to the grid circuit of a vacuum-tube amplifier?

2. Reproduce the circuit for a solid-state pressure transducer and explain its function.

3. Explain the principles involved in a bonded strain gauge.

4. Why is an LDR cell a photoconductive device?

5. Why is a ribbon microphone also called a *velocity* microphone?

6. Reproduce the drawing of the magnetic playback head and explain how it picks up signals. Why is this a transducer?

7. What is an inductive differential transducer used for in industrial electronics?

8. Explain the basic principles of a tachometer.

9. Why must a-c be used for the bridge circuit of the capacitive differential transducers shown in Fig. 21-9?

10. Explain how liquid level and thickness sensing is accomplished electronically in industry.

11. Discuss the characteristics of ferroelectric capacitors.

12. Reproduce drawings at two industrial output transducers (other than tube types) and explain their function.

13. Reproduce the drawings of two tube-type output transducers and explain their function.

14. If the lower-right ferrite core in Fig. 21-15 is to be energized, what amplitude signal voltages must be applied, and to what terminals?

15. Explain the purpose of a *sense wire* in a ferrite-core computer storage.

22

TEST

INSTRUMENTS

INTRODUCTION

In all activities involving design, maintenance, or the modification and improvement of electronic devices, the technician must utilize various units of test instruments as functional tools. By use of test equipment one can evaluate circuit function in terms of the voltage, current, and resistance units which are present. Test equipment also expedites trouble shooting, since it permits readings that can localize circuit faults. This is done by ascertaining which component values or unit measurements do not coincide with the pre-established values indicated by the manufacturer. Test equipment also permits the proper adjustment and alignment of various electronic circuits encountered in transmitting, receiving, and industrial electronic applications.

Test instruments are available in a variety of models, from the basic combination meters that read voltage, resistance, and current, to the more complex oscilloscopes, signal generators, and other devices. With, however, even the simplest equipment, a competent technician familiar with the gear can gather much information regarding the performance of a specific circuit. In such readings, however, when the necessity arises for delving deeper into complex circuitry, or when more precise measurements are needed, more elaborate test equipment must be utilized. Thus, even though the technician may be exposed only to a minimum of test equipment in the initial aspects of his professional activity, he should be familiar with the various units of test equipment which are generally available for the completion of various tests and measurements. A knowledge of the manner in which such equipment is used, plus an understanding of the limitations and applications of each particular piece of test equipment, will not only enable the technician to utilize such instruments, but he will also be able to evaluate the merits of the test equipment, and thus be in a better position to judge whether or not it will perform the precise functions which the occasion demands.

MULTIMETERS

When it becomes necessary to read voltages and currents, and to take resistive measurements, the basic individual meters for such purposes, as described in Chapter 5, can be employed. The acquisition of an individual meter for each type of test, however, becomes a costly affair, and a single meter with proper circuitry can be utilized for making all such tests. The most inexpensive type of test equipment which performs the measurement functions involved in voltage, current, and resistance is the *multimeter*. Since this is a combination meter reading *volts-ohms-milliamperes,* it is often referred to as a "VOM." In its most basic form, the multimeter utilizes a 0-1-milliampere meter. With proper combinations of shunt resistances and switches, the basic milliammeter becomes a multirange instrument capable of reading current values from a few milliamperes to several amperes. (Virtually all basic measuring devices use the so-called *D'Arsonval* meter movement which, basically, consists of a small inductance pivoted so it can turn freely between the poles of a permanent magnet. The indicating needle is fastened to the coil.)

Besides being capable of current measurements, this instrument may also be converted to a voltmeter by switching various resistors in series with the meter. The meter also functions as an a-c voltmeter, by employing a germanium- or silicon-diode rectifier to convert the a-c to d-c, for application to the meter.

Figure 22-1 shows a typical volt-milliampere switching circuit. The range selection switch is the two-pole rotary type as shown. For voltage readings, the switch selects various series resistors for the ranger required. When in the current-reading position, appropriate resistors shunt the meter as described in Chapter 5. In the position shown in Fig. 22-1, the switch shunts resistor R_2 across the meter and converts the latter to a 0-10-milliampere scale meter. With the switch at the 50-microampere range, no

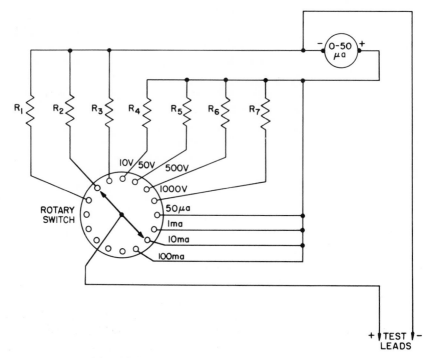

Fig. 22-1. Volt-milliampere switching circuit.

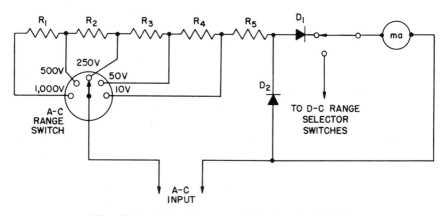

Fig. 22-2. A-C voltmeter switch circuit of VOM.

resistance shunts the meter because this is the basic meter full-scale current range.

The basic a-c voltmeter switch circuit for a VOM is shown in Fig. 22-2. Even though two diodes are used, the rectification is of the half-wave type, with diode D_1 being the meter rectifier. Diode D_2 shunts the opposite polarity alternation of the a-c being measured and thus removes the reverse-polarity voltage from across the D_1 rectifier and the meter. This inverse peak voltage could alter meter accuracy and performance. In the switch position shown, 250 volts is the maximum a-c scale range, using resistors R_3, R_4, and R_5 in series to provide the necessary voltage drops. In the 10-volt range, only R_5 is in series, while on the 1,000-volt range, all resistors are in series.

For a-c meters the scales are calibrated so that rms values of current and voltage are indicated. The average current (or voltage) for an alternation is 0.636 × peak. For half-wave rectification the average value occurs only for one-half of each cycle; hence the average value over a complete cycle (and successive cycles) is half of 0.636. Thus, for a 10-milliampere peak value (rms = 7 milliamperes) the average value is $6.36/2 = 3.18$ miliamperes, and meter calibration must take this into consideration. With multimeters using full-wave rectification, both alternations of the a-c are rectified and the average value is the full 0.636 of peak value. When full-wave rectification is utilized, the common method is to employ the bridge-type rectifier described earlier in Chapter 14.

If a multimeter has a 1,000-ohm-per-volt unit (see Chapter 5), the input resistance is rather low for voltage measurements, so that the device loads down the circuit to which it is attached. Such loading occurs because the amount of current which flows through the multimeter represents a current *shunt* across the resistor, or other device where voltage is to be measured. If, for instance, the 50-volt scale is utilized, the ohmmeter presents a resistance of 50 × 1,000, or 50,000 ohms. If the meter is used to measure the voltage across a 50,000-ohm resistor, its application to the resistor would be the same as though the resistor were shunted by another having the same 50,000 ohm value. Thus, the 50,000 ohms represented by the resistor in the circuit would be reduced to 25,000 ohms and, in consequence, double the amount of current would be drawn than would otherwise be the case. For this reason, such a multimeter gives rise to some inaccuracy when making voltage measurements. The resistance of the meter, however, rises with higher scales and, for the 2,500-volt scale, the shunting resistance as represented by the meter would be 2.5 megohms. A better multimeter is formed if it uses a 20,000-ohm-per-volt meter, which has considerably less loading effect on circuits. Even less loading effect is produced by the costlier multimeters employing 50,000-ohm-per-volt meter movements.

The ohmic ranges of the multimeters are obtained by the methods described earlier in Chapter 5. In most multimeters several flashlight cells are used for the ohmmeter circuitry. Again, appropriate switches are used for selection of ranges, or for changing from ohmic readings to voltage or current.

From the foregoing, it is evident that multimeters can be employed for the measurement of d-c currents flowing in the cathode, plate, screen, and other vacuum-tube circuits, as well as transistor circuits. The tester can also be employed for measuring the various d-c voltage drops across resistors and at the bleeder sections of power supplies. Besides such measurements, the meter can also be employed to read the a-c voltage across power-supply transformers, as well as the a-c filament voltages of the various tubes. In addition, the ohmic values of resistors, transformer windings, and other units can be measured. The ohmmeter scale is also useful for checking continuity in circuits. While this process is essentially that of taking resistance readings, it will establish whether or not an open or short circuit exists and, hence, proves useful in trouble-shooting work. The limitations of the multitester are imposed by the ranges of the various scales, as well as the loading effect.

A typical VOM is shown in Fig. 22-3, and is the Model 260 of Simpson Electric Company. The d-c and a-c voltage ranges extend to 5,000; current readings in milliamperes to 500 and ampere ranges to 10. A basic 50-microampere meter movement is employed. Resistance ranges extend as

Fig. 22-3. Volt-ohm-milliammeter.
(Courtesy Simpson Electric Company.)

high as 20 megohms. The decibel ranges (1mw − 600 ohms) extend from a −8 to +50. Various accessories are available, including probes for extending voltage readings to 50,000. The dimensions are 5¼ inches × 7 inches × 3⅛ inches and the weight is less than 4 pounds.

Variations among commercial VOM models which are encountered consist primarily in a rearrangement of the terminals. The instructions which accompany the multitester should be consulted with respect to the loading which is to be expected. The instruction sheets also indicate the ranges of the scales, and explain procedures recommended for proper measurements of voltages, currents, and resistances.

TYPICAL APPLICATIONS

When the multimeter is employed as a continuity-checking device, the ohmmeter scale is utilized, and the equipment to be checked *is shut off or disconnected from the power mains.* If, for instance, the continuity of a power supply is to be checked, the ohmmeter can be placed across the a-c plug, as shown in Fig. 22-4. With the switch open, no reading should

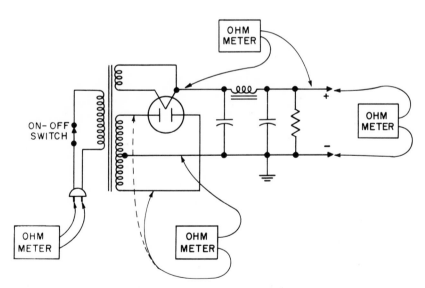

Fig. 22-4. Continuity checks on power supply.

be obtained and, when the switch is closed, a low ohmic value should be present. This is a continuity check of both the primary of the transformer and the switch. It indicates whether or not the switch is operating properly, and also shows whether or not the primary winding is open. This is the extent of a continuity check and, if there is reason to suspect that some of the transformer windings are shorted, the ohmic value as read by the meter would have to be compared with the value shown in the service notes or indicated by the manufacturer.

With the power shut off, a similar continuity check can be made of each secondary winding. The rectifier tube can also be removed and a continuity check made of the filaments, which would indicate whether or not the tube is burned out. (This will not indicate whether the tube has good emission, but merely provides a check of whether the filament is open.) An additional continuity check can then be made from the filament of the rectifier tube to the B+ output terminal, as shown in Fig. 22-4. Such a check will establish whether the filter choke (or filter resistor) is open. By placing the ohmmeter across the output of the power supply, a continuity check will indicate whether the filter capacitors are establishing an abnormal load (due to leakage), and are thus creating a partial short. An open bleeder section can also be ascertained by this procedure.

Similar continuity checks can be made on other circuits in identical fashion. With the receiver shut off, an amplifier stage, such as shown in Fig. 22-5, can be checked for continuity by placing the ohmmeter from

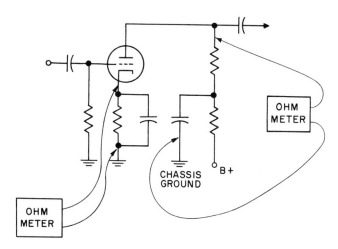

Fig. 22-5. Continuity check on an amplifier.

the anode of the tube to the chassis. A meter-needle deflection will indicate that no open circuit condition exists in the decoupling resistor or load resistor, while a short may indicate a defective decoupler capacitor or internal short within the tube. A check from cathode to ground will indicate if the cathode resistor is open, or the bypass capacitor shorted.

Continuity checks are made to establish whether an open or short circuit exists, and the actual ohmic values obtained are of little consequence, since in most instances the continuity for several series resistors or inductances may be involved. When a continuity check has localized the defect to a particular circuit, individual ohmic checks can be made of the various resistors, inductances, and other units involved.

VACUUM-TUBE VOLTMETER

The vacuum-tube voltmeter (VTVM) is similar to the multitester, since it is a single instrument which performs a number of measuring functions. The VTVM, however, has greater ranges with respect to voltage and resistance readings, and hence is more versatile. The VTVM also has a high input resistance and, for this reason, does not load down circuits as much as the multitester.

In a more inexpensive VTVM, only the d-c voltage scale uses the VTVM principle, while the a-c readings are obtained in similar fashion to that employed for the multitester. The more expensive VTVM, however, has a number of refinements which includes the VTVM principle for the a-c scale, as well as provisions for reading peak-to-peak voltages.

Since the vacuum-tube voltmeter has such a high input impedance, with little loading on the circuits under test, the more accurate readings which are obtained have made this instrument the most popular with technicians for trouble shooting radio and television receivers, as well as for laboratory work involving research and design. Because of the high sensitivity of the VTVM instrument, the ohmmeter range is capable of measuring resistances up to 1,000 megohms.

Special probes are also available for use with the vacuum-tube voltmeter, for extending the useful range of the various scales to permit a greater scope of tests. A conventional VTVM does not incorporate a milliampere or ampere scale. Current values can, however, be ascertained by use of Ohm's law. Thus, a voltage reading across a resistor, if the resistance value is known, will indicate current, when the voltage is divided by the resistance. Since the VTVM also incorporates an accurate ohmmeter, the unknown resistance can also be read, when it is necessary to establish the amount of current flowing therein.

Other probes are also available as accessories to the vacuum-tube voltmeter, one of which is the R-F probe. This probe contains a germanium- or silicone-diode crystal which converts R-F energy to d-c, so that the calibrated values can be read on the VTVM scale. The R-F probe permits direct measurement of audio, supersonic, and R-F voltages. Most such probes are of the peak-indicating type; that is, they will indicate a value almost equal to the positive peak voltage of the signal which is measured.

Some probes of this type will read amplitudes of signals having frequencies ranging between 20 cycles and 300 megacycles, which means that readings can be obtained for voltages from the low audio range to the upper limits of the 13 channel television frequencies. Other probes extend the d-c voltage-measurement range of the VTVM to as high as 50,000 volts, which is useful for reading the high picture tube anode voltages encountered in television receivers.

As with the multimeter, the instruction sheets accompanying the VTVM should be referred to, so that the full capabilities of the instrument can be utilized. The VTVM can also be employed for continuity checking, in similar fashion to the methods detailed for the multimeter.

There are a number of different types of VTVM on the market, including a number of units which come in kit form. Virtually each one is an excellent example of modern electronic design and, when accurately calibrated, becomes a valuable tool for the technician. Since vacuum tubes are employed in the VTVM, a power supply is necessary and, for this reason, many vacuum-tube voltmeters must be plugged into the a-c power mains. Some, however, operate on batteries for portable applications.

A typical VTVM is that shown in Fig. 22-6, and is the RCA *Voltohmyst* type WV-77E. The d-c voltmeter ranges for this instrument have an input resistance of 11 megohms. The VTVM reads d-c and a-c voltages to 1,500 volts, and peak-to-peak values of sine waves to 4,000 volts. Frequency response is ±5% from 40 cps to 5 megacycles. A single 1.5 cell is used for the ohmmeter circuits and resistance readings up to 1,000 megohms are possible in seven ranges.

TUBE CHECKERS

There are a variety of tube checkers on the market, and a typical one is illustrated in Fig. 22-7. This instrument is the Heathkit model IT-21 which is an emission-type tester. It uses a roll chart listing the switch settings necessary for the tube to be tested and checks for emission, shorts, leakage, open element, and filament continuity. A 1-milliampere meter is used, indicating bad tubes, questionable ones, and good ones.

The simplest and most inexpensive method for testing tubes is by the emission process. The tester connects all tube grids together with the anode, and the cathode; emission is then compared to the value considered as a standard for the tube under test. A more costly tube tester is the transconductance type wherein standard voltage values are applied to each tube element. The resultant plate-current value indicates the transconductance of the tube under test for static conditions. A dynamic transconductance test consists of setting up the tube elements as with the static test, but

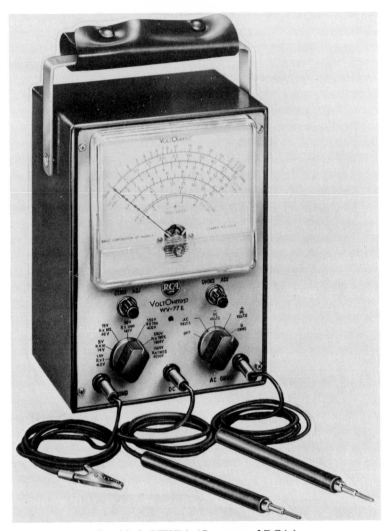

Fig. 22-6. VTVM. (Courtesy of RCA.)

also applying an a-c signal to the tube so that the anode current compares to that experienced in actual electronic circuitry. Thus, the anode current varies in relation to the signal applied to the grid, and represents a dynamic transconductance condition. A companion tube tester to that shown in Fig. 22-7 is available from the Heath Company and is a transconductance type, model TT-1A.

Most tube checkers have provisions for modernizing the checker, as newer tubes are produced by the various manufacturers. Where a roll chart is used for ascertaining the various settings for a particular tube,

Fig. 22-7. Tube checker. (Courtesy of Health Co.)

a new roll chart may be issued periodically, to keep the instrument up to date.

Since the physical make-up of the various tube checkers differs to a considerable extent, it is essential that the instruction manual which accompanies the tube checker be referred to, in order to utilize the instrument to its fullest capabilities. Unfamiliarity with the manner in which the tube checker should be employed may result in damage to the tubes. An abnormal application of filament potentials to the heaters of the tube to be checked can mean a tube burn-out, while excessive plate potentials could impair the emission characteristics of the cathode structure. For this reason, a careful study should be made of the operational principles before a tube is inserted.

CAPACITOR CHECKER

A capacitor checker is a useful device for servicing and laboratory work, since it gives a reading of the value of a capacitor as well as indicating its power factor in terms of leakage resistance.

Capacitor checkers usually employ a balanced-bridge circuit which compares the value of the unknown capacitor to that of precision-value capacitors in the instrument. A magic-eye type of indicating tube is usually employed, such as shown on the panel of the capacitor checker in Fig.

22-8. The probes of the checker are applied across the capacitor to be tested, and the approximate range is selected. The dial is then rotated until the shadow area of the magic-eye tube indicates a balanced bridge. The value of the capacitor, in microfarads or micromicrofarads, is then read directly on the scale. Most capacitor checkers also permit the application

Fig. 22-8. Capacitor checker. (Courtesy of Health Co.)

of voltage to the capacitor, for breakdown and leakage testing. The leakage is read by the power-factor method. Paper, ceramic, and mica capacitors should have a very low power-factor and, in most instances, no reading will be obtained for these, when they have no internal leakage. Electrolytic capacitors, such as employed for power supplies, have a much higher power factor (ranging from three to 15). An excessive power factor reading indicates an abnormal leakage and, in such an instance, the capacitor should be replaced by one having a power factor reading within the range specified by the manufacturer.

Some capacitor checkers also utilize the bridge circuit for measuring inductance values. The usual method, in such an instance, is to employ an inductance of known value and utilize it for balancing the bridge, to ascertain the value of the unknown inductance.

The instrument shown in Fig. 22-9 is the Model 383-A *Capacohmeter* of Simpson Electric Co. which measures leakage resistance of defective paper, mica, or ceramic capacitors over a range of 10 micromicrofarads to 10 miscrofarads. With this unit, measurements can be made on capacitors while they are in their circuit, thus testing under actual load conditions. A pulse technique is utilized for detecting marginal performance capacitors.

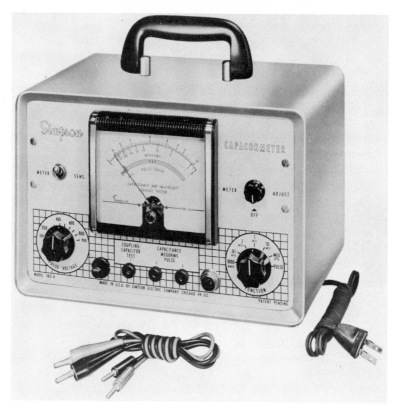

Fig. 22-9. Capachometer. (Courtesy of Simpson Electric Co.)

THE OSCILLOSCOPE

The oscilloscope is an electronic instrument which is capable of giving a visual indication of a signal waveform. For this reason, it is a valuable instrument for research, design, test and maintenance. With an oscilloscope, the waveshape of a signal can be studied with respect to amplitude, distortion, and deviations from the normal. In addition, the oscilloscope can also be employed as a voltmeter and a signal tracing device.

Shortly after the oscilloscope was first manufactured, its usefulness was confined to laboratory applications, but since the advent of industrial electronics and control, television, radar, and other specialized branches of electronics, the oscilloscope has become a valuable instrument for wideband i-f alignment, trouble shooting, signal waveform observation and inspection, and other similar applications.

SCOPE FUNCTION

The heart of the oscilloscope is the cathode-ray tube. The internal construction of a typical tube of this type is shown in Fig. 22-10. As with other vacuum tubes, the filament heats the cathode to the degree where the latter emits electrons. The conrol grid influences the amount of current flow, as in standard vacuum tubes. Two anodes are employed, each having a positive d-c potential applied to it. These anodes accelerate the electrons and form them into a beam. The intensity of the beam is regulated by the potential applied to the control grid.

The cathode consists of a nickel cylinder, at the end of which an emitting element is fused. This element is made of either barium or strontium oxide, and permits a sufficient release of electrons for the formation of an electron stream.

The grid structure, while controlling electron flow as in conventional tubes, differs from the wire mesh of receiving tubes and consists of a cylinder with a tiny circular opening, to keep the electron stream small in size. The beam is focused into a sharp pinpoint by controlling the voltage on the first anode. The two anodes of the cathode-ray tube can be compared to a glass lens system, such as employed in movie projectors, because the anodes focus the beam to a pinpoint at the face of the tube. A high voltage is applied to the second anode, so that the electron stream will attain high velocity for increased intensity and visibility when it strikes the tube face. The beam-forming section of the tube is known as an *electron gun*.

As shown in Fig. 22-10, two sets of plates are present within the tube, beyond the second anode. These plates are for deflecting the electron beam both horizontally and vertically. If, for instance, a voltage is applied across the horizontal deflection plates, it will influence the beam, because the negative potential on one of the horizontal plates will repel the electron stream, while the positive potential on the other horizontal deflection plate will attract the beam. If such a voltage is a sawtooth type, the gradually rising potential of the sawtooth will pull the beam gradually toward the positive horizontal deflection plate. Hence, the electron beam is made to *scan* across the face of the tube. Also, any potential applied to the vertical deflection plates will cause the beam to move vertically.

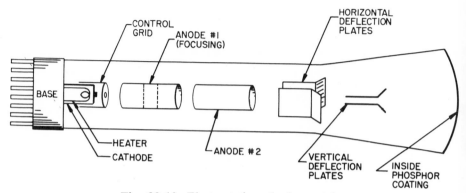

Fig. 22-10. Electrostatic cathode-ray tube.

As shown in Fig. 22-10, the inside of the tube face is coated with phosphor so that, when electrons strike this coating, it will fluoresce and emit light. After the exciting electron stream has left the area, the fluorescing characteristics which emit light rapidly decay, and the light level declines. The chemical composition of the coating, however, can be such that the emitted light persists for an appreciable interval, so that visual observation can be made of the light. Since the beam is swept across the tube at a fairly rapid rate, the light must persist for a sufficient time interval so that it leaves a complete trace of the waveform drawn on the picture-tube face. At the same time, the persistence of the phosphorescent coating should be sufficiently short so that, if the beam stops, the pattern which is traced on the tube will disappear very rapidly. The regular standard numbering system is utilized within the tube designation code, for ready identification of the phosphor characteristics. If 3AP1 is a cathode-ray tube's numerical designation, for instance, it indicates that the tube has a 3-inch face, because the first number identifies the face diameter. The P1 designation indicates a medium persistence phosphor, which has a green glow when excited. The A in the 3AP1 numerical designation refers to the internal construction of the tube and indicates that this particular tube has some structural changes with respect to a 3P1 cathode ray tube.

A typical oscilloscope is shown in Fig. 22-11. The various knobs are for controlling the size, brilliance, and number of images which appear on the screen. One knob regulates the bias on the control grid and, as mentioned earlier, affects the electron stream intensity. Hence, such a control is known as the *intensity* control, and permits adjustment of the image, with respect to making it brighter or dimmer. A focus control is also provided, which permits focusing the beam into a sharp pinpoint of light.

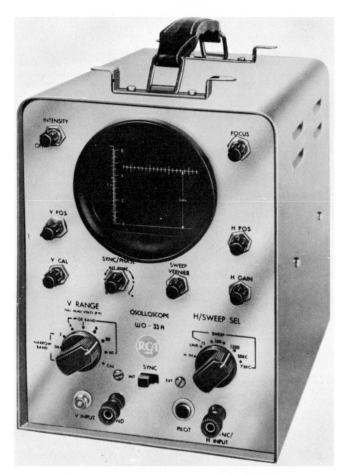

Fig. 22-11. Oscilloscope. (Courtesy of RCA.)

The focus control regulates the potential applied to the first anode of the cathode-ray tube. Another knob, the horizontal position control, regulates the amplitude of the d-c potential which is applied to the horizontal deflection plates, in addition to the usual sawtooth voltage. The d-c potential permits positioning the image which appears on the screen, so that the image can be moved to the right or left, as required. A vertical position control regulates the amplitude of a d-c voltage applied to the vertical plates, in addition to any signal voltage which may be impressed thereon. The d-c voltage on the vertical plates permits movement of the image in a vertical plane.

The signals to be observed are applied to the vertical input terminals and are amplified within the oscilloscope, before such signals arrive at the vertical deflection plates. The gain of the internal vertical signal ampifier can also be regulated from the front panel of the oscilloscope. An internal oscillator is present, which generates a sawtooth of voltage for application to the horizontal plates of the cathode-ray tube. The amplitude and the frequency of this horizontal sweep oscillator can also be regulated by the front panel controls of the oscilloscope. The relative position of the various controls on the front of an oscilloscope varies from one manufacturer to another. All models however, have the basic controls just mentioned.

Fig. 22-12 shows how an oscilloscope traces out a sinewave on the screen, when such a signal is applied to the vertical input of the scope. In (A), the sinewave applied at the vertical input of the oscilloscope is shown. If the internal horizontal sweep generator is turned off, the rising positive potential of the first alternation of the input signal would cause the electron beam to move upward, as shown in (B). When the negative alternation of the input signal arrives at the vertical deflection plates, the electron beam is pulled downward, as also shown in (B). The rapid rise and fall of the signal alternations cause the electron beam to move up and down the face of the cathode ray tube very rapidly, leaving a vertical line trace, as shown.

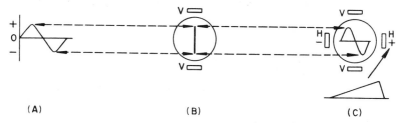

Fig. 22-12. Formation of sinewave on oscilloscope tube.

If the horizontal oscillator within the oscilloscope is now turned on, a sawtooth of voltage, as shown in (C), will be applied to the horizontal deflection pates. As shown in (C), the rising potential of the sawtooth voltage causes the right horizontal plate to become positive, and the left horizontal plate to become negative. The negative left plate and the horizontal right plate cause the beam to move from left to right, because the beam is repelled by the negative plate and attracted by the positive plate. If one sawtooth occurs for each cycle of the sinewave signal, the beam will be pulled across the face of the tube once for each cycle. Thus, as the first alternation of the input cycle rises in amplitude, the electron beam would normally rise in a vertical plane, as shown in (B). The sawtooth on the horizontal plates, however, gradually pulls the beam from left to right and, hence, traces out in visual form the waveshape of the input signal. Similarly, waveshapes of square waves, pulses, or any other types of signals, can be observed on the face of the oscilloscope screen. If the input signal has a frequency twice that of the sawtooth applied to the horizontal plates, two cycles will appear on the screen, because the beam is pulled across the screen only once for each two cycles of the input signal. Hence, by regulating the ratio of the input signal frequency to the sawtooth sweep frequency, portions of the input signal, or a number of cycles of the input signal, can be made visible on the screen. By calibrating the frequency of the horizontal sweep waveform so that its exact frequency is known, the frequency of the input signals to the oscilloscope can be ascertained. For instance, if four cycles of a sine-wave appear on the screen and the sawtooth generator is set for 100 cycles, the frequency of the signal applied at the input of the oscilloscope is 400 cycles per second.

PEAK-TO-PEAK READINGS

The oscilloscope can be utilized for reading the peak-to-peak voltages of a-c signals, just as some of the more expensive VTVM units can be utilized for this purpose. For reading peak-to-peak voltages, a transparent plastic screen is attached to the face of the oscilloscope. The screen is marked off with vertical and horizontal lines in the form of a graph. To calibrate the oscilloscope, an a-c voltmeter or VTVM of known accuracy is employed initially. A low-voltage a-c signal must be available for calibration purposes. Some oscilloscopes have a terminal, on the front panel, which supplies such an a-c reference voltage. If the reference voltage is 5 volts, for instance, this voltage is applied to the vertical input terminals of the oscilloscope. The internal horizontal sweep generator is shut off, so that a vertical trace, as shown in Fig. 22-12(B), is visible on the screen. This vertical line represents the peak-to-peak voltage of the input signal. The vertical height control is now adjusted so that the line is two or three squares high, and the control is left in this position after calibration. Knowing the rms value of the applied a-c calibrating voltage, the peak-to-peak voltage can be ascertained by multiplying the rms value by 1.41 to obtain the peak value, then doubling the peak value to obtain the peak-to-peak value. Once the oscilloscope has been calibrated, it can be utilized to read the peak-to-peak value of other voltages applied to the two vertical input terminals of the scope. Ordinary a-c voltmeters are accurate only for 60-cps signals, but a calibrated oscilloscope can read peak-to-peak voltages of signals having other frequencies. If the vertical amplifier of the oscilloscope has a fairly flat response up to 50 kilocycles, it will maintain accuracy with respect to peak-to-peak readings of signals whose frequencies range up to 50 kilocycles.

SIGNAL GENERATOR

A signal generator is a calibrated variable-frequency oscillator producing a simulated carrier signal, which can be employed in place of the
type of signal obtained from a broadcast station. Thus, the signal generator
is a useful device, when it is necessary to align a receiver or to track the
tuner.

Alignment refers to the tuning of the resonant circuits of the i-f amplifiers of superheterodyne receivers. Such tuning is made to "align" the
resonant frequencies of the tuned circuits to the necessary i-f frequency
specified for the receiver. *Tracking* refers to tuning the R-F, mixer, and
oscillator circuits of the receiver to the proper frequencies, so that the right
i-f signal frequencies are produced, regardless of whether a low-frequency
or a high-frequency station is tuned in.

The signal generator can also be employed for signal-tracing purposes,
since a signal can be injected into the input of a stage and its presence
(or absence) checked at the output. A signal generator also incorporates
an amplifier, in addition to the oscillator, to bring the signal levels up to
those desired. Such signal-level output is adjusted by a knob on the front
panel. Fig. 22-13 illustrates a typical signal generator panel layout for
AM and FM standard broadcast receiver applications.

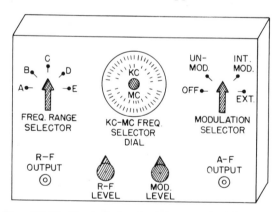

Fig. 22-13. Typical signal generator panel layout.

Signal generators also have a means for modulating the carrier signal
which is produced, so that a simulated AM waveform can be obtained.
The audio signal employed for modulation usually consists of a 400-cycle
tone which modulates the carrier produced by the oscillator. As a rule,
the modulation is no more than approximately 30%, and a switch is
provided for turning the modulation on or off. This is necessary because,

in some applications, a single signal is desired which utilizes only a narrow portion of the spectrum. On other occasions, the modulated signal is useful for producing an audible tone in the receiver during test procedures. In some units, the degree of modulation can be regulated.

The more elaborate signal generators also have an extended frequency range and, in addition, provide a means for frequency-modulating the carrier signal generated by the oscillator, so that the instrument can also be employed in conjunction with FM receivers.

The most general use of the signal generator is for alignment purposes. When employed for alignment, the generator should be calibrated accurately if any doubt exists regarding its accuracy. Calibration necessitates checking the frequency of the output signal against some standard signal from a special calibrator device or from a broadcast station, as described in the following discussion.

RECEIVER ALIGNMENT

Alignment procedures for various radio receivers differ somewhat, because of the characteristics of the receiver and the manner in which it was designed. For this reason, the service sheets for the receiver to be aligned should be referred to when this procedure (as well as tuner tracking) is necessary. To familiarize the reader with the general considerations applying to alignment procedures, however, basic factors are discussed herein for reference and study purposes. While such procedures are applicable to virtually all AM receivers, the schematic for the receiver to be aligned, as well as service notes for it, should be referred to when actual alignment procedures are undertaken. This is necessary in order to ascertain the location of the various adjusting screws and slugs, and to establish the proper frequency employed in the i-f stages.

Initially, the calibration of the signal generator should be checked by tuning to a station, and bringing the output terminals of the signal generator close to the antenna terminals of the receiver. The signal generator should then be adjusted so that its output frequency (or harmonic) coincides with that of the station which is tuned in. The signal generator should be coupled sufficiently to the antenna terminals, so that the signal from the generator can be heterodyned with that of the station. (If the signal cannot be heard by bringing the output probe of the generaor close to the terminals, a small capacitor can be used to couple the probe directly to the antenna terminals.) The squeal which is heard indicates the relative position of the signal-generator frequency. The dial is then adjusted until zero beat is obtained, at which time the frequency of the generator will coincide with that of the station. The dial can then be read to ascertain how accurate an indication it gives of the generator frequency. Since an

AM broadcast station maintains its frequency within 20 cycles of its assigned frequency, the station provides an exceptionally accurate means for checking the calibration of the signal generator.

After the generator has been accurately calibrated, tracking and alignment procedures can be employed, in similar fashion to the procedures which follow.

Basically, *alignment* refers to the process of adjusting the various R-F, mixer, and i-f stages of a receiver, so that they are at proper resonance for the frequencies involved. Thus, alignment consists in tuning up the aforementioned stages so that their resonant frequencies are aligned with respect to each other, for maximum performance. *Tracking* consists of adjustments to the receiver, so that the resonance of the various stages will remain "in tune" for different stations which are to be received.

Improper alignment can be caused by aging of component parts, drifting off resonance because of faulty or unstable circuits, and a general change in the characteristics of the various stages over appreciable time intervals. Improper alignment and tuner tracking will result in lowered signal output from the receiver, increased noise output, and poor selectivity. Misalignment and improper tracking can also contribute to interference from stations adjacent to the desired station, and to an impairment of tone quality, because all the sidebands of the station are not being received.

The normal order of procedure for alignment consists in first tuning the i-f circuits, and then tuning and tracking the R-F and oscillator stages. Usually, the method of applying the output from the signal generator consists in connecting the latter through an isolating 0.05-microfarad capacitor to the grid of the mixer tube. An indicating device must be employed, and this can consist of a VTVM connected across the avc circuit, with the VTVM adjusted for reading d-c. An oscilloscope can also be used to observe the output waveform obtained from across the output audio transformer of a radio, or the oscilloscope can be placed across the volume control circuit. Since best operational procedures are secured when the avc is grounded, the latter circuit does not lend itself to alignment procedure measurements.

The signal generator is adjusted to supply a modulated signal having the same frequency as the i-f of the receiver. The secondary of the output i-f transformer should now be adjusted, by using an alignment tool to turn the set screws provided. Adjustments should be made for maximum signal output, as observed on the VTVM or oscilloscope. The primary of the output i-f transformer should then also be adjusted for maximum signal output. If more than one i-f stage is present, the others should also be tuned, the sequence of tuning procedures being from the detector toward the mixer tube.

Some technicians dispense with an indicating device, and utilize the loudspeaker to indicate the modulated sound level produced by the signal generator. Regardless of the indicating device utilized, however, it is necessary during the alignment procedures to keep the signal strength from the signal generator at a low level, so as to prevent overloading of the stages which are being aligned.

After the i-f transformers have been aligned for maximum signal output at the proper frequency, tuner tracking should be undertaken. In some instances, the tuner will consist of only a mixer and oscillator stage, while some receivers will have an additional R-F amplification stage.

The oscillator must be adjusted so that its frequency will always be different from the incoming station frequency by the proper amount which allows the required i-f signal to be produced. A variation in the *difference* frequency will result in improper tracking and poor performance.

Tracking procedures consist in adjusting the small shunt and series capacitors which are associated with the major tuning capacitors of the R-F, mixer, and oscillator stages. The series capacitor is called a *padder,* and has an appreciable effect at the low-frequency end of the dial. At the same end of the dial, a shunt capacitor has little effect, because its capacity is relatively small, as compared to that of the major tuning capacitor when the plates of the latter are meshed for tuning to the low-frequency end of the dial. The shunt capacitor is called a *trimmer.*

When tuning at the high-frequency end of the dial, the major tuning capacitor has a small capacity, since the plates are unmeshed. Such small capacity means that the series padder has little effect on the frequency. The capacity of the shunt trimmer, however, is now appreciable as compared with that of the tuning capacitor, and thus is effective in tracking at the high-frequency end of the band.

For alignment procedures, the signal generator is connected to the antenna terminals of the receiver, again using an 0.05 microfarad isolating capacitor. The signal generator is adjusted to produce a signal at the high-frequency end of the dial, such as 1,400 kilocycles. The receiver dial should also be set for the latter frequency. The trimmer capacitor, which shunts the tuning capacitor of the lower oscillator stage, should now be adjusted for maximum signal output. The signal generator is now tuned so that its output signal corresponds to a frequency near the low frequency section of the dial, such as 600 kilocycles. The receiver should be tuned for maximum output when the dial is set at 600 kilocycles. The oscillator trimmer may have to be adjusted slightly for maximum output. The padder capacitors are also adjusted for maximum signal output. When an R-F stage is present, the trimmer and padder capacitors must also be adjusted for maximum output at the high- and low-frequency ends of the dial, respectively. After adjustments of the low-frequency tracking, the high-frequency tracking should be rechecked so that peak adjustments can be secured. A check should also be made to ascertain whether the dial indicator is properly set to cover the full tuning range. In some receivers, the variable-tuning-capacitor end plates are slotted, so that they can be bent out slightly at either the high-frequency or low-frequency end of the tuning range, for more precise adjustments of tuner tracking.

SWEEP AND MARKER GENERATORS

A sweep generator is a signal generator which has provisions for frequency-modulating the signal generated within the unit. Thus, the frequency of the signal produced by the generator is alternately swept above and below the frequency established by the oscillator within the unit, in similar fashion to the FM signal which is generated by FM alignment generators.

Sweep generators are useful for obtaining a visual indication of the bandpass characteristics of the R-F or i-f stages of FM and television receivers. They can also be used for observation of the bandpass characteristics of other electronic amplifying devices.

The sweep generator is applied to the i-f stages, for instance, and will furnish an output signal which will vary in frequency sufficiently to span slightly below and above the i-f bandpass of the receiver. An oscilloscope is then placed across the detector circuit of the receiver under alignment. The horizontal sawtooth sweep of the oscilloscope is synchronized with the sweep generator, so that the oscilloscope beam is swept across the face of the cathode-ray tube as the sweep generator sweeps from its lowest to its highest frequency. Since the gain of the i-f stages is such that the various frequencies are amplified to a different degree, the beam of the oscilloscope will rise and fall to correspond to the amplification of the sweep signals being injected into the i-f stages. Thus, the oscilloscope traces out the bandpass characteristics of the i-f stages. Fig. 22-14 shows a typical sweep waveform for a television receiver.

To identify frequency points along this waveform, an additional generator known as a marker generator is employed. The marker generator is a single-signal AM type of generator such as is incorporated in the unit shown in Fig. 22-13. By injecting this single signal a small section of a waveform on the oscilloscope is broken into a slight ripple known as a *marker pip*. This can be seen in the sweep waveform shown in Fig. 22-14.

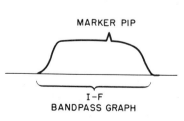

Fig. 22-14. Sweep waveform.

By varying the output frequency of the calibrated marker, the relative position of the pips which are produced will indicate the respective frequency of such points on the waveform. Hence, the band width, as well as the points of increased or decreased amplification along the response curve, are visually indicated. Alignment can then be undertaken to correct the waveform, so that it corresponds to the pattern illustrated in the service notes for the receiver under alignment. The pips supplied by the marker produced by a marker generator are equivalent guideposts of frequency along the bandpass waveform traced on the face of the oscilloscope tube.

DOT AND BAR GENERATORS

Other generators are also employed for testing alignment, and for design purposes. For television alignment and adjustment procedures, a cross-bar or dot-bar generator is also useful. Horizontal and vertical bars, or a combination of both, are available for adjusting the linearity of the television scanning process producing the picture. Adjustments to the receiver consist of manipulation of the vertical and horizontal linearity controls, in conjunction with the height and width controls, until both the horizonal and vertical bars produced on the television screen by the generator are equally spaced. For convergence adjustments in a color-television receiver, white dots are produced on the screen by the dot-bar generator.

Another type of generator useful for color-television servicing, maintenance, and adjusting is the color-bar generator which produces vertical bars having various colors. The proper color sequence of such bars is used as a reference for adjusting the color rendition of the receiver, and for ascertaining the circuits which are involved when improper hues or colors are observed.

INDUSTRIAL INSTRUMENTS

The instruments used in the fields of industrial control, computers, automation, and other allied branches of electronics have the same basic purposes as the instruments previously described. In research and design laboratories the test equipment is usually of the more costly type, since a greater accuracy is required than encountered in general tests, measurements, and circuit analysis. Oscilloscopes, for instance, may have a much wider frequency response range and sensitivity for accurate measurements of pulse signal durations, rise time, and repetition rates. Special circuits are often used to control more precisely the frequency of internal sweep

To identify frequency points along this waveform, an additional generator known as a marker generator is employed. The marker generator is a single-signal AM type of generator such as is incorporated in the unit shown in Fig. 22-13. By injecting this single signal, a small section waveforms. Some oscilloscopes also have *triggered* sweep control, whereby the sweep signal is triggered to start at an exact time in relation to the signal waveform that will be observed. With automatic triggering, the internal sweep circuits of the oscilloscope will synchronize automatically with the frequency of the input signal with no manual adjustments of the sweep frequency control necessary. Thus, even though the input signal frequency varies, the pattern on the screen will remain locked in.

Besides the basic type VOM and VTVM units discussed earlier, digital-type voltmeters are also encountered in industrial electronics. The digital voltmeter automatically displays the value of the voltage under measurement directly in large numbers. Some units have internal selection of ranges so that no range-selection by switches is necessary. The test probes are placed across the voltage to be measured, and the device senses the polarity and range, and switches internally to the proper circuitry for visual display of the voltage values. A typical digital voltmeter is shown in Fig. 22-15. In this instrument both positive and negative voltages are displayed with high accuracy with a range of 0.1 volt to 999 volts.

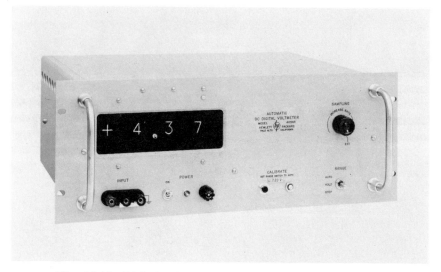

Fig. 22-15. Digital voltmeter. (Courtesy of Hewlett Packard.)

In some industrial electronic-measurement practices, counter-type instruments are also used, with visual display of the count accomplished by the beam-switching tube described earlier in Chapter 21. (See also Fig. 24-7.) Such a device will total the number of times certain industrial processes are repeated, or will count pulse rates and other periodic changes which need to be evaluated. A typical counter of this type is shown in Fig. 22-16. This Model R counter has a speed of 5,000 counts per second. Selector knobs are provided for establishing a present quantity to be counted.

In industrial electronics various plotters are also encountered to give a visual indication of variations (both electrical and mechanical) along X

Fig. 22-16. Model R counter. (Courtesy of Veeder-Root, Inc.)

and Y axes, thus performing graphing functions. Figure 22-17 shows such a function plotter produced by the Minneapolis Honeywell Regulator Company. The device uses a strip-chart single-pen recorder which is actuated by one signal, and the second signal controls chart movement. The chart, as with the pen, can respond to either a positive or negative position. Hence, the chart can be driven up or down in response to changes in one variable, while the recording pen moves to

Fig. 22-17. Brown electronic function plotter. (Courtesy of Minneapolis-Honeywell Regulator Co.)

the left or right for changes in the second signal variable. Both the recorder pen and chart can be energized by any d-c source. The plotter is useful in plotting hysteresis loops as well as speed-versus-torque variations, stress-versus-strain, temperature-versus-pressure, force-versus-motion, and any other X- and Y-axis graph plottings.

REVIEW QUESTIONS

1. What type of measurements can be made with a multimeter?

2. Briefly explain the advantages of a 20,000-ohm-per-volt meter, as compared to a 1,000-ohm-per-volt meter.

3. How can a multimeter be used for continuity checking?

4. Briefly explain the differences between a VTVM and a VOM.

5. Does the standard VTVM employ a means for measuring current?

6. Briefly explain what measurements can be made with a capacitor checker.

7. What type of tube is employed in an oscilloscope?

8. What is meant by the "gun" of a cathode-ray tube?

9. Describe at least three oscilloscope controls and explain their purpose and function.

10. To what oscilloscope terminals is a signal applied for observation on the screen?

11. Briefly define "persistence" with respect to the phosphorescent coating of a cathode-ray tube.

12. How can an oscilloscope be used as a voltmeter? Explain briefly.

13. What type of waveform is generated within an oscilloscope?

14. What is the purpose for a single-signal generator?

15. How may a signal generator be calibrated for accuracy?

16. Where is a sweep generator employed?

17. Explain the basic difference between an AM signal generator and a sweep generator.

18. What is the purpose for a marker generator?

19. Briefly explain the purpose for a crossbar generator.

20. What are some of the refinements which may be found in an industrial oscilloscope as compared to a general-purpose type?

21. Explain briefly the features of a digital voltmeter.

22. How does a counter display visually a total count?

23. List some of the uses for an *X-Y* function plotter.

23

SWITCHING
AND
GATING

INTRODUCTION

In addition to the amplification and modification of signals, there are numerous instances where signals or voltages must be switched or gated to other circuits or devices. This is particularly true in such branches of electronics as automation, computer systems, nuclear reactor control, electronic organs, closed-circuit commercial television, radar, and numerous other applications.

The purpose for the switching and gating systems is not to originate signals, but rather to hold them in abeyance until such a time that they are to be applied to other circuits or devices. Included among the switching and gating circuits is the so-called *logic* type which is extensively used in computer systems, but also finds applications in other branches of electronics where it is necessary to gate signals in or out of subsequent stages as required. This chapter covers the mechanical switching devices, as well as the electrical and electronic.

ELECTROMECHANICAL SWITCHING

The relay at Fig. 23-1(A) is a basic electromechanical switch. It has a coil, with a metal core (forming what is known as a solenoid), and is part of the switching assembly as shown. When d-c is applied to the solenoid, it energizes the latter and an electromagnet is formed. The electromagnet now pulls down the spring metal contact section which is part of the T_1. The other terminal T_2 attaches to the other contact point represented by the arrow. Thus, when the relay is energized it closes the circuit for T_1 and T_2 and in consequence a closed switch condition is initiated when the current circulates in the solenoid.

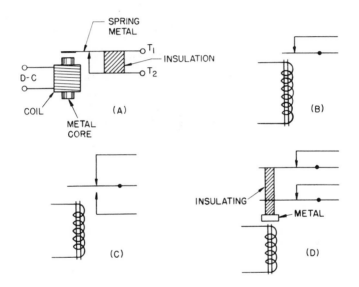

Fig. 23-1. Electromechanical relays.

The relay shown at (A) is known as an *open-circuit* type, since terminals T_1 and T_2 are in an open-circuit condition until the relay is energized. At (B) is shown a *closed-circuit* relay representation. Both the open-circuit and the closed-circuit shown are also known as a *single-pole single-throw switch,* since only one spring metal section is thrown (the pole). At Fig. 23-1(C) is shown a single-pole double-throw switch. Here, the moveable section, the pole, can be thrown to the lower or the upper position; hence it is a double-throw type. At (D) is shown a double-pole single-throw type relay. Here, two moveable pole sections are only thrown to a single contact point, establishing the single-throw factor.

A typical commercial relay is shown in Fig. 23-2. This is a single-pole double-throw relay. Terminal lugs at the bottom are for the application of the energizing voltage to the solenoid, while terminals at the rear and side of the top portion are for making contact with the switch section. Abbreviations are usually used for the switch identification. Thus, a single-pole single-throw switch is abbreviated SPST, a triple-pole, double-throw switch is indicated as TPDT, etc.

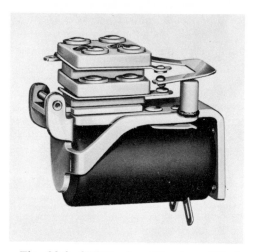

Fig. 23-2. SPDT relay. (Courtesy Allied Control Co., Inc.)

There are occasions in industrial electronics, computer systems, and other services when a-c or d-c signals are to be switched to a load circuit only when specific conditions exist. One of these conditions, for instance, could be that no power or signal waveforms of any type may be applied to the load circuit until two other voltages occur or are applied simultaneously. Another condition may be that the load gets continuous power (or signal waveforms) unless two other voltages or signals are present. One such circuit is shown at Fig. 23-3(A). Here, an a-c signal or a d-c voltage is impressed across the input terminals at the left as shown. In series with the load resistor are two open-circuit SPST switches controlled by the two relays.

If relay No. 1 is energized, the upper switch will close, but since the lower relay switch is open, no signal energy is applied to the load circuit. Similarly, if the lower switch is closed but the upper open, no energy is applied to the load. When, however, both relays are energized, a closed-circuit loop is formed and the input signal is applied to the load circuit. Thus, we need a *coincidence* of energy applied to both relays in order to close the circuit. Hence, this type of circuit is often referred to as a

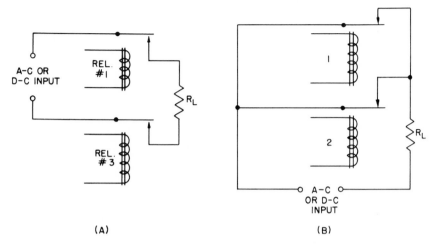

Fig. 23-3. Coincidence relay switching.

coincidence switching system. In computers, an electronic counterpart (nonmechanical) is utilized as described later. When such a coincidence circuit is used in computers, it is known as an AND circuit. The coincidence or AND must have both the upper *and* the lower switch closed for application of power to the load circuit.

Another coincidence relay switching circuit is shown at Fig. 23-3(B). Here, signal energy is applied to the load circuit continuously unless relay No. 1 *and* relay No. 2 are both energized simultaneously. As shown, normally-closed relays are utilized here in contrast to the normally-open relays shown at (A).

ELECTRONIC SWITCHING

The zener diode described in Chapter 14 can also be used as a switching device, as shown at Fig. 23-4(A). Here a zener diode is in series with the relay solenoid as shown. Upon the application of a negative signal having an amplitude sufficient to reach the zener region, the diode will conduct heavily and thus energize the relay. A normally-closed relay is shown, though a normally-open type could, of course, be used.

A tube or transistor can also be used as a switching device. If the bias is at the cutoff region, a positive pulse can be used to trigger the relay switch as shown at (B). Here, there is no forward bias applied to the transistor, hence the transistor is functioning with a class B characteristic. Since class B operation is at the cutoff point, the solenoid of the relay is not energized and the switch is in the normally-opened position as shown. When a positive pulse is applied, it makes the base positive with respect to the emitter, and thus the signal energy supplies the required forward bias for transistor conduction. Since the collector side already has the necessary reverse bias, the collector-emitter circuit conducts and the relay is energized.

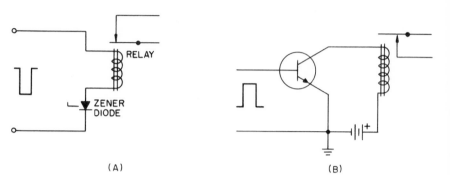

Fig. 23-4. Solid-state switching.

The thyratron or the solid-state silicon-controlled rectifier can also be used in switching circuitry. A basic thyratron-tube switching system is shown in Fig. 23-5. Here, the negative potential applied to the grid circuit prevents the thyratron from conducting. Thus, no energy is applied to the load circuit. For rapid triggering of the energy to the load circuit, a differentiating input is employed, consisting of capacitor C_1 and resistor R_1 as shown. These have the long time constant as previously explained, and the resultant sharp positive spike appearing at the grid causes thyratron conduction and the application of the d-c power to the load circuit. As detailed in Chapter 14, once the thyratron conducts, a negative potential at the grid is ineffectual in stopping conduction.

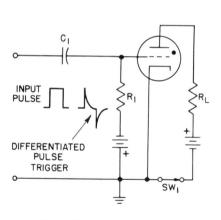

Fig. 23-5. Thyratron switch.

Hence, the negative spike of the differentiated pulse will not remove the power applied to the load circuit. To cause the thyratron to stop conducting, the switch SW_1 must be opened to remove the anode-cathode potential.

A widely-used circuit capable of switching, gating, and counting is the Eccles-Jordan flip-flop. One of its primary applications is in the field of digital computers, where it performs arithmetic operations, stores numbers, and provides open- or closed-gate conditions. A typical vacuum-tube flip-flop circuit is shown in Fig. 23-6. Superficially, it resembles the *r-c* relaxation oscillator circuit discussed earlier. Actually, however, it is not a generator or oscillator, and produces no output, except when input pulses are applied, as discussed below.

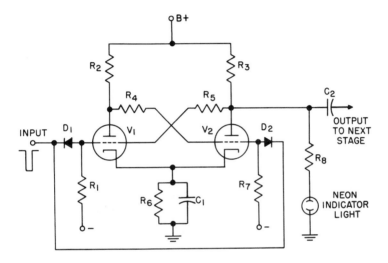

Fig. 23-6. Basic flip-flop circuit.

The flip-flop circuit is also referred to as a bistable device, because it has two stable states, known as the "off" and the "on" states. In the "off" state, vacuum tube V_1 is nonconducting, and vacuum tube V_2 is conducting at saturation. The circuit will remain in this off state until triggered by the application of a pulse at the input.

The reason the circuit remains in one stable state, and does not oscillate, is the particular circuit design utilized. Note that the plate of V_1 is directly coupled to the grid of V_2 via resistor R_4. Also, the plate of V_2 is coupled to the grid of V_1 via resistor R_5. The grid of V_1 has a negative potential applied to the bottom of the grid leak R_1, as does the grid of V_2 via R_7. When V_1 is in a nonconducting state, the full positive B potential appears at the plate of V_1, because there is no current flow through R_2 and, hence, no voltage drop across the latter. This high positive B potential also appears at the grid of V_2, overcoming the negative potential applied at the bottom of R_7. Hence, V_2 has no negative bias applied to it and, consequently, the tube has maximum plate-current flow and is operating at saturation. The plate current for V_2 also flows through the plate resistor R_3, and develops a large voltage drop across the latter. Consequently, the plate voltage for V_2 is low, and this low plate voltage also appears at the grid of V_1. The low plate voltage from V_2 is insufficient to overcome the negative potential applied to the grid of V_1 via R_1. Therefore, V_1 is biased beyond cutoff, and no current flows in this tube. Thus, a stable condition exists, with V_1 at cutoff and V_2 at saturation. Since a steady-state voltage exists at V_2, there is no output, because C_2 blocks the d-c potential. From the anode of V_2, a resistor R_8 is in series with a neon indicator light. This light is out, because of the low plate voltage of V_2. Hence, the fact that the bulb is not lit gives a visual indication that the circuit is in its "off" state.

If a negative pulse is now applied to the input, as shown, it will appear at the grid of V_1, and also at the grid of V_2. The diodes D_1 and D_2 allow the entry of only negative pulses to the grids. When the negative pulse appears at the grid of V_1, it has no effect on this tube, because the tube is already at cutoff, and the increase in negative potential at the grid will not alter the state of this tube. The negative pulse at the grid of V_2, however, will increase the negative potential at the grid and, in consequence, will cause this tube to reach cutoff. When V_2 reaches cutoff, plate voltage rises, and this rise in plate voltage also appears at the grid of V_1, because of coupling through R_5. The increasing positive potential at the grid of V_1 overcomes the negative potential applied through R_1, and hence V_1 comes out of its cutoff state and is permitted to conduct. The positive potential at the grid causes V_1 to conduct heavily, at saturation. The heavy current flow through the plate resistor R_2 creates a voltage drop across the latter and, hence, the plate voltage at V_1 declines. The lowered plate voltage of V_1 also appears at the grid of V_2, but is insufficient in amplitude and cannot overcome the negative potential appearing at the grid via resistor R_7. Thus, the negative potential at the grid of V_2 holds the latter at cutoff. A second stable state of the flip-flop circuit has been achieved. This new state is the "on" state. Because V_2 is now at cutoff, there is no voltage drop across R_3, and plate voltage for V_2 is high. Consequently, there is sufficient voltage amplitude appearing in the neon indicator light circuit to light the bulb and show that the circuit is in its "on" state.

When the circuit flipped over from its "off" state to its "on" state, the voltage at the plate of V_2 rose sharply. This sudden change of voltage from a low value to a high one produced a pulse at the output that had a positive polarity. The output from the stage shown in Fig. 23-6 would be applied to another stage similar in design to the one shown. When a positive pulse is applied to the next flip-flop, however, it is blocked from arriving at the grids of the circuit, because of the diodes in each grid, which block the positive pulses and permit entry of negative pulses only.

Hence, the production of a positive pulse when the circuit is flipped to its "on" state will not affect the next stage.

The circuit can be cleared and returned to its "off" state by the application of another pulse to the input of the circuit shown in Fig. 23-6. The negative pulse again appears at the grid of V_1 and V_2. Because V_2 is at cutoff, however, the negative pulse at its grid will have no effect; V_1, however, is at saturation, and the negative pulse will cause this tube to change from its saturation state to its cutoff state. When V_1 attains the cutoff state, no current flows through R_2 and no voltage drop occurs across this resistor. Hence, the plate voltage for V_1 is high. This voltage also appears at the grid of V_2, and causes the latter tube to attain the saturation state. When V_2 reaches saturation, the high current through R_3 again reduces the plate voltage. The reduced plate voltage causes the neon indicator light to go out, registering the zero state of the flip-flop circuit. When V_2 went into its saturation state, the anode voltage dropped from a high level to a low level, and developed an output pulse of negative polarity. This pulse, appearing at the next stage, can pass the grid diodes and flip the next stage into the "on" position. With the first stage of the series of flip-flops in its "off" state, and the second in its "on" state, the states of the two circuits indicate that two pulses have been applied to the input of the series flip-flops. Because only the negative pulses are the significant ones utilized in this particular circuit, one negative pulse will appear at the output of a flip-flop for every two negative pulses entered. Hence, the circuit is capable of scaling a particular sequence of digits. In other words, for every four pulses entered, only two negative pulses will appear at the output, etc.

When a particular number has been entered into the flip-flop to register an "on" state, the neon bulb will light and the circuit will *store* this number for as long as power is supplied to the circuit. A series of flip-flops will not only scale, but will also accumulate a series of counts representing pulses applied to the input, and will store such accumulated counts.

The flip-flop circuit can also be used to turn some device on and off at a given rate by virtue of the change in plate-current flow or plate voltage of either tube. Just as the neon light is turned on and off, so can a relay be tripped by wiring the latter into either plate circuit of the flip-flop. A transistorized flip-flop using dual relays is shown in Fig. 23-7. Normally-open relays are shown, though normally-closed relays could also be used. Also, one relay could be a normally-closed type and the other a normally-open type for meeting specific switching needs.

For purposes of analysis, assume the flip-flop shown in Fig. 23-7 is in its zero state. With the normally-open relays shown, relay No. 1 remains open since the transistor circuit T_1 is nonconducting. For the second relay in the collector circuit of T_2, however, the current circulating in the solenoid closes the relay. Now when the flip-flop stage is triggered to the 'one'

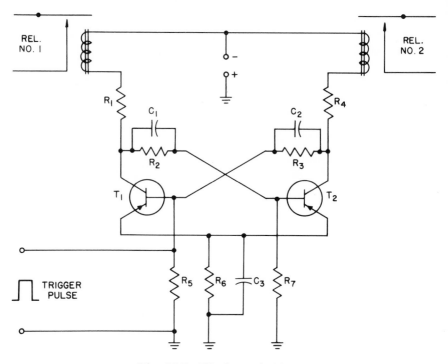

Fig. 23-7. Flip-flop switching.

state, the current flow in T_1 closes relay No. 1 and at the same time T_2 reaches cutoff, and relay No. 2 assumes its normally-open condition.

If the relays are to perform alternate switching functions, that is, with one providing an open circuit during the time the other provides a closed circuit, then relay No. 1 could be a normally-closed type, and relay No. 2 a normally-open type, or vice-versa, depending on switching requirements.

In industrial electronic switching, plate-sensitive relays (relays very sensitive to small changes of current values) are employed and often these in turn open or close larger relays where higher power is to be switched ultimately. The output terminals of the relays shown in Fig. 23-7 can also be applied to silicon-control rectifiers for triggering these devices and thus switching high power to other circuits or devices as required.

The operation of the transistor flip-flop shown in Fig. 23-7 is similar to that of the vacuum-tube type previously discussed. When transistor T_1 is conducting, a voltage drop occurs across resistor R_1 and the voltage at the base of transistor T_2 is low. This results in a reduction of the forward bias on the base of T_2 and this causes this transistor to go into its non-conducting state. Collector voltage for T_2 increases and this is felt at the base of T_1, where the increase in the negative potential raises the amplitude of the forward bias and increases conduction an additional amount. Eventually transistor T_1 reaches the saturation conduction level and T_2 remains at cutoff. When a triggering pulse is applied to the input resistor R_5, the positive potential of the input signal appears at the base circuits of each transistor. Transistor T_2, however, is already in its nonconduction state and the reverse bias appearing at its base is ineffectual. For T_1, however, the positive base potential becomes sufficient for the reverse bias to cut current flow to zero through this transistor. When nonconduction occurs, the collector voltage at T_1 rises to a high negative value and applies forward bias to T_2 causing the latter to conduct. Now, a large voltage drop occurs across R_4, and the voltage at the base of T_1 becomes less negative. Hence, in a fraction of a second, T_1 is driven into cutoff, and T_2 into saturation. The application of another positive pulse at the input will again flip the circuit over and it reverts to its original zero state.

PHOTOELECTRIC SWITCHING

The light-dependent resistor, a photoelectric transducer, has already been described in Chapter 21. In this unit, however, the resistive change for variations in light intensity do not have the rapid switching capabilities of vacuum-tube or transistor photoelectric devices. Thus, in industrial electronic applications where fast switching rates are essential, the phototubes or transistor devices are extensively employed. Phototubes may be either vacuum types or gas-filled types, and both have a cathode in the form of a curved elongated plate, as shown at Fig. 23-8(A). This cathode structure is coated with a photosensitive material which exhibits photoemission characteristics, that is, free electrons are liberated when light strikes the material.

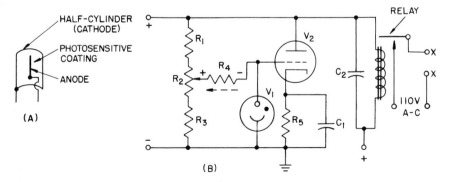

Fig. 23-8. Photoelectric relay circuit.

Switching and Gating

A vertical wire is suspended within the curved section of the cathode cylinder, and this vertical wire forms the anode of the diode phototube. Generally, gas-filled tubes are more sensitive than high-vacuum tubes, though the gas-filled types exhibit poorer response to variations in the intensity of the light striking the photosensitive material.

Phototubes have numerous applications, among which are those in motion pictures, burglar alarms, assembly line counters, and other similar applications where the electronic circuit must perform indicating, counting, or actuating functions related to light sources.

In motion-picture work, the sound which accompanies the picture is identified by light and dark areas at the edge of the film strip. When a beam of light is projected through this strip onto a phototube, the variations of shading in the strip will cause a variation of current flow from the phototube. Such variations form the audio signal.

When a phototube is used to perform the functions of counting or signalling, a circuit similar to that shown in Fig. 23-8(B) is utilized. Here, a gas-filled phototube, V_1, is wired into the circuit so that the cathode is at ground potential and the anode is connected to the grid of a vacuum tube V_2, as well as to resistor R_4. The current flow is in the direction shown by the arrows, during the time a light beam strikes the cathode of V_1. A negative voltage is developed across R_4 which is sufficiently high to prevent V_2 from conducting.

The SPST (single-pole, single-throw) switch of the relay can be connected to the 110-volt a-c line or other power source, as shown, and the points marked x can be connected to a light bulb, buzzer, or other indicating device.

If the circuit shown in Fig. 23-8(B) is used as a burglar alarm, the beam of light which is focused on V_1 can be aimed across a door. When the light is interrupted by someone passing through the door, the bias will be removed from the grid of V_2, because of the nonconduction of the phototube. The reduction of negative-grid voltage at V_2 will cause the latter to conduct. The current flow through the relay will actuate the switch and flash a light or ring a buzzer or bell.

The SPST switch can be replaced by a mechanical counter, which is tripped every time the relay lever is pulled downward. In the latter application, each interruption of the beam will actuate the relay and, hence, the counter device. In this manner, the circuit can be used to count the number of items going past an assembly line.

The relative degree of sensitivity is adjusted by the potentiometer R_2. The degree of sensitivity also depends on the type of phototube used and the circuit values.

Photosensitive transistors can also be employed in the same applications as phototubes. The phototransistor functions on the principle of the conductivity of germanium being altered by incident light energy. This permits the fabrication of an extremely small photocell which operates on the point-contact transistor principle. Instead of the emitter acting as an input circuit for an electric signal, however, the emitter input is a beam of light which causes current flow. The basic circuit is illustrated in Fig. 23-9.

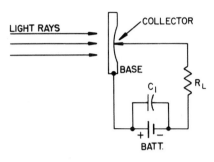

The concave-shaped transistor is mounted in a metal shell which forms the base connection. The current flow from the negative side of the battery goes through the load resistor and to the collector, and then to the base. The phototransistor has only an extremely small area of

Fig. 23-9. Photoelectric transistor.

light-sensitive surface. The light area centers around the section opposite the collector contact point, and the light-sensitive area is usually 0.01 inch in diameter.

GATING CIRCUITS

Gating circuits are usually employed to regulate the interval of time during which signal information is either applied to another circuit or device, or prevented from reaching another circuit or device. As such, they can also be considered as switching units as with the previous systems discussed. Switching circuits, however, are often used to turn devices on and off in addition to handling or transferring signals. The gating circuits are primarily concerned with the handling of pulse or square-wave signals and can be used to gate such signals in or to gate them out as required. A typical diode coincidence gate is shown in Fig. 23-10. Here, two solid-state diodes are used, and in the absence of a signal at the input terminals T_1 and T_2, both diodes conduct fully because they are in parallel with the load resistor and source voltage. The current flow for

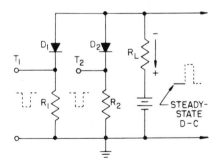

Fig. 23-10. Diode coincidence gate.

both diodes is from the ground terminal upward, and the current for both flows through the load resistor in the direction shown by the arrow. Because of the current flow through the load, there is a large voltage drop across the latter, establishing a steady-state d-c output in the absence of a signal input.

When a pulse of sufficient amplitude is applied to terminal T_1, its negative-polarity voltage drop across R_1 overcomes the battery potential across the series diode network composed of D_1 and R_1. Since this potential is opposite in polarity to the battery potential, it stops conduction of D_1. Diode D_2, however, conducts and hence only a slight change in voltage drop occurs across the load resistance. The same small change would occur if a negative pulse were applied to terminal T_2 only.

When input pulses appear simultaneously at terminals T_1 and T_2, both diodes stop conducting, and hence current flow through the load resistor drops to zero. Now, the supply potential from the battery predominates, and a rising positive polarity representative of the signal amplitude change occurs at the output. The output signal will have a flat-top wave shape equaling the duration of the pulse input signal. Instead of a pulse waveform input, steady-state d-c potentials can also be applied simultaneously to the input terminals to cause a change in output potential.

A pentode coincidence gate is shown in Fig. 23-11. Here, the screen grid does not have a positive potential applied to it as in the case in normal pentode amplifier circuitry. Instead, the screen is used as an additional input terminal and the screen-grid resistor is returned to ground as is the control-grid resistor at terminal T_1. A positive potential is applied across the cathode resistor R_2 so that a sufficiently high grid bias is established to reach the cutoff region. Because both the control grid and the screen grid are returned to the ground circuit, both are biased negatively, and in consequence either one has the ability to hold the tube at cutoff

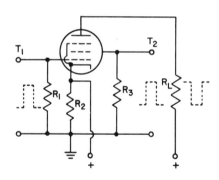

Fig. 23-11. Pentode coincidence gate.

independent of the other. Thus, if a positive pulse is applied to the control grid as shown by the dotted outline, it is ineffectual in causing tube conduction because the screen grid still has a sufficiently high negative potential applied to it to prevent conduction. Similarly a positive pulse applied to the screen-grid terminal T_2 only would be ineffectual because the negative bias developed for the control grid would not permit conduction. Thus, to cause conduction, a potential or signal waveform must be applied to both grids and have a sufficiently positive amplitude to overcome the negative potentials established by the voltage applied to the cathode. Hence, when signal *coincidence* prevails, the tube conducts and an amplified pulse signal appears across the load as shown in the dotted outline. The output pulse, in typical amplifier fashion, has a 180-degree phase reversal with respect to the input signal. The signal applied to terminal T_2 can be considered as being *gated in* by the signal at terminal T_1. As mentioned earlier, when such coincidence circuits are utilized in computers, they are known as AND gates or circuits. The circuit shown in Fig. 23-11 can also be modified to behave as a gating-out circuit. A positive steady-state potential is applied to the screen, causing the tube to conduct and thus permitting any signals applied to T_1 to develop across the load. When such signals are to be gated out, a negative potential is applied to terminal T_2, driving the screen grid into the negative region and cutting the tube off. Thus for the duration of the signal applied to terminal T_2 there will be a gating out of a pulse train appearing at T_1.

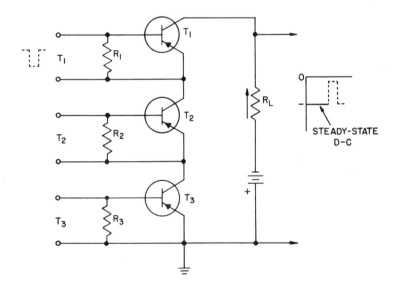

Fig. 23-12. Three-input AND gate.

The coincidence, or so-called AND gate, can be made up of two or more input terminals as desired. A typical three-input AND gate is shown in Fig. 23-12. Here, reverse bias for the collectors of the transistors is provided by the battery in series with the load resistance as shown. Forward bias, however, is omitted for each transistor. Consequently, each transistor acts as a class B system, since the absence of forward bias causes a cutoff state to prevail. Only when forward bias is applied will the high-potential barrier in the collector side permit current flow through the transistor. Hence, the gating signal must have a negative polarity, so the base will be negative with respect to the emitter.

When a negative voltage or pulse signal is applied to the input terminal T_1 as shown by the dotted outline, the upper transistor has the necessary forward bias to conduct but is unable to do so because its conduction path is also through the collector and emitter circuits of the lower transistors. Hence, if no signals are applied simultaneously to the lower terminals, no conduction can occur through any of the transistors. Similarly, the application of signals to T_2 only, or T_3 only, will not cause conduction. When negative-polarity signals are applied simultaneously to all three terminals, the necessary forward- and reverse-bias conditions prevail and all transistors conduct. The current flow which now occurs through the load resistance causes a voltage drop to occur across the latter and hence the normal steady-state d-c output declines from its high negative value to a lower value. This represents a positive change and thus the output signal has a polarity opposite to that of the input signal.

In computers, the phase-reversal of a signal across a circuit is sometimes referred to as NOT characteristic. This means that the phase of the output signal is *not* the same as that of the input signal. Thus, the circuit shown in Fig. 23-12 is sometimes known as an AND-NOT gate or circuit.

Another type of gate circuit is that known as the OR gate illustrated in Fig. 23-13. This circuit will have an output developed when a pulse input or other signal waveform is applied to T_1 *or* T_2, *or* both.

As shown, a positive potential is applied to the cathode resistor R_2 having a sufficient amplitude to bias both grids to cutoff. Hence, in the absence of input signals, there is no conduction. Now, when a positive-polarity signal is applied to T_1 as shown by the dotted outline, the triode at the left of the dual-triode tube conducts and current flows through the load resistor. The current change will conform to that of the input signal and in consequence the output pulse will be opposite in polarity to that of the input pulse. Similarly, if a positive pulse is applied to T_2, the right-side diode conducts and again an ouput signal is developed. If pulses are applied to both input terminals at the same time, both diode sections conduct and again an output pulse is developed. Thus, an output is obtained for T_1, *or* T_2, *or* both. Since there is a phase reversal, in computer terminology this circuit is sometimes referred to as a NOR circuit, since it combines the functions of the NOT circuit (signal reversal) as well as the OR circuit.

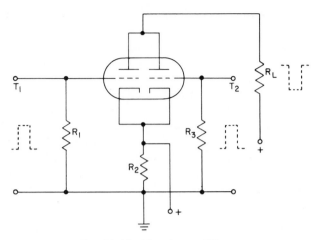

Fig. 23-13. Two-input OR gate.

As with the coincidence circuits, more than two terminals can be employed if so desired. A three-input OR gate is shown in Fig. 23-14. More inputs can be obtained by adding additional transistors. For the circuit shown, the necessary reverse bias for the collectors of the three transistors

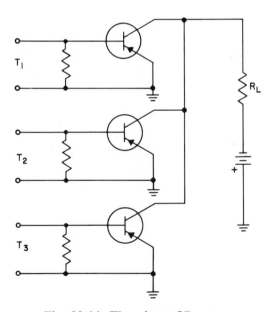

Fig. 23-14. Three-input OR gate.

is supplied by the battery in series with the load resistor R_L. In contrast
to the three-input AND gate shown earlier in Fig. 23-12, the collectors
for the OR gate are in parallel instead of in series as for the AND gate.
Again, no forward bias is applied to any transistor. Thus, if a signal of
negative polarity is applied to terminal T_1, it will make the base of the
top transistor negative with respect to the emitter. Thus, the forward-bias
requirements are supplied by the input waveform, and this transistor then
conducts causing a voltage to appear across the load resistor. Similarly,
if a signal of negative polarity is applied to terminal T_2, the center transistor conducts and an output signal is developed across the load. If signals
are applied to all inputs at one time, an output signal is again developed.
Thus, an output is developed for a signal applied to T_1, *or* to T_2, *or* to T_3,
or to all three inputs.

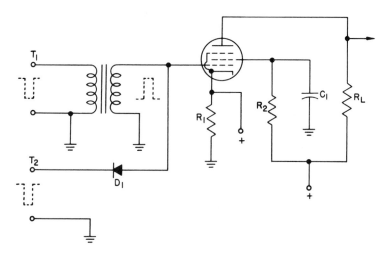

Fig. 23-15. Gating-out circuit (inhibitor).

A computer-type gating-out circuit is shown in Fig. 23-15. Here, again
the cathode is made sufficiently positive so that the grids will be negative
in respect to the cathode and will cut off tube conduction. The input T_1
is coupled to a transformer primary where the phase of the signal is inverted as shown by the dotted outline. Thus, a transformer functions as
a NOT circuit for reversing the polarity of the input pulse. Any signal
applied to terminal T_1 will, therefore, apply a positive signal to the grid
and cause tube conduction. In consequence, the signal will appear across
the load resistor R_L. If a signal is applied only to terminal T_2 as shown by
the dotted outline, it will have no effect on circuit performance because the

negative-polarity signal will drive the tube into cutoff to a greater degree than established by the bias, hence conduction would still not occur. When a signal appears at both inputs T_1 and T_2, the signal input at T_2 will *inhibit* the signal entered at T_1 and prevent it from causing tube conduction. Thus, this circuit in computer applications is often referred to as an INHIBITOR circuit or gate. In other applications, the circuit serves to gate out any portions of the input signal as desired. Thus, for a pulse-train input at T_1, certain pulses or groups of pulses can be gated out as desired. Because of the transformer arrangement, negative signals are employed at both T_1 and T_2. In the absence of the transformer, a positive signal would have to be applied to terminal T_1.

Two other gating circuits are shown in Fig. 23-16. The circuit shown at (A) can be used either as a keying-in or a keying-out device. As illustrated, however, the circuit performs as a keying-in unit. If a series of pulses is applied to input No. 1, there will be no output unless a gating

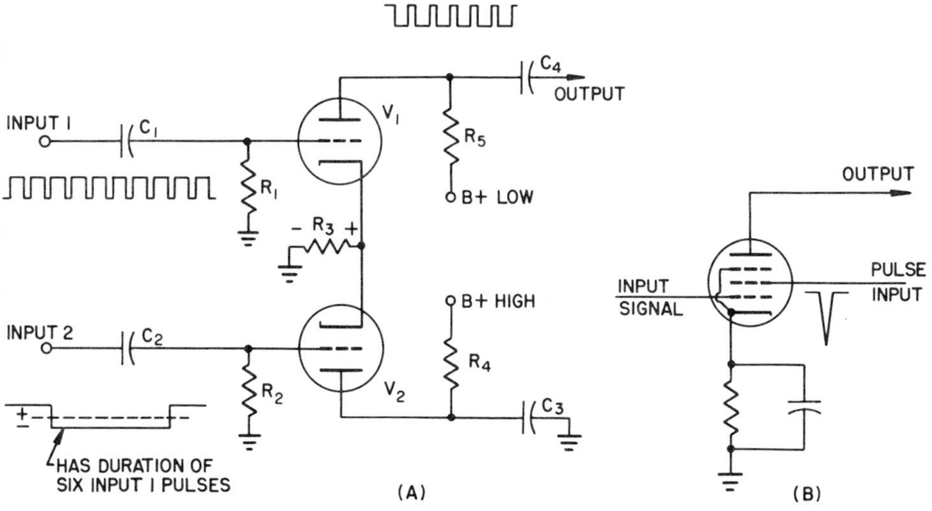

Fig. 23-16. Gating circuits.

pulse is applied to input No. 2. The duration of this gating pulse will determine how many of the pulses which are applied to input No. 1 will arrive at the output. This circuit is useful where only a precise amount of pulses is to be applied to some subsequent circuit or device. One application is in television transmitting systems, where it is necessary to insert synchronizing pulses into the video signal.

Note that the cathodes of V_1 and V_2 have a common resistor. The anode voltage for V_2, being higher than the anode voltage of V_1, causes the plate current for V_2 to produce a large voltage drop across resistor R_3, with a polarity as shown. This voltage drop across R_3 is sufficient to increase the bias for V_1 to the point where the latter tube is at cutoff. (Tube V_1 will cut off sooner for a given bias than V_2, because V_1 has a lower anode voltage.) Because V_1 is held at cutoff, due to the high current flow through V_2, no pulses appear at the output.

Assume that, in this gating circuit, it is required that only six pulses appear at the output at periodic intervals. Thus, when the six pulses are to appear at the output, a negative pulse is applied to input No. 2, this negative pulse having a duration equal to six pulses applied at intput No. 1. The application of a negative pulse to input No. 2 decreases the bias potential of V_2 and, hence, decreases current flow through the latter tube. The decline in V_2 current flowing through R_3 decreases the voltage drop across the latter resistor. The decreased voltage across R_3 also reduces the bias on V_1 and, hence, the latter is permitted to conduct. During conduction of V_1, all input pulses appearing at its grid will be amplified, and will appear at the output as shown. (These pulses are inverted, because of the phase difference across a vacuum amplifier tube.) When the negative-going pulse at V_2 ends, the bias at the grid of V_2 will again decrease and, in consequence, current flow through V_2 rises again. Once more, the additional current through the cathode resistor R_3 will increase the bias on V_1 and cause the latter to be cut off. Hence, only six of the input pulses appear at the output of V_1. From the foregoing, it is obvious that the entire circuit acts as a gate, which is closed for any input signals applied at input No. 1, and is opened only at certain intervals, to permit a specific number of pulses to pass through V_1.

When the circuit is operated in the manner just described, it is known as a keying-in device. The circuit in Fig. 23-16(A), however, can also be used as a keying-out circuit, by replacing the high anode B voltage of V_2 with a lower anode voltage. Also, the anode voltage of V_1 is raised when the device is to be used as a keying-out circuit. With lower plate voltage on V_2, less current is drawn and, with high anode voltage on V_1, higher current flows through the latter. Consequently, V_1 will not be at cutoff, and will pass all pulses applied to input No. 1. When, however, the pulses are to be keyed out, that is, prevented from appearing at the output, a positive pulse is applied to the grid of V_2, via input No. 2. The positive pulse will decrease the bias on the grid of V_2 and, hence, increased current flows through the latter tube. The increased current also flows through cathode resistor R_3 and raises the bias on V_1 to cutoff. When V_1 is at cutoff, the output will be zero for the duration of the positive pulse applied at input No. 2.

A simpler type of gating circuit is shown in Fig. 23-16(B). Here, a pentode tube is employed in a conventional amplifier circuit, except that the screen grid has provisions for the application of a signal. The signal input at the control grid will appear in its amplified version at the output at all times, except when a negative pulse is applied to the screen grid. When such a negative pulse is applied to the screen grid it stops conduction because of the high negative potential at the screen during the time interval the pulse is present. (As mentioned earlier, a negative voltage on the screen grid has the ability to produce cutoff, just as a negative bias applied to the control grid does.)

During the presence of a pulse at the screen grid, of course, no signal output appears and hence this circuit is a gating-out device. As such it performs an inhibiting function because a pulse applied to the screen will inhibit the entry of a pulse or other signal at the control grid. For comparison with the AND circuit, see Fig. 23-11.

LOGIC-GATE FUNCTIONS

Some of the functions of logic gates with respect to pulse handling are shown in Fig. 23-17. At (A) is shown an AND gate (coincidence circuit) where five pulses are applied to the upper terminal. At the lower terminal, the pulse train is interrupted and two pulse signals are missing as shown. Since, during the time the lower pulse signals are missing, there

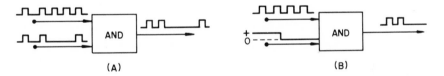

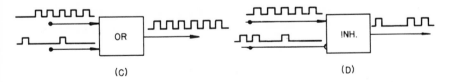

Fig. 23-17. Logic gate functions.

is no coincidence, there will be no output for this time interval. Hence the third and fourth pulses at the upper terminal will not appear at the output. The input pulses to either of the terminals of the circuit at (A) need not be a continuous pulse train. Letting the number "one" represent a pulse, assume that the pulse signals applied to the upper terminal at (A) are 101011. If the pulse signals now applied to the lower input terminal are 100101, the output pulse signal would be 100001. Since there is coincidence only between the first pulse signals and the last which enter the two terminals, there will be no output pulses between the two time intervals from the start of the signal input to the conclusion.

The circuit will also function by using steady-state signals at one terminal with respect to the other. This is shown at (B), where a positive voltage at the lower terminal exists for two of the pulses applied at the upper terminal. The positive voltage at the lower terminal will therefore provide a voltage coincidence with the upper input signals and hence the output waveform will consist of the two initial pulses as shown. Since the steady-state d-c voltage at the lower terminal drops to zero for the last two pulses, no coincidence prevails and there is no output for this time interval.

A representative pulse input to an OR circuit is shown at Fig. 23-17(C). Here, a pulse input at the upper or lower terminals will result in an output. Hence, the output pulse formation consists of six pulses as shown, because at the lower terminal one pulse extends to the left beyond the upper pulse train which provides an additional output. Where two pulses occur simultaneously, as at the third pulse input for the upper terminal, a single output pulse is available. Here again, if we let numbers represent pulses, an application of pulses having an order of 10001 at the upper terminal, plus pulses having a representation of 01110 at the lower terminal, will result in an output of 11111.

The inhibiting function is shown at Fig. 23-17(D). Here, five pulses are present at the upper terminal. At the lower terminal, the pulse to the left of the upper train will not appear at the output, since the inhibiting input does not produce tube or transistor conduction as discussed earlier. In the upper train, however, the pulse at the left is inhibited by the simultaneous pulse appearing at the lower terminals. Similarly, the third pulse of the upper pulse train is inhibited because of the appearance of a pulse during this time interval at the lower input terminal. Hence the output is as shown.

REVIEW QUESTIONS

1. Draw a schematic of a TPDT relay.

2. Explain how relays can be used to perform coincidence switching. Reproduce the schematics of the two types discussed in the text.

3. Explain how a zener diode may be used in a switching circuit.

4. Reproduce the schematic of a flip-flop circuit and indicate which tube or transistor is conducting when the device is in the 'one' state.

5. For the circuit shown in Fig. 23-7, which relay is closed when the flip-flop is in the "one" state?

6. For the circuit shown in Fig. 23-8, is the relay switch closed or open when light strikes the phototube?

7. Reproduce the schematic shown in Fig. 23-10, and modify it to accept positive pulse inputs. Briefly explain how this circuit functions.

8. Why is a coincidence gate also called an AND circuit?

9. Draw a schematic of a two-input transistor AND gate, using *N-P-N* transistors. Explain how the circuit functions and show the polarity of the input pulses as well as the polarity of the output pulses.

10. Draw a two-input transistor OR gate using *N-P-N* transistors. Explain how the circuit functions and illustrate the type waveform applied to the input and that produced at the output.

11. Explain the differences in function between an inhibitor circuit and a NOT circuit.

12. Reproduce the schematic shown at Fig. 23-16(A) but modify it to function as a gating-out circuit. Briefly explain its operation.

13. Using numbers to represent pulses, what output would be obtained from an AND circuit if the input to one terminal is 10111 and the input to the other terminal is 00111?

14. What would be the output from an OR circuit if the same input pulse signals were applied to it as in Problem 13?

15. Using the input signals for Problem 13, what would be the output pulses obtained from an inhibitor circuit?

16. Explain how a long-duration pulse can be used with an inhibitor circuit for gating out several pulses of a pulse train applied to one of the terminals.

24

MISCELLANEOUS CIRCUITS

INTRODUCTION

In the preceding chapters the fundamental aspects of a number of circuits and components have been covered with respect to specific categories. In amplifiers, for instance, both the voltage and power amplifiers were analyzed and illustrated, and the characteristics relating to the broad field of electronics were covered. There are, however, other types of amplifiers used in automation and industrial control which do not have the linear characteristics of those previously discussed, and hence are not suitable for the reproduction of sound or the amplification of carrier signals. Instead, such special amplifiers are primarily used to control the amount of power applied to industrial hardware, such as motors, control systems, and other units such as power supplies. Also, there are numerous occasions in industrial electronics where a specific frequency of a signal, or the pulse-repetition rate, must be altered by either increasing or decreasing the frequency to meet specific requirements. All of these circuits are utilized in some phases of automation, computer systems, nuclear reactor control, closed-circuit commercial television, radar, and in numerous other applications. In this chapter the circuits and operating principles of such amplifiers and frequency modifiers are covered to round out the circuit and component discussions in the preceding chapters.

CONTROL AMPLIFICATION

In industrial electronic devices, it is often necessary to vary a large amount of electric power in accordance with variations which occur at low-power levels. This is essentially an amplifying process similar to that performed by vacuum tubes and transistors. Instead of using the latter, however, a magnetic amplifier is employed because of its large power handling capability and its simplicity. A basic magnetic amplifier circuit is shown in Fig. 24-1. The heart of the magnetic amplifier is a device which resembles a transformer, but actually functions as a variable inductance. A coil is wound on each of the three legs of the core as shown. Inductance

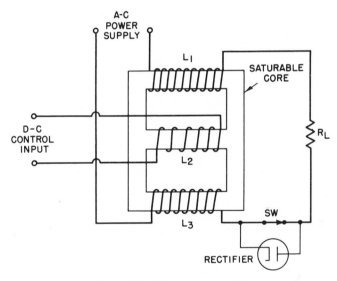

Fig. 24-1. Magnetic amplifier.

L_2 acts as a control winding, and sufficient current is circulated in this coil for operation around the saturation level of the core material in a manner similar to the swinging choke described in Chapter 14 on Power Supplies. The a-c power which is to be controlled is applied to the terminals shown, one of which is connected to coil L_1 in series with coil L_3. Each of these coils is wound in a direction opposite to the other, so that the fields established by the individual coils are effectively cancelled. This lessens the influence of these coils on the core and also minimizes interaction between these coils and the control winding coil L_2. The a-c power is fed through these coils and is applied to the output load, shown as a resistor R_L in Fig. 24-1. The actual load can consist of a large motor or other device in which the amount of a-c power which is applied must be regulated and controlled.

When a control voltage is applied to coil L_2, a certain degree of core saturation is produced, depending on the amount of current flow created by the control voltage. With the core at a certain saturation level, the inductances of L_1 and L_3 are lower in value than would be the case with no core saturation. In consequence, the inductive reactance is also lower than would normally be the case. Because inductances L_1 and L_3 are in series with the load circuit and the power source, the power factor is altered by the amount of inductance present. Hence, the power applied to the load will be determined by the amount of inductance which is in series. If the voltage applied to the control winding is increased, more current flows through the latter and the core flux density increases toward the saturation level. Permeability (and inductance) decreases, and hence more power is applied to the load circuit. For a reduction of the control voltage, less current circulates through the control winding and flux density drops to a level farther below the saturation level. Consequently, inductance values of L_1 and L_3 increase and less power is applied to the load circuit. From the foregoing, it is evident that variations in the low d-c input voltage produce high-value variations in the output, and hence this device is an amplifier.

The magnetic amplifier is sometimes known as a control device, since a large amount of power can be controlled by a relatively low-power value. If d-c output is required, the switch shown at the bottom of the load resistance can be opened, so that the vacuum-tube rectifier is in series with the load circuit. Because of the rectifying action, pulsating d-c will be applied to the load resistance instead of a-c. The pulsating d-c can be filtered to obtain relatively pure d-c if such is required.

As with tube and transistor amplifiers, feedback can also be employed with the magnetic amplifier. The feedback can be regenerative or degenerative as required. Thus, a portion of the amplified signal is fed back to the magnetic amplifier in order to alter its characteristics. With positive feedback, regeneration occurs, and the sensitivity as well as the gain of the magnetic amplifier is increased. When negative feedback is used, degeneration occurs, and the amplified signal waveform is more faithfully reproduced, although, as with tube and transistor amplifiers, the over-all gain is decreased in proportion to the amplitude of the signal which is fed back.

A typical magnetic amplifier with feedback is shown in Fig. 24-2. Here, a four-legged type of core is employed in contrast to the three-legged type shown earlier in Fig. 24-1. The additional core leg permits the inclusion of a feedback winding marked L_4 in the illustration. The bridge rectifier provides an output consisting of pulsating d-c which can be filtered, as with conventional power supplies, to provide relatively ripple-free d-c.

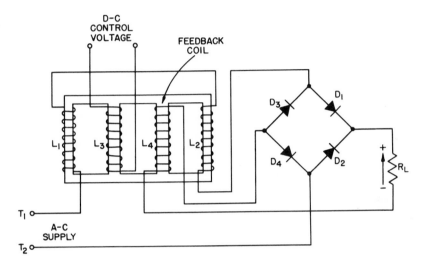

Fig. 24-2. Magnetic amplifier with feedback.

The operation of the amplifier can be more easily understood by assuming instantaneous values of a-c applied to the input terminals T_1 and T_2. Assume that the instantaneous value of the a-c is negative at terminal T_1 and positive at terminal T_2. With such a polarity at the input terminals, current flows from terminal T_1 and through the inductance L_1 and L_2, to the junction of the solid-state rectifiers D_1 and D_3. The current must complete its circuit to the positive terminal T_2, hence it flows through diode D_3, and through the feedback coil L_4, to the bottom of the load resistance R_L. The current flow through the load resistor establishes a voltage with a polarity as shown, and the current then completes the circuit to terminal T_2 by flowing through diode D_2.

When the a-c signal at the input terminal changes polarity, a negative potential appears at T_2 and a positive potential at T_1. Now, current flows from terminal T_2 to the junction of diodes D_2 and D_4. Since terminal T_1 is positive, the direction of the current path must be toward this terminal. Hence current flows through diode D_4, through the control winding L_4, and again to the bottom of the load resistor R_L. Again, the direction of current through the load resistor is the same as before, producing the second pulsating d-c alternation. Now the current flows through diode D_1 and through inductors L_2 and L_1 to terminal T_1. (Note that when this current had arrived at the junction of diodes D_1 and D_2 it would appear that either diode could conduct. The current will not flow through D_2, however, because the return path must be to the positive terminal T_1. Hence, conduction for this instantaneous a-c is through D_1.)

If the feedback is degenerative, the circuit can be changed to a regenerative one simply by transposing the leads from the feedback coil L_4. If the circuit has been set up to be regenerative, the feedback current fields will cause the current flow through the control winding to increase and hence a greater control change occurs. Thus, an increase in the current through the control winding will raise the flux density to the near-saturation point, and the saturation level increase over and above that which would occur without feedback, provides a greater change in the amplified power output. If the current through the control winding decreases, the signal energy at the load circuit decreases and hence the current through the feedback coil L_4 also decreases, causing a reduction in flux density to a greater degree than would occur for a change of current in the control winding L_3 without feedback.

Similarly, if the feedback-coil polarity is such that the circuit is degenerative, the current flow through L_4 would establish magnetic lines of force which oppose the control winding L_3. Consequently, the core saturation level would be decreased below the level which prevails for current through the control winding L_3 without feedback. For instance, a decrease in the control current flow through L_3 would mean that the flux density of the core also decreases to a given level. The feedback current through L_4, however, also causes an additional decrease, with the end result that the flux density would not decline to as low a level as would be the case without degeneration.

Another type of power-control amplifier used in industrial electronics is the so-called *Hall effect* amplifier shown in Fig. 24-3. The heart of the amplifier is a semiconductor crystal slab, as shown at (A), composed of intermetallic components such as indium arsenide and indium antimonide. These components have *magnetoresistive* characteristics and have what is known as a high *mobility* of the conduction material. With ordinary conductors the Hall effect is very slight and the voltages set up are insufficient in amplitude to be of any practical use.

As shown at (A), the conductive slab has attached to it two independent circuits. The circuit containing the battery or other supply causes current flow as shown by the arrows and identified as I_c, *control current*. When a magnetic field is applied to the conductive crystal slab so that the magnetic lines of force are at right angles to the slab, the electrons are forced aside as shown by the dotted outline at Fig. 24-3(A). This results in an excessive amount of electrons on that side (negative charge) while on the other side there is a deficiency of electrons creating a positive charge. Thus, the magnetic field creates a potential difference across the edges of the crystal opposite to the potential difference applied by the battery. Thus, a current flows up through the crystal slab and this Hall-effect current (HE_C) flows down through the load resistor in the direction shown by the arrows, with its return path to the plus terminal of the supply source. Hence this characteristic can be employed in industrial measurements of magnetic field strength, instruments, and power control amplification.

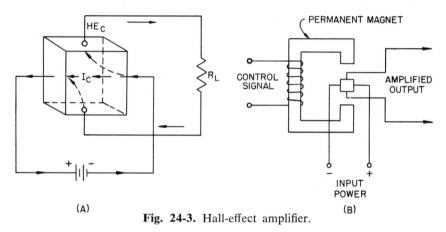

Fig. 24-3. Hall-effect amplifier.

The basic amplifier circuit is shown at Fig. 24-3(B). With the permanent magnet arrangement as shown, the high magnetic-flux density is impressed across the crystal slab as shown. The control signal is applied to an inductor wound around the permanent magnet. Thus, the magnetic flux between the pole pieces of the permanent magnet can be increased or decreased by the control-signal voltage applied to the coil. If the applied signal voltage produces a magnetic field which aids that of the magnet, the increase in magnetic flux between the pole pieces will cause a greater deflection of the electron stream within the slab, with an increase in the current flow through the load circuit. If, however, the voltage applied to the coil is reversed in polarity, the magnetic field produced by the coil will oppose that of the field of the magnet and hence the flux density between the pole pieces decreases. Hence, there is a decrease in the electron-stream deflection, and the current through the load circuit will decrease. As with other amplifiers, a signal of low power applied to the coil will produce a signal of considerably greater power at the output. The input signal can be either d-c or a-c to produce an amplified output signal of either type as required.

SIGNAL-FREQUENCY MULTIPLICATION

In AM, FM, and TV broadcasting, as well as in radar and other electronic applications, it is often necessary to increase the frequency of a particular R-F signal. A common frequency multiplier used is the Class C amplifier previously discussed. Figure 24-4 shows the Class C triode amplifier in a frequency-doubler application. Here, an oscillator generating a frequency of 2,000 kilocycles is applied to the Class C doubler circuit, so that the oscillator frequency may be increased to 4,000 kilocycles, as shown.

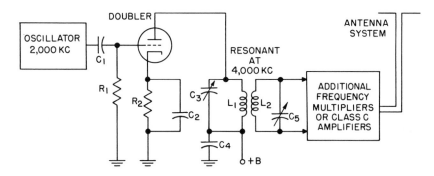

Fig. 24-4. Signal-frequency multiplication.

Oscillators, Class C amplifiers, and other similar devices operate on the nonlinear portion of the tube's characteristics and, hence, generate a high order of harmonics in addition to the fundamental frequency. In consequence, a Class C amplifier can be employed which is tuned to one of the harmonics of the fundamental, so that it will develop across its resonant circuit a primary signal of the harmonic, rather than of the fundamental impressed at the input. Such is the case with the doubler circuit shown in Fig. 24-4. The oscillator is generating a frequency of 2,000 kilocycles, but the resonant circuit of the doubler, composed of C_3 and L_1, is tuned to 4,000 kilocycles. Because the harmonics of the oscillator are lower in amplitude than the fundamental signal, less driving power is applied to the grid circuit of the doubler tube. Consequently, the doubler circuit does not have the high efficiency of the regular Class C amplifier.

The input resonant circuit to a subsequent stage (L_2 and C_5) is tuned to the multiplied frequency of 4,000 kilocycles. Additional doubler stages can be employed to increase the signal frequency to a higher value, if desired. The Class C amplifier will also function as a tripler, multiplying the input frequency three times. As a tripler, however, the efficiency is increasingly lower than in the normal Class C amplifier or the doubler circuit.

Frequency multipliers, because of the difference in the frequency of the signals applied to the input and those generated at the output, are not subject to undesired oscillations and hence rarely require neutralization as is the case with triode Class C amplifiers.

FREQUENCY DIVIDERS

Often, in industrial electronics, the pulse frequency (repetition rate) must be divided for purposes of industrial control, synchronization of oscillator circuits, counting, timing, pulse-rate comparisons, and for the operation of circuits operating at lower frequencies than the pulse repetition rate. One method for accomplishing frequency division is by use of the relaxation oscillators described in Chapter 17. If, for instance, a blocking oscillator is employed, its free-running frequency can be set at one-half of the repetition rate of the pulses applied to its sync input. This is shown in Fig. 24-5. Here, assume the sync input pulses have a repetition rate of 6,000 pulses per second (pps). The blocking oscillator, however, has its characteristics designed so that it has a free-running frequency of 3,000 pps. Hence, alternate sync input pulses will keep the oscillator in synchronization as shown by the grid-signal waveform in Fig. 24-5. Every other sync pulse will drop below the tube conduction level and hence will be ineffectual in causing tube conduction. Only the pulses near the free-running frequency are effective in causing tube conduction and thus permitting synchronization. Thus, this system acts as a pulse-repetition-rate divider since the output pulses are synchronized by pulses having a repetition rate twice that of the output.

The flip-flop circuits discussed in Chapter 23 are also capable of pulse-repetition-rate division, and are also utilized in computers and industrial electronic applications. As detailed in Chapter 23, the flip-flop circuit will produce one negative output pulse for every two negative pulses applied to the input circuit. (With appropriate circuit wiring, positive pulses can also be employed. For the purpose of this discussion, assume that the circuit is as shown earlier in Fig. 23-6, where the grid diodes are so wired that negative pulses are the gating signals.) Thus, when a flip-flop is in its "zero" state and triggered to its "one" state, a positive pulse develops at the output of the flip-flop, but such a pulse polarity has no effect on a second-stage flip-flop, because only negative pulses are instrumental in triggering. When a second pulse is applied to a flip-flop stage, it will trigger the latter into the "zero" state again, while at the same time a negative output pulse is developed. The latter, when applied to the next flip-flop stage, will trigger it to its 'one' state.

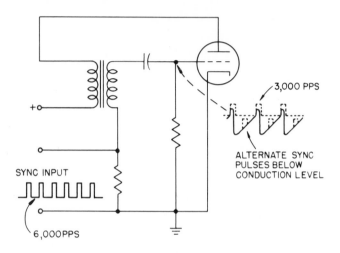

Fig. 24-5. Blocking oscillator frequency division.

Assume, for instance, that five flip-flop circuits are connected as shown in Fig. 24-6. If two pulses are entered into the first flip-flop at the left, the output negative pulse will trigger the second stage to its "one" state. The latter will then produce a positive output pulse, but again such a pulse polarity has no effect on the third stage because of the grid diodes. Upon the application of a third pulse to the first flip-flop stage, it will again be triggered into its "one" state, but again the positive output pulse has no effect on the second flip-flop. Upon the application of a fourth pulse to the first stage, however, the negative output pulse which is applied to the second flip-flop will trigger the latter to its "zero" state, and hence this second stage will send a negative pulse to the third stage which is then triggered to the "one" state.

Hence, it is obvious that successive pulses applied to the first flip-flop will produce one negative output pulse for every two entered. Thus, if four are entered into the first stage, two pulses will be produced at the

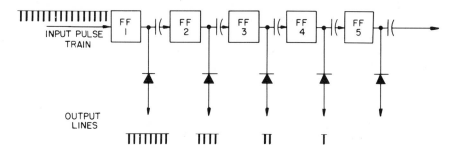

Fig. 24-6. Flip-flop scaling.

output. If eight are entered, four output pulses will be produced, and if 16 are entered, eight will be available at the output. Hence, a series of flip-flop stages has the ability to *count down,* or *scale.* As shown in Fig. 24-6, when 16 pulses are entered into the first flip-flop, the eight which are produced at its output terminal are also applied to the input of the second flip-flop. (The diodes in the output leads also prevent any positive pulses from appearing.) Since eight pulses are applied to the second flip-flop, four pulses are produced at its output and applied to the third flip-flop. The third produces two output pulses which are applied to the fourth flip-flop, and the latter produces one output pulse as shown.

This pulse-repetition-rate dividing characteristic of a series of such flip-flop stages is not only a useful characteristic in digital computers, but also in industrial control applications. As discussed in Chapter 23, relays can be placed in the anode of circuits in the various stages to perform count-down functions and close or open circuits at predetermined intervals. For industrial applications, the input pulses to the first flip-flop stage can be obtained from photocells or other transducers described in Chapter 21. The photocell, with a suitable light beam impinging on it, will produce a series of pulses when the beam of light is interrupted periodically. Such pulse signals, when applied to the series flip-flop stages, can be used in control applications for purposes of counting, fabrication, sorting, and other various processes.

The flip-flop stages shown in Fig. 24-6 operate on what is known as the *binary* system, sometimes referred to as the "8-4-2-1 system." Here, the scaling is in terms of two raised to some power. For instance, two to the zero power equals one, two to the first power equals two, two to the second power equals four, two to the third power equals eight, two to the fourth power equals 16, etc. On occasion, however, it is preferable to have the division in terms of our decimal system having a base 10 instead of a base two. This is done by appropriate circuit changes and modifications which usually consist of using feedback loops within four flip-flop stages, so that such a four-stage group will trigger to zero at the count of 10. When this is done, an equivalent decimal system is established as shown in Fig. 24-7.

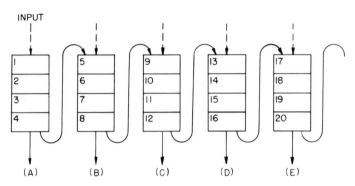

Fig. 24-7. Flip-flop decade counters.

The flip-flop stages with circuit modifications, and in the arrangement shown in Fig. 24-7, are known as *decade counters*. If 10 pulses are applied to the input terminal of the first flip-flop, an output pulse would be procured from terminal A, and such an output pulse will also be applied to the input of the fifth flip-flop as shown. At the same, the first four flip-flop stages will clear to their 'zero' state. Thus, this series of flip-flop stages will produce an output from any decade group of four, for 10 pulses which enter at the top of the flip-flop decade. For an output to be procured from terminal B, 100 pulses would have to be applied to the input terminal of the first decade counter. With this number applied to the input, there would be 10 pulses procured from A, and since these are also applied to the second decade counter, the input to the fifth flip-flop would receive 10 pulses, and one output pulse would be obtained from B. At the same time, the output pulse from the eighth flip-flop would also be applied to the ninth. Thus, the system operates as a decade device, and divides down by 10 for each successive flip-flop decade group.

The output terminals from the individual decade counters can be indicated visually by utilization of the indicators described in Chapter 21. As with the flip-flops previously discussed, any numbers which are entered are stored for as long a time as power is supplied to the circuits. The various stages can be cleared of the stored number, and in computer applications the numbers can be channeled to read-out devices such as electric typewriters or printers.

The Dekatron tube or other beam-switching tubes can also be utilized as decade counters or dividers by placing them in series as shown in Fig. 24-8. As discussed in Chapter 21, when pulses are applied to such tubes,

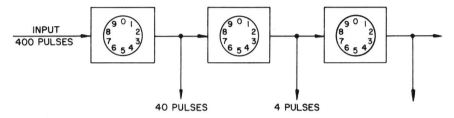

Fig. 24-8. Beam-switching tube divider.

the internal construction is such that there is successive switching from zero to nine. At the application of the tenth pulse, the tube switches to zero and an ouput pulse is produced. Thus, the tube is basically a 10-to-one divider. As shown, if 400 pulses are applied to the first beam-switching tube at the left, 40 pulses would be produced at the output and applied to the second beam-switching tube. At the output from the second tube, four pulses would be produced and also applied to the third tube. There would be no output from the latter until the count of 10 was reached.

The beam-switching tubes are compact and versatile, and will operate at frequencies ranging up to several megacycles. As many tubes as necessary can, of course, be connected together in sequence as shown in Fig. 24-8, or in reverse order for counting purposes.

Another type of pulse-rate divider using logic circuits is shown in Fig. 24-9. Here the input train of pulses is applied to an AND gate as shown, and as described in Chapter 23. The output from the AND gate is also applied to a delay line composed of series inductances and shunt capacitances. A pulse entering such a line, will be delayed in proportion to the amount of inductors and capacitors constituting the delay circuit. The output from the delay line is applied to one of the grid terminals of a flip-flop as shown. The output from the AND gate is also applied directly to the grid of the second tube of the flip-flop stage. The anode of the second tube V_2, is applied to the input of the AND gate, forming the second input terminal to this coincidence circuit.

Assume that positive pulses are employed as shown. When a train of pulses is applied to the upper terminal of the AND circuit, such positive pulses would produce no output unless the positive potential were also present at the lower input to the AND circuit. Note that this condition is satisfied when the flip-flop is in the state where V_1 is conducting and V_2

is nonconducting. With V_2 nonconducting, there would be no voltage drop across the plate resistor, and a high positive voltage is present at its plate. This positive voltage, also appearing at the lower input terminal of the AND gate, will provide the necessary signal polarity coincidence to open the AND gate and permit the first pulse to go through. The positive pulse which appears at the output of the AND gate represents the first positive output pulse obtained from the full circuit. This initial pulse is marked (x) for identification purposes. Note that this initial pulse also enters the delay line, as well as appearing at the grid of V_2. The positive pulse (x) at V_2 will overcome the cutoff bias on this tube and will trigger the flip-flop into its opposite state.

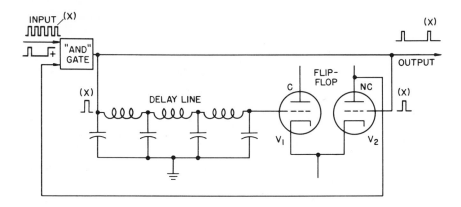

Fig. 24-9. Gated pulse-rate divider.

When the flip-flop triggers to the opposite state, V_1 will be nonconducting, and V_2 will now be conducting. With V_2 conducting, there will be a large voltage drop across the plate resistor, and in consequence, the anode voltage for V_2 will drop to a low level as discussed earlier in Chapter 23. This decrease in the positive voltage will also be felt at the lower input terminal to the AND gate, and in consequence the gate will be closed, since no coincidence now prevails. Thus, for successive input pulses, the AND gate will have no output until coincidence again prevails. In the interim, the first pulse (x) goes through the delay line and finally arrives at the grid of V_1. Since this tube is now in its nonconducting state, a positive pulse will trigger the flip-flop back into its initial state. Now, V_1 will conduct, and V_2 will again be nonconducting. Thus, a positive voltage is once more applied to the lower input terminal of the AND gate, and the coincidence thus produced permits another pulse to enter the

AND gate. The new pulse will appear at the output and again at the delay line and at the grid of V_2. Since V_2 has resumed being nonconducting, the positive pulse will retrigger the flip-flop and will remove the positive potential from the lower terminal of the AND gate. Again, there is no coincidence, and again there will be several pulses appearing at the AND gate which will not be able to go through it.

The operation just described indicates that this is a pulse-rate divider. As shown in Fig. 24-9, with a specific delay, there would only be one output pulse produced for every four input pulses. If the time delay is increased, there would be one pulse produced for six, seven, or eight input pulses, depending on the amount of time delay. Thus, the division can be varied by changing the amount of delay which the input pulse to the delay line encounters.

Several delay lines can be employed with predetermined delay intervals, and switched into the circuit as required for the amount of division needed. As discussed in Chapter 23, the flip-flop stage acts as a switch, which successively opens and closes the AND gate. The latter, in turn, acts as a switch or gate to switch to the output line the required number of pulses which are to be divided.

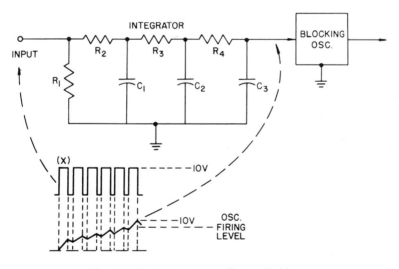

Fig. 24-10. Integrator-oscillator divider.

Another dividing system using a blocking oscillator is shown in Fig. 24-10. Here an integrator circuit is employed, the output of which is applied to the grid of a blocking oscillator. As detailed in Chapter 17, an integrator circuit has a long time constant in relation to the pulse duration. Thus, successive pulses are required to charge the integrator capacitors to an amplitude equal to the peak pulse amplitude. For purposes of analysis, assume that the firing level of the blocking oscillator requires a signal amplitude at the grid of approximately 8 volts. The incoming pulses have a 10-volt peak level as shown. Upon arrival of the first pulse identified by (x), the integrator capacitors will start to charge for the duration of the incoming pulse. Because of the long time constant, however, the charge which builds up is only a small percentage of the peak voltage of the incoming pulse. During the interval between pulses, the capacitors will discharge through the resistive network composed of R_1 and R_2. Since the duration between the pulses is shorter than the pulse width, however, the capacitors only discharge a small percentage of the charge which they obtained when the pulse was present. Thus, the second pulse will cause the integrator capacitors to charge an additional amount and during the interval between the second and third pulses there again is a slight discharge as shown in Fig. 24-10. Eventually, the incoming pulses will build up an amplitude sufficiently high to reach the firing level of the blocking oscillator, and hence will cause blocking-oscillator tube conduction and thus synchronize the free-running frequency of the blocking oscillator.

Thus, if this device has a free-running frequency of one-sixth the repetition rate of the input pulses, a six-to-one division occurs. When the blocking-oscillator tube or transistor conducts, the integrator capacitors discharge through the low impedance of the conducting tube.

In this circuit the amount of pulse-repetition rate division depends on the time constant of the integrator circuit, the pulse duration, repetition rate, and similar factors. An adjustment of the bias or the free-running frequency of the blocking oscillator will also influence the division rate. This system is utilized in the vertical sweep systems of television receivers and some industrial control applications.

For the system shown in Fig. 24-10, the input must consist of a pulse train without long time intervals between groups of pulses. Any appreciable time interval will result in the discharge of the integrator capacitors through the shunting R_1 and R_2 resistors. If the decline in the charge between pulse intervals is to be avoided, the circuit shown in Fig. 24-11 is utilized. This is a *staircase*-type divider or pulse counter, because the signal waveform appearing at the grid of the tube (or the base of the transistor) appears as an ascending, sharply-defined waveform resembling a staircase.

Note that the input pulses are of short duration; the time interval is longer than it was in the previously discussed circuit. Here, the input circuit consists of a coupling capacitor C_1, a shunting diode D_1, a series diode D_2, and the staircase charging capacitor C_2. The tube can be a part of a blocking-oscillator circuit, or it can consist of a thyratron or silicon-

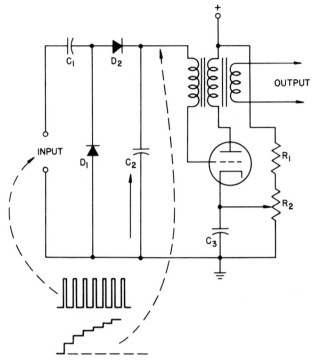

Fig. 24-11. Staircase divider-counter.

controlled rectifier which will be fired when the signal amplitude applied to the control grid reaches a predetermined amplitude.

Upon the arrival of a pulse to the input of the circuit shown in Fig. 24-11, the positive rise of the pulse waveform will cause diode D_2 to conduct, and current flow will be toward capacitor C_2 in the direction shown by the arrow. Thus, capacitor C_2 as well as C_1 starts to charge. Since, however, the pulse duration is short compared to the long time constant of the circuit, only a small charge builds up across C_2 and C_1. During the interval between the first and second pulse, the charge remains on C_2, hence the signal waveform developed between grid and ground levels off as shown in the staircase waveform drawing. Capacitor C_1, having been charged with a negative polarity toward the top of the diode and a positive polarity toward the bottom of D_1 (through the input coupling network) will now cause diode D_1 to conduct and thus discharge C_1. Capacitor C_2, however, is unable to discharge because the top plate of C_2 is positive with respect to the bottom plate, and hence it has no conduction path through either D_1 or D_2. If the input waveform is of the square-wave type instead of the pulse type, diode D_1 would conduct for the negative half cycle of the square waves, again discharging C_1 but not affecting the charge on C_2.

During the second positive input pulse, the charge on capacitor C_2 is increased by an additional amount in step fashion as shown by the staircase waveform. Even though the intervals between pulses were substantially longer in duration, there would be no discharge of C_2 during such intervals (provided the reverse resistance of D_2 approached that of the vacuum-tube open-circuit condition). Since the capacitor C_2 charges exponentially, the charge-voltage amplitude decreases for successive steps of the staircase waveform as shown.

Because capacitor C_2 is coupled to the grid of the tube through the transformer primary, it will cause tube conduction when the staircase signal amplitude reaches a sufficiently high level to overcome the negative-bias potential of the tube. When the tube fires, the conduction establishes a low-impedance path for discharge of the staircase capacitor. The negative bias for the tube is set by resistor R_2, which applies a positive potential to the cathode and thus establishes the point at which the tube is cut off. Thus, an adjustment of R_2 will alter the operational characteristics of the circuit, since it will establish the bias level and hence the amplitude of the staircase necessary for overcoming bias. Since R_2 adjusts the firing level, it regulates the amount of division which is procured. Hence, one output pulse is delivered for a predetermined number of input pulses. As discussed in Chapter 17, the output waveform may be modified by clipping or other wave-shaping procedures to procure the type of signal required. This may be necessary, since the output waveform from a blocking oscillator does not resemble the input pulses shown in Fig. 24-11. If a thyratron or silicon-controlled rectifier is used instead of a blocking oscillator, the staircase amplitude will fire the thyratron when it reaches an amplitude sufficient to release the holding characteristics of the control grid. Once capacitor C_2 has discharged, however, the thyratron will still conduct, as explained earlier, and means must be provided to interrupt the plate-current flow to cause the thyratron to stop conducting again.

REVIEW QUESTIONS

1. Reproduce a schematic of a magnetic amplifier and summarize its operating characteristics.

2. In what manner may a magnetic amplifier be modified to permit either regenerative or degenerative feedback?

3. Explain what is meant by the *Hall effect*.

4. Explain in what manner a doubler circuit produces an output which is higher in frequency than the input signal.

5. When triode tubes or transistors are used for doubler circuits, why is neutralization unnecessary?

6. Explain in what manner a blocking oscillator can be utilized as a frequency divider.

7. Explain the manner in which the series of flip-flop circuits can perform scaling functions.

8. Explain the basic differences between a binary scaler and a decade scaler.

9. Draw a block diagram of four beam-switching tubes wired to perform dividing functions. Indicate the number of input pulses which must be applied to the first tube in order to procure one pulse from the output of the last tube.

10. Draw a block diagram of a divider system using a logic AND gate and flip-flop, and indicate a division ratio of 12 to one.

11. Explain how an integrator can be utilized with a relaxation oscillator for pulse-rate division.

12. Draw a schematic of a staircase-type divider which is utilized in conjunction with a gas-tube thyratron.

APPENDIX

Element	Symbol	Atomic Number	Atomic Weight
Actinium	Ac	89	227
Aluminum	Al	13	26.98
Americium	Am	95	*243
Antimony	Sb	51	121.76
Argon	A	18	39.944
Arsenic	As	33	74.91
Astatine	At	85	*210
Barium	Ba	56	137.36
Berkelium	Bk	97	*249
Beryllium	Be	4	9.013
Bismuth	Bi	83	209.00
Boron	B	5	10.82
Bromine	Br	35	79.916
Cadmium	Cd	48	112.41
Calcium	Ca	20	40.08
Californium	Cf	98	*249
Carbon	C	6	12.011
Cerium	Ce	58	140.13
Cesium	Cs	55	132.91
Chlorine	Cl	17	35.457
Chromium	Cr	24	52.01
Cobalt	Co	27	58.94
Copper	Cu	29	63.54
Curium	Cm	96	*245
Dysprosium	Dy	66	162.51
Einsteinium	Es	99	*255
Erbium	Er	68	167.27
Europium	Eu	63	152.0
Fermium	Fm	100	*255
Fluorine	F	9	19.00
Francium	Fr	87	*223
Gadolinium	Gd	64	157.26
Gallium	Ga	31	69.72
Germanium	Ge	32	72.60
Gold	Au	79	197.0
Hafnium	Hf	72	178.50
Helium	He	2	4.003
Holmium	Ho	67	164.94
Hydrogen	H	1	1.0080
Indium	In	49	114.82
Iodine	I	53	126.91
Iridium	Ir	77	192.2
Iron	Fe	26	55.85
Krypton	Kr	36	83.80
Lanthanum	La	57	138.92
Lead	Pb	82	207.21
Lithium	Li	3	6.940
Lutecium	Lu	71	174.99
Magnesium	Mg	12	24.32
Manganese	Mn	25	54.94

Mendelevium	Md	101	*256
Mercury	Hg	80	200.61
Molybdenum	Mo	42	95.95
Neodymium	Nd	60	144.27
Neon	Ne	10	20.183
Neptunium	Np	93	*237
Nickel	Ni	28	58.71
Niobium	Nb	41	92.91
Nitrogen	N	7	14.008
Nobelium	No	102	*253
Osmium	Os	76	190.2
Oxygen	O	8	16.000
Palladium	Pd	46	106.4
Phosphorus	P	15	30.975
Platinum	Pt	78	195.09
Plutonium	Pu	94	*242
Polonium	Po	84	210
Potassium	K	19	39.100
Praseodymium	Pr	59	140.92
Promethium	Pm	61	*145
Protactinium	Pa	91	231
Radium	Ra	88	226.05
Radon	Rn	86	222
Rhenium	Re	75	186.22
Rhodium	Rh	45	102.91
Rubidium	Rb	37	85.48
Ruthenium	Ru	44	101.1
Samarium	Sm	62	150.35
Scandium	Sc	21	44.96
Selenium	Se	34	78.96
Silicon	Si	14	28.09
Silver	Ag	47	107.880
Sodium	Na	11	22.991
Strontium	Sr	38	87.63
Sulfur	S	16	32.066
Tantalum	Ta	73	180.95
Technetium	Tc	43	*99
Tellurium	Te	52	127.61
Terbium	Tb	65	158.93
Thallium	Tl	81	204.39
Thorium	Th	90	232.05
Thulium	Tm	69	168.94
Tin	Sn	50	118.70
Titanium	Ti	22	47.90
Tungsten	W	74	183.86
Uranium	U	92	238.07
Vanadium	V	23	50.95
Xenon	Xe	54	131.30
Ytterbium	Yb	70	173.04
Yttrium	Y	39	88.92
Zinc	Zn	30	65.38
Zirconium	Zr	40	91.22

* Denotes isotope weight value for most stable type.

TRIGONOMETRIC RELATIONSHIPS

Trigonometry is the study of various angles, and that branch of trig-onometry relating to *right angles* is reviewed here. As shown at Fig. A-1(A), the sides of a triangle are assigned specific names, *using the angle*

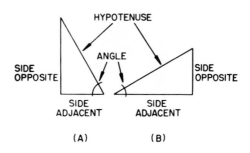

Fig. A-1.

as the reference. Thus, if we are calculating for the angle at the lower right of (A), then the horizontal line extending from this angle is desig-nated as the *side adjacent* to the angle. The vertical line opposite the angle is called the *side opposite,* and the diagonal line from the side opposite to the angle is known as the *hypotenuse.* The angle is the reference point and, as shown at (B), the designations follow a similar pattern as in Fig. A-1(A).

In electronic work, the angles involved in a-c are often of importance in circuit analysis and design, since the opposition to a-c offered by capaci-tors and inductances must be calculated on the basis of simple trigonometry.

A useful form of trigonometry consists in solving for unknown lengths of a triangle, by employing the known angle in conjunction with the length of one of the sides. The relationships of the sides can also be employed to ascertain the angles. For instance, the ratio of the length of the side opposite to the length of the hypotenuse determines the angle. Relation-ships also hold for the ratio of the opposite side to the adjacent side, etc. When such ratios are set down in table form (see the trigonometric table of ratios which follows), the various angles of triangles can be ascertained by calculating the ratio of lengths of the sides. The following are some of the most frequently used ratios:

$$\frac{\text{Opposite side}}{\text{Hypotenuse}} = \sin \theta \text{ (sine of the angle)}$$

$$\frac{\text{Opposite}}{\text{Adjacent}} = \tan \theta \ (\text{tangent of the angle})$$

$$\frac{\text{Adjacent}}{\text{Hypotenuse}} = \cos \theta \ (\text{cosine of an angle})$$

Another characteristic of the right angle is the Pythagorean theorem, which states that the sum of the squares of the side adjacent and the side opposite of a right triangle is equal to the square of the hypotenuse. This theory was formulated by the Greek scholar *Pythagoras* (about 500 B.C.) and the formula related to this theorem may be stated as follows:

$$a^2 + b^2 = c^2$$

In the foregoing formula, a represents the side opposite, b the side adjacent, and c the hypotenuse. Thus, by mathematical rearrangement of the symbols and powers shown above, the hypotenuse can be ascertained from the following formula:

$$c = \sqrt{a^2 + b^2}$$

This equation, except for the substitution of electronic symbols instead of the a, b, and c symbols, is used extensively.

TABLE OF TRIGONOMETRIC RATIOS
(Sines, Cosines, and Tangents)

Degrees	$\frac{(opp)}{(hyp)}$ Sine	$\frac{(adj)}{(hyp)}$ Cosine	$\frac{(opp)}{(adj)}$ Tangent	Degrees	$\frac{(opp)}{(hyp)}$ Sine	$\frac{(adj)}{(hyp)}$ Cosine	$\frac{(opp)}{(adj)}$ Tangent
0	0.0000	1.0000	0.0000	45	0.7071	0.7071	1.0000
1	.0175	.9998	.0175	46	.7193	.6947	1.0355
2	.0349	.9994	.0349	47	.7314	.6820	1.0724
3	.0523	.9986	.0524	48	.7431	.6691	1.1106
4	.0698	.9976	.0699	49	.7547	.6561	1.1504
5	.0872	.9962	.0875	50	.7660	.6429	1.1918
6	.1045	.9945	.1051	51	.7771	.6293	1.2349
7	.1219	.9925	.1228	52	.7880	.6157	1.2799
8	.1392	.9903	.1405	53	.7986	.6018	1.3270
9	.1564	.9877	.1584	54	.8090	.5878	1.3764
10	.1736	.9848	.1763	55	.8192	.5736	1.4281
11	.1908	.9816	.1944	56	.8290	.5592	1.4826
12	.2079	.9781	.2126	57	.8387	.5446	1.5399
13	.2250	.9744	.2309	58	.8480	.5299	1.6003
14	.2419	.9703	.2493	59	.8572	.5150	1.6643
15	.2588	.9659	.2679	60	.8660	.5000	1.7321
16	.2756	.9613	.2867	61	.8746	.4848	1.8040
17	.2924	.9563	.3057	62	.8829	.4695	1.8807
18	.3090	.9511	.3249	63	.8910	.4540	1.9626
19	.3256	.9455	.3443	64	.8988	.4384	2.0503
20	.3420	.9397	.3640	65	.9063	.4226	2.1445
21	.3584	.9336	.3839	66	.9135	.4067	2.2460
22	.3746	.9272	.4040	67	.9205	.3907	2.3559
23	.3907	.9205	.4245	68	.9272	.3746	2.4751
24	.4067	.9135	.4452	69	.9336	.3584	2.6051
25	.4226	.9063	.4663	70	.9397	.3420	2.7475
26	.4384	.8988	.4877	71	.9455	.3256	2.9042
27	.4540	.8910	.5095	72	.9511	.3090	3.0777
28	.4695	.8829	.5317	73	.9563	.2924	3.2709
29	.4848	.8746	.5543	74	.9613	.2756	3.4874
30	.5000	.8660	.5774	75	.9659	.2588	3.7321
31	.5150	.8572	.6009	76	.9703	.2419	4.0108
32	.5299	.8480	.6249	77	.9744	.2250	4.3315
33	.5446	.8387	.6494	78	.9781	.2079	4.7046
34	.5592	.8290	.6745	79	.9816	.1908	5.1446
35	.5736	.8192	.7002	80	.9848	.1736	5.6713
36	.5878	.8090	.7265	81	.9877	.1564	6.3138
37	.6018	.7986	.7536	82	.9903	.1392	7.1154
38	.6157	.7880	.7813	83	.9925	.1219	8.1443
39	.6293	.7771	.8098	84	.9945	.1045	9.5144
40	.6428	.7660	.8391	85	.9962	.0872	11.4301
41	.6561	.7547	.8693	86	.9976	.0698	14.3007
42	.6691	.7431	.9004	87	.9986	.0523	19.0811
43	.6820	.7314	.9325	88	.9994	.0349	28.6363
44	.6947	.7193	.9657	89	.9998	.0175	57.2900
45	.7071	.7071	1.0000	90	1.0000	.0000	....

LOGARITHMS

In Chapter 2, under the discussion on abbreviated forms, it was shown that 10 could be expressed as 10^1, 100 as 10^2, 1,000 as 10^3, etc. Obviously, intermediate power values for numbers between 10 and 100, or between 100 and 1,000, also exist. Similarly, powers for numbers below 10 are also in existence, and can be represented by 10 to some fractional power. Inasmuch as 10^0 is equal to one, and 10^1 is equal to 10, the exponent of a number between one and 10 would be a fractional exponent, since it must be less than one. A *logarithm table* shows the powers for these intermediate numbers. A logarithm (abbreviated "log") is the exponent of the intermediate number, without the base written in. The left-hand vertical column of numbers in the log table represents the intermediate numbers for which the logarithm is to be found, and the succeeding vertical columns show the logarithm or exponent without the base. For instance, the logarithm of the number three is 0.4771. This means that, instead of expressing three as 10 to the 0.4771 power, the 0.4771 is written without the base 10, and hence is known as the logarithm or "log of 3." Since the base is 10, the log of 30 or 300 or 3,000 would contain the same digits as for log 3, except for the decimal point. When 10 is expressed as 10^1, and 100 is expressed as 10^2, it is obvious that the exponent of numbers between 10 and 100 must fall between one and two. For the same reason, then, the logarithm of a number between 10 and 100 must be between one and two. Hence, to express the log of 30, the original 0.4771 number is employed, but it must be added to the original exponent in 10^1 and, therefore, would equal 1.4771. Since the power of 10 for the number 100 is 10^2, the power of 10 for 300 would be $10^{2.4771}$. Hence, the logarithm of 300 is 2.4771. Therefore, the logarithm at the right of a decimal point does not change when additional zeros are added to the original number. The number at the left of the decimal point, however, increases by a numerical value of one each time the original number is multiplied by 10. The fractional portion of the logarithm (at the right of the decimal point) is known as the *mantissa*. The whole number to the left of the decimal point is known as the *characteristic*.

Numbers may not be single digits followed by zeros. For instance, to find the logarithm of 2,720, the number 27 is located in the left-hand column of the table. Along the horizontal row of columns, the logarithm under 2 is now found, to complete the logarithm of 272. This is found to be 4346. To place the decimal point, the decimal point in the original number is moved to the left until the remaining number lies between one and 10. Thus, the decimal point is placed in the original number so that the latter is 2.720. Since the decimal place was moved three places, this number forms the characteristic of 3. Hence, the logarithm of 2,720 is 3.4346. As another example, to find the logarithm of 60,000, locate the number 60 in the left-hand column. Since the original number has no additional digits, read the number 7,782 in the zero column next to the original number 60. Point off the original number to the left until only one digit (between one and 10) remains. This requires the pointing off of four places. Hence, the characteristic is four, and the log of 60,000 is 4.7782.

The logarithm of fractional powers can also be ascertained. As an illustration, assume that the logarithm of the number 0.0015 is to be found. Number 15 is located in the left-hand column and, since there are no additional digits following this number, the initial logarithm obtained is 1761. This is expressed as 0.1761; the decimal place in the original number is moved to the right until a single digit remains to the left of the decimal number. Thus, the decimal number is moved to the right three places in the original number, indicating that the characteristic is three. Hence, the log of 0.0015 is $-3 + 0.1761$. The latter number can also be expressed as 7.1761 minus 10.

Knowing the logarithm for a given number, the original number can be ascertained from the log table. This process is known as finding the *antilogarithm* and, in such a procedure, the original number which produced the logarithm is known as the antilog. For instance, to find the antilog of 2.6599, the .6599 portion of the number is located in the logarithm table. This provides the number 457. The latter number must be assumed to be a number between one and 10 and, hence, it is considered to be 4.57. Since the characteristic of the number for which the antilog is to be found is two, the decimal place is moved over two points and gives 457 for the antilog. The foregoing represents a summary of the basic logarithm principles for use in this book. For more advanced work with respect to interpolation, and to the use of logarithms for multiplication and division, reference should be made to a standard mathematical text.

COMMON LOGARITHM TABLE

N	0	1	2	3	4	5	6	7	8	9
10	0000	0043	0086	0128	0170	0212	0253	0294	0334	0374
11	0414	0453	0492	0531	0569	0607	0645	0682	0719	0755
12	0792	0828	0864	0899	0934	0969	1004	1038	1072	1106
13	1139	1173	1206	1239	1271	1303	1335	1367	1399	1430
14	1461	1492	1523	1553	1584	1614	1644	1673	1703	1732
15	1761	1790	1818	1847	1875	1903	1931	1959	1987	2014
16	2041	2068	2095	2122	2148	2175	2201	2227	2253	2279
17	2304	2330	2355	2380	2405	2430	2455	2480	2504	2529
18	2553	2577	2601	2625	2648	2672	2695	2718	2742	2765
19	2788	2810	2833	2856	2878	2900	2923	2945	2967	2989
20	3010	3032	3054	3075	3096	3118	3139	3160	3181	3201
21	3222	3243	3263	3284	3304	3324	3345	3365	3385	3404
22	3424	3444	3464	3483	3502	3522	3541	3560	3579	3598
23	3617	3636	3655	3674	3692	3711	3729	3747	3766	3784
24	3802	3820	3838	3856	3874	3892	3909	3927	3945	3962
25	3979	3997	4014	4031	4048	4065	4082	4099	4116	4133
26	4150	4166	4183	4200	4216	4232	4249	4265	4281	4298
27	4314	4330	4346	4362	4378	4393	4409	4425	4440	4456
28	4472	4487	4502	4518	4533	4548	4564	4579	4594	4609
29	4624	4639	4654	4669	4683	4698	4713	4728	4742	4757
30	4771	4786	4800	4814	4829	4843	4857	4871	4886	4900
31	4914	4928	4942	4955	4969	4983	4997	5011	5024	5038
32	5051	5065	5079	5092	5105	5119	5132	5145	5159	5172
33	5185	5198	5211	5224	5237	5250	5263	5276	5289	5302
34	5315	5328	5340	5353	5366	5378	5391	5403	5416	5428
35	5441	5453	5465	5478	5490	5502	5514	5527	5539	5551
36	5563	5575	5587	5599	5611	5623	5635	5647	5658	5670
37	5682	5694	5705	5717	5729	5740	5752	5763	5775	5786
38	5798	5809	5821	5832	5843	5855	5866	5877	5888	5899
39	5911	5922	5933	5944	5955	5966	5977	5988	5999	6010
40	6021	6031	6042	6053	6064	6075	6085	6096	6107	6117
41	6128	6138	6149	6160	6170	6180	6191	6201	6212	6222
42	6232	6243	6253	6263	6274	6284	6294	6304	6314	6325
43	6335	6345	6355	6365	6375	6385	6395	6405	6415	6425
44	6435	6444	6454	6464	6474	6484	6493	6503	6513	6522
45	6532	6542	6551	6561	6571	6580	6590	6599	6609	6618
46	6628	6637	6646	6656	6665	6675	6684	6693	6702	6712
47	6721	6730	6739	6749	6758	6767	6776	6785	6794	6803
48	6812	6821	6830	6839	6848	6857	6866	6875	6884	6893
49	6902	6911	6920	6928	6937	6946	6955	6964	6972	6981
50	6990	6998	7007	7016	7024	7033	7042	7050	7059	7067
51	7076	7084	7093	7101	7110	7118	7126	7135	7143	7152
52	7160	7168	7177	7185	7193	7202	7210	7218	7226	7235
53	7243	7251	7259	7267	7275	7284	7292	7300	7308	7316
54	7324	7332	7340	7348	7356	7364	7372	7380	7388	7396
N	0	1	2	3	4	5	6	7	8	9

N	0	1	2	3	4	5	6	7	8	9
55	7404	7412	7419	7427	7435	7443	7451	7459	7466	7474
56	7482	7490	7497	7505	7513	7520	7528	7536	7543	7551
57	7559	7566	7574	7582	7589	7597	7604	7612	7619	7627
58	7634	7642	7649	7657	7664	7672	7679	7686	7694	7701
59	7709	7716	7723	7731	7738	7745	7752	7760	7767	7774
60	7782	7789	7796	7803	7810	7818	7825	7832	7839	7846
61	7853	7860	7868	7875	7882	7889	7896	7903	7910	7917
62	7924	7931	7938	7945	7952	7959	7966	7973	7980	7987
63	7993	8000	8007	8014	8021	8028	8035	8041	8048	8055
64	8062	8069	8075	8082	8089	8096	8102	8109	8116	8122
65	8129	8136	8142	8149	8156	8162	8169	8176	8182	8189
66	8195	8202	8209	8215	8222	8228	8235	8241	8248	8254
67	8261	8267	8274	8280	8287	8293	8299	8306	8312	8319
68	8325	8331	8338	8344	8351	8357	8363	8370	8376	8382
69	8388	8395	8401	8407	8414	8420	8426	8432	8439	8445
70	8451	8457	8463	8470	8476	8482	8488	8494	8500	8506
71	8513	8519	8525	8531	8537	8543	8549	8555	8561	8567
72	8573	8579	8585	8591	8597	8603	8609	8615	8621	8627
73	8633	8639	8645	8651	8657	8663	8669	8675	8681	8686
74	8692	8698	8704	8710	8716	8722	8727	8733	8739	8745
75	8751	8756	8762	8768	8774	8779	8785	8791	8797	8802
76	8808	8814	8820	8825	8831	8837	8842	8848	8854	8859
77	8865	8871	8876	8882	8887	8893	8899	8904	8910	8915
78	8921	8927	8932	8938	8943	8949	8954	8960	8965	8971
79	8976	8982	8987	8993	8998	9004	9009	9015	9020	9025
80	9031	9036	9042	9047	9053	9058	9063	9069	9074	9079
81	9085	9090	9096	9101	9106	9112	9117	9122	9128	9133
82	9138	9143	9149	9154	9159	9165	9170	9175	9180	9186
83	9191	9196	9201	9206	9212	9217	9222	9227	9232	9238
84	9243	9248	9253	9258	9263	9269	9274	9279	9284	9289
85	9294	9299	9304	9309	9315	9320	9325	9330	9335	9340
86	9345	9350	9355	9360	9365	9370	9375	9380	9385	9390
87	9395	9400	9405	9410	9415	9420	9425	9430	9435	9440
88	9445	9450	9455	9460	9465	9469	9474	9479	9484	9489
89	9494	9499	9504	9509	9513	9518	9523	9528	9533	9538
90	9542	9547	9552	9557	9562	9566	9571	9576	9581	9586
91	9590	9595	9600	9605	9609	9614	9619	9624	9628	9633
92	9638	9643	9647	9652	9657	9661	9666	9671	9675	9680
93	9685	9689	9694	9699	9703	9708	9713	9717	9722	9727
94	9731	9736	9741	9745	9750	9754	9759	9763	9768	9773
95	9777	9782	9786	9791	9795	9800	9805	9809	9814	9818
96	9823	9827	9832	9836	9841	9845	9850	9854	9859	9863
97	9868	9872	9877	9881	9886	9890	9894	9899	9903	9908
98	9912	9917	9921	9926	9930	9934	9939	9943	9948	9952
99	9956	9961	9965	9969	9974	9978	9983	9987	9991	9996
N	0	1	2	3	4	5	6	7	8	9

RESISTOR AND CAPACITOR COLOR CODES

Resistors and capacitors are coded with bands of various colors which correspond to certain numbers. By understanding the method by which resistors and capacitors are color-coded, the actual value of the component, as well as the tolerance and voltage ratings, can be ascertained. Many molded composition resistors and molded capacitors have similar appearances, but their color coding differs, as shown in Fig. A-2.

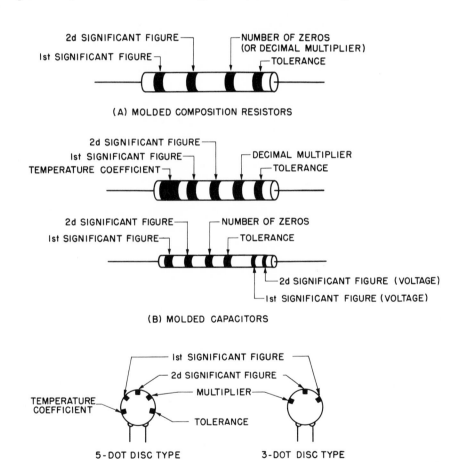

Fig. A-2. Resistor and capacitor color codes.

While the electronic industry has set up standard color codes, many variations will appear in the field, because of the nonuniformity and lack of standardization encountered in imported units, or in those made for special services and later sold over the counters of wholesale houses as surplus material. The color codes presented herein, however, represent those standardized for modern types of components, and will, therefore, serve as a guide for conventional makes. When any doubt exists, however, measurements should be made with a calibrated ohmmeter for resistors, and with a capacitance checker for the various types of capacitors encountered.

The color-code listings for the resistors and capacitors shown in Fig. A-2 will follow. For the molded composition type capacitor shown in (A), all the color bands are usually of the same width and are spaced at equal distances. In (B), the upper molded capacitor has a wide band at the left, which is used for indicating the temperature coefficient of the capacitor. Significant figures and decimal multipliers then follow in sequence, ending with the tolerance band at the right. The second type of molded capacitors shown in (B) has all bands of the same width, with the last two bands showing the voltage tolerance of the capacitor. Sometimes, this particular capacitor may be furnished with the latter two bands omitted.

For the upper capacitor shown in Fig. A-2(B), the correct sequence of colors exists when the wide band is at the left. For the second capacitor shown in (B), the proper sequence of colors holds when the two bands which are separated from the other bands are toward the right.

The first two significant figures in the color code of capacitors are in micromicrofarads. The third digit indicates the number of zeros which follow. When voltage bands are shown on the molded capacitor, the voltage rating is identified by a single-digit number for ratings through 900 volts, and by a two-digit number for ratings above 900 volts. It must be understood that two zeros follow the significant figure or figures which are obtained from the color code.

STANDARD RESISTOR VALUES

Ohms	Ohms	Ohms	Ohms	Ohms	Ohms	Megs	Megs	Megs
—	1.0	10	100	1,000	10,000	0.1	1.0	10
—	1.1	11	110	1,100	11,000	0.11	1.1	11
—	1.2	12	120	1,200	12,000	0.12	1.2	12
—	1.3	13	130	1,300	13,000	0.13	1.3	13
—	1.5	15	150	1,500	15,000	0.15	1.5	15
—	1.6	16	160	1,600	16,000	0.16	1.6	16
—	1.8	18	180	1,800	18,000	0.18	1.8	18
—	2.0	20	200	2,000	20,000	0.20	2.0	20
—	2.2	22	220	2,200	22,000	0.22	2.2	22
0.24	2.4	24	240	2,400	24,000	0.24	2.4	—
0.27	2.7	27	270	2,700	27,000	0.27	2.7	—
0.30	3.0	30	300	3,000	30,000	0.30	3.0	—
0.33	3.3	33	330	3,300	33,000	0.33	3.3	—
0.36	3.6	36	360	3,600	36,000	0.36	3.6	—
0.39	3.9	39	390	3,900	39,000	0.39	3.9	—
0.43	4.3	43	430	4,300	43,000	0.43	4.3	—
0.47	4.7	47	470	4,700	47,000	0.47	4.7	—
0.51	5.1	51	510	5,100	51,000	0.51	5.1	—
0.56	5.6	56	560	5,600	56,000	0.56	5.6	—
0.62	6.2	62	620	6,200	62,000	0.62	6.2	—
0.68	6.8	68	680	6,800	68,000	0.68	6.8	—
0.75	7.5	75	750	7,500	75,000	0.75	7.5	—
0.82	8.2	82	820	8,200	82,000	0.82	8.2	—
0.91	9.1	91	910	9,100	91,000	0.91	9.1	—

COLOR CODE FOR MOLDED (FIXED) RESISTORS

Color	Significant figure	Multiplying value
Black	0	1
Brown	1	10
Red	2	100
Orange	3	1,000
Yellow	4	10,000
Green	5	100,000
Blue	6	1,000,000
Violet	7	10,000,000
Gray	8	100,000,000
White	9	1,000,000,000
Gold	$\pm 5\%$ tolerance	0.1
Silver	$\pm 10\%$ tolerance	0.01
No Color	$\pm 20\%$ tolerance	

COLOR CODE FOR MOLDED AND CERAMIC CAPACITORS

Color	Significant figure	No. of zeros following significant figure	Capacity tolerance
Black	0		$\pm 20\%$
Brown	1	0	
Red	2	00	
Orange	3	000	$\pm 30\%$
Yellow	4	0000	$\pm 40\%$
Green	5	00000	$\pm 5\%$
Blue	6	000000	
Violet	7		
Gray	8		
White	9		$\pm 10\%$

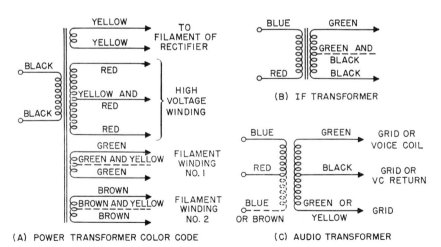

Fig. A-3. Transformer color codes.

PROPERTIES OF COPPER WIRE CONDUCTORS*
(AMERICAN WIRE GAUGE)

Size (gauge no.)	Diam in mils at 20°C, 68°F	Area circular mils	Ohms per 1,000 ft. 25°C, 77°F
16	50.82	2,583.0	4.094
17	45.26	2,048.0	5.163
18	40.30	1,624.0	6.510
19	35.89	1,288.0	8.210
20	31.96	1,022.0	10.35
21	28.46	810.1	13.05
22	25.35	642.4	16.46
23	22.57	509.5	20.76
24	20.10	404.0	26.17
25	17.90	320.4	33.00
26	15.94	254.1	41.62
27	14.20	201.5	52.48
28	12.64	159.8	66.17
29	11.26	126.7	83.44
30	10.03	100.5	105.2
31	8.93	79.70	132.7
32	7.95	63.21	167.3
33	7.08	50.13	211.0
34	6.31	39.75	266.0
35	5.62	31.52	335.5
36	5.00	25.00	423.0
37	4.45	19.83	533.4
38	3.96	15.72	672.6
39	3.53	12.47	848.1
40	3.14	9.89	1,069.0

* Only wire sizes found in conventional electronic circuitry are listed. For sizes larger or smaller than shown, refer to Circular 31, National Bureau of Standards, or to the National Electrical Code pamphlet of the National Board of Fire Underwriters.

STANDARD BROADCAST STATION ALLOCATIONS

AM Broadcast Band

550 kilocycles to 1,600 kilocycles
(Nominally 10 kilocycles per station)

FM Broadcast Band

88 megacycles to 108 megacycles
(200 kilocycles per station)

VHF Television Station Frequencies

Channel number	Frequency in megacycles	Video carrier	Sound carrier
1	(Not allocated)		
2	54–60	55.25	59.75
3	60–66	61.25	65.75
4	66–72	67.25	71.75
5	76–82	77.25	81.75
6	82–88	83.25	87.75
7	174–180	175.25	179.75
8	180–186	181.25	185.75
9	186–192	187.25	191.75
10	192–198	193.25	197.75
11	198–204	199.25	203.75
12	204–210	205.25	209.75
13	210–216	211.25	215.75

UHF Television Station Band

Channels 14 to 83 inclusive.
Total frequency span: 470 megacycles to 890 megacycles.
Each station allocated a 6-megacycle spectrum space, as with VHF stations.

Frequency Spectrum Designations

VLF	(very low frequencies)	3 to	30	kilocycles
LF	(low frequencies)	30 to	300	kilocycles
MF	(medium frequencies)	300 to	3,000	kilocycles
HF	(high frequencies)	3,000 to	30,000	kilocycles
VHF	(very high frequencies)	30 to	300	megacycles
UHF	(ultra-high frequencies)	300 to	3,000	megacycles
SHF	(super-high frequencies)	3,000 to	30,000	megacycles
EHF	(extra-high frequencies)	30,000 to	300,000	megacycles

Military Frequency Spectrum Designations

P-band	225 to	390	megacycles
L-band	390 to	1,550	megacycles
S-band	1,550 to	5,200	megacycles
X-band	5,200 to	10,900	megacycles
K-band	10,900 to	36,000	megacycles
Q-band	36,000 to	46,000	megacycles
V-band	46,000 to	56,000	megacycles

ANSWERS TO PRACTICAL PROBLEMS

Chapter 1. **1.** 7,200 dynes. **2.** 1,800 dynes.

Chapter 2. **1.** 0.65 ampere. **2.** 4.5 volts. **3.** 800 ohms. **4.** 125 watts, 250 volts. **5.** 0.2 watt, 0.05 ampere. **6.** 40 ohms, 200 volts. **7.** 20 millivolts. **8.** 5 kilovolts. **9.** 30 milliampere. **10.** 0.4 milliampere. **11.** 50,000 watts. **12.** 0.2 watt. **13.** 0.00025 volt. **14.** 90,000,000 cycles.

Chapter 3. **1.** 0.5 ampere, 240 ohms. **2.** 10,000 ohms, 2,500 ohms; total $= 12,500$ ohms. **3.** $R_1 = 4$ watts, $R_2 = 1$ watt. **4.** 10 milliamperes. **5.** $I = 0.03$ ampere, $R_1 = 50$ ohms, $R_2 = 100$ ohms. **6.** 20,000 ohms, 0.05 ampere. **7.** $R_1 = 0.075$ ampere; $R_2 = 0.3$ ampere, $R_3 = 0.15$ ampere, $I_T = 0.525$ ampere, $R_T = 285.7$ ohms. **8.** 285.7 ohms. **9.** 50 watts. **10.** 78.75 watts. **11.** 315 watts. **12.** $R_1 = 5$ ohms, $R_2 = 10$ ohms, $R_T = 3.33$ ohms. **13.** 15 cells in series. **14.** 13.5 volts.

Chapter 4. **1.** $R_T = 400$ ohms, $E_{R_1} = 200$ volts, $E_{R_2} = 600$ volts. **2.** $I = 0.5$ ampere, $R_T = 1,000$ ohms, $E_T = 500$ volts. **3.** 125 ohms. **4.** 130, 65, and 26 ohms. (one solution of many) **5.** 40 ohms total; E across 18-ohm resistor $= 36$ volts. **6.** $R_e = 1,078$ ohms, $I_L = 0.01$ ampere. **7.** 0.01 ampere.

Chapter 5. **1.** 0.04 volt. **2.** 2,000 ohms. **3.** 20 ohms. **4.** 49,900 ohms. **5.** 8,000 ohms. **6.** 6 decibels. **7.** -10 decibels. **8.** 18 decibels. **9.** 4.77 decibels. **10.** -9.54 decibels.

Chapter 6. **1.** 0.003 henrys. **2.** 3.14 gilberts. **3.** 12.56 gilberts. **4.** 50.24. **5.** 7.536. **6.** 18 microfarads. **7.** 0.05 microfarad. **8.** 0.05 second. **9.** 300 microseconds. **10.** 150 volts.

Chapter 7. **1.** 32 volts. **2.** 212 volts. **3.** 176.25 volts. **4.** 240.38 volts. **5.** 211.5 volts. **6.** 44.54 volts. **7.** 338.4 volts.

Chapter 8. **1.** 7,536 ohms. **2.** 17 milliamperes. **3.** 7 watts. **4.** 12.5 ohms. **5.** 7,000 ohms. **6.** 30 volts. **7.** 40 ohms. **8.** 3,500 ohms. **9.** 8 millihenrys. **10.** 60 to 1. **11.** 6.5 millihenrys. **12.** 21.5 millihenrys. **13.** 25

microseconds. **14.** 8 microfarads, 600 working volts. **15.** 24 microfarads, 450 working volts. **16.** Yes, 1 ohm. **17.** No, 600 ohms. **18.** Two capacitors of 0.02 microfarad in series, shunted by 0.05 microfarad. **19.** 63 volts; 1.65 watts approx. **20.** 31.5 volts; 20 milliamperes, 1,575 ohms. **21.** 680 milliamperes, 200 ohms. **22.** 21 microfarads (approx). **23.** 12 henrys: $L_X = 16 \dfrac{1500}{2000}$.

Chapter 9. **1.** 8 amperes, 36 degrees. **2.** 120 volts. **3.** (a) $X_L = 18,840$ ohms, $X_C = 200,000$ ohms; (b) $X_L = 37,680$ ohms, $X_C = 100,000$ ohms; (c) $X_L = 75,360$ ohms, $X_C = 50,000$ ohms; (d) $X_L = 150,720$ ohms, $X_C = 25,000$ ohms; (e) $X_L = 301,440$ ohms, $X_C = 12,500$ ohms. **4.** 155 ohms. **5.** X_L total $= 1,256,000$ ohms, $I = 10$ milliamperes, $Z = 500$ ohms. **6.** $Z = 192$ ohms, $I = 50$ milliamperes. **7.** $Z = 360$ ohms,

Chapter 10. **1.** 2 milliamperes, 0.2 watt; $X_L = 23,000$ ohms, at 180 cps, $X_L = 69,000$ ohms. **2.** 200, 20, the 10-ohm resistor. **3.** 15.92 cps. **4.** 4,000 kilocycles. **5.** 10,000 kilocycles. **6.** At 5 megacycles. **7.** 1,000 kilocycles. **8.** 600-kilocycle resonance and frequency of signal at load. **9.** 4.4, 335 kilocycles.

Chapter 11. **1.** Mu $= 7.3$. **2.** $r_p = 1,333$ ohms (approx.). **3.** $g_m = 0.0025$ mho. **4.** Mu $= 20$. **5.** $r_p = 6,250$ ohms. **6.** 0.001 mho. **7.** 800 ohms. **8.** 0.002 mho or 2,000 micromhos. **9.** Mu $= 25$. **10.** No. 1 at mu of 100. No. 2 has a mu of only 50.

Chapter 12. **1.** 450 volts. **2.** 150,000 ohms. **3.** 398,000 ohms. **4.** 141 vols. **5.** 60 degrees. **6.** 0.6 microsecond. **7.** 115 ohms. **8.** 65 to 1. **9.** 0.01 second. **10.** 67.5 ohms. **11.** 2,860 ohms, 30 milliamperes. **12.** 20. **13.** 3 megacycles. **14.** 50. **15.** 10,000 ohms.

Chapter 13. **1.** Current gain $= 32$. **2.** $\mathcal{B} = 25$. **3.** $A_i = 66.6$. **4.** $R_i = 2,100$ ohms. **5.** $A_e = 230$. **6.** $A_p = 15,318$. **7.** $A_i = 80$. **8.** $A_i = 100$.

Chapter 14. **1.** Two 16-microfarad, 450-working-voltage capacitors in series. (This provides 8 microfarads at 900 volts. If the other 16 microfarads were used in series the working voltage would only be 300 and this would not allow for any voltage increase variations.) **2.** Choke No. 3. (No. 1 and No. 3 are the only ones with adequate current ratings and the choice would be No. 3 because of its higher henry rating.) **3.** $R_1 = 4,000$ ohms, $R_2 = 20,000$ ohms; $\mathbf{R}_{L_1} = 5,000$ ohms. **4.** Two 16-microfarad, 300-working-volt capacitors in series, paralleled by a duplicate series section. **5.** 1,057.5-volt $(375 \times 1.41 \times 2)$ charged input capacitor contributes an additional peak voltage. **6.** 15,072 ohms. (With full-wave rectification the ripple frequency is 120, hence $X_L = 6.28 \times 120 \times 20$). **7.** At 60 cps, $X_L =$ one-half of the value in Problem 6, or 7,536 ohms. **8.** 25%. **9.** 25% $((2,000 - 1600)/1600 = 0.25 \times 100 = 25\%)$. Regulation was improved, because at 33%, the 2,000 volts dropped to approximately 1,500 volts with same load current. **10.** 50,000 ohms.

Chapter 15. **1.** 66.6. **2.** 80. **3.** 980. **4.** 7,000 **5.** −2.7. **6.** 260.8 volts. **7.** 8.7 watts.

Chapter 16. **1.** 8,333 ohms. **2.** 20 milliamperes. **3.** 5 watts. **4.** 26 to 1. **5.** 2,400 ohms. **6.** 12 watts. **7.** 0.8 alpha. **8.** 4,000 ohms. **9.** 22.5 to 1. **10.** $I = 50 + 50 = 100$ milliamperes, $R = E/I = 10/0.1 = 100$ ohms. $P = EI = 10 \times 0.1 = 1$ watt.

Chapter 17. (Part 1) **1.** 1,428.5 kilocycles. **2.** 1,000 kilocycles. **3.** 7,500 kilocycles. **4.** 40 ohms; yes. **5.** 600 kilocycles **6.** 75,360 ohms.

Chapter 17. (Part 2) **1.** 0.002. **2.** 0.01 watt. **3.** 0.005 watt. **4.** 200-kilocycle base frequency ($1/dura = 1/0.000005 = 200,000$) 40 kilocycles is lowest frequency. **5.** 0.2. **6.** 5 microseconds. **7.** 100 microseconds.

Chapter 18. **1.** 1,000.5 kilocycles, 999.5 kilocycles, 1,002.6 kilocycles, 997.4 kilocycles. **2.** 5.2 kilocycles. **3.** Modulation index = 2. **4.** *SSB* = 4. **5.** 3.5 microhenrys. **6.** 100 kilocycles, 900 kilocycles, 1,900 kilocycles, 200 kilocycles. **7.** 40,000.4 kilocycles or 39,999.6 kilocycles. **8.** 20,231 kilocycles.

Chapter 20. **1.** 300 ohms. **2.** 552 ohms. **3.** 82.8 ohms. **4.** 41.5 ohms. **5.** 8 feet. **6.** 492 megacycles. **7.** 3 inches.

INDEX